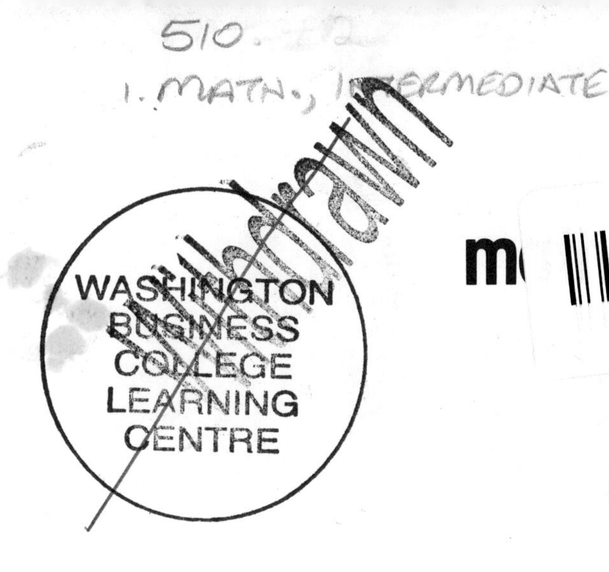

m... ...sion and practice

second edition

mathematics: revision and practice

second edition

R. Elvin
formerly Head of Mathematics, Thomas Sumpter School, Scunthorpe
C. Oliver
formerly Thomas Sumpter School, Scunthorpe
S. K. Whitehead T.D., B.Sc.,
formerly Senior Lecturer, Derby College of Further Education

Oxford University Press

Oxford University Press, Walton Street, Oxford OX2 6DP
Oxford New York Toronto
Delhi Bombay Calcutta Madras Karachi
Petaling Jaya Singapore Hong Kong Tokyo
Nairobi Dar es Salaam Cape Town
Melbourne Auckland
and associated companies in
Beirut Berlin Ibadan Nicosia

Oxford is a trade mark of Oxford University Press

ISBN 0 19 832620 3

First published 1977
Reprinted (with additions and corrections) 1977
Second edition 1979
Reprinted 1981, 1982, 1983
Reprinted (with additions and corrections) 1984
Reprinted 1986, 1987

Printed in Great Britain
at the University Printing House, Oxford
by David Stanford
Printer to the University

Preface

This book provides a comprehensive range of carefully graded examples for students preparing for GCSE, and similar examinations in mathematics. Each section also includes brief notes and worked examples which review the methods and processes required.

The sections are arranged within the book under general headings for ease of reference: the order does not represent any particular teaching approach. A set of miscellaneous exercises is included under each heading and all answers are provided at the end of the book.

The aim of the authors has been to provide ample practice in all topics normally associated with mathematics at this level. They believe that such practice brings both confidence and familiarity with the mathematical skills needed in the examination.

December 1976

R.E.

C.O.

S.K.W.

In this second edition the opportunity has been taken to include practice in Part 9 on all the topics required by the newer examination syllabuses in a similar form to the rest of the book.

February 1979

R.E.

C.O.

S.K.W.

Contents

Part 6 Trigonometry

Part 7 Calculus

Part 8 Further mathematics

Part 9 Modern mathematics

Part 1 Arithmetic

1.1 Whole numbers

Example 1 126 × 53

Multiplying by left-hand digit first	Multiplying by right-hand digit first
$\begin{array}{rl} 126 & \\ \times\ \ \underline{53} & \\ 6300 & (126 \times 50) \\ \underline{378} & (126 \times 3) \\ \underline{\underline{6678}} & \end{array}$	$\begin{array}{rl} 126 & \\ \times\ \ \underline{53} & \\ 378 & (126 \times 3) \\ \underline{6300} & (126 \times 50) \\ \underline{\underline{6678}} & \end{array}$

Example 2 5232 ÷ 48

$$\begin{array}{r} 109 \\ 48\overline{)5232} \\ \underline{48\downarrow\downarrow} \\ 432 \\ \underline{432} \\ \cdots \end{array}$$

Example 3 132 ÷ (12 × 3 − 15 ÷ 5)

Remember that the order of operation is:
brackets, division, multiplication, addition, subtraction.

$$\begin{aligned} & 132 \div (12 \times 3 - 15 \div 5) \\ = {} & 132 \div (36 - 3) = 132 \div 33 = 4 \end{aligned}$$

Exercise 1.1

Add the following groups of numbers

1. 27 9	**2.** 36 41	**3.** 85 76	**4.** 192 49
5. 286 132	**6.** 377 284	**7.** 506 729	**8.** 1062 985
9. 234 538 778	**10.** 476 984 867	**11.** 5632 4815 8547 6474	**12.** 1273 9639 3469 6382
13. 16 432 28 071 43 185 82 153	**14.** 20 159 17 861 33 922 14 015	**15.** 82 756 4 981 8 265 14	**16.** 62 479 31 159 27 183 8 006

17.	18.	19.	20.
64 145	63 214	76 823	17 580
17 813	38 694	23 413	48 152
36 714	41 362	64 328	41 899
48 957	84 721	18 231	23 122

Find the difference between the following pairs of numbers

21.	22.	23.	24.
28	36	41	106
14	24	39	87

25.	26.	27.	28.
213	862	108	165
101	173	47	79

29.	30.	31.	32.
418	732	957	758
155	525	868	749

33.	34.	35.	36.
478	196	823	1003
389	168	455	998

37.	38.	39.	40.
8231	4823	6728	2413
6407	1946	4343	1825

Multiply together the following pairs of numbers

41. 19×4 **42.** 21×8 **43.** 36×9 **44.** 82×8
45. 26×12 **46.** 42×15 **47.** 84×23 **48.** 92×45
49. 104×63 **50.** 240×84 **51.** 206×302 **52.** 946×146
53. 603×237 **54.** 264×804 **55.** 217×405 **56.** 1064×98
57. 2816×362 **58.** 1937×168 **59.** 4206×107 **60.** 1025×168

Divide the following pairs of numbers

61. $336 \div 4$ **62.** $343 \div 7$ **63.** $729 \div 9$ **64.** $1672 \div 11$
65. $1848 \div 12$ **66.** $867 \div 17$ **67.** $2116 \div 23$ **68.** $2457 \div 117$
69. $4182 \div 123$ **70.** $17\,688 \div 201$ **71.** $43\,424 \div 236$ **72.** $20\,402 \div 101$
73. $4053 \div 193$ **74.** $14\,976 \div 288$ **75.** $17\,856 \div 372$ **76.** $13\,561 \div 191$
77. $614\,384 \div 304$ **78.** $429\,070 \div 214$ **79.** $965\,247 \div 321$ **80.** $481\,293 \div 477$

Find the value of:

81. $2 + 3 \times 6$ **82.** $(4 + 8) \times 8$ **83.** $21 - 7 \times 3$ **84.** $19 - 7 + 3$
85. $21 \div 3 + 7$ **86.** $64 \div 8 - 4$ **87.** $(28 - 14) \times 2$ **88.** $35 \div 5 \times 7$
89. $16 \times 64 \div 8$ **90.** $12 \times 8 + 15 \div 5$ **91.** $12 \times (8 + 15) \div 4$ **92.** $7 \times (8 + 21 \div 3)$
93. $144 \div (14 - 6 \div 3)$ **94.** $343 \div (4 \times 3 - 15 \div 3)$
95. $(7 \times 8) \div (64 \div 8)$ **96.** $24 \times 8 \div 64 \div 3$
97. $81 \div (9 \times 3) + 7$ **98.** $12 - [4 \times (20 - 3 \times 6)]$
99. $12 \times [4 + (20 - 3) \times 6]$ **100.** $12 \times [(4 + 20) - 3 \times 6]$

1.2 Decimal fractions

Addition and subtraction

Make sure that all like quantities appear in the same column by putting the decimal points underneath each other.

Example 1

Add 12, 1·36 and 0·768.

```
 12·0
  1·36
  0·768
 ______
 14·128
 ======
```

Example 2

Subtract 0·423 from 36.

```
 36·0
  0·423
 ______
 35·577
 ======
```

Exercise 1.2a

Add the following groups of numbers

```
 1.   3·1        2.   6·07       3.   81·6       4.  124
      1·04            1·14            19·7            16·8
     _____           _____           _____          _____

 5.  67·2        6.  72·9        7.    10·62     8.  64·07
      1·96            6·17            214·8          90·44
     _____           _____           ______         _____

 9.   98·4      10.  73·12      11.  976·2      12. 1652
     815             63·99           951·3            265·8
      63·82          84·14           600·8            220·9
     ______          _____           _____          ______

13.  286·02     14.   19·063
     141·97          981·4
     604·13            1·008
     790·04           18·016
     ______          _______
```

15. 1067 + 82·406 + 13·04 + 987·6
16. 17·04 + 866·15 + 1004·06 + 72·977
17. 0·001276 + 0·08601 + 0·0723 + 0·1044
18. 1·0046 + 0·0287 + 6·1432 + 18
19. 0·10621 + 0·36004 + 0·00822 + 0·01464

Find the difference between the following pairs of numbers

20.	3·1 2·7	**21.**	0·062 0·043	**22.**	1·771 0·902	**23.**	34·64 0·007
24.	82·14 1·15	**25.**	196·2 87·1	**26.**	1·004 0·823	**27.**	17·22 9·022
28.	14·23 0·0486	**29.**	226·8 14·73	**30.**	779·2 604·86	**31.**	3·519 3·406

32. 7601 and 0·1632
33. 74·06 and 9·044
34. 9·044 and 74·06
35. 4·218 and 2·739
36. 29·007 and 416·3
37. 0·004963 and 0·000137

Multiplication

To multiply by 10, move the figures one place to the *left*.
To multiply by 100, move the figures *two* places to the left.

To multiply any two decimals, leave out the decimal point, then multiply the two numbers together. Position the decimal point in the answer so that the same number of figures appear after it as the total number of figures that appear after the decimal point in *both* decimals being multiplied.

Example 2·8 × 0·32

$$\begin{array}{r} 28 \\ \times\ 32 \\ \hline 56 \\ 840 \\ \hline 896 \\ \hline\hline \end{array}$$

2·8 × 0·32 = 0·896

There are 3 figures altogether after the two decimal points. Therefore, there are 3 figures after the decimal point in the answer.

Exercise 1.2b

1. Multiply each of the following (a) by 10, (b) by 100.
(i) 6·3 (ii) 8·04 (iii) 0·61 (iv) 0·037 (v) 0·065

Multiply together the following pairs of numbers

2. 6·8 × 20
3. 0·25 × 40
4. 0·125 × 80
5. 2·1 × 0·6
6. 63 × 0·08
7. 0·36 × 0·12
8. 64 × 0·08
9. 0·042 × 1·2
10. 1·042 × 0·0012
11. 96·1 × 0·11
12. 0·832 × 0·09
13. 0·0942 × 1·5
14. 0·8602 × 0·032
15. 1·471 × 0·65
16. 62·16 × 0·107
17. 8·621 × 1·22
18. 421·8 × 0·0324
19. 0·6134 × 1·62
20. 0·060 02 × 146
21. 0·002 671 × 0·0321
22. 0·106 04 × 2·071
23. 621·07 × 0·0146
24. 4·701 × 0·0562

Division

To divide by 10, move the figures one place to the *right*.
To divide by 100, move the figures *two* places to the right.

To divide any decimal (the dividend) by another decimal (the divisor), multiply both by 10, or 100, or 1000 etc. to make the divisor a whole number. Then divide in the normal way.

Example

46·731 ÷ 0·37 = 4673·1 ÷ 37 (multiplying by 100 to make the divisor a whole number)

```
     126·3
 37/4673·1
    37
     97
     74
     233
     222
      111
      111
      ...
```

46·731 ÷ 0·37 = 126·3

Decimal places

To approximate a number to a given number of places
(a) Calculate the answer to 1 more place than required
(b) If this last figure is less than 5, discard it; if it is 5 or more, add 1 to the figure before it.

Examples

3·766 = 3·77 to two decimal places (2 D.P.)
0·0404 = 0·040 to three decimal places (3 D.P.)

Significant figures

The first non-zero digit of any number is the first significant figure, so 0·0236 has three significant figures.

Examples

5276 = 5280 to three significant figures (3 S.F.)
0·04042 = 0·0404 to three significant figures (3 S.F.)

Standard form

Very large or very small numbers may be more conveniently written in the form

$$a \times 10^n$$

where a is a number between 1 and 10 and n is an integer.

Examples

$$527\,600\,000 = 5{\cdot}276 \times 100\,000\,000 = 5{\cdot}276 \times 10^8$$
$$0{\cdot}000\,042 = 4{\cdot}2 \times \frac{1}{100\,000} = 4{\cdot}2 \times 10^{-5}$$

Exercise 1.2c

1. Divide each of the following (a) by 10, (b) by 100
   (i) 6·3 (ii) 66 (iii) 0·61 (iv) 0·301 (v) 1764·29

Solve the following

2. 3·4 ÷ 20
3. 0·76 ÷ 50
4. 2·6 ÷ 25

Divide the following pairs of numbers to the degree of accuracy indicated

5. 10 ÷ 3 to 3 places of decimals
6. 10 ÷ 3 to 2 significant figures
7. 18 ÷ 7 to 1 place of decimals
8. 167 ÷ 11 to 2 significant figures
9. 283 ÷ 12 to 2 places of decimals
10. 821 ÷ 12 to 4 significant figures
11. 10·6 ÷ 0·214 to 1 place of decimals
12. 59·31 ÷ 1·04 to 4 significant figures
13. 3·14 ÷ 19·6 to 3 places of decimals
14. 8·22 ÷ 11·8 to 2 significant figures
15. 0·0286 ÷ 31·2 to 5 places of decimals
16. 64·7 ÷ 0·0267 to 3 significant figures
17. 0·634 ÷ 0·0492 to 1 place of decimals
18. 0·0819 ÷ 0·0401 to 4 significant figures
19. 7·009 ÷ 0·671 to 1 place of decimals
20. 14 850 ÷ 0·742 to 4 significant figures
21. 4962 ÷ 583 11 to 2 places of decimals
22. 1346 ÷ 0·08101 to 3 significant figures
23. 0·08 267 ÷ 0·004 173 to 1 place of decimals
24. 0·002 641 ÷ 14 310 to 3 significant figures
25. Write the following in standard form
    (a) 186 000 (b) 63 360 (c) 31 536 000
    (d) 0·000 062 (e) 0·0002 (f) 0·000 000 002 13
26. Write the following as ordinary numbers
    (a) $1{\cdot}8 \times 10^2$ (b) $4{\cdot}52 \times 10^3$ (c) $8{\cdot}69 \times 10^5$
    (d) $1{\cdot}8 \times 10^{-2}$ (e) $4{\cdot}52 \times 10^{-3}$ (f) $8{\cdot}69 \times 10^{-5}$
27. Write each of the following in standard form
    (a) 36 900 (b) 0·001 64
    and hence or otherwise evaluate 369 000 ÷ 0·001 64 leaving the answer in Standard Form.
28. How many pieces of string, 11·6 cm long can be cut from a ball of string 50 m long?
29. Find the cost of 259 therms of gas, when 1 therm costs 14·07p. (Answer to the nearest p.)
30. A book of trading stamps contains 30 pages and each page holds 40 stamps. If a stamp is worth 0·033p calculate the value of the stamps in a full book.

1.3 Vulgar fractions

A *vulgar fraction* is a quantity such as $\frac{5}{7}$, where 5 is called the numerator and 7 is called the denominator.

$\dfrac{5}{7}$ means $5 \div 7$.

An *improper fraction* is one in which the numerator is greater than the denominator, e.g. $\frac{10}{3}$.
It can be simplified to give a *mixed number*, e.g. $\frac{10}{3} = 3\frac{1}{3}$.

A vulgar fraction is unchanged in value when both the numerator and the denominator are multiplied by the same number. It is equally unchanged in value when both are divided by the same number.

Examples

$$\frac{2 \times 8}{3 \times 8} = \frac{16}{24}; \qquad \frac{16 \div 8}{24 \div 8} = \frac{2}{3}$$

Addition and subtraction of fractions

These operations can only be carried out when all fractions have a common denominator.

Example $3\frac{2}{5} + 1\frac{1}{2} - 2\frac{3}{10}$

$$= 3\tfrac{4}{10} + 1\tfrac{5}{10} - 2\tfrac{3}{10}$$
$$= 2\tfrac{6}{10} = 2\tfrac{3}{5}$$

Multiplication and division of fractions

(a) These operations can only be carried out with vulgar fractions or with improper fractions, e.g. $\frac{3}{5}$, $\frac{10}{3}$; but not with mixed numbers, e.g. $3\frac{1}{3}$.
(b) To multiply fractions, multiply the numerators together and then the denominators together. Simplify by cancelling where possible.
(c) To divide, multiply by the inverse of the divisor. For example, the inverse of $\frac{2}{5}$ is $\frac{5}{2}$; the inverse of $3\frac{1}{3}$ is $\frac{3}{10}$.

Example 1 $3\frac{1}{3} \times 1\frac{1}{5} \div 2\frac{1}{2}$

$$= \frac{10}{3} \times \frac{6}{5} \div \frac{5}{2}$$

$$= \frac{\cancel{10}^{2}}{\cancel{3}_{1}} \times \frac{\cancel{6}^{2}}{\cancel{5}_{1}} \times \frac{2}{5}$$

$$= \frac{8}{5} = 1\tfrac{3}{5}$$

(d) To change a vulgar fraction into a decimal fraction, divide the numerator by the denominator. The answer may be an exact decimal (example 2). But it may be a recurring decimal (example 3) or may only recur after many decimal places; these are usually expressed to a given number of decimal places.

Example 2

Change $\frac{3}{8}$ into a decimal fraction.

$$\begin{array}{r} 0{\cdot}375 \\ 8\overline{)3{\cdot}000} \\ \underline{24} \\ 60 \\ \underline{56} \\ 40 \\ \underline{40} \\ .. \end{array}$$

$$\tfrac{3}{8} = 3 \div 8 = 0{\cdot}375$$

Example 3

Change $\frac{5}{11}$ into a decimal fraction

$$\begin{array}{r} 0{\cdot}4545\ldots \\ 11\overline{)5{\cdot}0000} \\ \underline{44} \\ 60 \\ \underline{55} \\ 50 \\ \underline{44} \\ 60 \\ \underline{55} \\ 5 \end{array}$$

$$\tfrac{5}{11} = 5 \div 11 = 0{\cdot}4545\ldots$$
$$= 0{\cdot}\dot{4}\dot{5}$$

(e) To change a decimal fraction into a vulgar fraction, write each digit as a vulgar fraction. Then add the fractions together and give the answer in its simplest form.

Example 4

Change 0·375 into a vulgar fraction

$$0{\cdot}375 = \frac{3}{10} + \frac{7}{100} + \frac{5}{1000}$$

$$= \frac{375}{1000} = \frac{3 \times \cancel{125}^{1}}{8 \times \cancel{125}_{1}}$$

$$= \frac{3}{8}$$

Exercise 1.3

Add the following

1. $\frac{1}{2}+\frac{1}{3}$
2. $\frac{2}{3}+\frac{1}{4}$
3. $\frac{3}{4}+\frac{4}{5}$
4. $\frac{5}{6}+\frac{3}{8}$
5. $\frac{2}{3}+\frac{3}{7}$
6. $\frac{3}{5}+\frac{1}{9}$
7. $\frac{5}{8}+\frac{2}{11}$
8. $\frac{3}{13}+\frac{1}{2}$
9. $1\frac{3}{4}+2\frac{4}{9}$
10. $3\frac{1}{2}+1\frac{15}{16}$
11. $2\frac{3}{7}+4\frac{5}{21}$
12. $2\frac{3}{8}+1\frac{1}{12}$
13. $3\frac{1}{2}+2\frac{2}{3}+6\frac{1}{6}$
14. $4\frac{1}{4}+1\frac{5}{6}+\frac{3}{8}$
15. $1\frac{3}{10}+2\frac{2}{15}+3\frac{1}{25}$
16. $1\frac{1}{3}+4\frac{5}{6}+2\frac{2}{7}$
17. $2\frac{2}{9}+3\frac{1}{12}+2\frac{1}{18}$
18. $4\frac{3}{16}+2\frac{1}{24}+\frac{3}{8}$
19. $3\frac{1}{14}+1\frac{5}{8}+2\frac{3}{28}$
20. $3\frac{5}{6}+4\frac{2}{9}+\frac{7}{36}+\frac{1}{72}$

Evaluate the following

21. $\frac{1}{2}+\frac{1}{3}-\frac{1}{4}$
22. $\frac{1}{3}-\frac{4}{5}+\frac{1}{2}$
23. $1\frac{15}{16}-\frac{3}{4}-\frac{1}{8}$
24. $3\frac{1}{3}+1\frac{5}{6}-4\frac{2}{9}$
25. $5\frac{1}{4}-6\frac{5}{6}+3\frac{3}{8}$
26. $4\frac{2}{3}+5\frac{4}{21}-6\frac{1}{6}$
27. $4\frac{2}{9}+3\frac{5}{12}-6\frac{13}{18}$
28. $\frac{6}{25}-3\frac{7}{15}+4\frac{1}{10}$
29. $1\frac{3}{16}+2\frac{5}{24}-\frac{7}{8}$
30. $(2\frac{9}{14}+3\frac{3}{8})-(1\frac{5}{28}-\frac{3}{14})$

Simplify

31. $\frac{2}{3}\times\frac{9}{8}$
32. $\frac{4}{7}\times\frac{14}{8}$
33. $\frac{3}{5}\times\frac{25}{21}$
34. $\frac{6}{7}\times\frac{21}{54}$
35. $1\frac{1}{2}\times 2\frac{1}{3}$
36. $2\frac{1}{5}\times 2\frac{21}{22}$
37. $3\frac{1}{3}\times 4\frac{4}{5}$
38. $2\frac{1}{7}\times 4\frac{1}{5}$
39. $3\frac{1}{2}\times\frac{14}{15}\times 2\frac{13}{21}$
40. $\frac{3}{5}\times 4\frac{1}{6}\times 2\frac{4}{7}$
41. $\frac{2}{3}\div\frac{4}{9}$
42. $\frac{3}{8}\div\frac{9}{16}$
43. $\frac{7}{8}\div\frac{21}{4}$
44. $\frac{5}{9}\div\frac{75}{72}$
45. $3\frac{3}{5}\div 2\frac{1}{4}$
46. $2\frac{6}{7}\div 1\frac{1}{14}$
47. $1\frac{5}{12}\div 3\frac{3}{16}$
48. $1\frac{4}{15}\div 1\frac{31}{45}$
49. $\frac{7}{2}\div\frac{15}{14}\div\frac{21}{55}$
50. $1\frac{4}{5}\div 3\frac{6}{25}\div 6\frac{2}{3}$
51. $\frac{1}{2}+\frac{1}{3}\times\frac{3}{4}$
52. $\left(\frac{1}{2}+\frac{2}{3}\right)\times\frac{3}{4}$
53. $\frac{1}{2}\div\frac{2}{3}\times\frac{3}{4}$
54. $\frac{1}{2}\div\left(\frac{2}{3}\times\frac{3}{4}\right)$
55. $\frac{3}{5}+\frac{5}{6}\div\frac{7}{12}-\frac{23}{35}$
56. $\left(\frac{3}{5}+\frac{5}{6}\right)\div\frac{7}{12}-\frac{23}{35}$
57. $(\frac{3}{5}+\frac{5}{6})\div(1\frac{2}{5}-\frac{5}{12})$
58. $2\frac{5}{6}+\frac{1}{2}$ of $(4\frac{1}{4}-2\frac{1}{3})$
59. $\frac{2}{3}$ of $7\frac{1}{2}\div\frac{3}{4}$ of $2\frac{1}{7}$
60. $\left(\frac{3}{4}-\frac{5}{9}\right)\div\left(\frac{1}{2}+\frac{1}{4}\div\frac{2}{3}\right)$

Change the following into decimal fractions, giving the answer to 3 decimal places if necessary.

61. $\frac{5}{8}$
62. $\frac{3}{5}$
63. $\frac{1}{20}$
64. $\frac{5}{16}$
65. $\frac{3}{32}$
66. $\frac{23}{32}$
67. $\frac{3}{25}$
68. $\frac{19}{25}$

69. $\frac{17}{50}$ 70. $\frac{21}{40}$ 71. $\frac{7}{11}$ 72. $\frac{2}{3}$

73. $\frac{5}{6}$ 74. $\frac{5}{17}$ 75. $\frac{4}{13}$

Change the following into vulgar fractions

76. 0·125 77. 0·875 78. 0·15 79. 0·85
80. 0·05 81. 0·002 82. 0·5625 83. 0·735
84. 0·842 85. 0·1065

86. A boy has 87 marbles. If he loses 27 of them in a game, what fraction of the original number has he left?
87. There are 42 chocolates in a box and $\frac{3}{14}$ of them have 'hard centres'. How many chocolates are not hard-centred?
88. A girl spends $\frac{1}{4}$ of her pocket money on tights, $\frac{1}{8}$ on sweets and $\frac{3}{16}$ on bus fares. If she spends 24p on bus fares, how much did she spend on tights?
89. A woman spends $\frac{3}{5}$ of her money on food, and $\frac{3}{4}$ of the remainder on clothes. If she has £2·61 left, how much did she start with?
90. A water tank is $\frac{2}{3}$ full. When 15 000 litres are taken out it is $\frac{3}{7}$ full. What volume of water has still to be run out, so that the tank is $\frac{1}{4}$ full?
91. The value of π to six decimal places is 3·141 593. Calculate each of the following as a decimal correct to 6 decimal places, and give the difference from π in each case
(a) $\frac{22}{7}$ (b) $3\frac{17}{120}$ (c) $\frac{355}{113}$
92. The value of π correct to 8 decimal places is 3·141 592 65.
Show that this is approximately equal to

$$3 + \frac{1}{8} + \frac{1}{64} + \frac{1}{1024}$$

and express the difference as a decimal fraction of π to two significant figures.
93. Find the difference between $\frac{17}{25}$ and $\frac{19}{300}$ giving the answer:
(a) as a vulgar fraction (b) as a decimal fraction correct to 3 S.F.
(c) in standard form.
94. $\frac{3}{5}$ of the pupils in a school are boys. If 10 more girls join the school, then the fraction of boys becomes $\frac{29}{50}$. How many girls are now in the school?
95. $\frac{2}{5}$ of the pupils in a school study French, $\frac{3}{4}$ of the remainder study Latin. If 195 pupils study no language, how many learn Latin?

1.4 Ratio and proportion

The ratio of one quantity to another is either written $a : b$ or as the fraction $\frac{a}{b}$.

The two quantities in a ratio must always be expressed in the *same* units, and the answer must be given in its simplest form.

It is essential that the order in which the comparison is being made is clear, e.g. $a : b$ does not equal $b : a$.

Example 1

Express as simply as possible the ratio of £1·50 to £5·25.

$$150\text{p} : 525\text{p} = 2 : 7$$

or $$\frac{150\text{p}}{525\text{p}} = \frac{2}{7}$$

Example 2

Increase £2·50 in the ratio 3 : 2.

Let £x be the new amount; then £x : £2·50 = 3 : 2.

$$\frac{x}{\text{£}2{\cdot}50} = \frac{3}{2}$$

$$2x = \text{£}7{\cdot}50$$

$$x = \text{£}3{\cdot}75$$

Example 3

In a sale, all prices are reduced by 15p in the £. If an article was reduced by £3·75, what was the original price?

Let x pence = the original price

then $$15 : 100 = 375 : x$$

$$\frac{15}{100} = \frac{375}{x}$$

$$15x = 37\,500$$

$$x = 2500$$

$\therefore$ the original price was £25.

Exercise 1.4

In questions 1 to 10 express, as simply as possible, the ratio of the first quantity to the second in the form (a) $\frac{m}{n}$ and (b) $m : n$.

1. 36 : 48
2. 18 : 27
3. 24 : 20
4. 81 : 36
5. £10 : £75
6. £5·50 : £2·20
7. 51cm : 17cm
8. 27g : 6g
9. 27 days : 21 days
10. 42g : 560g

In questions 11 to 17 express each pair of ratios in the form $m : 1$ (giving m correct to two places of decimals). Which of each pair is the greater ratio?

11. 4 : 3 3 : 2
12. 20 : 16 25 : 21
13. 18 : 4 20 : 5
14. £25 : £10 24p : 8p
15. 14kg : 3kg 16g : 5g
16. 51km : 10km 17m : 3m
17. 4 days : 4 hours $3\frac{1}{2}$ days : 3 hours
18. Increase 12 in the ratio 2 : 1
19. Decrease 16 in the ratio 3 : 4
20. Increase 18 in the ratio 3 : 2
21. Decrease 15 in the ratio 4 : 5
22. Increase £6 in the ratio 9 : 4
23. In what ratio must 24 be increased to become 32?
24. In what ratio must 15 be increased to become 25?
25. In what ratio must 51 be decreased to become 8·5?
26. In what ratio must 72 be decreased to become 68?
27. A school contains 520 boys and 360 girls. Find the ratio of the number of boys to the number of girls and of the number of boys to the total number of pupils.
28. A man pays £490 in tax on an income of £1400. What ratio is this?
29. A hotel charges £5 a day in the winter and £42 a week in the summer. Find the ratio of summer to winter prices.
30. An alloy contains 84 g of copper and 96 g of zinc. Find the ratio of the weight of copper to the weight of alloy.
31. Using the data of question 30 find the weight of zinc in 1kg of alloy.
32. A car can travel 52 km in one hour. How far can it travel in 18 minutes at the same speed?
33. A journey takes 10 hours if travelled at 56 km/h. How long will it take if travelled at 48 km/h?
34. Rail fares are increased from 2p a mile to $2\frac{1}{2}$p a mile. What was the old fare for a journey which now costs 85p?
35. A man earns £30 for working a 48 hour week. What should he earn for a 44 hour one?
36. The rail fare for 2 adults and 3 children (half fare) is £14·42. What is the fare for 1 adult and 1 child?
37. A shopkeeper allows 10p in the £ off the marked price for cash. At what price was an article marked for which a customer paid £16·20 cash?
38. After selling 95 copies of a book for every 100 printed a publisher finds he has 150 left. How many were sold and how many were originally printed?
39. A bankrupt is able to pay 56p in the £ to his creditors. How much does a creditor lose who is owed £20?
40. Three men win £10 000 on the football pools. They agree to share this sum in the same ratio as their weekly stake i.e. 2 : 3 : 5. How much does each receive?

1.5 Percentage

Percentage (or %) means 'out of a hundred'.

e.g. 3 per cent $= 3\% = \dfrac{3}{100}$

Any fraction or decimal fraction can be converted into a percentage by multiplying the fraction by 100.

Example 1

$$\frac{1}{5} = \frac{1}{5} \times 100\ \% = 20\%$$

$$0{\cdot}025 = 0{\cdot}025 \times 100\ \% = 2{\cdot}5\% \text{ or } 2\tfrac{1}{2}\%$$

A percentage can be converted into a fraction by dividing the percentage by 100.

Example 2

$$7\tfrac{1}{2}\% = \frac{7\frac{1}{2}}{100} = \frac{15}{200} = \frac{3}{40}$$

$$18\tfrac{3}{4}\% = 18{\cdot}75\% = \frac{18{\cdot}75}{100} = 0{\cdot}1875$$

To find a percentage of a given quantity, change the percentage to a fraction, and calculate the fraction of the quantity.

Example 3

Find 66% of £250.

$$66\% \text{ of } £250 = \frac{\overset{33}{\cancel{66}}}{\underset{\underset{1}{\cancel{50}}}{\cancel{100}}} \times \overset{5}{\cancel{250}} = £165$$

To express one quantity as a percentage of another, first express that quantity as a fraction of the other. Then change this fraction into a percentage.

Example 4

Express £19 as a percentage of £80.

$$\text{Required percentage} = \frac{19}{\underset{4}{\cancel{80}}} \times \overset{5}{\cancel{100}} = \frac{95}{4} = 23\tfrac{3}{4}\%$$

Example 5

Express 4 km as a percentage of 750 m.

$$\text{Required percentage} = \frac{\overset{800}{\cancel{4000}}}{\underset{\underset{3}{\cancel{15}}}{\cancel{750}}} \times \overset{2}{\cancel{100}} = \frac{1600}{3} = 533\tfrac{1}{3}\%.$$

Exercise 1.5

Convert the following fractions to percentages

1. $\frac{1}{2}$ $\frac{1}{4}$ $\frac{3}{4}$ **2.** $\frac{1}{3}$ $\frac{2}{3}$ **3.** $\frac{1}{5}$ $\frac{2}{5}$ $\frac{3}{5}$ $\frac{4}{5}$ **4.** $\frac{1}{6}$ $\frac{5}{6}$
5. $\frac{1}{7}$ $\frac{3}{7}$ $\frac{5}{7}$ **6.** $\frac{1}{8}$ $\frac{3}{8}$ $\frac{5}{8}$ $\frac{7}{8}$ **7.** $\frac{1}{9}$ $\frac{5}{9}$ $\frac{7}{9}$ **8.** $\frac{1}{11}$ $\frac{3}{11}$ $\frac{7}{11}$
9. $\frac{3}{13}$ $\frac{7}{15}$ **10.** $\frac{3}{23}$ $\frac{17}{29}$

Change the following decimal fractions to percentages

11. 0·65 0·25 **12.** 0·02 0·09
13. 0·125 0·455 **14.** 0·0025 0·0075 **15.** *1·325 4·675*

Convert the following percentages to fractions

16. 5% 10% 80% **17.** 12% 18% 48%
18. $33\frac{1}{3}\%$ $81\frac{1}{3}\%$ **19.** 125% $128\frac{4}{7}\%$ **20.** $6\frac{2}{3}\%$ $14\frac{3}{8}\%$

Convert the following percentages to decimal fractions

21. 75% 83% **22.** 6% 1%
23. $12\frac{1}{2}\%$ $87\frac{1}{2}\%$ **24.** $6\frac{1}{4}\%$ $3\frac{3}{4}\%$ **25.** 136% $618\frac{1}{2}\%$

Find the value of the following

26. 15% of £1 **27.** 23% of 15 g **28.** 94% of 16 m **29.** 37% of 1 h 10 min.
30. 205% of 14 km/h **31.** 135% of 40p
32. $12\frac{1}{2}\%$ of £11·20 **33.** $68\frac{3}{4}\%$ of 2·56 m
34. $108\frac{1}{3}\%$ of 75 m **35.** $109\frac{1}{11}\%$ of £33·22

Express the first quantity in each of the following pairs as a percentage of the second

36. 15 75 **37.** 18 48 **38.** 82 96 **39.** 140 65
40. 286 180 **41.** 20p £1·50 **42.** 1 km 850 m **43.** 22 min 1 h 10 min.
44. 16 mm 14 m **45.** 23 cm^2 1 m^2

46. A man pays income tax at the rate of 30% on his salary of £3250 per annum. How much does he pay?

47. In a crate of 144 eggs, $4\frac{1}{6}\%$ were bad. How many were good?

48. A student gains 70 marks out of a possible 150 in an examination. What percentage is this? If he needs 40% to pass, did he pass or not?

49. A man whose income is £1200 per annum, spends 30% of it on rent. How much has he left?

50. In an election there were two candidates. They received 51% and 26% of the votes of the total electorate respectively. If 4600 voters failed to vote, how many in all could have voted?

1.6 Profit and loss

Cost price is the price of an article paid by the shopkeeper. *Selling price* is the price for which the shopkeeper sells the article.

$$\text{Profit} = (\text{selling price}) - (\text{cost price})$$

$$\text{Percentage profit} = \frac{\text{profit}}{\text{cost price}} \times 100\ \%$$

Example 1

Calculate the percentage profit when a shopkeeper buys a chair for £50 and sells it for £66·50.

$$\text{Selling price} = £66{\cdot}50;\ \text{cost price} = £50$$

$$\therefore \text{Profit} = £66{\cdot}50 - £50 = £16{\cdot}50$$

$$\%\ \text{profit} = \frac{£16{\cdot}50}{£50} \times 100\ \% = 33\%$$

$$\text{Loss} = (\text{cost price}) - (\text{selling price})$$

$$\text{Percentage loss} = \frac{\text{loss}}{\text{cost price}} \times 100\ \%$$

Example 2

A car costing £1200 was sold for £800. Calculate the percentage loss.

$$\text{Cost price} = £1200;\ \text{selling price} = £800$$

$$\therefore \text{Loss} = £1200 - £800 = £400$$

$$\%\ \text{loss} = \frac{\overset{100}{\cancel{£400}}}{\underset{\cancel{12}\ 3}{\cancel{£1200}}} \times \overset{1}{\cancel{100}}\ \% = \frac{100}{3} = 33\tfrac{1}{3}\%.$$

Profit and loss problems are most often calculated on the cost price as 100%. On this basis:

(a) a profit of 6% means that the cost price has been increased in the ratio 100 : 106.

(b) a loss of 6% means that the cost price has been reduced in the ratio 100 : 94.

Example 3

A shopkeeper loses 4% by selling a coat for £48. At what price should he have sold the coat to make a profit of 4%?

$$\text{Selling price is } 96\% = £48$$

$$\text{Cost price is } 100\% = £48 \times \frac{100}{96}$$

$$\therefore \text{ new selling price is } 104\% = £48 \times \frac{100}{96} \times \frac{104}{100}$$

$$= £52$$

Exercise 1.6

Calculate the percentage profit in each case

1. Cost price £15 profit 50p
2. Cost price £22 profit £1
3. Cost price £12·50 profit £1·50
4. Cost price £260 profit £6·50
5. Cost price £840 profit £7
6. Cost price £10 selling price £13
7. Cost price £12 selling price £18
8. Cost price £25 selling price £27
9. Cost price £105 selling price £120
10. Cost price £3000 selling price £3500

Calculate the selling price in each case

11. Cost price £20 profit 9%
12. Cost price 28p profit 25%
13. Cost price £75 profit 8%
14. Cost price £75 loss 8%
15. Cost price £125 loss 15%
16. Cost price £2500 profit $12\frac{1}{2}\%$
17. Cost price £36·50 loss 35%
18. Cost price £19·80 profit 15%

Calculate the cost price in each case

19. Selling price £12 loss 4%
20. Selling price £21 gain 5%
21. Selling price £180 loss 10%
22. Selling price £56 gain $6\frac{2}{3}\%$
23. Selling price £102 gain $13\frac{1}{3}\%$
24. Selling price £196 loss 51%
25. Selling price £72 gain $12\frac{1}{2}\%$
26. Selling price £34 gain 36%
27. Selling price £20·50 loss 18%
28. Selling price £51 loss $23\frac{1}{2}\%$
29. By selling an article for £3·24, a man makes 35% profit. Find the selling price at which he would make 20% profit.
30. A merchant gains 110% by selling goods at £70 per tonne. What would he need to sell them at to make 140% profit?
31. A man sold an article for £60·48 at a profit of 12%. Find his gain per cent if he had sold it for £67·50.
32. *A* sells a car to *B* at a loss of 10%. *B* sells it to *C* at a loss of 12%. If *C* paid £495 for it, how much did *A* pay when he first bought it?
33. *A* sells to *B* at a profit of 12%. *B* sells to *C* at a profit of 10% and *C* sells to *D* at a profit of $7\frac{1}{2}\%$. If *A* had sold directly to *D* at the same price *D* paid *C*, what would *A*'s percentage profit have been? Give your answer to the nearest whole number.
34. A milkman buys 400 litres of milk for £40. He adds 40 litres of water, but then spills 5% of the mixture. If he now sells it at $6\frac{1}{2}$p per half litre what is his percentage profit?
35. Potatoes cost £100 a tonne today. By next week they will have risen in price by 5%, but may fall by 5% next year. What will the price then be? Answer to the nearest penny.

1.7 Simple interest

If £P is the sum invested (the principal), then the profit return on this investment (the interest I) when invested at Simple Interest over a number of years Y is given by the formula

$$I = \frac{P \times R \times Y}{100} = \frac{PRY}{100}$$

where R is the percentage return each year or the rate per cent per annum.

Note that: amount = principal + interest

Example 1

Find the simple interest on £440 for 6 months at $12\frac{1}{2}\%$ p.a.
i.e. find I when P = £440, R = $12\frac{1}{2}\%$, Y = $\frac{1}{2}$ year.

$$\therefore\ I = \frac{440 \times 12\frac{1}{2} \times \frac{1}{2}}{100} = \frac{\overset{11}{\cancel{\overset{22}{\cancel{440}}}} \times \overset{5}{\cancel{25}} \times 1}{\underset{\cancel{20}}{\cancel{100}} \times \underset{1}{\cancel{2}} \times 2}$$

$$= £\frac{55}{2} = £27\frac{1}{2} = £27{\cdot}50$$

Example 2

Find the percentage rate at which £440 will gain £51 interest in 9 months.
i.e. find R when P = £440, Y = $\frac{3}{4}$ year, I = £51

$$\text{Changing the formula, } R = \frac{100 \times I}{P \times Y}$$

$$= \frac{100 \times 51}{440 \times \frac{3}{4}}$$

$$= \frac{\overset{10}{\cancel{100}} \times \overset{17}{\cancel{51}} \times \overset{1}{\cancel{4}}}{\underset{11}{\cancel{\underset{110}{\cancel{440}}}} \times \underset{1}{\cancel{3}}}$$

$$= \frac{170}{11} = 15\tfrac{5}{11}\%$$

Exercise 1.7

Find the simple interest and the amount at simple interest on

1. £100 for 2 years at 3%
2. £200 for 3 years at 2%
3. £400 for 6 years at 2%
4. £500 for 4 years at 3%
5. £700 for 3 years at 5%
6. £150 for 3 years at 4%
7. £200 for 4 years at $2\frac{1}{2}\%$
8. £250 for $3\frac{1}{2}$ years at 3%
9. £125 for $4\frac{1}{2}$ years at 2%
10. £130 for 2 years at $7\frac{1}{2}\%$

Find, to the nearest penny, the simple interest on

11. £46 for 2 years at $2\frac{1}{2}$%

12. £132 for 3 years at $3\frac{1}{2}$%

13. £108 for 3 years at $3\frac{1}{2}$%

14. £162 at 2 years at $2\frac{3}{4}$%

15. £192 for 4 years at $3\frac{1}{4}$%

16. £42·50 for 3 years at 6%

17. £2006 for 5 years at $6\frac{1}{2}$%

18. £1822 for 4 years at $5\frac{3}{4}$%

19. £8462 for 3 years at $5\frac{1}{4}$%

20. £4123 for 5 years at $4\frac{3}{4}$%

Find the unknown quantities in questions **21** to **30**

	Principal	*Interest*	*Amount*	*Time*	*Rate per cent*
21.	£100	£9	–	3 yrs	–
22.	–	£12	–	3 yrs	4%
23.	£150	£50	–	–	$2\frac{1}{2}$%
24.	–	£70	£210	–	6%
25.	£1000	£81	–	$4\frac{1}{2}$ yrs	–
26.	£850	–	£867	–	4%
27.	–	£102	–	$2\frac{1}{2}$ yrs	$5\frac{1}{3}$%
28.	£500	–	£605	6 yrs	–
29.	£600	£126	–	–	6%
30.	£192	£8·80	–	–	$2\frac{3}{4}$%

31. A man borrows £100 at 4% per month simple interest. After a year he pays back £100. How much does he still owe?

32. A man buys a car for £650. At the end of a year it has depreciated in value by 10% and at the end of the second year by a further 8% of its value at the end of the first year. What is it now worth?

33. A man borrows £200 on condition that he pays back £250 after 9 months. At what rate per annum was interest charged?

34. If a Building Society increases its rate of interest from $6\frac{1}{4}$% to $6\frac{1}{2}$% per annum how much extra is paid on a deposit of £5000.

35. If the rate of interest is decreased from 6% to $5\frac{3}{4}$% find how much less is paid per half year on a loan of £8000.

36. The rate of interest on a loan is raised from 4% to $5\frac{1}{2}$%. This produces £54 more income. What was the original loan?

37. How long will it take a sum of money invested at 6% simple interest to increase in value by 15%?

38. A man buys a house for £10 000. He pays a 10% deposit and the remainder in instalments over 20 years. If simple interest is charged at 5% on the whole sum not paid at the time of purchase for the 20 years what did the man pay in all?

39. A man deposited £500 in a bank and at the end of the first year £25 interest was added. The whole sum was left in the bank for a further year and interest again added at the same rate. What did the sum amount to at the end of this time?

40. A man is paid an annual salary of £5000 for 4 years. At the end of the first year he invests 6% of his income for that year in a Building Society which pays interest at the rate of 6%. He does this again at the end of each of the next two years. What has he received in all at the end of the fourth year?

1.8 Compound interest

In this method of investment, the interest is added to the principal at the end of each period of time.
Thus the amount at the end of each period becomes the principal for the next period.
To calculate the interest
either (a) use repeated simple interest
or (b) use the formula $A = P\left(1 + \frac{r}{100}\right)^n$

where A is the amount,
P is the principal
r is the rate per cent per annum
n is the time in years.

This calculation is usually done using logarithms.

Example 1

Find the compound interest on £400 for 3 years at 10% p.a., using the simple interest method.

Principal (in £'s)	=	400
Interest in 1st year	=	40
Principal for 2nd year	=	440
Interest in 2nd year	=	44
Principal for 3rd year	=	484
Interest in 3rd year	=	48·40
Amount	=	532·40
Principal	=	400·00
Compound interest	=	£132·40

Example 2

Find the compount interest on £876 for 10 years at 6% p.a.

In the formula $A = P\left(1 + \frac{r}{100}\right)^n$, P = £876, r = 6%, n = 10 years.

$\therefore A = 876\left(1 + \frac{6}{100}\right)^{10}$

$= 876\,(1{\cdot}06)^{10}$

$= 1570$ (3 S.F.)

No.	Log.
$(1{\cdot}06)^{10}$	0·0253 X 10
	0·2530
876	2·9425
1569	3·1955

$\therefore$ compound interest = amount − principal
= £1570 − £876
= £694

Exercise 1.8

Find the compound interest (payable annually) on the following sums. (Give answers to the nearest penny where applicable.)

1. £180 for 2 years at 5%
2. £210 for 3 years at 4%
3. £135 for 2 years at 3%
4. £50 for $3\frac{1}{2}$ years at 6%
5. £2500 for 2 years at $3\frac{1}{2}$%
6. £1750 for 3 years at $5\frac{1}{2}$%
7. £1000 for $2\frac{1}{2}$ years at $4\frac{1}{2}$%
8. £825 for 2 years at $4\frac{3}{4}$%
9. £190 for 3 years at $2\frac{3}{4}$%
10. £84 for $2\frac{1}{2}$ years at $5\frac{3}{4}$%

Use the formula to find the amount at compound interest.

11. £100 for 10 years at $2\frac{1}{2}$%
12. £125 for 9 years at 3%
13. £78 for 12 years at 4%
14. £132 for 15 years at 5%
15. £184 for 8 years at 4%
16. £2672 for 6 years at $2\frac{1}{2}$%
17. £346 for 5 years at 3%
18. £826 for 20 years at $2\frac{1}{2}$%
19. £1620 for 4 years at $2\frac{1}{2}$%
20. £930 for 25 years at 4%
21. A car depreciates in value by 10% each year. If a new car costs £1200 how much is it worth at the end of three years?
22. A piece of machinery depreciates at the rate of 5% per year. If it costs £12 000 when new what is its value at the end of two years?
23. In how many years (correct to the nearest whole year) does it take a sum of money to double in value if compound interest is paid at the rate of 5%?
24. In how many years will a sum of money increase by half its value if compound interest is added at 4%?
25. The population of a certain town increases from 20 000 to 25 000 in 5 years. As accurately as you can, using the tables available, find the annual growth factor. (i.e. the percentage rate of increase at "compound interest".)
26. Find the difference between the simple and compound interest on £1500 for 3 years at 3% per annum.
27. Find the amount on a principal of £1000 in 2 years at 6% per annum, compound interest the interest being added half yearly.
28. In how many years will a sum of money double itself if invested at 4% per annum compound interest?
29. A sum of money was invested for 2 years at compound interest. At the end of the first year the money plus interest had amounted to £792, and at the end of the second year, including interest it had amounted to £871·20.
    Find (a) the rate % per annum at which the interest was paid; (b) the original sum of money invested.
30. The value of a car depreciates each year by 15% of its value at the beginning of the year. If the present value of the car is £1700, calculate (a) its value in two years time; (b) its value a year ago.

1.9 Averages

The *mean* is the sum of any number of quantities divided by the number of quantities.

$$\text{i.e. mean} = \frac{\text{sum}}{\text{total number of quantities}}$$

The *median* is the middle term of a set of quantities arranged in order of size, and is not necessarily a member of that set.

If there are n terms, then the median is the $\left(\frac{n+1}{2}\right)$th term.

The *mode* is the most frequent (most popular) item in a set of quantities.

Example 1

Find the mean, median, and mode of 23, 22, 22, 21, 20, 22, 18, 18, 21, 23.

$$\text{Mean} = \frac{23 + 22 + 22 + 21 + 20 + 22 + 18 + 18 + 21 + 23}{10}$$

$$= \frac{210}{10} = 21$$

The numbers in order of size are: 18, 18, 20, 21, 21, 22, 22, 22, 23, 23

$$\text{Median} = \frac{10 + 1}{2} = 5\tfrac{1}{2}\text{th term.}$$

∴ the median is halfway between the fifth and the sixth term.

$$= \frac{21 + 22}{2} = \frac{43}{2} = 21\tfrac{1}{2}$$

Mode. The most popular number is 22.

$$\text{Average speed} = \frac{\text{total distance travelled}}{\text{total time taken}}$$

Note that: when the distance is measured in kilometres, the time is measured in hours. When the distance is measured in metres, the time is measured in seconds.

Example 2

A man bicycles 2 km to the station at an average speed of 12 km/h. He then travels 48 km by train at an average speed of 80 km/h. Calculate the average speed for the whole journey.

$$\text{Time taken to bicycle} = \frac{2}{12}\text{ h} = 10\text{ mins.}$$

$$\text{Time taken by train} = \frac{48}{80}\text{ h} = 36\text{ mins.}$$

$$\therefore \text{ total time } = 46 \text{ min} = \frac{46}{60} \text{ h}$$

$$\text{total distance} = 48 + 2 = 50 \text{ km}$$

$$\therefore \text{ average speed} = \frac{50}{\frac{46}{60}} = \overset{25}{\cancel{50}} \times \frac{60}{\underset{23}{\cancel{46}}}$$

$$= \frac{1500}{23} = 65{\cdot}22 \text{ km/h}$$

Exercise 1.9

1. Find the average of the following
   (a) 2 4 6 8 10 (b) 5 km 7 km 19 km 23 km 48 km
   (c) 2·1 g 3·8 g 4·7 g 19·1 g 6 g (d) 15 h 8 h 16 h 48 h 81 h
   (e) $8°9'$ $19°1'$ $22°26'$ $36°4'$ $7°42'$
2. A man earns £50 for 8 days work. Find his average daily earnings.
3. A clock loses $2\frac{1}{2}$ minutes a day. What is the average time lost per hour correct to the nearest one hundredth of a second?
4. A batsman scores 576 runs in 24 innings. What was his average score?
5. A trader buys 50 sacks of potatoes at £5 a sack and 100 sacks at £4·80 a sack. What is the average price per sack, correct to the nearest penny?
6. A greengrocer sells 25 kg of apples at 21p per kg, 28 kg at 22p per kg and 46 kg at 23p per kg. What is the average price per kg, correct to the nearest penny?
7. A batsman scores 24, 15 and 48 runs in successive innings. What must he score in his next innings if he is to maintain an average of 25 runs per innings?
8. Seven members of a rowing eight weigh respectively 50, 48, 52, 59, 54, 56 and 60 kg. What is the weight of the eighth member if their average weight is 55 kg?
9. A cyclist rides 75 km at 15 km/h and a further 60 km at 12 km/h. What is his average speed?
10. A man walks round the four sides of a square park at 4, 3, 2 and 1 km/h respectively. What is his average speed?
11. A motorist drives at 64 km/h for 2 hours and then 84 km/h for half an hour. What is his average speed?
12. A train is timed to make a journey of 60 km at 80 km/h. It starts 5 minutes late. At what speed must it run to arrive on time?
13. A train normally runs 16 km in 24 minutes. What is its average speed? On a particular journey, owing to track repairs, after running at its normal speed for 4 km it has to travel the next 500 m at 10 km/h. What must its average speed be during the rest of the journey so that it may arrive on time?

Find the mean, mode and median of each of the following

14. 1, 1, 1, 2, 2, 2, 2, 2, 3, 4
15. 1, 1, 2, 2, 2, 2, 3, 3, 10, 14
16. 1, 2, 3, 7, 9, 2, 7, 11, 13
17. 3, 5, 5, 4, 8, 6, 5, 5, 4, 5
18. 12, 12, 11, 38, 37, 39, 13, 14
19. 2, 3, 4, 7, 5, 7, 3, 3, 10, 4, 9
20. 24, 21, 20, 25, 21, 27
21. 3, 3, 1, 2, 2, 3, 2, 4, 5, 4, 3, 4, 2, 3, 3, 4
22. 86, 82, 78, 93, 86, 84, 90, 85, 79, 86, 85, 88, 81, 87

1.10 Squares, square roots, reciprocals

The square of 4 is 16.
It is written $4^2 = 4 \times 4 = 16$
The square of 40 is 1600
It is written $40^2 = 40 \times 40 = 1600$
The square root of 16 is 4
It is written $\sqrt{16} = 16^{\frac{1}{2}} = 4$
The square root of 160 is 12·65 (to 4 S.F.)
It is written $\sqrt{160} = 160^{\frac{1}{2}} = 12{\cdot}65$ (to 4 S.F.)
The square root of 1600 is 40
It is written $\sqrt{1600} = 1600^{\frac{1}{2}} = 40$

Be careful to use the appropriate square root table. Check your answer with a rough estimate.

The reciprocal of 4 is 0·25
It is written $\frac{1}{4}$ or $4^{-1} = 0{\cdot}25$
The reciprocal of $\frac{1}{4}$ is 4
It is written $(\frac{1}{4})^{-1} = \frac{4}{1} = 4$

When using four-figure tables of reciprocals, remember to *subtract* the mean difference.

When using tables of squares, square roots, or reciprocals, always find a rough estimate (R.E.) of the answer to avoid careless mistakes.

Examples

$(24{\cdot}21)^2 = 586{\cdot}1$ R.E. $20^2 = 400$
$(0{\cdot}002\,421)^2 = 0{\cdot}000\,005\,861$ R.E. $(0{\cdot}002)^2 = 0{\cdot}000\,004$
$\sqrt{242{\cdot}1} = 15{\cdot}56$ R.E. $\sqrt{225} = 15$
$\sqrt{24{\cdot}21} = 4{\cdot}920$ R.E. $\sqrt{25} = 5$
$\sqrt{0{\cdot}2421} = 0{\cdot}4920$ R.E. $\sqrt{0{\cdot}25} = 0{\cdot}5$
$\sqrt{0{\cdot}024\,21} = 0{\cdot}1556$ R.E. $\sqrt{0{\cdot}02} = 0{\cdot}14$
$\frac{1}{242{\cdot}1} = 242{\cdot}1^{-1} = 0{\cdot}004\,130$ R.E. $\frac{1}{200} = 0{\cdot}005$
$\frac{1}{0{\cdot}024\,21} = 0{\cdot}024\,21^{-1} = 41{\cdot}30$ R.E. $\frac{1}{0{\cdot}02} = 50$

Exercise 1.10

1. Without using tables, write down the squares of the following numbers

(a) 20	(b) 60	(c) 500	(d) 0·2	(e) 0·12
(f) 30	(g) 90	(h) 700	(i) 0·6	(j) 1·1
(k) 40	(l) 120	(m) 800	(n) 0·07	(o) 2·5

2. Without using tables, write down the square roots of the following numbers

(a) 16 (b) 0·25 (c) 400 (d) 0·64 (e) 0·0036
(f) 49 (g) 0·09 (h) 900 (i) 1·44 (j) 0·0009
(k) 81 (l) 0·01 (m) 3600 (n) 1·69 (o) 0·0001

3. Without using tables, write down the reciprocals of the following

(a) 5 (b) 4 (c) 8 (d) 0·5 (e) $2\frac{1}{5}$
(f) 10 (g) 100 (h) $\frac{1}{2}$ (i) 0·25 (j) 0·01
(k) 20 (l) 1000 (m) $\frac{1}{10}$ (n) 0·125 (o) 0·000 001

4. Use tables to write down the square of the following numbers

(a) 19 (b) 76 (c) 84 (d) 122 (e) 384
(f) 821 (g) 3·45 (h) 5·87 (i) 39·8 (j) 381·4
(k) 826·9 (l) 0·4592 (m) 43·88 (n) 1·367 (o) 0·0056
(p) 0·1062 (q) 98 100 (r) 0·060 79

5. Use tables to write down the square root of the following numbers

(a) 1·2 (b) 6·33 (c) 8·35 (d) 2·607 (e) 5·441
(f) 8·365 (g) 15 (h) 72 (i) 36·8 (j) 85·79
(k) 22·46 (l) 62·99 (m) 12 680 (n) 4822 (o) 821
(p) 0·8934 (q) 0·067 98 (r) 0·000 8267

6. Use tables to write down the reciprocal of the following numbers

(a) 3·4 (b) 77 (c) 690 (d) 824 (e) 6946
(f) 132 (g) 81·45 (h) 0·079 26 (i) 6·892 (j) 0·003 862
(k) 8615 (l) 36 920 (m) 0·004 576 (n) 79 630 (o) 1·594
(p) 265·8 (q) 0·1793 (r) 0·8211

7. Evaluate the following

(a) $\dfrac{1}{2{\cdot}643}+\dfrac{1}{3{\cdot}793}$ (b) $\dfrac{1}{86{\cdot}33}+\dfrac{1}{246{\cdot}7}$

(c) $\dfrac{1}{0{\cdot}0284}-\dfrac{1}{0{\cdot}3679}$ (d) $\dfrac{1}{\sqrt{600{\cdot}8}}-\dfrac{1}{(5{\cdot}692)^2}$

(e) $\dfrac{1}{\sqrt{(14{\cdot}9^2+26{\cdot}3^2)}}$

8. Find the value of x when $\dfrac{1}{x} = (6{\cdot}83)^2-(6{\cdot}38)^2$.

9. When $\dfrac{1}{R} = \dfrac{1}{r_1}+\dfrac{1}{r_2}+\dfrac{1}{r_3}$, find R if $r_1 = 0{\cdot}25$, $r_2 = 0{\cdot}35$, $r_3 = 0{\cdot}45$.

10. Evaluate $\sqrt{\left(\dfrac{1}{(0{\cdot}374)^2}+\dfrac{1}{0{\cdot}002\,43}\right)}$.

1.11 Logarithms

The logarithm of a number consists of a whole number called the *characteristic*, which can be either positive or negative and a decimal part called the *mantissa* which is always positive.

Example 1

The logarithm of 200 is 2·3010, where 2 is the characteristic and ·3010 is the mantissa.
The value of the characteristic is found by inspection and the value of the mantissa from tables of logarithms.
To multiply numbers together using logarithms, add their logarithms.
The answer is the antilogarithm of this sum.

Example 2 10·4 × 7·8
= 81·12

No.	Log.
10·4 × 7·8	1·0170 + 0·8921
81·12	1·9091

To divide one number by another, subtract their logarithms.
The answer is the antilogarithm of this subtraction.

Example 3 10·4 ÷ 7·8
= 1·333

No.	Log.
10·4 ÷ 7·8	1·0170 − 0·8921
1·333	0·1249

To raise a number to a given power, multiply the logarithm of the number by the power. The answer is the antilogarithm of this product.

Example 4 $(10{\cdot}4)^3$
= 1125

No.	Log.
$(10{\cdot}4)^3$	1·0170 × 3
1125	3·0510

To find a root of a number, divide the logarithm of the number by the required root. The answer is the antilogarithm of this division.

Example 5 $\sqrt{10{\cdot}4}$
$= (10{\cdot}4)^{\frac{1}{2}}$
= 3·225

No.	Log.
$\sqrt{10{\cdot}4}$	1·0170 ÷ 2
3·225	0·5085

To divide $\bar{2}{\cdot}3020$ by 3, write $\bar{2}{\cdot}3020$ as $\bar{3} + 1{\cdot}3020$.

Hence $$\frac{\bar{2}{\cdot}3020}{3} = \frac{\bar{3} + 1{\cdot}3020}{3} = \bar{1}{\cdot}4340$$

Calculations are usually presented in tabular form as follows, and answers given correct to 3 significant figures.

Example 6

Evaluate $\dfrac{\sqrt{0\cdot0074} \times (1\cdot42)^2}{0\cdot036} = 4\cdot82$ (3 S.F.)

No.	Calculation	Log.
$\sqrt{0\cdot0074}$	$\bar{3}\cdot8692 \div 2$	$\bar{2}\cdot9346$
$\times\ (1\cdot42)^2$	$0\cdot1523 \times 2$	$+\ 0\cdot3046$
		$\bar{1}\cdot2392$
$\div\ 0\cdot036$		$-\ \bar{2}\cdot5563$
$4\cdot818$		$0\cdot6829$

Exercise 1.11

1. 24×81
2. 75×49
3. 821×477
4. $564\cdot6 \times 39\cdot67$
5. $3\cdot469 \times 23\cdot68$
6. $569\cdot3 \times 9\cdot358$
7. $36\cdot58 \times 6\cdot459$
8. $56\cdot35 \times 7\cdot369$
9. $3\cdot559 \times 784\cdot6$
10. $6\cdot498 \div 4\cdot662$
11. $48\cdot69 \div 34\cdot22$
12. $981\cdot3 \div 567\cdot4$
13. $4\cdot893 \div 2\cdot557$
14. $82\cdot45 \div 76\cdot37$
15. $473\cdot2 \div 466\cdot5$
16. $378\cdot2 \div 366\cdot4$
17. $8\cdot662 \div 7\cdot399$
18. $9429 \div 5673$
19. $(10\cdot55)^2$
20. $(345\cdot8)^3$
21. $(9862)^{\frac{1}{2}}$
22. $(32\cdot68)^{\frac{1}{3}}$
23. $\sqrt{1178}$
24. $\sqrt{24\cdot79}$
25. $\sqrt{8\cdot239}$
26. $\sqrt[3]{567\cdot2}$
27. $\sqrt[4]{9982}$
28. $\dfrac{246\cdot8 \times 3\cdot496}{43\cdot69}$
29. $\dfrac{8\cdot274 \times 34\cdot99}{10\cdot59}$
30. $\dfrac{10\cdot09 \times 36\cdot22}{21\cdot08 \times 12\cdot46}$
31. $\dfrac{8234 \times \sqrt{9\cdot472}}{68\cdot49 \times 4\cdot592}$
32. $\dfrac{\sqrt[3]{462\cdot3}}{(1\cdot044)^2 \times 1\cdot6}$
33. $\dfrac{306\cdot2 \times \sqrt{34\cdot69}}{(2\cdot396)^3}$
34. $0\cdot268 \times 0\cdot923$
35. $0\cdot4583 \times 13\cdot22$
36. $467\cdot3 \times 0\cdot0034$
37. $76\cdot34 \times 0\cdot0935$
38. $0\cdot09482 \times 16\cdot39$
39. $8160 \times 0\cdot000\,6792$
40. $56\cdot77 \times 0\cdot009\,347$
41. $0\cdot3492 \times 56\cdot77$
42. $0\cdot007\,834 \times 81\cdot62$
43. $8631 \div 9962$
44. $5\cdot782 \div 0\cdot3492$
45. $0\cdot8935 \div 0\cdot05628$
46. $0\cdot4592 \div 0\cdot006\,739$
47. $23\cdot59 \div 478\cdot9$
48. $0\cdot005639 \div 0\cdot3492$
49. $6\cdot339 \div 594\cdot7$
50. $10\cdot88 \div 0\cdot7359$
51. $36\cdot45 \div 2897$
52. $(0\cdot4566)^2$
53. $(0\cdot029\,77)^3$
54. $(0\cdot6733)^4$
55. $\sqrt{0\cdot06733}$
56. $\sqrt{0\cdot09458}$
57. $\sqrt{0\cdot04388}$
58. $\sqrt{0\cdot8744}$
59. $\sqrt{0\cdot4388}$
60. $\sqrt{0\cdot7933}$
61. $\sqrt[3]{0\cdot7699}$
62. $\sqrt[3]{0\cdot09644}$
63. $\sqrt[4]{0\cdot006\,733}$
64. $\dfrac{3677 \times 4599}{4896 \times 5539}$
65. $\dfrac{821 \times \sqrt{0\cdot6735}}{(367\cdot8)^2}$
66. $\dfrac{4422 + \sqrt{3497}}{6217}$
67. $\dfrac{1}{0\cdot9688} + \dfrac{1}{0\cdot06635}$
68. $\dfrac{0\cdot07643 - 0\cdot06649}{\sqrt{0\cdot7633} + \sqrt[3]{0\cdot8462}}$
69. $4\cdot962 - \dfrac{(0\cdot7633)^3}{\sqrt[4]{3\cdot779}}$
70. $(0\cdot5788)^{1\frac{1}{2}}$

1.12 Rates and taxes

The 'product of a penny rate' is the amount of money raised when a rate of 1p in the £1 is levied on each £1 of Rateable Value (R.V.). Every property in the area of a Local Authority is given a Rateable Value dependent on its size and amenities, i.e. the property is assessed.

rates payable = R.V. × (rate in the £1)

Example 1

The total Rateable Value of a Local Authority is £27 500 000.

(a) How much would be raised from a penny rate?

(b) The cost to the Local Authority of the Social Services is £3 162 500. Calculate the rate in the £1 which has to be levied to meet this cost.

Product of penny rate = 27 500 000p = £275 000

Social Services rate $= \frac{3\,162\,500}{275\,000} =$ 11·5p in the £1

Exercise 1.12a

1. A man's house is assessed at £190 and last year the rate in the £ was 90p. How much was his rate bill?
2. A man whose house is assessed at £150 paid a half-yearly rate bill of £84. What rate in the £ did this represent?
3. The rateable value of a certain house is assessed at two-fifths of the annual rent. If the rent is £5 a week and the 'rates' are 85p in the £ how much is the annual rate bill?
4. The 'rates' are 94p in the £ on a house assessed at £240. If education is paid for by a 17p rate, how much is the annual rate bill for the house and how much of it goes to pay for education?
5. The rateable value of a house used to be £120 when the rate in the £ was 85p. On reassessment the rateable value was increased to £200 but the rate in the £ reduced to 45p. How much more or less is the new annual rate bill?
6. The rateable value of a certain town is £4374 500. What rate in the £ (to the nearest penny) must be levied to produce an annual revenue of £885 425? At this rate what must be paid each half year by a householder whose house is assessed at £140?
7. A borough with a rateable value of £4 821 000 has to raise the sum of £98 562 for road works. How much, to the nearest penny, will have to be added to the annual rate in the £. How much more will this cost a man whose house is assessed at £175 per annum?
8. How much is raised by a penny rate in a borough of total rateable value £5 846 200?
9. In a certain town a penny rate brings in £48 200. If 28p in the £ is allocated to education, what is the total cost of this service? How much towards this does a householder pay whose house is assessed at £82 per half year?
10. A rate of 1·7p in the £ is levied to pay for the public libraries in a town whose total rateable value is £2 840 000. Find the cost of running these libraries. Another town needs £37 200 and has to levy the same 1·7p in the £. How much, correct to the nearest £, is the rateable value of this town?

Income Tax is a percentage of taxable income.

taxable income = (gross income) − (allowances)

Example 2

A married man is allowed to deduct £955 from his income before paying tax. If his taxable income is taxed at 35%, how much tax will he pay when he earns £5600 in a year?

Taxable income = £5600 − £955 = £4645

Tax paid = 35% of £4645 = £1625·75

Exercise 1.12b

1. A man's salary is £3500 a year. His taxable income is found by deducting the following amounts from that sum
   (a) Married man's allowance of £750.
   (b) Childrens' allowance of £400 for each of two children
   (c) Interest on mortgage repayments £240
   (d) Two fifths of life insurance premium of £40.
   He pays income tax at 30%. How much tax does he pay?
2. A single man earns £1200 a year. Before paying tax at $33\frac{1}{3}$% he is able to make the following deductions
   (a) Single man's allowance £605
   (b) Dependent relative's allowance £100
   (c) Clothing and equipment necessary for his work £80.
   How much does he have left after paying tax? (Correct to the nearest penny.)
3. With allowances already mentioned in questions 1 and 2, find how much tax a married man with one child and one dependent relative must pay if the standard rate of income tax is 30% and his income is £2500 per annum.
4. How much extra tax must the man in question 3 pay if his salary is increased by £100 per annum?
5. The man in question 1 now moves to another job for which the salary is £4500 per year. However, he has to pay 5% of this to a superannuation scheme; this sum not being subject to tax. What is his new net salary after tax?
6. A taxpayer has an Income Tax Code Number 143, i.e. the first £1430 of his annual income is tax free. If he pays tax at the standard rate of 35p in the £, calculate
   (a) the amount of tax he pays when his annual income is £5782
   (b) the percentage of his total income he then pays in tax
   (c) his total income if he pays £1715 in tax.
7. A citizen has an Income Tax Code Number 121. If he pays income tax at the standard rate of 35p in the £ on all his taxable income up to £4500, and at the rate of 40p in the £ on the remainder, calculate
   (a) the amount of tax he pays each week when his annual income is £6725. (Answer to the nearest p).
   (b) the percentage of his total income he pays in tax.

1.13 Foreign exchange

In the British system of decimal currency, the pound (£) is the basic unit.

100 pence = 1 pound sterling
100p = £1

All other major currency systems use the decimal system also.

Questions usually involve the use of simple ratios based upon current rates of exchange. In this exercise, the following rates of exchange will be used, though these rates are constantly changing.

Country	Monetary unit	Exchange rate
Belgium	100 centimes = 1 franc	BF 70 = £1
Canada	100 cents = 1 dollar	C$ 1·76 = £1
France	100 centimes = 1 franc	Fr. 8·67 = £1
Germany (Federal Republic)	100 pfennig = 1 mark	DM 4·42 = £1
Hong Kong	100 cents = 1 dollar	HK$ 8·8 = £1
Japan	yen	Y 512 = £1
Malaysia	100 sen = 1 ringgit	M$ 4·55 = £1
Nigeria	100 kobo = 1 naira	₦ 1·68 = £1
Portugal	100 centavos = 1 escudo	Es. 55 = £1
South Africa	100 cents = 1 rand	R 2·1 = £1
Switzerland	100 centimes = 1 franc	Fr. 4·34 = £1
U.S.A.	100 cents = 1 dollar	US $ 1·8 = £1

Example 1

If the rate of exchange is 1·76 dollars to the £1, how many dollars would a man receive for £52·50?

$$\text{Number of dollars} = 52{\cdot}5 \times 1{\cdot}76 = 92{\cdot}40$$

Example 2

In England, petrol costs 80p per gallon. What would be the equivalent cost per litre in France? (Take 1 litre = 0·22 gallon and £1 = 8·67 francs).

$$\text{80p per gallon} = 0{\cdot}8 \times 8{\cdot}67 = 6{\cdot}94 \text{ francs}$$

$$1 \text{ gallon} = \frac{1}{0{\cdot}22} = 4{\cdot}55 \text{ litres}$$

$$\therefore \quad \text{cost per litre} = \frac{6{\cdot}94}{4{\cdot}55} = 1{\cdot}52 \text{ francs (to 2 D.P.)}$$

Exercise 1.13

1. Convert the following sterling amounts
   (a) £38 into Swiss francs
   (b) £16·45 into Malaysian dollars
   (c) £16·75 into Nigerian naira
   (d) £2369 into Canadian dollars
   (e) £1546 into Japanese yen
   (f) £19·40 into Hong Kong dollars
   (g) £34·32 into U.S. dollars
   (h) £22·41 into German marks
2. Convert the following into sterling
   (a) 1820 Belgian francs
   (b) 3400 Swiss francs
   (c) 2300 Nigerian naira
   (d) 10 500 U.S. dollars
   (e) 140 South African rand
   (f) 1650 Canadian dollars
   (g) 1200 Portuguese escudos
   (h) 5400 Hong Kong dollars
   (i) 3765 French francs
   (j) 500 German marks
3. Find the sterling equivalent (to the nearest $\frac{1}{2}$p) of the unit of currency of the following.
   (a) French franc
   (b) U.S. dollar
   (c) Japanese yen
   (d) Swiss franc
   (e) Hong Kong dollar
   (f) Malaysian dollar
   (g) German mark
   (h) South African rand
   (i) Nigerian naira
   (j) Belgian franc
   (k) Canadian dollar
   (l) Portuguese escudo
4. A crate of 500 cricket bats is exported from Hong Kong to England through an agent who sells them to a shopkeeper for a total of HK$ 3344. If the shopkeeper sells them for 95p, what is his profit on each bat?
5. A certain spare part of a car engine is sold to a Nigerian agent at £2·20 each. If the agent orders 800 of these parts and he wishes to make a total profit of ₦500, at what price (in naira) should he sell them?
6. A Malaysian businessman flies from Kuala Lumpur to London, a total distance of 10 500 km and pays a fare of M$1570. If he now flies on to New York, another 5500 km, what extra fare in sterling would he expect to pay?
7. A man bought 15 watches in Switzerland for 700 francs. Find, to the nearest penny the value of each watch in England.
8. How many U.S. dollars are equivalent to 590 Canadian dollars?
9. How many Swiss francs are equivalent to (a) 1000 French francs? (b) 890 Belgian francs?
10. Butter in England costs 25p per kg. In Germany it costs 4 DM per kg. In which country is butter cheaper and by how much?
11. An English firm sold 8 cars at £1200 each to an Indian importer. If the rate of exchange was 8·6 rupees to the £1 and the importer wishes to make a profit of 25%, at what price would he have to sell each car in India?
12. A family spent a holiday in France, taking with them £400 which they changed into francs. They spend 3158 francs and changed the rest back to sterling at only 6·2 francs to the £1. What did the holiday cost?
13. If the distance from London to Brighton is 51 miles and the railway fare is £1·24, what would be the equivalent fare between two Belgian towns which are 47 km apart? (take 8 km = 5 miles).

Miscellaneous exercise 1

1. Consider the three decimal fractions 0·375, 0·385, 0·405.
   (a) What is the sum of these three decimal fractions?
   (b) Write down 0·375 as a vulgar fraction in its lowest terms.
   (c) How many millimetres is 0·385 of a kilometre?
   (d) Calculate the average of the three fractions as a decimal correct to two significant figures.
2. The cost of 1 tonne of coal was raised from £105 to £113·40. What was the % price increase?
3. Simplify the following, giving the answer as a fraction in its lowest terms: $\dfrac{3\frac{1}{3} \times 1\frac{1}{5}}{3\frac{7}{12} - 1\frac{3}{4}}$.
4. The cost of the theatre tickets for a party of 16 adults and 24 children was £88. If a child's ticket cost two-thirds of that of an adult, find the cost of an adult ticket.
5. (a) Without using tables, find the value of: $\dfrac{(4{\cdot}7 \times 0{\cdot}25) + (4{\cdot}7 \times 9{\cdot}75)}{4{\cdot}7 \times 0{\cdot}25}$.

   (b) Use tables to find the value (correct to 3 significant figures) of: $\dfrac{27{\cdot}29 + 63{\cdot}21}{27{\cdot}29 \times 63{\cdot}21}$.
6. A speedometer gives a correct reading when tyres of circumference 180 cm are used. If oversize tyres of circumference 190 cm are fitted, what is the true length of a journey which is recorded as 50 km? (Give your answer to 3 significant figures).
7. The Rateable Value of all the property in a small town is £2 175 000. The total cost of the library service is £76 125. What rate on the £ must be levied for this service?
8. The average sales in a shop for the first 11 weeks of a quarter was £868·30 per week. The sales for the two remaining weeks of the quarter averaged £846·85 per week. What was the average weekly sales for the quarter?
9. When petrol cost 16p per litre, a motorist used 24 litres per week. When the price of petrol was increased by $12\frac{1}{2}$%, the motorist decided to buy 4 litres less per week. How much is the difference between his old and his new weekly petrol bill?
10. (a) A packet of biscuits contains $7\frac{1}{2}$ ounces or 213 grams. Using these equivalent quantities calculate, correct to 3 significant figures, the number of grams in 1 lb.
    (b) In France, petrol costs 2·06 francs per litre. Calculate the equivalent cost per gallon in £ sterling correct to 2 decimal places (4·55 litres = 1 gallon; £1 = 8·26 francs).
11. (a) Calculate the sum £300 amounts to in 8 years @ 5% per annum compound interest.
    (b) Find the amount of interest earned by £1000 in 2 years @ 14% per annum compound interest.
    (c) In how many years will £400 amount to £463·05 at 5% per annum compound interest?
    (d) Calculate the sum repayable after 7 months if £1000 is borrowed at a rate of 1·5% per month compound interest. (Answer to the nearest £).
12. *A* is 50% older than *B*. By what per cent is *B* younger than *A*?
13. A retailer buys 27 portable television sets at £48 each. His marked selling price is 30% above this cost price. He sells 23 of them at this price, but, in order to clear his stock, he sells the remaining 4 in a sale at £42·96 each. Calculate his profit as a percentage of the cost price of the sets.

14. A class consists of 14 boys and 16 girls. In a mathematics examination the average mark of the boys was 59·5 and the average mark of the girls was 60·75. Find the average mark of the whole class to 3 S.F.

15. The cost of producing a carpet is divided between material and labour in the ratio 7 : 8. If the cost of material increases by 20% and the cost of labour increases by 11%, find the resulting percentage increase in the total cost of producing the carpet.

16. Two men X and Y invest £14 000 and £15 600 respectively in a business. As managing director X draws a salary of £5600 out of the total profits, and 7·5% of the remaining profit is put aside for depreciation of equipment. The remainder of the profit is then divided between the two men in the ratio of the amount of capital they invested.
Calculate (a) the total amount each man received when the total profit was £21 600.
(b) the total amount received by X, if Y had received £11 778.

17. In making raspberry jam a cook used:
6 kg of raspberries at 67·5 pence per kilo, 6 kg of sugar at 25 pence per kilo, and 3 lemons at 9 pence each.
In cooking the jam she used 2·5 therms of gas costing 17·2 pence per therm. She obtained 11·75 kg of jam. How much per kilo did the jam cost her? (Answer to the nearest penny.)

18. The distance the Earth moves round the Sun in 365 days is approximately 467 000 000 km. Calculate the distance travelled by the Earth in the month of August (31 days). Give the answer in Standard Form correct to 3 significant figures.

19. In a sale a shopkeeper gives a discount of 12 pence in the pound for all articles he sells for cash.
(a) What is the sale price of an article listed at £37·50?
(b) What is the sale price of an article which is reduced by £1·50?
(c) How much is saved by buying a record player in the sale whose sale price is £59·40?

20. A chronometer loses 0·0073 seconds every day. If it is correct at 12 noon on January 1st, 1977, what will be the correct time when the chronometer shows 12 noon on January 1st, 1978? (Answer to 3 decimal places).

Part 2 Mensuration

2.1 Simple areas

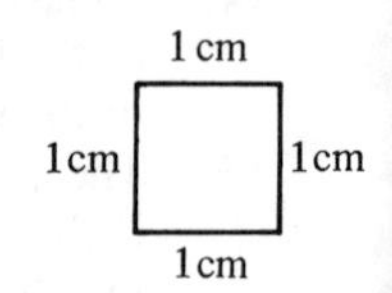

The unit of area is the square e.g. the area of the square shown is 1 cm^2.

Areas of rectilinear shapes (those with straight edges) are found as follows

(a) *Rectangle*

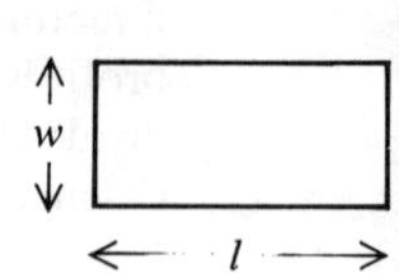

Area $= l \times w$
Perimeter $= 2l + 2w = 2(l + w)$

(b) *Parellelogram*

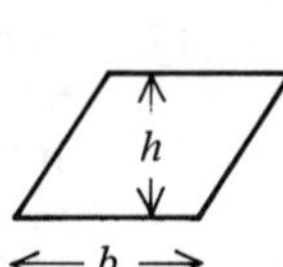

Area $= b \times h$, where h is the perpendicular distance between two parallel sides.

(c) *Rhombus*

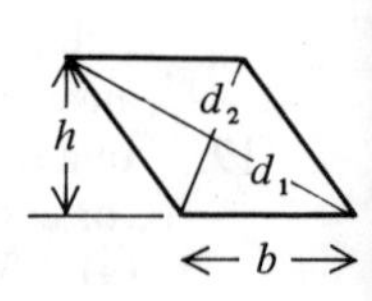

Area $= b \times h$,

or area $= \dfrac{d_1 \times d_2}{2}$, where d_1 and d_2 are the lengths of the diagonals.

(d) *Trapezium*

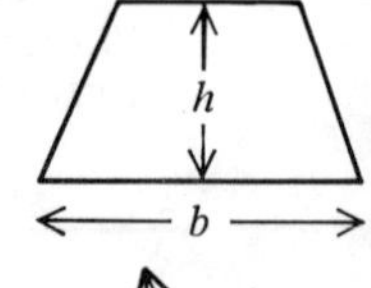

Area $= \left(\dfrac{a + b}{2}\right)h$, where a and b are the lengths of the parallel sides and h is the perpendicular distance between them.

(e) *Triangle*

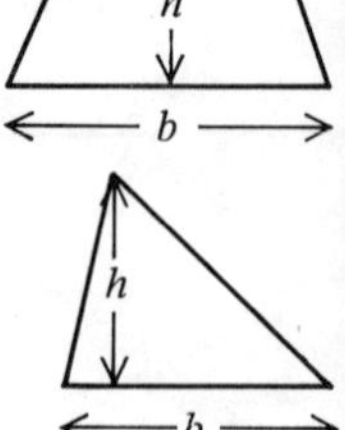

Area $= \dfrac{b \times h}{2}$

To find the area of an irregular shape, split the figure into rectilinear shapes.

Example 1

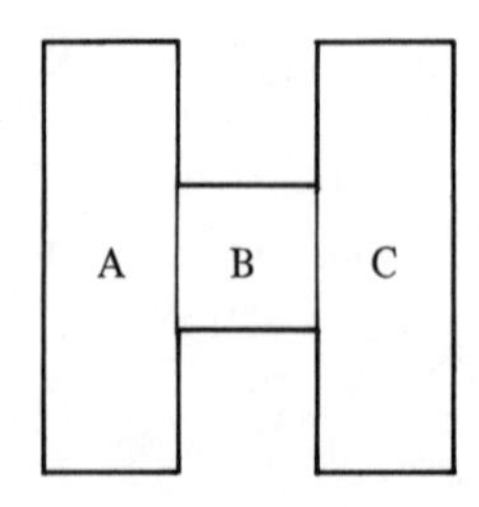

Area = area of A + area of B + area of C

Example 2

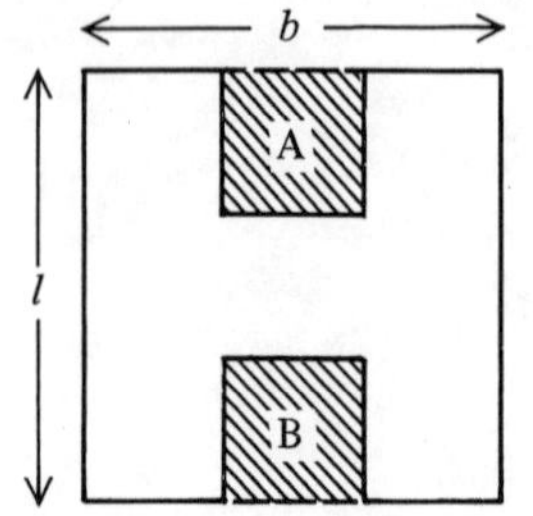

Area $= (l \times b) - ($area A + area B$)$

Exercise 2.1

1. Find the areas and perimeters of squares with the following sides
(a) 2 cm (b) 6 cm (c) 8·5 cm (d) 19·8 cm
2. Find the areas and perimeters of the following rectangles
(a) 4 cm by 6 cm (b) 8 cm by 12 cm (c) 9·5 cm by 8 cm (d) 6·5 cm by 2·5 cm
3. Find the areas of the figures below

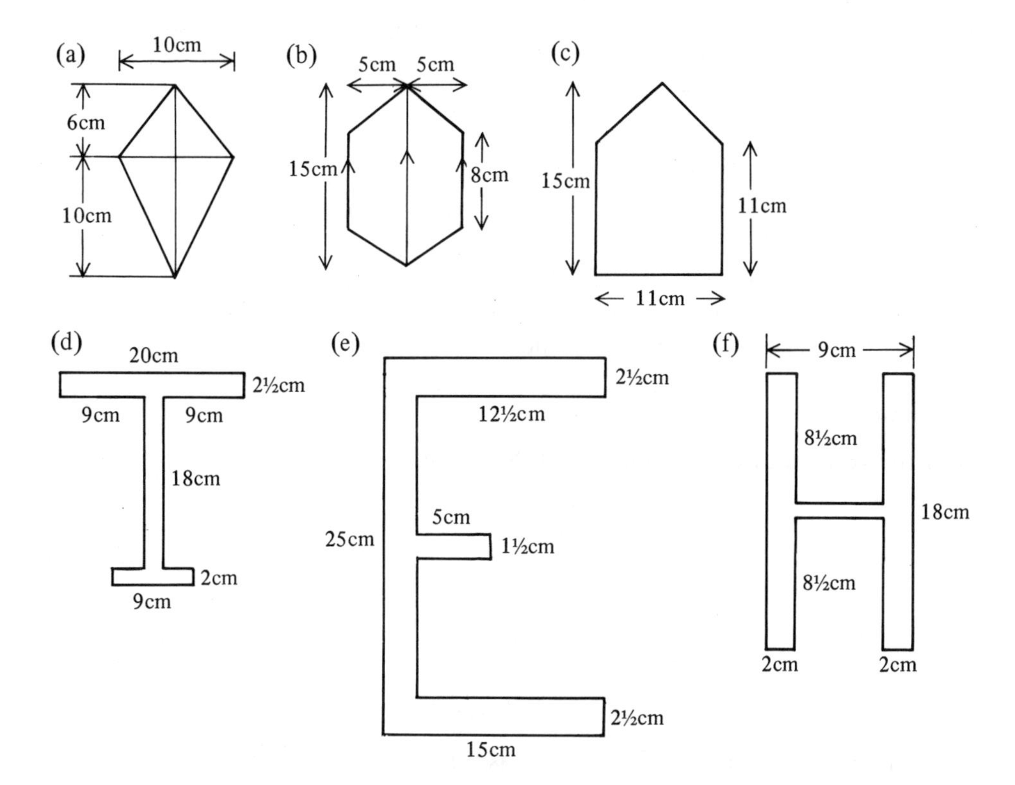

4. A rectangular pool 10 m by 5 m is surrounded by a path 1 m wide. What is the area of the path?
5. How many square tiles each of side 8 cm are needed to tile a floor 22 m 40 cm long by 12 m 80 cm wide?
6. How many complete tiles of side 12 cm must be used to cover a floor 3 m by 2 m? What area must now be covered by cut tiles?
7. Find the areas of the following triangles
(a) base 15 cm height 18 cm (b) base 7·5 cm height 21 cm (c) base 6·1 cm height 8·7 cm
(d) base = height = 6·25 cm
8. Find the area of the following parallelograms
(a) base 6 cm perpendicular height 8 cm (b) base 12 cm perpendicular height 9 cm
(c) base 4·8 cm perpendicular height 5 cm (d) base 7·2 cm perpendicular height 3·7 cm
9. Find the areas of the following trapeziums
(a) parallel sides 4 cm and 6 cm distance apart 3 cm
(b) parallel sides 9 cm and 12 cm distance apart 5 cm
(c) parallel sides 8·5 cm and 6·5 cm distance apart 4 cm
(d) parallel sides 16·1 cm and 18·1 cm distance apart 12·2 cm.

2.2 Volumes

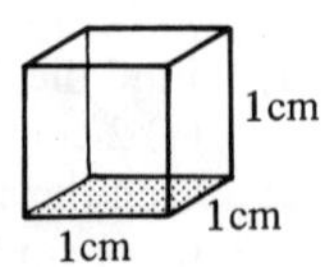

The unit of volume is the cube e.g. the volume of the cube is 1 cm³.

A prism is a solid which has uniform cross section throughout its length, as shown in the following examples.

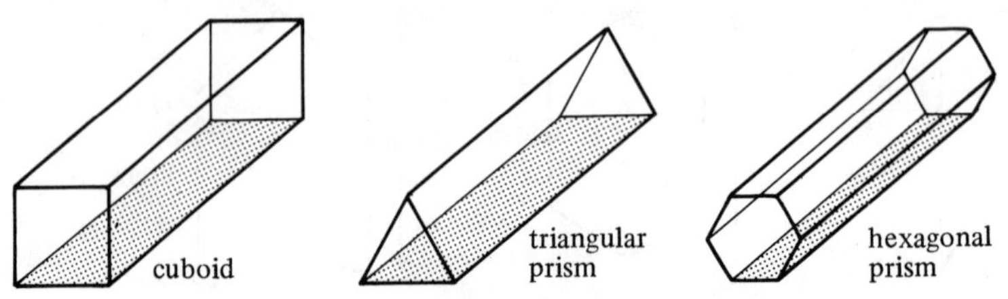

The *volume* of a prism = (area of cross section) × length
= (area of end) × length

Example

Find the volume of a triangular prism 8·4 cm high with its base 7·2 cm wide and 20 cm long.

$$\text{Area of end} = \frac{7\cdot2 \times 8\cdot4}{2}\ \text{cm}^2$$

$$\therefore \quad \text{volume} = \frac{7\cdot2 \times 8\cdot4}{\overset{}{\cancel{2}}_{\,1}} \times \overset{10}{\cancel{20}}\ \text{cm}^3$$

$$= 60\cdot48 \times 10 = 604\cdot8\ \text{cm}^3$$

8·4cm
20cm
7·2cm

Capacity is the volume of liquid, measured in litres, which a vessel of the same shape and size as a solid can hold.

1 litre is equivalent to 1000 cm³.

Hence the capacity of the triangular prism in the example is 0·6048 litres.

Density is the mass (or weight) in grams of 1 cubic centimetre of a substance and is measured in g/cm³. Water has a density of 1 g/cm³.

Exercise 2.2

1. Find the volumes of cubes of the following sizes
   (a) 3 cm (b) 8 cm (c) 19 cm (d) 84 cm
2. Find the volumes of the following rectangular solids
   (a) 2 cm by 3 cm by 4 cm (b) 5 cm by 8 cm by 9 cm (c) 21 cm by 19 cm by 17 cm
   (d) 6·2 cm by 8·1 cm by 3·4 cm

3. Find the volume of the following triangular prisms
   (a) end a right-angled triangle 3 cm by 4 cm by 5 cm, length 6 cm
   (b) end a triangle base 10 cm, height 8 cm, length 9 cm
   (c) end a triangle base 6·4 cm, height 14 cm, length 11 cm
   (d) end a triangle base 3·1 cm, height 2·7 cm, length 4·8 cm.
4. Find the volume of wood used in making an open wooden box 20 cm by 10 cm by 5 cm high if the wood used is $\frac{1}{2}$ cm thick throughout.
5. Find the weight of the box described in question 4 if the wood weighs 0·4 g per cm^3. (Give your answer correct to 3 significant figures.)
6. Find the volume and weight of wood used in making a closed box 25 cm by 15 cm by 12 cm high if the wood used is 0·75 cm thick throughout and weighs 0·5 g per cm^3. (Give your answer correct to 4 significant figures.)
7. Find the volume of water which can be contained in a trough 2 m long. The end of the trough is a trapezium of top and bottom 30 cm and 50 cm and height 20 cm. (Give your answer in m^3.)
8. Find the weight of a triangular steel wedge whose base is a square of side 3 cm and its length is 5 cm. Steel weighs 7·8 g per cm^3.
9. A rectangular tank 1 m by 90 cm contains water to a depth of 40 cm. If a 12 cm cube is now lowered into it how far does the water level rise?
10. A swimming bath is 30 m long by 10 m wide. It is 3 m deep at the deep end and 1 m deep at the shallow end. The floor slopes uniformly. It can be filled by a pipe which delivers 10 m^3 of water per minute. How long will it take (a) for the floor to be just covered and (b) for the bath to be completely filled?
11. Find the volume of gravel needed to make a 1 m wide path 5 cm deep round a lawn 24 m by 12 m.
12. An ingot of copper 24 cm long by 5 cm wide by 4 cm thick is drawn out into a wire of cross-sectional area 1·5 mm^2. How long is the wire?
13. In question 12 the copper weighs 8·9 g/cm^3. Find the weight of 100 m of the wire.
14. Two cubes have sides in the ratio 1 : 2. What is the ratio of (a) their surface areas and (b) their volumes and (c) their weights if the larger cube is only half as dense as the smaller one?
15. A jug 20 cm high holds $\frac{3}{4}$ of a litre. How much (in cm^3) will a jug of similar shape but only 15 cm high hold? (Give your answer to the nearest cm^3.)
16. A house has a rectangular floor plan 12 m by 8 m. The ridge of the roof is 13 m high and the eaves are 8 m from the ground. What percentage of the total interior volume of the house is wasted in the roof space? Will the answer be different if the house is 15 m long?
17. With the data of question 10 what volume of water must be run off to expose half the floor?
18. A room is 5 m long by 4 m wide by $2\frac{1}{2}$m high. Find the area of its walls allowing 6 m^2 for doors and windows.
19. A cardboard box 25 cm by 12 cm by 8 cm high is closed by a lid which has a 1 cm overlap. Find the total area of cardboard used in making the box.
20. A gardener uses a chemical fertilizer costing £1·20 per sack. Each sack covers 15 m^2. His garden is 30 m long by 10 m wide but has a path $\frac{3}{4}$m wide down one side and across the bottom. How much did the fertilizer cost? (He can only buy complete sacks.)

2.3 Circles, cylinders and pipes

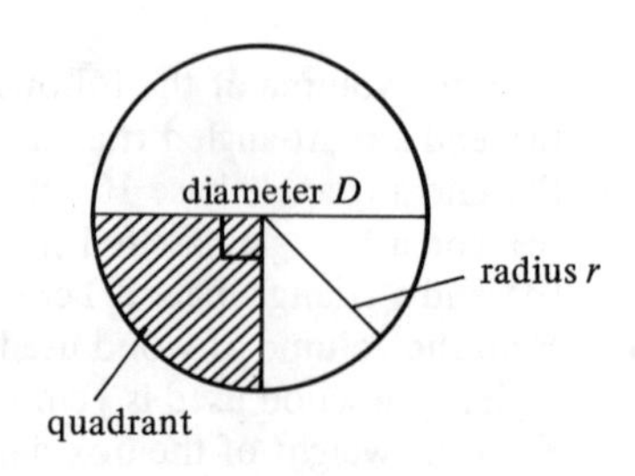

The circle

Circumference of a circle $= \pi D$ or $2\pi r$

Area of a circle $= \pi r^2$ or $\dfrac{\pi D^2}{4}$

Example

Find (a) the circumference (b) the area of a circle radius 14 cm $\left(\pi = \dfrac{22}{7}\right)$

(a) Circumference $= 2\pi r$

$$= 2 \times \frac{22}{7} \times 14 = 88 \text{ cm}$$

(b) Area $= \pi r^2 = \dfrac{22}{7} \times 14 \times 14 = 616 \text{ cm}^2$

The cylinder

Fig. 1

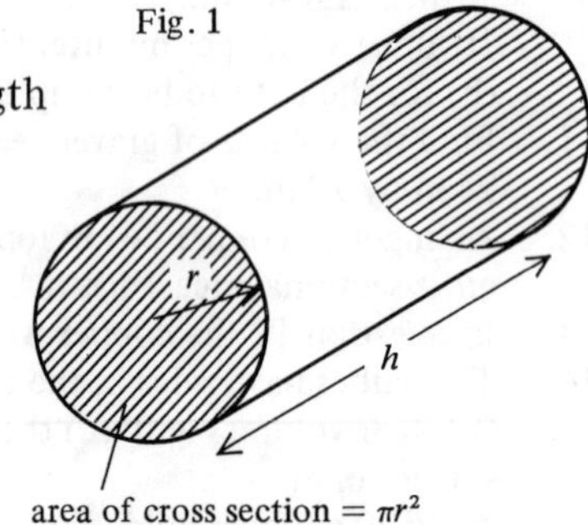

Volume of cylinder $=$ (area of cross section) $\times$ length

$= \pi r^2 h$ (Fig. 1)

Total surface area $=$ area of curved surface + area of ends

$= 2\pi rh + 2\pi r^2$

$= 2\pi r(h + r)$ (Fig. 2)

Example

Find the volume and total surface area of a solid cylindrical rod, radius 7 cm and length 21 cm $\left(\pi = \dfrac{22}{7}\right)$

Volume $= \pi r^2 h = \dfrac{22}{7} \times 7 \times 7 \times 21 = 3234 \text{ cm}^3$

Surface area $= 2\pi rh + 2\pi r^2$

$= 2\pi r(h + r)$

$= 2 \times \dfrac{22}{7} \times 7\,(21 + 7)$

$= 2 \times \dfrac{22}{7} \times 7 \times 28 = 1232 \text{ cm}^2$

Fig. 2

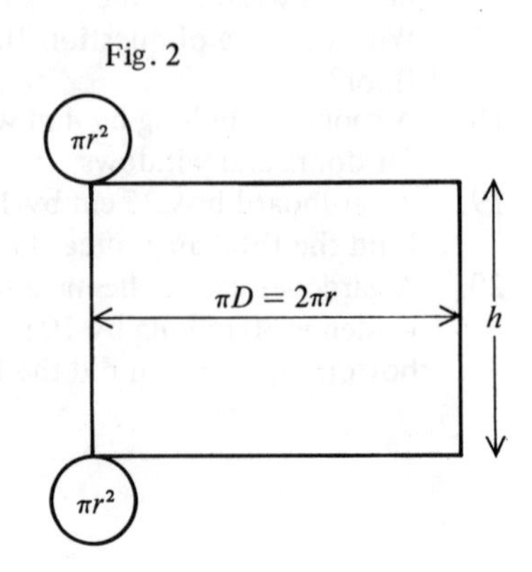

Exercise 2.3a

Take $\pi = 3{\cdot}142$ when you use logarithms and $\frac{22}{7}$ when you do not. Give your answers correct to 4 significant figures.

Find the circumferences and areas of circles with the following radii

1. 7 cm **2.** 28 cm **3.** 10 cm **4.** 19·61 cm **5.** 1·062 cm

Find the radii of the circles whose circumferences are

6. 11 cm **7.** 99 cm **8.** 104 cm **9.** 8·266 cm **10.** 0·8142 cm

Find the volumes and curved surface areas of the following cylinders

11. $r = 7$ cm $h = 9$ cm **12.** $r = 14$ cm $h = 2$ cm

13. $r = 9$ cm $h = 5$ cm **14.** $r = 1{\cdot}66$ cm $h = 3{\cdot}21$ cm

15. $r = 18{\cdot}51$ cm $h = 16{\cdot}27$ cm

The annulus

The area of an annulus (or ring) is the difference between the areas of two circles with the same centre.

$$\text{Area} = \pi R^2 - \pi r^2$$
$$= \pi (R + r)(R - r)$$
$$= \pi (R + r)\,t$$

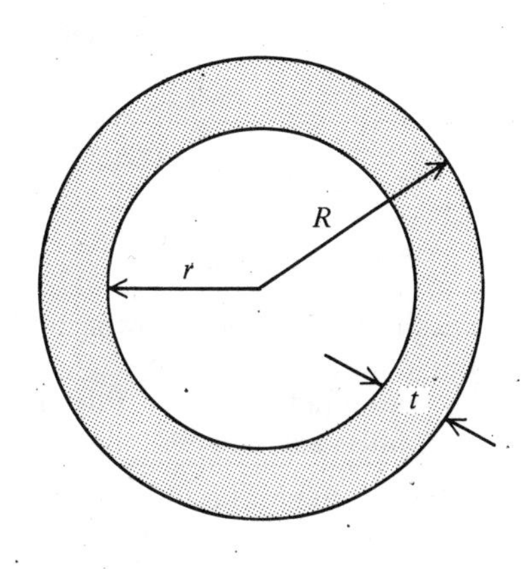

Example 1

Two concentric circles (circles with the same centre) have radii of 6·4 cm and 3·6 cm respectively. Find the area of the annulus. ($\pi = 3{\cdot}142$).

$$\text{Area} = \pi R^2 - \pi r^2$$
$$= \pi (R + r)(R - r)$$
$$= 3{\cdot}142\,(6{\cdot}4 + 3{\cdot}6)(6{\cdot}4 - 3{\cdot}6)$$
$$= 3{\cdot}142 \times 10 \times 2{\cdot}8$$
$$= 31{\cdot}42 \times 2{\cdot}8 = 87{\cdot}98\ \text{cm}^2$$

The volume of material in a pipe = (area of cross section of annulus) × length.

Example 2

A piece of rubber tubing has its outer diameter 40 mm and inner diameter 10 mm. If the tubing is 1 m long, find the volume of rubber in the pipe (π = 3·142).

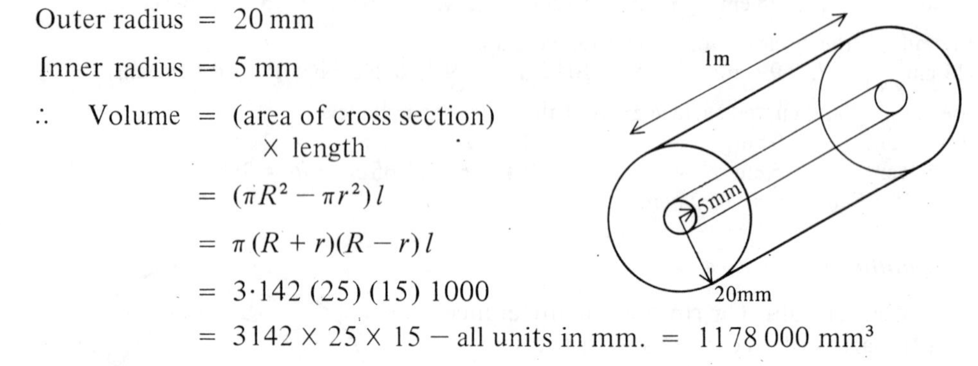

Outer radius = 20 mm

Inner radius = 5 mm

∴ Volume = (area of cross section) × length

$= (\pi R^2 - \pi r^2) l$

$= \pi (R + r)(R - r) l$

$= 3{\cdot}142\ (25)\ (15)\ 1000$

$= 3142 \times 25 \times 15$ — all units in mm. $= 1178\,000\ \text{mm}^3$

Exercise 2.3b

Find the areas of the following annuli

1. radii 7 cm and 8 cm
2. diameters 4 cm and 11 cm
3. outer radius 11 cm thickness 2 cm
4. outer diameter 15·2 cm thickness 3·1 cm
5. inner radius 14 cm thickness 3·6 cm

Find the volume of lead required to make the following lengths of pipe

6. inner and outer radii 2 cm and 2·5 cm length 100 m
7. inner and outer radii 4 cm and 4·2 cm length 12 m
8. inner and outer radii 10 cm and 11 cm length 95 cm
9. inner diameter 5 cm thickness 0·5 cm length 8 cm
10. outer diameter 7·2 cm thickness 0·4 cm length 2 m
11. Find the weight of each of the pieces of piping in questions 6 to 10 if lead weighs 11·37 g/cm^3.

Flow through pipes

The volume of water passing through a pipe in a given unit of time is given by:
(speed of flow of water) × (area of cross section of pipe)
In all calculations, units must always be the same, e.g. metres with metres, seconds with seconds, etc.

Example

Find the volume of water in litres flowing in 6 minutes through a pipe of internal radius 10 cm at a speed of 5 m/s (π = 3·142)

Volume in 1 second $= 500 \times \pi r^2\ \text{cm}^3$

$= 500 \times 3{\cdot}142 \times 10 \times 10\ \text{cm}^3$

$= \dfrac{500 \times 3{\cdot}142 \times 10 \times 10}{1000}$ litres

$$\text{Volume in 6 minutes} = \frac{500 \times 3{\cdot}142 \times 10 \times 10 \times 360}{1000} = 314{\cdot}2 \times 180$$

$$= 56\,560 \text{ litres (4 S.F.)}$$

Exercise 2.3c

1. How many revolutions per second does a wheel of 42 cm diameter make if it is travelling at 55 km/h?
2. A wheel of diameter 14 cm is making 1000 revolutions per second. Find the speed of a point on its rim in m/s.
3. A quadrant of radius 21 cm is cut away from each of the four corners of an ornamental table 150 cm long by 75 cm wide. Find its new perimeter and new area.
4. Find the total surface area of a cylinder of diameter 14 cm and height 9 cm.
5. Find the circumference of a circle whose area is 2464 cm^2.
6. Find the radius of a circle whose area is equal to the sum of the areas of two circles of diameter 64 cm.
7. A rectangular table top 150 cm by 75 cm has its corners rounded off by quadrants of 7 cm radius. By what percentage is its perimeter reduced?
8. A railway tunnel has a cross section consisting of a rectangle 7 m across and 8 m high surmounted by a semi-circle of radius 3·5 m. Find the area of its walls and roof if it is $2\frac{1}{2}$ km long. If this area is lined with bricks 22 cm by 7 cm (including the mortar) how many will be needed?
9. A cylindrical water butt of diameter 63 cm contains water. By how much will the water level rise if 12 roof tiles each 30 cm long by 20 cm broad by 1 cm thick fall into it?
10. Water is pumped into a cylindrical reservoir of diameter 8 m at the rate of 5000 litres per minute. How long does it take the water to rise 10 cm? (Give your answer correct to the nearest second.)
11. A garden roller has diameter 60 cm and width 50 cm. The metal of which it is made is 4 cm thick throughout and weighs 7 g/cm^3. How heavy, correct to the nearest kg does it weigh?
12. A round bar of diameter 2 cm is replaced in a certain engine by a tube of the same length and weight of external diameter 4 cm. What is its internal diameter?
13. Water is flowing at 2 m/s in a pipe of internal diameter 2 cm. How many litres pass a point in 5 minutes?
14. Water is flowing at 5 m/s in a pipe of internal diameter 3 cm. How long will it take to fill a tank holding 100 litres?
15. Water flows through a pipe of internal diameter 6 cm at 1 m/s. How many litres pass a point in one second?
16. How many litres per hour will a pump put into a water tower if the water flows through a 5 cm diameter pipe at 2 m/s?
17. A pipe of internal diameter 6 cm is used to fill a reservoir holding 300 000 litres in one hour. At what speed must the water flow in the pipe?
18. Water flowing through a pipe of internal diameter 5 cm takes four hours to raise the water level by 3 m in a cylindrical reservoir of internal diameter 4 m. What is the speed of flow of the water in the pipe?
19. A 5000 litre tank is filled in 30 minutes through a 5 cm diameter pipe. Find the speed of flow of the water.
20. Water is delivered through a pipe of internal diameter 3 cm. Find the speed of flow if 20 000 litres are delivered per hour. (Give your answer in km/h.)

2.4 The parts of a circle

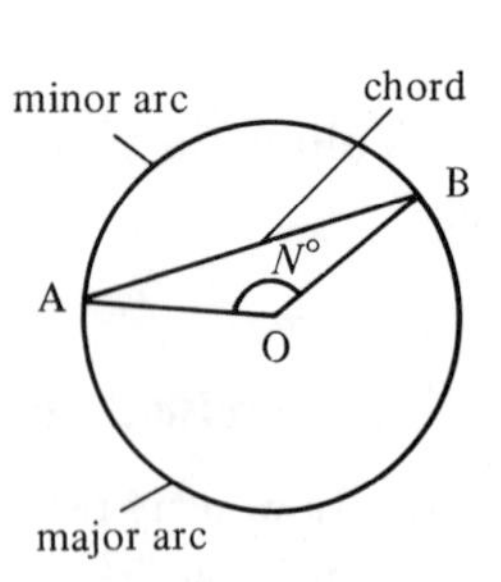

An *arc* is any portion of the circumference of a circle. In the diagram, the arc AB subtends an angle of $N°$ at the centre O. The length of arc AB is $\frac{N°}{360°}$ of the circumference of the circle.

If d is the diameter of the circle, arc AB $= \frac{N}{360} \times \pi d$.

Example 1

An arc AB subtends an angle of 45° at the centre of a circle of radius 7 cm. Calculate its length (take $\pi = \frac{22}{7}$).

$$\text{Length of arc} = \frac{45}{360} \text{ of } \pi d = \frac{\overset{1}{\cancel{45}}}{\underset{\cancel{8}\,\cancel{4}\,2}{\cancel{360}}} \times \frac{\overset{11}{\cancel{22}}}{\underset{1}{\cancel{7}}} \times \overset{\cancel{2}\,1}{\cancel{14}}$$

$$= \frac{11}{2} = 5\tfrac{1}{2} \text{ cm.}$$

A *sector* is the area of a circle bounded by two radii.

The smaller area (shaded) is called the *minor sector* and the larger area is the *major sector.* If the arc of the sector AB subtends an angle of $N°$ at the centre

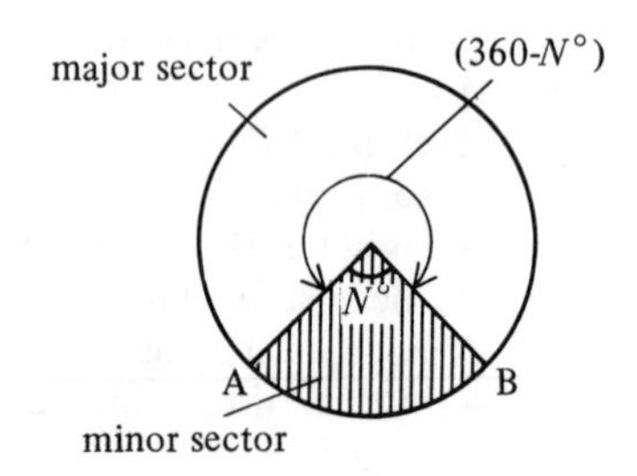

$$\text{the area of the minor sector} = \frac{N}{360} \text{ of the area of the circle}$$

$$= \frac{N}{360} \times \pi r^2 \text{ where } r \text{ is the radius}$$

$$\text{the area of the major sector} = \frac{(360 - N)}{360} \text{ of the area of the circle}$$

$$= \frac{(360 - N)}{360} \times \pi r^2$$

Example 2

An arc AB subtends an angle of 45° at the centre O of a circle of radius 7 cm. Calculate the area of the minor sector AOB $\left(\text{take } \pi = \frac{22}{7}\right)$

$$\text{Area of minor sector} = \frac{45}{360} \times \pi r^2$$

$$= \frac{45}{360} \times \frac{22}{7} \times 7 \times 7$$

$$= \frac{77}{4} = 19\tfrac{1}{4}\ \text{cm}^2$$

A *segment* is that part of a circle which lies on either side of a chord. The smaller part (shaded) is called the *minor segment* and the larger part is the *major segment.*

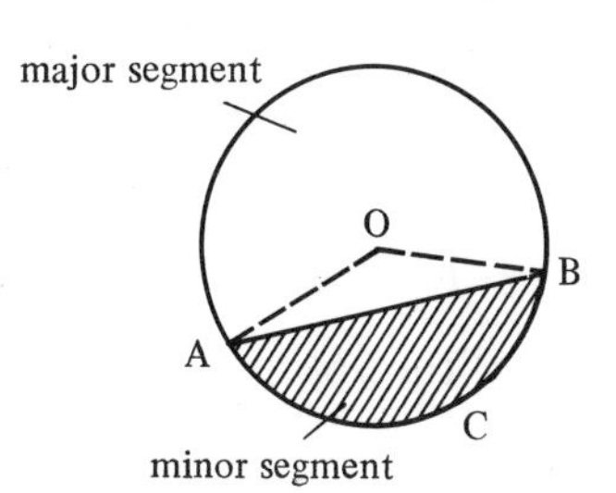

The area of the segment ABC is

(area of sector OACB) − (area of triangle OAB)

Exercise 2.4

Use $\pi = \frac{22}{7}$, unless otherwise stated.

1. Find the arc length and the area of the sector of the circle giving the following
   (a) radius = 3·5 cm; angle at the centre = 45°
   (b) radius = 7 cm; angle at the centre = 60°
   (c) radius = 1·4 cm; angle at the centre = 110°
   (d) radius = 6·3 cm; angle at the centre = 24°
   (e) radius = 21 cm; angle at the centre = 225°

2. Find the radius of the circle, given the following
   (a) arc length = 4·4 cm; angle at the centre = 72°
   (b) arc length = 18·4 cm; angle at the centre = 189°
   (c) arc length = 23·1 cm; angle at the centre = 294°
   (d) arc length = 2·2 cm; angle at the centre = 70°
   (e) arc length = 16·5 cm; angle at the centre = 14°

3. Find the area of the minor segment of the circle, given the following
   (a) arc length = 3·5 cm; angle at the centre = 90°
   (b) arc length = 14·2 cm; angle at the centre = 30°
   (c) arc length = 5·6 cm; angle at the centre = 60°
   (d) arc length = 4·2 cm; angle at the centre = 72°
   (e) arc length = 10·5 cm; angle at the centre = 180°

4. Find how far the tip of the minute hand, 1·5 cm long, of a watch travels in
   (a) 10 minutes (b) 35 minutes (c) 75 minutes
   (d) 3 hours (e) 24 hours

5. Using $\pi = 3{\cdot}142$, find the angle subtended at the centre
   (a) by an arc 27 cm long in a circle of radius 20 cm
   (b) by an arc 34 cm long in a circle of diameter 12 cm.

2.5 Pyramids

A right pyramid is a pyramid in which the vertex V lies above the centre of the base.

Volume of a pyramid =

$$\frac{\text{area of base} \times \text{perpendicular height}}{3}$$

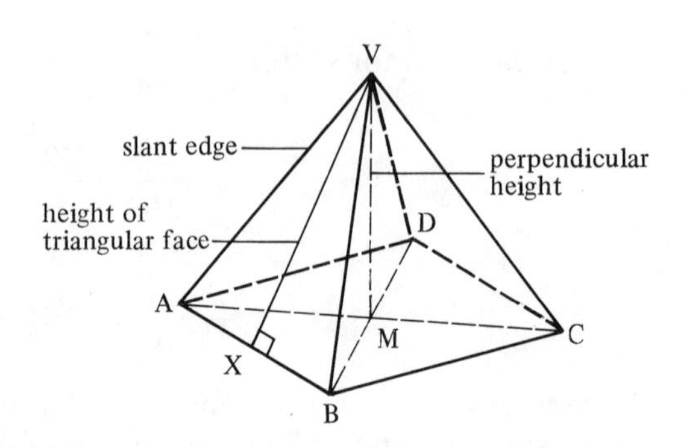

Example 1

Find the volume of a square-based pyramid VABCD in which AB = BC = CD = AD = 10 cm and the perpendicular height VM is 12 cm

$$\text{Volume} = \frac{10 \times 10 \times 12}{3}$$

$$= 400 \text{ cm}^3$$

The total surface area of a pyramid is

area of base + area of triangular faces.

Example 2

Find the total surface area of a square-based pyramid VABCD with perpendicular height VM = 6 cm and the slant edges VA = VB = VC = VD = 10 cm.

(i) Area of base ABCD.

First find the length of diagonal BD.

In triangle VMB,

$$10^2 = 6^2 + MB^2 \text{ (Pythagoras' theorem)}$$

$$100 - 36 = MB^2$$

$$64 = MB^2$$

$$8 = MB$$

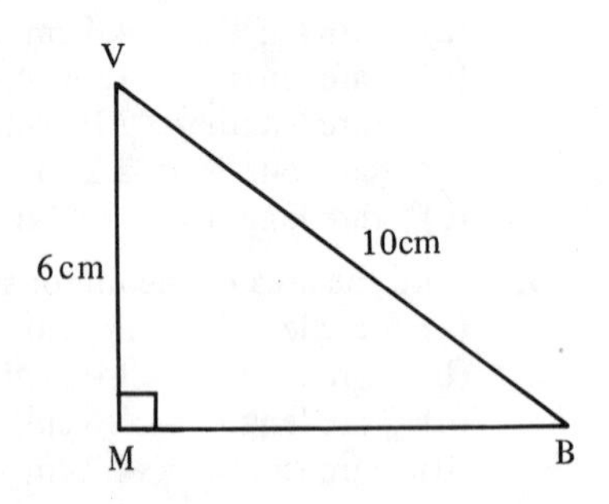

But M is the mid-point of BD, ∴ BD = 2 × 8 = 16 cm

In a square, the diagonals are equal

BD = AC = 16 cm

$$\text{Area of ABCD} = \frac{\text{product of diagonals}}{2}$$

$$= \frac{16 \times 16}{2} = 128 \text{ cm}^2.$$

(ii) Area of the four triangular sides.

In triangle VAB, $AB = \sqrt{128}$ cm

$$\text{Area of VAB} = \frac{AB \times VX}{2}$$

A V X B

In the right-angle triangle VXB

$$XB = \frac{\sqrt{128}}{2} \text{ and } VB = 10$$

$$VB^2 = VX^2 + XB^2 \text{ (Pythagoras' theorem)}$$

$$\therefore \quad 10^2 = VX^2 + \left(\frac{\sqrt{128}}{2}\right)^2$$

$$100 = VX^2 + \frac{128}{4}$$

$$100 - 32 = VX^2$$

$$68 = VX^2$$

$$\therefore \quad VX = \sqrt{68}$$

$$\therefore \text{ Area of triangle VAB} = \frac{\sqrt{128} \times \sqrt{68}}{2}$$

$$= \frac{\sqrt{8704}}{2}$$

$$= \frac{93{\cdot}3}{2} = 46{\cdot}65 \text{ cm}^2$$

$\therefore$ area of the four triangular faces

$$= 46{\cdot}65 \times 4 = 186{\cdot}6 \text{ cm}^2$$

$$\therefore \quad \text{total surface area} = 186{\cdot}6 + 128$$

$$= 314{\cdot}6 \text{ cm}^2$$

Exercise 2.5

Find the volumes of the pyramids in questions **1** to **5**.

1. Height 6 cm, square base 8 cm
2. Height 5 cm, rectangular base 5 cm by 6 cm
3. Height 7 cm, rectangular base 5 cm by 6 cm
4. Height 4 cm, triangular base 3 cm by 4 cm by 5 cm
5. Height 9 cm, triangular base 5 cm by 5 cm by 8 cm
6. Find the height of a pyramid of volume 100 cm^3 if it stands on a square base of side 10 cm.
7. Find the area of the base of a pyramid of volume 200 cm^3 if its height is 5 cm.
8. Find the total surface area of the right pyramid having the following dimensions: height 4 cm, square base of side 6 cm.

2.6 Cones

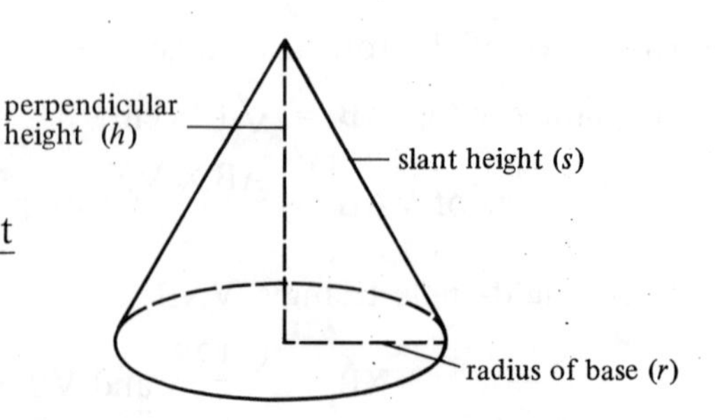

The volume of a cone is

$$= \frac{\text{area of base} \times \text{perpendicular height}}{3}$$

$$= \frac{\pi r^2 h}{3}$$

Example 1

Find the volume of a cone, with base radius 7 cm, and perpendicular height 12 cm $(\pi = \frac{22}{7})$

$$\text{Volume} = \frac{(\text{area of base}) \times (\text{perpendicular height})}{3}$$

$$= \frac{\frac{22}{\cancel{7}_1} \times \frac{\cancel{7}^1}{1} \times \frac{7}{1} \times \frac{12}{1}}{3}$$

$$= \frac{22 \times \cancel{12}^4 \times 7}{\cancel{3}_1} = 616 \text{ cm}^3$$

The total surface area of a cone is given by

$$(\text{area of curved surface}) + (\text{area of base})$$

$$= \frac{\text{circumference of base} \times \text{slant height}}{2} + \pi r^2$$

$$= \frac{2\pi rs}{2} + \pi r^2$$

$$= \pi rs + \pi r^2$$

$$= \pi r(s + r)$$

Example 2

Find the total surface area of a cone, with perpendicular height 24 cm and radius 7 cm (take $\pi = \frac{22}{7}$)

(i) Find the slant height VB

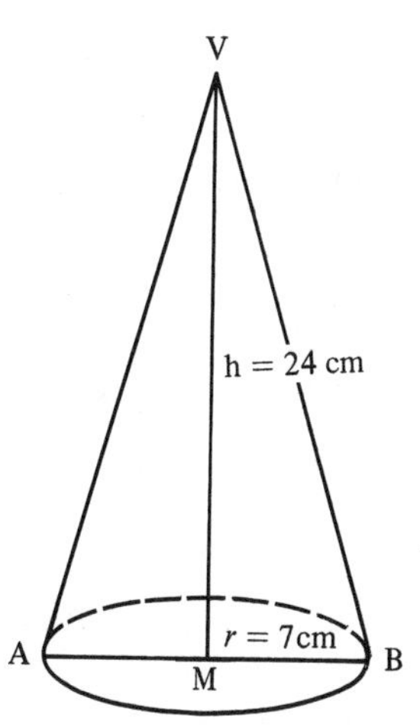

In triangle VMB

$$VB^2 = VM^2 + MB^2 \text{ (Pythagoras' theorem)}$$
$$= 24^2 + 7^2$$
$$= 576 + 49$$
$$= 625$$
$$VB = \sqrt{625} = 25 \text{ cm}$$

(ii) Calculate the surface area

$$\text{Surface area} = \pi r(s + r), \text{ where } s = 25, r = 7, \pi = \frac{22}{7}$$
$$= \frac{22}{7} \times 7\,(25 + 7)$$
$$= 22 \times 32 = 704 \text{ cm}^2$$

Exercise 2.6

Take $\pi = 3{\cdot}142$ when using logs and $\frac{22}{7}$ when you see the possibility of cancelling the 7.

Find the volumes of the following cones

1. Height 3 cm, area of base 21 cm^2
2. Height 5 cm, radius of base 12 cm
3. Height 2 m, radius of base 3·5 m
4. Height 21 cm, area of base 5 cm^2
5. Height 17 cm, radius of base 14 cm

Find the area of the curved surface of the following cones

6. Slant height 8 cm, base radius 6 cm
7. Slant height 16 cm, radius of base 14 cm
8. Height 4 cm, radius of base 3 cm
9. Height 8 cm, base diameter 12 cm
10. Height 12 cm, radius of base 5 cm

11. A conical block of silver has height 20 cm and base radius 12 cm. How many coins 4 cm in diameter and 3 mm thick can be cast from it?

12. If the cone described in question 11 were recast instead into spherical beads of diameter 4 mm, how many would there be?

13. A bird cage is in the shape of a cylinder of height 30 cm and radius 15 cm surmounted by a cone so that the total height is 40 cm. Find the volume of the cage.

14. A wine glass is conical in shape and holds 100 cm^3 of wine. If the diameter of its rim is 6 cm find its depth.

15. A circular piece of parchment of radius 30 cm is cut into three equal sectors each of which is made into a conical lamp shade. Find the base radius of each shade.

2.7 The sphere

The volume of a sphere is $= \frac{4}{3}\pi r^3$

Example 1

Find the volume of a sphere with diameter 20 cm (take $\pi = 3{\cdot}142$)

$$\text{Radius} = 20 \div 2 = 10 \text{ cm}$$

$$\therefore \text{ Volume} = \frac{4}{3} \times 10 \times 10 \times 10 \times 3{\cdot}142$$

$$= \frac{12568}{3} = 4189\tfrac{1}{3} \text{ cm}^3$$

The surface area of a sphere is $= 4\pi r^2$.

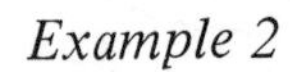

Example 2

Find the surface area of a sphere with radius 19 cm (take $\pi = 3{\cdot}142$)

$$\text{Surface area} = 4 \times 3{\cdot}142 \times 19 \times 19$$

$$= 4537{\cdot}048$$

$$= 4537 \text{ cm}^2 \text{ (to 4 S.F.)}$$

Exercise 2.7

Take $\pi = 3{\cdot}142$. Give your answers correct to 4 significant figures.

1. Find the volumes and surface areas of spheres of the following radii
   (a) 5 cm (b) 6·2 cm (c) 183 cm (d) 41·66 cm
2. Find the radius of the sphere whose volume is 3177 cm^3.
3. Find the radius of the sphere whose surface area is 265 cm^2.
4. Find the volume of the sphere whose surface area is 132 cm^2.
5. Ten spherical lead bullets of diameter 0·8 cm are melted down and recast into a single sphere. What is its diameter?
6. A measuring cylinder of diameter 4 cm contains water. 100 lead shot of diameter 2 mm are dropped in. By how much does the water level rise?
7. Find the total surface area of a solid hemisphere of radius 15 cm.
8. A buoy consists of a hemisphere of diameter 1 m surmounted by a cone of height 2 m. The circular bases of the cone and the hemisphere coincide. Find its volume and surface area.
9. The external diameter of a hollow sphere is 94 cm and its thickness is 2 cm. Find the diameter of a solid sphere of the same weight if it is made of material of twice the density of the hollow one.
10. Two spheres have volumes in the ratio 69 : 1. What is the ratio
    (a) of their radii and (b) of their surface areas?

11. Two spheres have surface areas in the ratio 8 : 1. What is the ratio of their volumes?
12. A hollow sphere of radius 20 cm contains a solid cone of height 30 cm. The vertex of the cone and the whole of the circumference of its base are in contact with the sphere. Show that the radius of the base of the cone is $10\sqrt{3}$ cm and find (a) the percentage of the volume of the sphere that lies within the cone and (b) the ratio of the curved surface area of the cone to that of the sphere.
13. A planetarium consists of a cylinder of base radius 14 m and height 3 m surmounted by a hemispherical top. Calculate
    (a) the volume of the planetarium
    (b) the volume of the architect's model of this planetarium which is made one tenth full size.

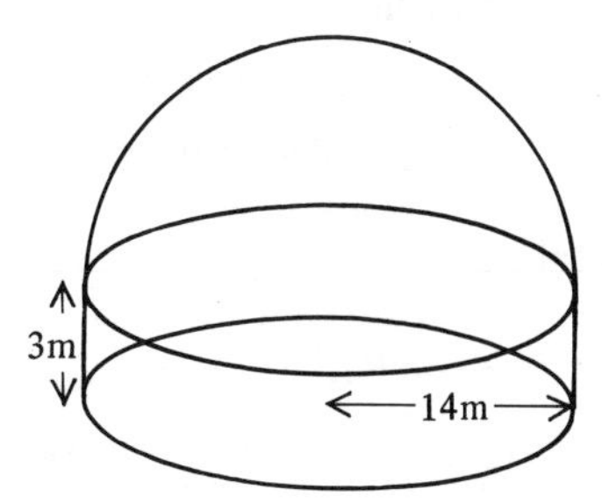

14. A metal rod 5 m long, 9 cm wide, and 8 cm thick, is melted down and cast into spherical ball bearings of diameter 15 mm. Assuming no metal is lost on casting, calculate how many ball bearings will be made.
15. 96 spheres, each of radius 32 mm are packed in a rectangular wooden box, 6 to a layer, as shown. Calculate
    (a) the volume of the smallest box required in cm^3,
    (b) the percentage of the total volume of the box filled by the spheres.

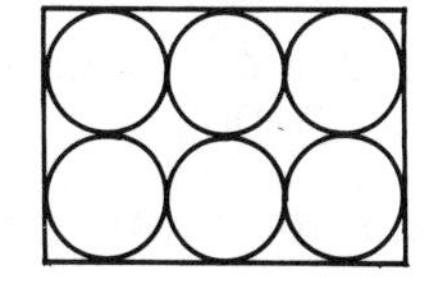

When unpacked, each of the spheres is coated with paint 0·001 mm thick. How many boxes of spheres can be painted with 1 litre of paint?

2.8 Map scales and contours

The *scale* of a map is usually given in the form of a ratio 1 : n where 1 is the distance on the map and n is the real distance in the same units.

Example 1

If the scale of a map is 1 : 40 000, this means that 1 cm on the map = 40 000 cm or 400 m on the ground.

If the scale of a plan is 10 : 1, this means that 10 cm on the plan represents a real distance of 1 cm.

The scale of a map can be expressed as a fraction, called the *representative fraction* (or R.F.).

Hence the scale 1 : 4000 has a R.F. $= \frac{1}{4000}$.

Areas on a map are proportional to the squares of the scale.

Example 2

Find the area on the ground (in km²) of an area of 6 cm² on the map, when the scale is 1 : 50 000.

1 cm² represents $(50\,000)^2$ cm² on the map

6 cm² represents $(50\,000)^2 \times 6$ cm² on the map

$$\therefore \; 6 \text{ cm}^2 \text{ represents } \frac{50\,000 \times 50\,000 \times 6}{100 \times 1000 \times 100 \times 1000} \text{ km}^2$$

$$= 1{\cdot}5 \text{ km}^2$$

A *contour line* is a line on a map joining places with equal heights. This height is usually written in metres on the contour line.

Example 3

On the map drawn to a scale of 1:50 000, find the gradient of the slope of the ground between A and B.

Remember that the gradient of a slope of the ground is the ratio

vertical height : sloping distance.

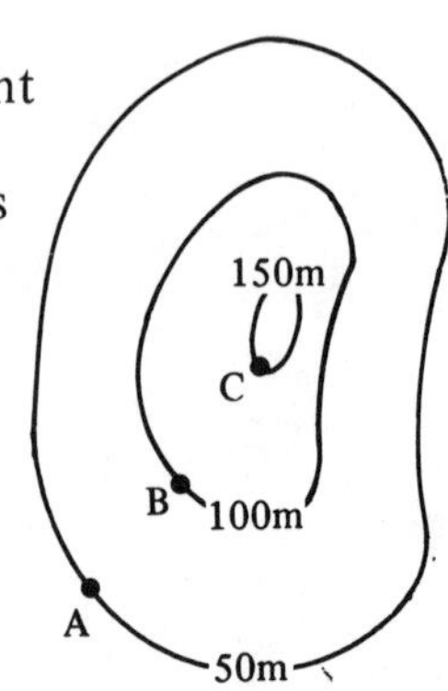

From the map, distance AB is 1 cm, and difference in heights 50 m, which is the vertical height

∴ actual distance AB is 50 000 cm, and using the same units,
difference in heights is 5000 cm.

The information can be shown as follows

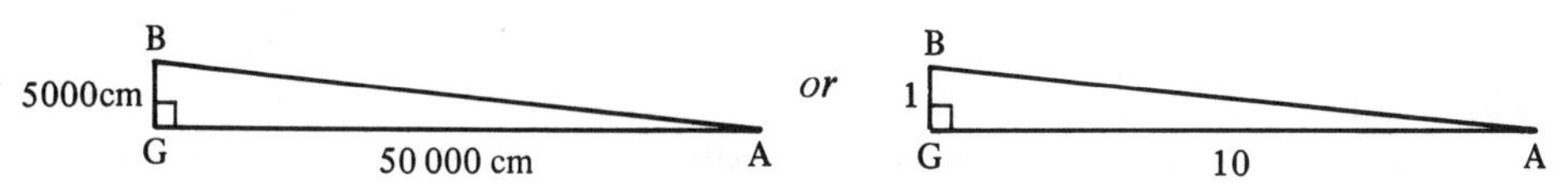

$\therefore\ AB^2 = 1^2 + 10^2$ where AB is the sloping distance

$AB^2 = 101$

$AB = \sqrt{101} = 10{\cdot}05$

$\therefore$ gradient is BG : BA

$$= 1 : 10{\cdot}05 \text{ or } \frac{1}{10{\cdot}05}$$

We say that the slope of the ground is 1 in 10·05. The angle of inclination of this slope of the ground is the angle whose sine is equal to $\frac{1}{10{\cdot}05}$ or 0·0995 which is 5° 42′.

Exercise 2.8

1. Find the representative fraction (R.F.) of maps drawn to the following scales
   (a) 10 cm to 1 km (b) 2 cm to 1 km (c) 1 inch to 1 mile
   (d) 1 cm to 1·5 km (e) 4 inches to 1 yard
2. The scale of a map is 1 : 50 000. Find in km the lengths on the ground of objects shown with the following lengths on the map
   (a) 2 cm (b) 1·4 cm (c) 9·3 cm (d) 6·14 cm (e) 7·27 cm
3. Find the length on a map of scale 1 : 20 000 of objects whose length on the ground is as follows
   (a) 1 km (b) 0·625 km (c) 840 m (d) 97 m
4. Find the areas on the ground (in km^2) of the following areas on a map of scale 1 : 50 000
   (a) 1 cm^2 (b) 1·6 cm^2 (c) 25 cm^2 (d) 100 cm^2 (e) 0·14 m^2
5. Find the area on the map (in cm^2) of the following areas on the ground
   (a) 1 km^2 scale of map 1 : 20 000 (b) 3·8 km^2 scale of map 1 : 30 000
   (c) 6·5 km^2 scale of map 1 : 15 000 (d) 14·6 km^2 scale of map 1 : 50 000
   (e) 76·4 km^2 scale of map 1 : 100 000
6. A surveyor measures the gradients of various roads and records them in the form 1 : n (1 vertically to n units measured along the ground). Find the angles at which the following roads are inclined
   (a) 1 : 10 (b) 1 : 4 (c) 1 : 7 (d) 1 : 15 (e) 1 : $3\frac{1}{2}$
7. A map of scale 1 : 50 000 has contours whose vertical interval is 50 m. Give the gradient in the form 1 : n and also the angle of inclination for slopes where the contours are the following distance apart
   (a) 1 cm (b) 2 cm (c) 4 mm (d) 7·5 mm (e) 3·4 cm
8. The scale of a map is 10 cm to 1 km. A builder pays £5 per square metre for a plot of land 15 cm^2 on the map. How much did he pay?
9. A car runs at 40 km/h up a gradient of 1 in 42. How many metres does it rise in 1 minute?
10. A pine wood is shown on a map of scale 1 : 20 000 as a square of side 4 cm. If two of its sides are parallel to the slope of the ground which is 1 in 3, find the actual area of the wood.

2.9 Latitude and longitude

The position of a point on the Earth's surface is given by its latitude and longitude.
A *great circle* is a circle whose radius is the same as the radius of the Earth.
A *meridian* is a great circle passing through the North pole and the South pole.
The *Equator* is the great circle, taken to be latitude 0°, which divides the Earth into the Northern hemisphere and the Southern hemisphere.
The *Greenwich meridian* is the great circle, taken to be longitude 0°, which divides the Earth into the Eastern hemisphere and the Western hemisphere.

The *latitude* of a place is the angular distance in degrees along a meridian measured north or south of the Equator. The range of latitude is 0° to 90° N or S of the Equator.

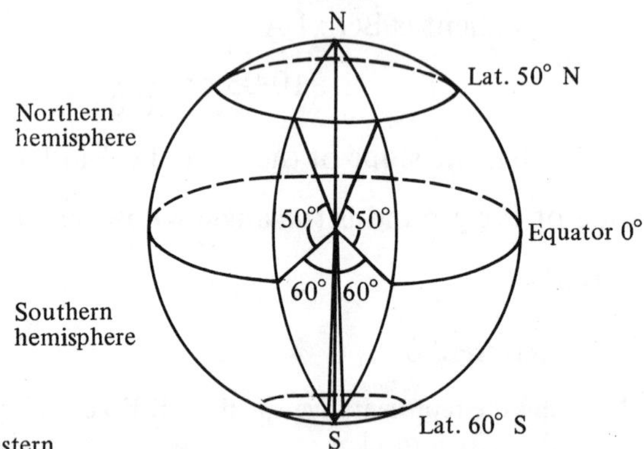

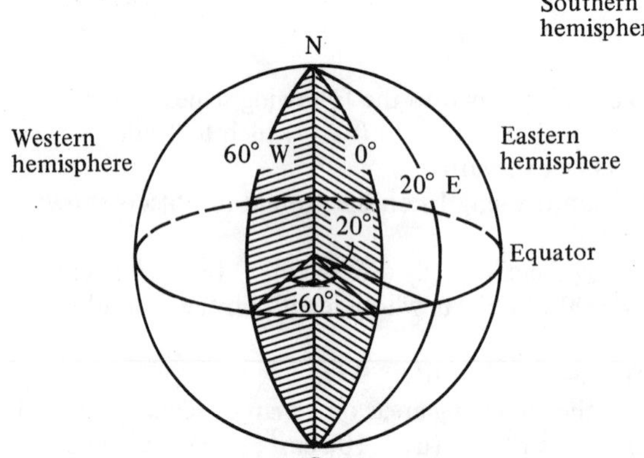

The *longitude* of a place is the angle in degrees between the plane of the meridian passing through the place and the plane of the meridian passing through Greenwich. The range of longitude is 0° to 180° E or W of Greenwich.

Most questions on latitude and longitude are based on finding the length of an arc of a circle.

From the diagram

$$\frac{\text{arc AB}}{\text{circumference of circle}} = \frac{\theta°}{360°}$$

$$\text{arc AB} = \frac{\theta}{360} \text{ of } 2\pi r.$$

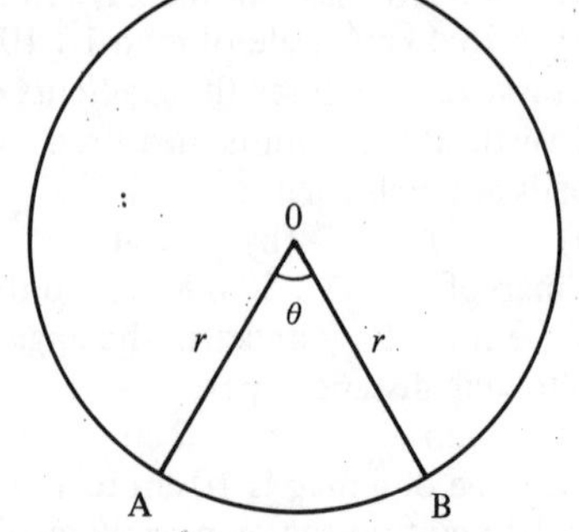

The distance between two places on the same meridian of longitude

Example 1

A is at 50° N, B is at 10° N, C is at 40° S. If A, B, and C are on the same meridian of longitude, find (a) the distance AB, (b) the distance AC (radius of Earth = 6400 km).

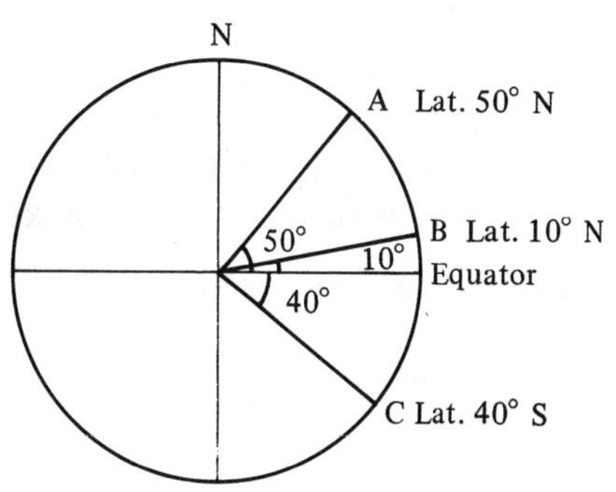

$$\text{Distance AB} = \frac{(50° - 10°)}{360°} \text{ of the}$$

circumference of the Earth.

$$= \frac{40}{360} \text{ of } 2\pi r = 4468 \text{ km}$$

$$\text{Distance AC} = \frac{(50° + 40°)}{360°} \text{ of the}$$

circumference of the Earth.

$$= \frac{90}{360} \text{ of } 2\pi r = 10\,050 \text{ km}$$

The distance between two places on the same circle of latitude

Note: the circumference of a circle of latitude is $2\pi r \cos\theta$, where θ is the angle of latitude and r is the radius of the Earth.

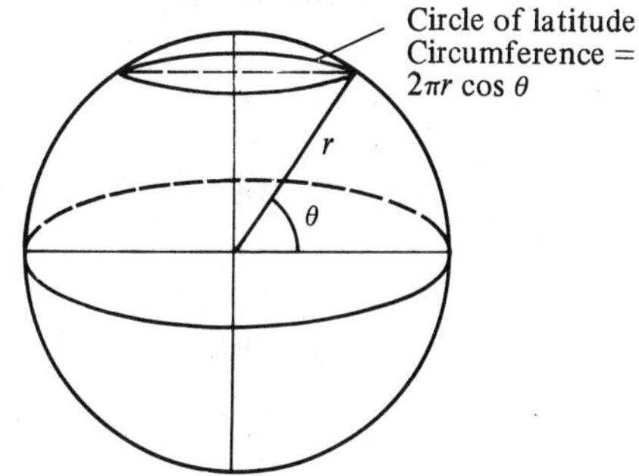

Example 2

A is at 40° W, B is at 10° W, C is at 20° E. If A, B, and C are on the same circle of latitude at 60° N, find (a) the distance AB, (b) the distance AC (radius of Earth = 6400 km).

$$\text{Distance AB} = \frac{(40° - 10°)}{360°} \text{ of the}$$

circumference of the circle of latitude.

$$= \frac{30}{360} \text{ of } 2\pi r \cos\theta$$

$$= \frac{1}{12} \times 2\pi \times 6400 \cos 60 = 1676 \text{ km}$$

$$\text{Distance AC} = \frac{(40° + 20°)}{360°} \text{ of the circumference of the circle of latitude}$$

$$= \frac{60}{360} \text{ of } 2\pi r \cos\theta \quad = \frac{1}{6} \times 2\pi \times 6400 \cos 60 = 3351 \text{ km.}$$

Example 3

An aircraft leaves A (34° E, 36° N) and flies due South to B (34° E, 24° S). From B, it flies 3200 km due West to C.
(a) What is the distance flown from A to B?
(b) What is the position of C?
(Take radius of Earth = 6400 km, π = 3·142)

Angular distance from A to B = 36° + 24° = 60°.

$$\therefore \text{ distance AB} = \frac{60^\circ}{360^\circ} \text{ of the circumference of the Earth}$$

$$= \frac{60}{360} \times 2\pi \times 6400$$

$$= 6700 \text{ km (to 3 S.F.)}.$$

Circumference of circle of latitude = 6400 cos 24°.
If $\theta°$ is the angular distance from B to C

then $\frac{\theta^\circ}{360^\circ}$ of the circumference of the circle of latitude = 3200 km.

$$\frac{\theta}{360} \times 2\pi \times 6400 \cos 24^\circ = 3200$$

$$\theta = \frac{360 \times \overset{1}{\cancel{3200}}}{2\pi \times \underset{2}{\cancel{6400}} \cos 24^\circ} = 31{\cdot}4^\circ$$

$$\therefore \text{ position of C} = (34^\circ - 31{\cdot}4^\circ)\text{ E, } 24^\circ \text{ S}$$

$$= 2{\cdot}6^\circ \text{ E, } 24^\circ \text{ S or } 2^\circ 36' \text{ E, } 24^\circ \text{ S}.$$

Exercise 2.9

Take the radius of the earth to be 6400 km and π = 3·142.

1. The following pairs of places lie on the same meridian and have latitudes as stated. Find their distance apart measured along the meridian.
   (a) 52° N, 68° N (b) 14° N, 18° S
   (c) 48° 16′ N, 17° 36′ S (d) 27° 18′ 10″ N, 84° 24′ 50″ N
2. Find the radii of the following circles of latitude
   (a) 50° N (b) 40° S (c) 54° N (d) 84° N (e) 27° 36′ S
3. Find the distance, measured along their lines of latitude, between pairs of points whose positions are as follows
   (a) Latitude 10° N, Longitude 30° W and longitude 20° E
   (b) Latitude 28° S, Longitude 46° W and longitude 140° W
   (c) Latitude 36° S, Longitude 10° E and longitude 59° E
   (d) Latitude 88° N, Longitude 0° and longitude 90° W.
4. An aeroplane flies 1000 km due West from London airport. (Latitude 51° 30′ N. Longitude 10′ W.) What is its new Longitude?
5. The distance measured along a parallel of latitude between two points one of longitude 12° W and the other of longitude 12° E is 2000 km. Find their latitude.

6. An aeroplane flies due East along the parallel of latitude 53° N for 150 km. By how much has its longitude changed?
7. Another aeroplane flies due North along the meridian through Greenwich for 150 km. By how much has its latitude changed?
8. Two Concordes fly from London airport (Lat. 51° 30′ N). One flies due West through 96° of longitude and the other due East through 104°. If they continue on their present courses at a speed of Mach one (1200 km/h) when will they meet?
9. A classroom globe is 30 cm in diameter. How far apart measured along the equator are the mouth of the Amazon (Lat. 0° Long. 50° W) and Cape Esterias (Lat. 0° Long. 10°E)? How far apart are they measured through a small hole drilled through the globe to join them?
10. A and B are two towns in latitude 43°N, their longitudes differing by 43°. Find
    (a) the distance between them measured along the circle of latitude,
    (b) the distance between them measured along the great circle joining them.
11. The position of X is (26°N 26°W) and the position of Y is (26°N 14°E). Find
    (a) the distance between them measured along the circle of latitude,
    (b) the shortest distance between them.
12. A is 68°N x°E and B is 68°N 32°W. B is 2678 km due West of A.
    (a) Find the longitude of A
    (b) The length of the chord AB, correct to the nearest km.

Miscellaneous exercise 2

1. A car wheel is 50 cm in diameter. How many revolutions does it make in travelling 1 km?
2. Following a storm water is pumped out of a flooded area through a 20 cm diameter pipe at the rate of 5000 litres per minute. Find the speed of flow through the pipe. If the water is known to contain 0·5 g per litre of mud what weight of mud is moved in three days of continuous pumping?
3. A horizontal water channel is in the shape of a trapezium. Its base is 8 cm wide and the width at the water surface is 12 cm. The water is 10 cm deep. Calculate the cross sectional area of the flowing water and its speed in k/h if the channel delivers 30 000 litres per hour.
4. Water from a flooded river overflows an embankment. It flows at 5 k/h and is 2 cm deep as it crosses the embankment which is 500 m long. How many litres are flooding over per second and how long will it take 10 pumps to pump all the water back into the river when the flood is over? The pumps can each deliver water at 5 m/s through pipes of diameter 20 cm and the flood lasted for 10 hours.
5. Find the area of the shaded part of each figure from the dimensions given

(a)

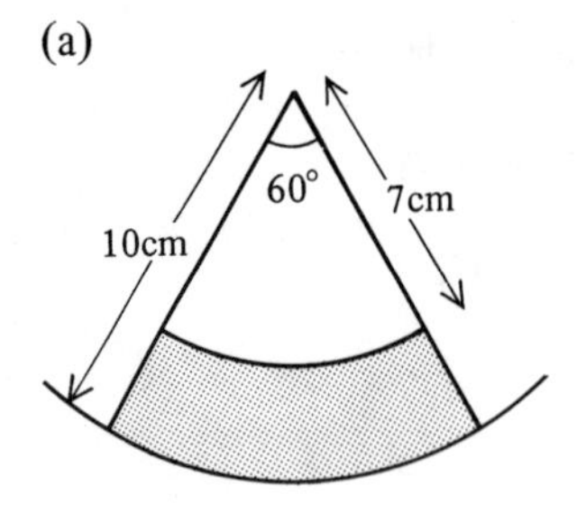

(b)

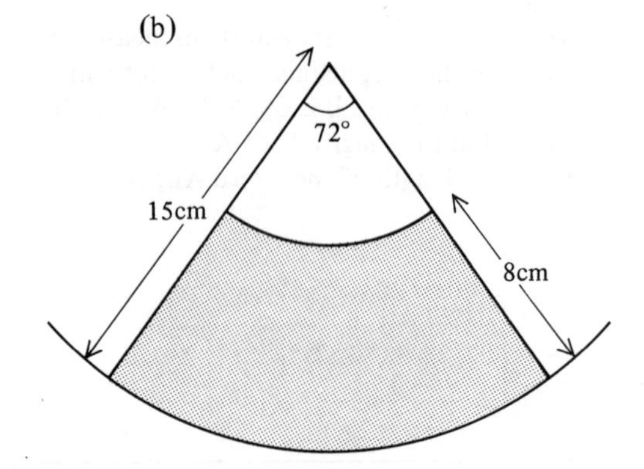

6. The length of the arc of a quadrant of a circle is 19·25 cm. Calculate
   (a) the circumference of this circle (b) the area of the quadrant
7. The pointer of a weighing machine is 27 cm long and moves through an angle of 70°. If a mass of 1 kg moves the pointer 2 cm, find the greatest mass that can be weighed on the machine.
8. Draw (a) a regular hexagon inside a circle of radius 4 cm
   (b) a regular octagon inside a circle of diameter 7·4 cm

   In each case find
   (i) the area of the circle
   (ii) the area of the regular figure
   (iii) the area of one of the segments between the figure and the circumference of the circle.
9. A swimming pool is 30 m long by 10 m wide. The water at the shallow end is 1 m deep and at the deep end 2 m deep. How many litres does the pool hold? If it can be filled in 12 hours by water flowing through a pipe of internal diameter 10 cm find the speed of the water in the pipe.
10. Find the areas of the following rhombuses
   (a) diagonals 5 cm and 6 cm (b) diagonals 19 cm and 21 cm
   (c) diagonals 7·5 cm and 8·6 cm (d) diagonals 3·25 cm and 7·5 cm

11. Three points A, B and C are on a map whose scale is 1 : 25 000. They form an isosceles triangle with AB = AC = 6 cm and BC = 4 cm. A is on the 50 m contour and B and C both on the 250 m contour. Find the general angle of slope of the hillside (assumed plane).

12. Eight cupfuls of water are emptied into a hemispherical bowl of diameter 30 cm. The cup is a cylinder of radius 4 cm and height 9 cm. What fraction of the bowl remains to be filled? How many whole ice cubes each of side 9 cm^2 can now be put in before the bowl overflows?

13. Find the volume of a right pyramid standing on a square base if its height is 6 cm and the length of its slant edge is 8 cm.

14. A rectangular tank 3 m by 2 m by 1 m high contains a pyramid of height 1 m and square base of side $1\frac{1}{2}$ m. The tank is now filled with water. By how much does the water level fall when the pyramid is removed?

15. In the diagram, the lines OA, OC and OV are mutually perpendicular (like the corner of a brick). OV = 3 cm, OA = 4 cm and OC = 5 cm.

Find the volume and total surface area of the solid VOABC.

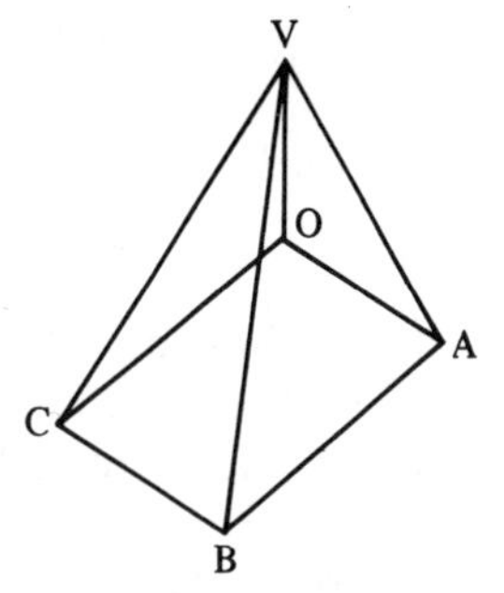

16. A solid pyramid VABCD has its eight edges each of length 24 cm. The vertex V is above the centroid of the square base. A plane horizontal cut is made through the points E, F, G and H which are the mid-points of VA, VB, VC and VD. The pyramid VEFGH is removed. Calculate (i) the surface area of the solid remaining
(ii) the volume of the solid removed.

17. Suppose that in question 15, V was vertically above the mid-point of OA and all the dimensions given were unchanged. Find the volume and surface area of the new solid so formed.

18. A bucket used for loading sand is shaped like the frustum of a square pyramid. Its top is 1 metre square and its base is 70 cm square. It is 50 cm deep. Find its volume and the weight of sand it will hold if sand weighs 2·51 g/cm^3.

19. (a) A is in latitude 45°N. Calculate the circumference of the circle of latitude which passes through A.
(b) B is a place with the same longitude as A, and the shortest distance from A to B is 20 000 km. What are the two possible latitudes of B? (Answer to the nearest degree). (Take $\pi = 3{\cdot}142$ and radius of earth 6400 km.)

20. A ream of duplicating paper consists of 500 sheets, weighing 85 g/m^2. Each sheet is a rectangle measuring 26 cm by 18 cm and is 0·13 mm thick.
Find
(a) the total area of all the sheets in the packet (in m^2),
(b) the total weight of the packet in kg.
Find the volume of paper removed if two circular holes of radius 6 mm are punched through all the sheets in the packet. (Take $\pi = 3{\cdot}142$.)

Part 3 Algebra

3.1 Generalized arithmetic

If x stands for an unknown number,

then 2 more than the number is written	$x + 2$
3 less than the number is written	$x - 3$
4 times the number is written	$4x$
the number multiplied by itself is written	x^2
half the number is written	$\frac{1}{2}x$ or $\frac{x}{2}$
y more than the number is written	$x + y$
y times the number is written	yx or xy

Example 1

How many pence in £Y?

In £1 there are 100 pence
In £2 there are (100×2) pence
In £Y there are $(100 \times Y)$ or $100Y$ pence.

Exercise 3.1a

1. What is 2 more than a?
2. What is 4 less than b?
3. What is 3 times a?
4. What is $\frac{1}{4}$ of b?
5. What is a more than b?
6. What is c less than d?
7. What is a times b?
8. What must be added to a to make 11?
9. What number multiplied by x will give 36?
10. How many metres in y kilometres?
11. What is the cost of 3 eggs if an egg costs x pence?
12. How many pence in £y?
13. How many metres in x centimetres?
14. How many grams in x kilograms?
15. What number multiplied by y will give 50?
16. What is the next highest number after x?
17. What is the next highest number after $(x + 2)$?
18. If I buy a car for £x and sell it for £y, how much more is the selling price than the buying price?
19. A man earns £A and spends £B. How much does he save?
20. How much change do I get from a £1 note, after buying 6 kg of sugar at x pence per kilogram?

Example 2

A man buys x kg of potatoes at y pence per kg and a kg of potatoes at b pence per kg. What is the average cost of all the potatoes he buys?

Cost of x kg at y pence per kg $=$ xy pence

Cost of a kg at b pence per kg $=$ ab pence

$$\therefore \text{ total cost of all the potatoes } = (xy + ab) \text{ pence}$$

$$\text{and total weight of all the potatoes } = (x + a) \text{ kg}$$

$$\text{Average cost per kg } = \frac{(xy + ab)}{(x + a)} \text{ pence}$$

Exercise 3.1b

1. A man is earning £y per week. After promotion he gets a further £2. How many pounds does he now earn?
2. A bus carries x passengers downstairs and y upstairs. How many passengers does it carry altogether?
3. I have £m in the bank. How much shall I have left if I spend
   (a) £n (b) a further £62 and (c) half of what is now left?
4. What is the total cost of m books at n pence each? Give your answer (a) in pence and (b) in £.
5. A motorist uses g litres of petrol to travel m kilometres. How many kilometres does he do to the litre?
6. A man is y years old. How old was he x years ago? How old will he be in z years time?
7. A man earns £k by doing m days work. How much is this per day?
8. A man earns £x an hour when he works for y hours spread over z days. What is his average daily earning?
9. In a test, p pupils each scored q marks, and r pupils each scores s marks. What was the average mark per pupil?
10. During a sale a shop offers a discount of p pence in the £. What must a customer pay for goods marked £Y?
11. If x articles cost £y, what will be the price of z articles at the same rate?
12. In a library b shelves each hold c books, d shelves each hold e books, and f shelves each hold g books. What is the average number of books per shelf?
13. A motorist uses p litres of petrol at q pence per litre in running r km. Another motorist uses s litres at t pence per litre in running u km. By how much per km does the second motorist pay less than the first?
14. If x denotes a number how would you express (a) twice the number and (b) two more than the number?
15. By how much is x less than 50?
16. By how much is 50 less than x?
17. The sum of two numbers is y. One of them is x. What is the other?
18. A man pays income tax at the rate of p pence in the £ on all except the first £F of his income of £I. How much has he left after paying tax?
19. When a is increased by 20%, it becomes b. When b is increased by 20%, it becomes c.
    (a) Express c as a percentage of b.
    (b) Express c as a percentage of a.
20. A regular hexagon of side x cm has a square of side x cm cut from it. Find an expression for the remaining area.

3.2 Directed numbers

Addition

$+2+3 = +5$
$-3-4 = -7$
$+3-2 = +1$
$+3-5 = -2$

Subtraction

$+2--+3 = +2-3 = -1$
$-3--4 = -3+4 = +1$
$+3--2 = +3+2 = +5$
$+3--5 = +3+5 = +8$

Multiplication

$+2 \times +3 = +6$
$-3 \times -4 = +12$
$+3 \times -2 = -6$
$-5 \times +3 = -15$

Division

$+6 \div +2 = +3$
$+12 \div -3 = -4$
$-6 \div -2 = +3$
$-15 \div +3 = -5$

Example 1

Add together -2, -3, and -4

$$-2+-3+-4 = -2-3-4 = -9$$

Example 2

Subtract the second quantity from the first: $(4-6)$ and $-(6-8)$.

$$(4-6)--(6-8) = (-2)--(-2) = -2+-2 = -2-2 = -4$$

Example 3

Multiply together $-\frac{1}{2}$ and $-\frac{2}{3}$.

$$-\tfrac{1}{2} \times -\tfrac{2}{3} = +\tfrac{1}{3}$$

Example 4

Divide $-4\frac{1}{2}$ by $+9$.

$$-4\tfrac{1}{2} \div +9 = -\tfrac{9}{2} \div +9 = -\tfrac{9}{2} \times +\tfrac{1}{9} = -\tfrac{1}{2}$$

Example 5

Evaluate $(-2)^5$

$$(-2)^5 = -2 \times -2 \times -2 \times -2 \times -2 = -32$$

Exercise 3.2

Add together the following groups of numbers

1. $2, -6$ **2.** $4, -3$ **3.** $-3, -5$ **4.** $6. -\frac{1}{2}$
5. $2, -7, 4\frac{1}{2}$ **6.** $-11, 4, 16$ **7.** $-9, -4\frac{2}{3}$ **8.** $5, -9, 6$
9. $-4, -7, -5$ **10.** $13, -6, -4$ **11.** $-9, -6, 23$ **12.** $16, -7, -11\frac{1}{2}$
13. $8\frac{2}{3}, -5, -\frac{1}{3}$ **14.** $\frac{1}{2}, \frac{1}{4}, -\frac{3}{4}$ **15.** $3\frac{1}{4}, -4\frac{7}{8}$ **16.** $3, -4\frac{5}{8}, 2\frac{1}{8}$
17. $\frac{2}{3}, \frac{2}{3}, -2$ **18.** $4\frac{1}{4}, -2, \frac{1}{8}$ **19.** $6, -2\frac{3}{8}, -\frac{5}{8}$ **20.** $3\frac{3}{4}, 4, -7\frac{7}{8}$

Subtract the second quantity from the first

21. $-4, 5$ **22.** $-4, -5$ **23.** $6, -8$ **24.** $4\frac{1}{2}, -4\frac{1}{2}$
25. $-4\frac{1}{2}, -4\frac{1}{2}$ **26.** $-4\frac{1}{2}, 4\frac{1}{2}$ **27.** $6, -(3+2)$ **28.** $6, -(3-2)$
29. $-7, -(4-6)$ **30.** $(5-6), -8$ **31.** $-(3-2), 4$ **32.** $(4-7), -(2-5)$
33. $2\frac{1}{2}, -(3-4\frac{1}{4})$ **34.** $0, -(2-4+3)$
35. $6, (-5+2)$ **36.** $-4, (3-6-2)$
37. $7, -(\frac{1}{3}-\frac{1}{2}+\frac{3}{4})$ **38.** $\frac{1}{8}, -(\frac{5}{8}-\frac{7}{8})$
39. $2{\cdot}1, -0{\cdot}09$ **40.** $-3{\cdot}66, -2{\cdot}901$

Multiply together the following groups of numbers

41. $2, -4$ **42.** $-2, 4$ **43.** $-2, -4$ **44.** $2, 4$
45. $6, 8$ **46.** $-6, -8$ **47.** $6, -8$ **48.** $-6, 8$
49. $-\frac{1}{2}, \frac{1}{4}$ **50.** $-\frac{1}{2}, -\frac{1}{4}$ **51.** $-2, -4, -5$ **52.** $-5, 2, -3$

Divide the first number by the second

53. $6, -3$ **54.** $-6, 3$ **55.** $-6, -3$ **56.** $-7\frac{1}{2}, 3$
57. $9, -4\frac{1}{2}$ **58.** $-7\frac{1}{2}, -1\frac{1}{2}$ **59.** $-14, 21$ **60.** $-5, -15$

Evaluate the following

61. $(-2)^2$ **62.** $(-4)^3$ **63.** $(-2)^3$ **64.** $(-\frac{1}{2})^4$

In the following questions use directed numbers to express your answers.

65. I have 20p in my pocket but I owe someone 30p. What am I really worth?

66. What are a man's assets if he has £500 in the bank but owes £600? By what amount is he in debt?

67. Taking distances and speeds due North and due East as positive express the following to show both magnitude and direction at the same time
(a) a distance of 5 km due North (b) a distance of 6 km due South
(c) a distance of 3 km due West (d) a speed of 3 km/h due East
(e) a speed of 5 km/h due South (f) a speed of 6 km/h due West

68. Write down the following temperature changes
(a) 12°C to −4°C (b) −2°C to −5°C
(c) −5°C to −2°C (d) −6°C to 45°C
(e) 10°C to 34°C

69. What is the average of $6, -4, 5, -7$?

70. In a 'multi-choice' examination paper, 3 marks are awarded for a correct response, −1 mark for an incorrect response, and −2 marks if the question is not attempted. Calculate the scores of the following pupils if there are 50 questions on the paper.
A 30 correct, 20 incorrect
B 32 correct, 15 incorrect
C 40 correct
D 20 correct, 10 incorrect
E 5 correct, 22 incorrect

3.3 Simple substitution

Points to remember:

$$2a = a + a = 2 \times a$$
$$a \text{ squared} = a^2 = a \times a$$
$$a \text{ cubed} = a^3 = a \times a \times a$$
$$3a^2 = a^2 + a^2 + a^2 = 3 \times a^2 = 3 \times a \times a$$
$$2ab = ab + ab = 2 \times ab = 2 \times a \times b$$
$$(2a)^2 = 2a \times 2a = 2 \times a \times 2 \times a = 2 \times 2 \times a \times a = 4 \times a \times a = 4a^2$$

The square root of a is written $\sqrt{a}$ or $a^{\frac{1}{2}}$

$$a \div 2 = \frac{1}{2} \text{ of } a \text{ or } \frac{a}{2}$$

Example 1 Find the value of $4x - 6$ if $x = 8$.

If $x = 8$, then $4x - 6 = (4 \times 8) - 6 = 32 - 6 = 26$.

Example 2 Find the value of $2a^2 + 3a$ if $a = 4$.

If $a = 4$, then $2a^2 + 3a = (2 \times 4 \times 4) + (3 \times 4) = 32 + 12 = 44$.

Example 3 Find the value of $\frac{3a - 2b}{4c}$ if $a = 3, b = 0, c = \frac{1}{2}$.

If $a = 3$, $b = 0$ and $c = \frac{1}{2}$, then $\frac{3a - 2b}{4c} = \frac{(3 \times 3) - (2 \times 0)}{(4 \times \frac{1}{2})}$

$$= \frac{9 - 0}{2} = \frac{9}{2} = 4\tfrac{1}{2}$$

Exercise 3.3a

If $a = 1, b = 2, c = 3, d = 4$, and $e = 0$, evaluate the following

1. $2b$ **2.** $3ac$ **3.** $c + d$ **4.** $2a + d$
5. $2a + 3b - 2d$ **6.** $ab + de$ **7.** $3bc + d$ **8.** $4ad - \frac{1}{2}bd$
9. $\frac{abc}{d}$ **10.** b^2 **11.** $3c^2$ **12.** $(3c)^2$
13. $e(a + b)$ **14.** $c(d - 3e)^2$ **15.** $2b^2(a + c)$ **16.** $\frac{2(2a + 3b + 4c)}{d}$
17. $\sqrt{d}$ **18.** $2\sqrt{(3c)}$ **19.** $\sqrt[3]{(bd)}$ **20.** $\sqrt{(4c + d)}$
21. $(16e)^2$ **22.** $2a(b + c)d$ **23.** $\frac{(3b + d)}{(4a - b)}$ **24.** $\frac{\sqrt{(4d - 3b - a)}}{2b}$

25. $\sqrt{(2a+b)^3}$ 26. $\sqrt[3]{(2b+e)^3}$ 27. $e^2(a+66b)$ 28. $(a+e)^2(a+66b)$

29. $\dfrac{b^2}{d^3}$ 30. $\left(\dfrac{b}{d}\right)^2$ 31. $\dfrac{1}{c}-\dfrac{1}{d}$ 32. $\dfrac{1}{d-c}$

33. $\dfrac{e}{3a+12c}$ 34. $\dfrac{a}{3e+12c}$ 35. $\dfrac{c}{e}$ 36. e^2

37. $\dfrac{c^2-b^2}{c^2b^2}$ 38. $\dfrac{c^2}{b^2}+\dfrac{b^2}{c^2}$ 39. $\dfrac{(c+b+e)^2}{(c+b)^2}$ 40. $\dfrac{c^2+b^3+e^4}{3a^3}$

Special care must be taken when the substitution involves negative numbers.

Example 4 Find the value of $4x-6$ when $x = -6$.

If $x = -6$, then $4x-6 = (4\times -6)-6 = -24-6 = -30$.

Example 5 Find the value of $2a^2+3a$ when $a = -4$.

If $a = -4$, then $2a^2+3a = (2\times -4\times -4)+(3\times -4) = 32-12 = 20$.

Example 6 Find the value of $4-x^2$ when $x = -3$.

If $x = -3$, then $4-x^2 = 4-(-3\times -3) = 4-9 = -5$.

Exercise 3.3b

If $x = -4$, evaluate the following

1. $2x$ 2. x^2 3. x^3 4. $x-4$
5. $4-x^2$ 6. $4x-x^2$ 7. x^2-4x-2 8. $2x^2+6x-9$
9. $4-3x-x^2$ 10. $\sqrt{(x^4)}$

If $a = -1$, $b = -2$, and $c = 6$, evaluate the following

11. $a+b+c$ 12. $a-b-c$ 13. abc 14. a^2+b^2
15. a^3-b 16. a^2b 17. $2a-a^2$ 18. a^2-2a
19. $\dfrac{c^2}{ab}$ 20. $\dfrac{a+b+c}{a}$ 21. $\dfrac{a}{b}+\dfrac{b}{a}$ 22. $\dfrac{1}{a}+\dfrac{1}{b}+\dfrac{1}{c}$

23. Find y when $y = mx+c$, $m = -2$, $x = 3$, and $c = 5$.
24. Find s when $s = ut+\frac{1}{2}ft^2$, $u = 0$, $t = 3$, and $f = 10$.
25. Find f when $\dfrac{1}{f} = \dfrac{1}{v}+\dfrac{1}{u}$, $v = 2$, and $u = 4$.
26. Find v when $v^2-u^2 = 2fs$, $u = -5$, $f = 10$, and $s = 7{\cdot}2$.
27. Find t when $t = 2\pi\sqrt{\dfrac{l}{g}}$, $\pi = 3{\cdot}14$, $l = 10{\cdot}24$, and $g = 32$.
28. Find m_2 when $F = \dfrac{m_1m_2}{d^2}$, $F = 6$, $d = 4$, and $m_1 = 0{\cdot}1$.
29. Find S when $S = \dfrac{2(u^2+uv+v^2)}{3(u+v)}$, $u = 0{\cdot}6$ and $v = 0{\cdot}4$.
30. Find T when $T = \sqrt{\dfrac{2hP}{g(P-mg)}}$, $h = 3$, $P = 500$, $g = 10$ and $m = 0{\cdot}25$.

3.4 Use of brackets

Terms are the parts of an expression which are connected by + or − signs. Like terms can be collected together, and replaced by a single term.

Example 1

$5x + 4x - 3x = 6x$

$-3a - 4a - 5a = -12a$

Unlike terms are those which cannot be collected together and replaced by a single term.

Example 2

$5x + 4y$ cannot be simplified

$4x^2 + 3x^3$ cannot be replaced by a single term.

$4\,xyz$ is only one term; x, y and z are *not* separate terms.
In all expressions, the term ab is the same as the term ba.
The *distributive law*, states that a term outside a bracket multiplies each of the terms inside the bracket.
Remember that a negative sign outside a bracket changes all the signs inside the bracket.
After removing brackets, the expression is simplified by collecting all the like terms together.

Example 3

$$x + 3(x + y) = x + 3x + 3y = 4x + 3y$$

$$x - 3(x + y) = x - 3x - 3y = -2x - 3y$$

$$x - 3(x - y) = x - 3x + 3y = -2x + 3y \text{ or } 3y - 2x$$

$$x + 3x(x + y) = x + 3x^2 + 3xy$$

$$\begin{aligned}(x + y)(x + y) &= x(x + y) + y(x + y)\\ &= x^2 + xy + yx + y^2 = x^2 + 2xy + y^2\end{aligned}$$

$$\begin{aligned}(a + 2b)(3a - 5b) &= a(3a - 5b) + 2b(3a - 5b)\\ &= 3a^2 - 5ab + 6ba - 10b^2 = 3a^2 + ab - 10b^2\end{aligned}$$

$$\begin{aligned}(4x + 3y)(4x - 3y) &= 4x(4x - 3y) + 3y(4x - 3y)\\ &= 16x^2 - 12xy + 12yx - 9y^2 = 16x^2 - 9y^2\end{aligned}$$

In a case where there are brackets inside brackets, the 'inside' brackets are removed first.

Example 4

$$4[(a+b)-3(b-a)] = 4[a+b-3b+3a] = 4[4a-2b] = 16a-8b$$

Exercise 3.4

Simplify the following by collecting like terms

1. $2x+3x$
2. $3y+4y+5y$
3. $a+6a-2a$
4. $2ab+7ba$
5. $2a+3b+a-2b$
6. $3p+q-p-4q$
7. $x-2y+12x-6y$
8. $x+3xy+2x$
9. $2pq+3qp$
10. $abc+2bca-2cab$

Simplify the following by removing the brackets and collecting like terms

11. $a+2(a+2b)$
12. $3x-2(x+y)$
13. $3x-2(x-y)$
14. $3x-(x+y)$
15. $3x-(x-y)$
16. $4p-(p-q)$
17. $18x+3(y-2x)$
18. $f-3(f+g)$
19. $ab+a(b+c)$
20. $3xy-2x(y-z)$
21. $3(x+2y)-2(y-x)$
22. $a(b+c)+b(a+c)$
23. $2(3+mn)+4(1-mn)$
24. $xy+yz-2y(x+z)$
25. $3m(2+n)-3n(2-n)$
26. $3xy(2+z)+4yz(2x+12)$
27. $r(p+2q)-2p(q-r)$
28. $x(x+y)-y(x-2y)$
29. $4x(x-y)-2y(x-2y)$
30. $(p-2q)r-2p(p-r)$
31. $2[(a+b)-2(b-c)]$
32. $3x[(x+y+z)-5]$
33. $a[(p+2q)-3(2p-q)]$
34. $2p[(1+q)+3(1-2q)]$
35. $x\left(\frac{1}{x}+\frac{1}{y}\right)$
36. $2ab\left(\frac{2}{a}-\frac{1}{b}\right)$
37. $mn\left(2+\frac{m+n}{2}\right)$
38. $(x+2)(x+3)$
39. $(x+3)(x-2)$
40. $(x-3)(x-2)$
41. $(x-3)(x+3)$
42. $(x-3)(x-3)$
43. $(x+3)(x+3)$
44. $(x+y)(x+2y)$
45. $(x-y)(x-2y)$
46. $(x-y)(x+y)$
47. $(a-b)(2a-3b)$
48. $(2x-y)(2x+3y)$
49. $(3p-4q)(2p+q)$
50. $(2a-4b)(3a-5b)$
51. $(m-5n)(5m+n)$
52. $3(a+2b)(3a-2b)$
53. $2(3x+y)(2x-3y)$
54. $(a+b)(a+b+c)$
55. $(3a+2b)^2$
56. $(2x-y)(3x+y+4)$
57. $(x+y)\left(\frac{1}{x}+\frac{1}{y}\right)$
58. $3(x+2)(2x-1)-2(3x-2)$
59. $(x+3)(4x-1)+(2x-3)(2x+3)$
60. $2x(x+3)-3(x-4)(x+3)$
61. $(3x-2y)^2$
62. $(5a-b)^2$
63. $4(2x+3)^2$
64. $3x[(x+y)^2-2y]$
65. $(a+b)^2-2(a-b)^2$

3.5 Simple equations

1. Simple linear equations can be solved by
(a) adding equal numbers to both sides of the equation
or (b) subtracting equal numbers from both sides of the equation
and (c) multiplying *or* dividing both sides of the equation by the same number.

Example 1 Solve $x - 3 = 9$

$$x - 3 + 3 = 9 + 3 \quad \text{(adding 3 to both sides)}$$
$$x = 12$$

Check: when $x = 12$, $12 - 3 = 9$

Example 2 Solve $2x + 4 = 6$

$$2x + 4 - 4 = 6 - 4 \text{ (subtracting 4 from both sides)}$$
$$2x = 2$$
$$x = 1 \quad \text{(dividing both sides by 2)}$$

Check: when $x = 1, 2 \times 1 + 4 = 2 + 4 = 6$

2. If the equation contains brackets, these should be removed first, using the methods given in 3.4.

Example 3 Solve $4(x + 4) - 3(2 - x) = 17$

$$4x + 16 - 6 + 3x = 17$$
$$7x = 17 + 6 - 16$$
$$7x = 7$$
$$x = 1$$

Check: when $x = 1$ in the original equation,
$4(1 + 4) - 3(2 - 1) = (4 \times 5) - (3 \times 1) = 20 - 3 = 17$

3. If the equation contains fractions, these fractions are removed by multiplying every term on *both* sides of the equation by the lowest common multiple (L.C.M.) of the denominators.

Example 4 Solve $\dfrac{3x - 4}{4} - \dfrac{3x - 2}{3} = 2$

The L.C.M. of the denominators is 12. Therefore the equation becomes

$$\frac{12(3x - 4)}{4} - \frac{12(3x - 2)}{3} = 2 \times 12$$
$$3(3x - 4) - 4(3x - 2) = 24$$

$$\begin{aligned} 9x - 12 - 12x + 8 &= 24 \\ 9x - 12x &= 24 + 12 - 8 \\ -3x &= 28 \\ x &= \frac{28}{-3} = -9\tfrac{1}{3} \end{aligned}$$

Check: when $x = -9\frac{1}{3}$ in the original equation,

$$\begin{aligned} \frac{3 \times -9\frac{1}{3} - 4}{4} - \frac{3 \times -9\frac{1}{3} - 2}{3} &= \frac{-28-4}{4} - \frac{-28-2}{3} \\ &= \frac{-32}{4} - \frac{-30}{3} \\ &= -8 - -10 \\ &= -8 + 10 = 2 \end{aligned}$$

Exercise 3.5

1. $x - 2 = 6$
2. $x - 4 = 11$
3. $x + 3 = 9$
4. $x + 11 = 21$
5. $2x = 14$
6. $7x = 49$
7. $\frac{1}{2}x = 3$
8. $\frac{1}{8}x = 2$
9. $\frac{x}{3} = 4$
10. $\frac{x}{4} = 2$
11. $2x - 9 = 11$
12. $3x + 2 = 17$
13. $\frac{2}{3}x - 2 = 7$
14. $\frac{1}{4}x + 8 = 16$
15. $2x + 3x = 25$
16. $6x - x = 15$
17. $4x + x - 2x = 27$
18. $5x - 2x = 12 - x$
19. $6x - 7x + 2x + 1 = 9$
20. $17x - 6 = 12x + 9$
21. $5x - 1\frac{1}{2}x = 21$
22. $3x + 8 = 28 - \frac{x}{3}$
23. $4x + \frac{1}{3}x - 2 = 24$
24. $\frac{x}{2} + \frac{x}{3} = 15$
25. $\frac{2x}{3} + \frac{x}{4} = 33$
26. $\frac{4x}{7} - \frac{x}{2} = 1$
27. $\frac{3}{8}x + \frac{1}{4}x - \frac{1}{3}x = 28$
28. $\frac{3}{5}x - \frac{1}{2}x = 3 - \frac{x}{10}$
29. $\frac{2x}{3} = \frac{7}{2}$
30. $\frac{4}{5}x = 1\frac{1}{2}$
31. $2(3x + 6) = 15$
32. $x + 2(x + 1) = 11$
33. $3x + 4(x - 6) + 3 = 0$
34. $3(2x - 1) + 4x = 7$
35. $5(x + 6) - 3x = 45$
36. $2(x - 1) + 3(2x + 3) = 31$
37. $3(2x - 3) - 2(1 - x) = 5$
38. $4(6 - 2x) + 3(3 - 2x) = 5$
39. $10(x + 4) + 9(2x - 5) = 0$
40. $2x + 6 + \frac{1}{2}(x + 1) = 7$
41. $\frac{2x + 1}{5} + 3x = 3\frac{3}{5}$
42. $\frac{1}{2}(3x + 1) + \frac{1}{3}(2x + 1) = 0$
43. $\frac{2}{3}(x + 4) + \frac{3}{5}(2x + 1) = 0$
44. $\frac{x + 1}{3} + \frac{2x - 1}{4} = 2$
45. $\frac{2(2x - 1)}{5} + \frac{x}{4} = 2$
46. $\frac{3(2x - 1)}{4} - \frac{2(x + 2)}{3} = 1$
47. $\frac{2}{5(2x + 1)} = 3$
48. $\frac{1}{6(x - 1)} - 4 = 0$

3.6 Simple equations (problems)

To solve an algebraic problem:

(a) Let a letter stand for the unknown.

(b) This letter must stand for a number and its units must be clearly stated;
e.g. let the length be x cm
let the cost be y pence

(c) Change each statement in the problem to a fact containing the unknown.

(d) Using these facts, build up an equation, solve it, and then give the answer to the question.
e.g. Bob's age is 16 years, *not* $x = 16$

(e) Check the answer by using the facts given in the question. It is a waste of time checking the equation.

Example 1

Find the number which, when it is trebled and 13 added, gives an answer of 40.
Let the number be x; then the number trebled is $3x$.

$$\therefore 3x + 13 = 40$$
$$3x = 27$$
$$x = 9$$

Therefore the number is 9.
Check: 9 trebled is 27, and 13 added gives 40.

Example 2

If a man walks to the station at 4 kilometres per hour, he misses his train by 1 minute. But if he runs at 8 kilometres per hour, he arrives $6\frac{1}{2}$ minutes early. How far is it to the station?
Let the distance to the station be x km.

Then the time taken to walk is $\frac{x}{4}$ hours and the time taken to run is $\frac{x}{8}$ hours.

$$\therefore \frac{x}{4} - \frac{1}{60} = \frac{x}{8} + \frac{6\frac{1}{2}}{60}$$
$$30x - 2 = 15x + 13$$
$$15x = 15$$
$$x = 1$$

Therefore the distance to the station is 1 kilometre.

Check: if the distance is 1 km, the time to walk is $\frac{1}{4}$ h or 15 min, and the time to run is $\frac{1}{8}$ h or $7\frac{1}{2}$ min.

Hence $15 - 1 = 14$, and $7\frac{1}{2} + 6\frac{1}{2} = 14$.

Exercise 3.6

1. A said to B 'I am thinking of a number. I doubled it and the answer is six.' What number was A first thinking of?
2. B replied to A 'I too am thinking of a number. I have halved it and then added six and the answer is 12.' What number was B thinking of?
3. Find three consecutive numbers whose sum is 24.
4. Find four consecutive odd numbers whose sum is 128.
5. There are three children in a family. Each is three years older than the next and the sum of their ages is 21 years. How old are they?
6. Divide £190 between A and B so that A receives £72 more than B.
7. A man is eight times as old as his son. In five years time he will be only four times as old. How old is the son now?
8. A man bought a house. When he sold it for £9000, he had gained one eighth of his purchase price. What did he pay for it?
9. A man walks a certain distance and then drives five times as far. His total journey is 48 miles. How far did he walk?
10. A room is 2 m longer than it is wide. If its perimeter is 32 m, how long is it?
11. A man buys an article costing £51 for which he pays a deposit and then twelve monthly instalments. If the deposit is equal to five monthly instalments how much was it?
12. Find the number which, when added to both the numerator and the denominator of the fraction thirteen-seventeenths, makes it equal to seven-ninths.
13. A cricketer makes 287 runs in 14 innings. How many runs must he make in the next innings if his average is to be 25?
14. There are 261 people in a village. There are 7 more men than women and 16 more children than men. How many men are there?
15. Two trains, one of which travels at 10 km/h more than the other, start towards each other at the same time from two places 325 km apart. They meet in $2\frac{1}{2}$ hours. Find the speed of the slower train.
16. A train leaves a station. One hour later another train follows it travelling 10 km/h faster. It overtakes the first train in 6 hours. What was the speed of the first train?
17. Eight years ago, B was three times as old as A. Four years from now, A's age will be five-ninths that of B. How old is A now?
18. Two tanks contain petrol, one holding twice as much as the other. When 5 litres are transferred from the lesser quantity to the greater, the ratio of the two quantities of petrol is 1 : 3. How much did the larger tank originally contain?
19. There are 50 coins in a box. Some are 50p pieces and the rest are 10p pieces. If the total value of all the coins is £21·80, how many more 50p pieces than 10p pieces are there in the box?
20. The same number is added to both the numerator and the denominator of the fraction $\frac{19}{25}$. If the fraction is then equal to $\frac{5}{6}$, find the number added.

3.7 Changing the subject

To change the subject of an expression, apply the following rules where necessary.

(a) Remove all fractions, brackets and roots.

(b) Put all the terms containing the new subject to one side of the expression, and all the rest to the other side.

(c) Simplify both sides of this new expression and if the new subject still appears in more than one term, take it out as a common factor.

(d) Divide both sides of the expression by the coefficient of the new subject.

Example 1 Make D the subject of $C = \pi D$

$\frac{C}{\pi} = D$ (dividing both sides by π: the coefficient of D)

Example 2 Make x the subject of $y = mx + c$

$y - c = mx$ (taking c from both sides)

$\frac{y-c}{m} = x$ (dividing both sides by m)

Example 3 Make a the subject of $\frac{x}{a} + \frac{y}{b} = 1$

$xb + ay = ab$ (multiplying both sides by the L.C.M.)

$xb = ab - ay$ (taking ay from both sides)

$xb = a(b - y)$ (a is a common factor)

$\frac{xb}{b-y} = a$ ($(b - y)$ is the coefficient of a)

Example 4 Make g the subject of $t = 2\pi\sqrt{\left(\frac{l}{g}\right)}$

$t^2 = 4\pi^2\frac{l}{g}$ (squaring both sides)

$gt^2 = 4\pi^2 l$ (multiplying both sides by g)

$g = \frac{4\pi^2 l}{t^2}$ (dividing both sides by t^2)

Example 5 Make r the subject of $A = P\left(1 + \frac{r}{100}\right)$

$A = P + \frac{Pr}{100}$ (removing brackets)

$100A = 100P + Pr$ (multiplying both sides by 100)

$$100A - 100P = Pr \qquad \text{(taking } 100P \text{ from both sides)}$$

$$\frac{100A - 100P}{P} = r \qquad \text{(dividing both sides by } P\text{)}$$

Example 6

If $A = \pi r^2$ and $C = 2\pi r$, express C in terms of A and π, i.e. eliminate r.

From $A = \pi r^2$, $\dfrac{A}{\pi} = r^2$.

From $C = 2\pi r$, $\dfrac{C}{2\pi} = r$. $\qquad \therefore \dfrac{C^2}{4\pi^2} = r^2$

$$\therefore \quad \frac{C^2}{4\pi^2} = \frac{A}{\pi}; \quad \pi C^2 = 4\pi^2 A$$

$$C^2 = 4\pi A$$

$$C = \sqrt{(4\pi A)}$$

Exercise 3.7

In each of the following questions rearrange the formula to make its subject the letter shown in the square brackets.

1. $A = LB\ [B]$
2. $A = \frac{1}{2}bh\ [b]$
3. $C = 2\pi r\ [r]$
4. $V = \frac{1}{3}\pi r^2 h\ [h]$
5. $S = \pi rL\ [L]$
6. $pv = c\ [v]$
7. $V = r^2 h\ [h]$
8. $V = abc\ [c]$
9. $\frac{1}{2}P = L + B\ [B]$
10. $v = u + ft\ [f]$
11. $v^2 - u^2 = 2fs\ [s]$
12. $s = ut + \frac{1}{2}ft^2\ [f]$
13. $s = \frac{1}{2}n(a + L)\ [L]$
14. $C = \frac{5}{9}(F - 32)\ [F]$
15. $s = \dfrac{u + v}{2}t\ [v]$
16. $V = \pi h(R + r)t\ [R]$
17. $xy + a = p\ [y]$
18. $x(y + a) = p\ [y]$
19. $V = \pi r^2 h\ [r]$
20. $A = 4\pi r^2\ [r]$
21. $H = \frac{a}{b}\sqrt{t}\ [t]$
22. $P = \dfrac{5M}{N^2}\ [N]$
23. $V = \frac{1}{3}\pi r^2 h\ [r]$
24. $A = \pi(R^2 - r^2)\ [r]$
25. If $P = \dfrac{mv - mu}{t}$ and $P = mf$, find v in terms of u, f and t only.
26. If $\dfrac{1}{p} - \dfrac{1}{q} = \dfrac{1}{10}$ and $p + q = z$, find z in terms of p only.
27. If $V = \pi r^2 h$ and $A = 2\pi rh$, find V in terms of A and r.
28. If $V = \frac{4}{3}\pi r^3$ and $A = 4\pi r^2$, find V in terms of A, and A in terms of V (π may appear but not r).
29. Given that $A = \dfrac{3K + 5M}{K + 2}$, find an expression for K in terms of M and A.
30. If $a^2 + b^2 = \left(\dfrac{x^2}{y} - b\right)^2$, find b in terms of a, x, and y.

3.8 Simultaneous equations

If two or more equations are true for the same values of the unknowns, they are called *simultaneous equations.*

Simultaneous equations are normally solved by equalizing coefficients of one of the unknowns, and then eliminating that unknown by subtracting (or adding) one equation from the other to find the second unknown. Sometimes this can be done by inspection, as in Example 1 below.

Example 1 Solve $x + y = 5$

$$x - y = 3$$

Hence $x = 4$ and $y = 1$.

Example 2 Solve $10x - 3y = 50 \quad \text{(i)}$

$$3x - 4y = -16 \quad \text{(ii)}$$

Step 1. Make the coefficients of y numerically equal by multiplying equation (i) by 4 and equation (ii) by 3.

$$40x - 12y = 200 \quad \text{(iii)}$$

$$9x - 12y = -48 \quad \text{(iv)}$$

Step 2. Subtract equation (iv) from equation (iii) to eliminate the terms in y.

$$31x = 248$$

$$\therefore x = 8$$

If the coefficients of y had opposite signs, it would have been necessary to add the two equations together.

Step 3. By replacing x by 8 in equation (i), this equation becomes

$$10 \times 8 - 3y = 50$$

$$80 - 3y = 50$$

$$30 = 3y$$

$$10 = y$$

Therefore $x = 8$ and $y = 10$.
Check: when $x = 8$ and $y = 10$ in both the original equations,

$$10x - 3y = 10 \times 8 - 3 \times 10 = 80 - 30 = 50$$

$$3x - 4y = 3 \times 8 - 4 \times 10 = 24 - 40 = -16$$

Note. It does not matter whether x or y is eliminated. If possible, choose whichever is the easier.

Exercise 3.8

Solve the following pairs of simultaneous equations

1. $x + y = 12$, $x - y = 6$

2. $2x + y = 10$, $x - y = 2$

3. $4x + y = 10$, $3x + y = 9$

4. $2x + 3y = 11$, $4x + y = 12$

5. $3x + 4y = 25$, $4x - 3y = 0$

6. $2x + 5y = 16$, $3x - 2y = 5$

7. $x + 2y = 4$, $3x + 7y = 11$

8. $5x - 6y = 8$, $y - 4x = 5$

9. $3x + 7y = 28$, $x + y = 5\frac{1}{3}$

10. $3x + 3y = 15$, $2x - y = 4$

11. $5x + y = -1$, $2x + y = -1$

12. $3x - 3y = 0$, $x + 5y = -6$

13. $4x + y = 3$, $4x - 2y = 0$

14. $x + y = 2$, $3x - 3y = 3$

15. $12x + 9y = 30$, $8x + 12y = 32$

16. $36x - 32y = 32$, $48x + 36y = -36$

17. $3(x + y) = 21$, $6(x - y) = 6$

18. $3x + 2y = 24$, $2x - 3y = 42$

19. $3y + 5x = 9$, $7x - 2y = 25$

20. $2x + 3y = 4$, $3x - 4{\cdot}5y = 6$

21. $x + y = 21$, $\dfrac{x}{4} + \dfrac{y}{3} = 6$

22. $x - y = 4$, $\dfrac{x}{5} + \dfrac{y}{3} = 4$

23. $x + 2y = 2$, $2x + \dfrac{y}{2} = \dfrac{25}{8}$

24. $\dfrac{x + y}{2} = \frac{1}{4}(y - x)$, $x + y = 2$

25. $\frac{1}{2}(x - 2y) = 3(x + 8y)$, $x + 2y = 4$

26. $x + 3y + 2 = 0$, $4(x + y) - 8 = 0$

27. $\dfrac{1}{x} + y = 8$, $\dfrac{3}{x} - 2y + 6 = 0$

28. $\dfrac{2}{x} + \dfrac{1}{y} = 7$, $\dfrac{3}{x} + \dfrac{2}{y} = 12\frac{1}{2}$

29. $\dfrac{1 + 2y}{x} = 5$, $\dfrac{3 + 4y}{2x} = 3\frac{1}{2}$

30. $8x - y = 2(x - y) = 20x - 3$

31. $\dfrac{x - y}{5} = \dfrac{x - 6}{3} = \dfrac{x - 3y}{3}$

32. $x + 18y = xy$, $\dfrac{1}{x} + \dfrac{1}{y} + \frac{8}{9} = 0$

33. If the equation $y = ax + b$ is satisfied by $x = 0, y = 2$ and also by $x = 3, y = 3\frac{1}{2}$ find the values of a and b.

34. If the equation $y = mx + c$ is satisfied by $x = 1, y = 5$ and also by $x = 4, y = 11$ find the values of m and c.

35. If $x + 2y = 7$ and $3x - y = 14$, find the value of $5x + 3y$ with as little working as possible.

36. If $3x + 4y = 4$ and $2x + 3y = 1\frac{1}{2}$, find the value of $13x + 18y$ with as little working as possible.

3.9 Simultaneous equations (problems)

Adapt the method outlined in Section 3.6 (page 68) to produce two different equations in two unknowns and solve them as outlined in Section 3.8 (page 72).

Example

3 apples and 2 bananas weigh 200 g and 4 apples and 4 bananas weigh 300 g. Find the weight of each.

Let x g be the weight of an apple and y g be the weight of a banana

then $3x + 2y = 200$ (i)

$4x + 4y = 300$ (ii)

$6x + 4y = 400$ (iii) Multiply equation (i) by 2

$2x = 100$ Subtract equation (ii) from equation (iii)

$x = 50$

Replace x by 50 in equation (i) $(3 \times 50) + 2y = 200$

$150 + 2y = 200$

$2y = 50$

$y = 25$

Therefore each apple weighs 50 g and each banana weighs 25 g.

Check:

3 apples weigh 150 g, 2 bananas weigh 50 g; $\therefore$ total is 200 g in equation (i)

4 apples weigh 200 g, 4 bananas weigh 100 g; $\therefore$ total is 300 g in equation (ii).

Exercise 3.9

1. Two loaves and three small fishes cost 65p. Three loaves and two small fishes cost 60p. What is the price of each?
2. A car and caravan cost £4000. Two cars and three caravans cost £9600. Find the price of one of each.
3. A bill for £53 is paid with £5 and £1 notes, thirteen notes being used in all. How many £5 notes were there?
4. The wages of 10 men and 4 boys amount to £100 a day while 5 men and 6 boys earn £70. What is the daily wage of each?
5. The rail fare for 10 adults and 2 children (half price) is £44. For 3 adults and 50 children it is £112. What is the fare for one child?
6. An alloy containing 6 cm^3 of iron and 8 cm^3 of lead weighs 130 g. Another alloy containing 5 cm^3 of iron and 7 cm^3 of lead weighs 112 g. What is the density in g/cm^3 of iron and of lead?
7. A man invests at simple interest a certain sum of money at 5% per annum and another sum at 6% per annum. His income was £43. If he had invested the whole sum at $5\frac{1}{2}$%, his income would have been £44. What sums did he invest?

8. I buy 200 stamps, some at $6\frac{1}{2}$p and the rest at $8\frac{1}{2}$p. The total cost is £14·60. How many of each kind did I buy?
9. Three magazines and four newspapers cost 65p. Half as many newspapers and three times as many magazines cost £1·45. Find the cost of six of each.
10. A is twice as old as B. In 20 years time the sum of their ages will be 85 years. How old will they be in 10 years time?
11. The ratio of the ages of A and B is 2 : 3. In 7 years time it will be 3 : 4. Find their present ages.
12. A second-hand furniture dealer buys a table and sells a chair thus making a profit of £10. He then sells the table at twice what he gave for it and buys another chair at three quarters of the original price, thus showing a profit of £70. What was the original price of each?
13. A number is made up of two digits whose sum is 9 and whose difference is 5. What is the number?
14. A number is made up of two digits whose sum is 9. If this number is now divided into the number made up of the same digits but in reverse order the result is six-fifths. Find the number.
15. A boat can travel at 20 knots with the tide and 10 knots against it. What speed can the boat make in still water?
16. A motor boat can travel 5 km upstream in 50 minutes and back in half an hour. What speed can the boat make in still water?
17. A rectangle has a perimeter of 62·5 cm. If the width is doubled and the length is halved, the new perimeter is 72·5 cm. What is the area of this rectangle?
18. At a Dog Show, there were a number of dogs and people, and between those present there were 400 heads and 1042 legs. How many dogs were at the Show?
19. When I invested £2750 in shares whose annual dividend was x%, and £2025 in shares whose annual dividend was y%, my total dividend was £613·50. Had I invested £2025 at x% and £2750 at y%, I should have gained £14·50. Find the values of x and y.
20. A man drives to a car park at an average speed of 40 km/h and then walks to his office at an average speed of 6 km/h. The total journey takes him 25 minutes.
One day his car breaks down and he has to walk three times as far, so arriving at his office 17 minutes late. How far is it to his office?

3.10 Factors

If $2x$ is multiplied by $(3x - 4)$, the product is $6x^2 - 8x$.

$$2x(3x - 4) = 6x^2 - 8x$$

The *factors* of $6x^2 - 8x$ are $2x$ and $3x - 4$.
The *highest common factor* (H.C.F.) of $6x^2 - 8x$ is $2x$.
The expression $6x^2 - 8x$ is called a *binomial* because it contains two terms.
When factorizing an expression, always take out the obvious highest common factor first.

Example 1

$3a + 6b = 3(a + 2b)$; $\quad 2ax^2 + 4bx = 2x(ax + 2b)$

To factorize an expression containing four terms (a tetranomial), arrange the expression into two pairs so that each pair has a common factor.

Example 2

$ax + ay + bx + by$
$= a(x + y) + b(x + y)$ — Here a is a common factor of the first pair and b of the second pair.
$= (x + y)(a + b)$ — $(x + y)$ is a common factor.

Example 3

$3ax + 2by + 3ay + 2bx.$
$= 3ax + 3ay + 2by + 2bx$ — The expression is rearranged.
$= 3a(x + y) + 2b(v + x)$ — $3a$ is a common factor of the first pair and $2b$ of the second.
$= (x + y)(3a + 2b)$ — $(x + y)$ is a common factor.

Note. $x + y$ is identical to $y + x$, but $x - y$ is *not* identical to $y - x$. Remember that $x - y = -(y - x)$.

Example 4

$3ay - bx - 3ax + by$
$= 3ay - 3ax - bx + by$ — The expression is rearranged.
$= 3a(y - x) - b(x - y)$ — $3a$ is a common factor of the first pair and $-b$ of the second.
$= 3a(y - x) + b(y - x)$ — $(y - x) = -(x - y)$.
$= (y - x)(3a + b)$ — $(y - x)$ is a common factor.

Note. If an expression contains 6 terms, try rearranging it into 3 pairs so that each pair has a common factor.

Exercise 3.10a

Factorize

1. $2a + 4b$
2. $6a + 9b$
3. $ax + ay$
4. $aby + abz$
5. $x^2 + xy$
6. $2x^2 + 8xy$
7. $3x^2y + 3xy^2$
8. $x^3 + x^2y + 2x^2z$
9. $2a^2b + ab^2c + abc^2$
10. $3p^3q^2 + 6p^2qrs$
11. $2x - 4y + 2z$
12. $3ax + 3b^2x - 6xc$
13. $10p^3 - 15p^2q - 5pr$
14. $17m^3n - 51\,mn^3 + 17\,mnp$
15. $39x^3y^2 - 13x$
16. $9a^3b - 9a^2bc + 36a^2c^2$
17. $4x^3z - 4x^2yz^2 + 8xz^3$
18. $6rs^3 - 9rst^2 + 3rs^2t$
19. $11x^3y - 22xy^3 - 11xyz^2$
20. $24pq^2 + 8pr^2 - 8ps^2$
21. $ac + bc + ad + bd$
22. $2x - 2y - xz + yz$
23. $pr + ps + 2qr + 2qs$
24. $ac - ad + 2bc - 2bd$
25. $3ac + 2bc + 3ad + 2bd$
26. $2ac - 3bc + 3bd - 2ad$
27. $2wx - wy + 4xz - 2yz$
28. $2mx - 2nx + 3my - 3ny$
29. $ac - 3ad + 2bc - 6bd$
30. $6xc - 4cy + 3xd - 2dy$
31. $x^2 + xy + xz + yz$
32. $xy + 2y^2 + 2xz + 4yz$
33. $x^2 - xy + 2xz - 2yz$
34. $ab - b^2 - ac + bc$
35. $2p^2 - 2pm - pn + mn$
36. $abp + 2p + 2q + abq$
37. $a^2b - a - ab^2 + b$
38. $2x^2y + 3x - 2xy^2 - 3y$
39. $ap - 2aq + bp - 2bq + 2pc - 4cq$
40. $xc - 3cy + cz - xd + 3dy - dz$

An algebraic expression that contains three terms is called a *trinomial.* In many instances, the product of two binomials gives a trinomial; in such cases, the two binomials are factors of the expression.

Example 5 $(x + 2)(x + 3) = x^2 + 5x + 6$

Therefore $(x + 2)$ and $(x + 3)$ are factors of the trinomial $x^2 + 5x + 6$.

The factors of a trinomial are usually found by trial and error, as shown below.

Example 6 Factorize $x^2 - 3x - 10$

Step 1. Because the first term is x^2, the expression must be of the form:

$(x \pm \quad)(x \pm \quad)$

Step 2. The product of the second part in each bracket must give -10. The possible factors are therefore:

$(-1, +10); (-10, +1); (-2, +5); (-5, +2)$

Step 3. The possible solutions are as follows:

$(x - 1)(x + 10)$ which gives $x^2 + 9x - 10$
$(x - 10)(x + 1)$ which gives $x^2 - 9x - 10$
$(x - 2)(x + 5)$ which gives $x^2 + 3x - 10$
$(x - 5)(x + 2)$ which gives $x^2 - 3x - 10$

$\therefore\ x^2 - 3x - 10 = (x - 5)(x + 2)$

Example 7 Factorize $2x^2 + 7x + 6$

Step 1. Because the first term is $2x^2$, the expression must be of the form:

$$(2x \pm \quad)(x \pm \quad)$$

Step 2. The product of the second part in each bracket must give +6. The possible factors are therefore:

$$(1, 6); (6, 1); (2, 3); (3, 2); (-1, -6); (-6, -1); (-2, -3); (-3, -2)$$

Step 3. The possible solutions are as follows:

$(2x + 1)(x + 6)$ which gives $2x^2 + 13x + 6$
$(2x + 6)(x + 1)$ which gives $2x^2 + 8x + 6$
$(2x + 2)(x + 3)$ which gives $2x^2 + 8x + 6$
$(2x + 3)(x + 2)$ which gives $2x^2 + 7x + 6$

The other four solutions give a negative middle term.

$$\therefore\ 2x^2 + 7x + 6 = (2x + 3)(x + 2)$$

With practice, much of this work can be avoided by picking out suitable factors and setting down as shown below.

Example 8 Factorize $3x^2 - 9x - 12$

Because 3 is a common factor, the expression becomes

$$3[x^2 - 3x - 4] = 3(x - 4)(x + 1).$$

Exercise 3.10b

Factorize

1. $x^2 + 3x + 2$ **2.** $x^2 + 5x + 6$ **3.** $x^2 + 7x + 12$
4. $x^2 + 5x + 4$ **5.** $x^2 + 4x + 4$ **6.** $x^2 + 4x + 3$
7. $x^2 + 8x + 15$ **8.** $x^2 + 8x + 12$ **9.** $x^2 + 10x + 21$
10. $x^2 + 11x + 18$ **11.** $x^2 + x - 2$ **12.** $x^2 + x - 12$
13. $x^2 + 4x - 12$ **14.** $x^2 - 4x + 3$ **15.** $x^2 + 5x - 6$
16. $x^2 - 6x + 8$ **17.** $x^2 - 3x - 18$ **18.** $x^2 - 9x + 18$
19. $x^2 - 12x + 32$ **20.** $x^2 + 8x - 9$

21. $2x^2 + 3x + 1$ **22.** $2x^2 + 5x + 3$ **23.** $6x^2 + 7x + 2$
24. $6x^2 + 11x + 3$ **25.** $3x^2 + 7x + 2$ **26.** $4x^2 + 7x + 3$
27. $4x^2 + 13x + 3$ **28.** $7x^2 + 9x + 2$ **29.** $9x^2 + 19x + 2$
30. $8x^2 + 19x + 6$

31. $2x^2 + x - 1$ **32.** $2x^2 - 5x - 3$ **33.** $3x^2 - x - 2$
34. $3x^2 - 5x + 2$ **35.** $4x^2 + x - 3$ **36.** $2x^2 - 7x + 6$
37. $4x^2 - 7x + 3$ **38.** $7x^2 - 15x + 2$ **39.** $9x^2 + 17x - 2$
40. $8x^2 - 19x + 6$ **41.** $4x^2 - 12x + 8$ **42.** $3x^2 - 12x - 36$
43. $5x^2 + 20x + 15$ **44.** $8x^2 - 14x + 6$ **45.** $18x^2 - 38x + 4$
46. $24x^2 - 62xy + 40y^2$ **47.** $x^2 + 2xy + y^2 + 3x + 3y$
48. $8(x + 1)^2 - 2(x + 1) - 10$

The expression $a^2 + b^2$ cannot be factorized.
The expression $a^2 - b^2$ can be factorized: it has the factors $(a + b)$ and $(a - b)$.

$$a^2 - b^2 = (a + b)(a - b)$$

The expression $a^2 - b^2$ is known as *the difference between two squares.*

Example 9

(a) Factorize $x^2 - 16$

$$x^2 - 16 = x^2 - 4^2$$
$$= (x + 4)(x - 4)$$

(b) Factorize $4x^2 - 9y^2$

$$4x^2 - 9y^2 = (2x)^2 - (3y)^2$$
$$= (2x + 3y)(2x - 3y)$$

The method of factorizing the difference between two squares is often useful in simplifying arithmetical calculations.

Example 10

(a)
$$78^2 - 22^2 = (78 + 22)(78 - 22)$$
$$= 100 \times 56$$
$$= 5600$$

(b)
$$0{\cdot}63^2 - 0{\cdot}37^2$$
$$= (0{\cdot}63 + 0{\cdot}37)(0{\cdot}63 - 0{\cdot}37)$$
$$= 1 \times 0{\cdot}26$$
$$= 0{\cdot}26$$

Exercise 3.10c

Factorize

1. $x^2 - y^2$
2. $a^2 - 4b^2$
3. $4p^2 - 9q^2$
4. $16m^2 - 81n^2$
5. $2x^2 - 8y^2$
6. $12x^2 - 27y^2$
7. $2x^2 - 50y^2$
8. $xy^2 - xz^2$
9. $2x^2 - 50$
10. $16x^2 - 4$
11. $12x^2 - 75y^4$
12. $a^2b^2 - c^2d^2$
13. $5a^2b^2 - 20$
14. $16a^2 - 36b^2c^2$
15. $8a^3 - 18ab^2$
16. $a^3b - 4ab^3$
17. $18x^3 - 2xy^2$
18. $x^4 - y^4$
19. $x^4 - 16y^4$
20. $81y^4 - 16z^4$

Find by factors the value of

21. $51^2 - 49^2$
22. $101^2 - 99^2$
23. $1001^2 - 999^2$
24. $79^2 - 21^2$
25. $987^2 - 13^2$
26. $841^2 - 159^2$
27. $501^2 - 499^2$
28. $500{\cdot}5^2 - 499{\cdot}5^2$
29. $(10\frac{1}{2})^2 - (9\frac{1}{2})^2$
30. $(15\frac{3}{8})^2 - (13\frac{5}{8})^2$

Factorize

31. $(a + b)^2 - 4$
32. $(4x + 3y)^2 - (2x + y)^2$
33. $(4x - 3y)^2 - (2x - y)^2$
34. $x^2 + 6x + 9 - 4y^2$
35. $x^2 + y^2 - a^2 - 2xy$

3.11 Fractions

An algebraic fraction, like a vulgar fraction, is not changed in value if the numerator *and* the denominator are multiplied or divided by the same quantity.

Example 1 Simplify the following:

(a) $\dfrac{xy}{2x} = \dfrac{y}{2}$ Here the numerator and the denominator are divided by the common factor x.

(b) $\dfrac{2a^2b^2}{4a^3b^3} = \dfrac{1}{2ab}$ Here the numerator and the denominator are divided by the common factor $2a^2b^2$.

To multiply algebraic fractions, factorize the numerator and the denominator where possible. Cancel down and then multiply out.

Example 2 Simplify the following:

$$\frac{a^2 + 2ab + b^2}{a^2 + ab} \times \frac{a}{a^2 - b^2} = \frac{\overset{1}{\cancel{(a+b)}}\overset{1}{\cancel{(a+b)}}}{\underset{1}{\cancel{a}}\underset{1}{\cancel{(a+b)}}} \times \frac{\overset{1}{\cancel{a}}}{\underset{1}{\cancel{(a+b)}}(a-b)}$$

$$= \frac{1}{a-b}$$

To divide algebraic fractions, factorize in the same way; then multiply by the inverse of the divisor.

Example 3 Simplify the following:

$$\frac{x^2b}{c} \div \frac{ab}{c^2} = \frac{x^2\overset{1}{\cancel{b}}}{\cancel{c}} \times \frac{\overset{c}{\cancel{c^2}}}{a\underset{1}{\cancel{b}}}$$

$$= \frac{x^2c}{a}$$

To add or to subtract algebraic fractions

(a) Find the L.C.M. of the denominators

(b) Express each fraction with this L.C.M. It may help to put all the binomial numerators in brackets.

(c) Simplify the numerator.

Example 4. Simplify the following:

$$\frac{a}{a-2} - \frac{4}{a+2} - \frac{a+6}{a^2-4}$$

$$= \frac{a}{a-2} - \frac{4}{a+2} - \frac{(a+6)}{(a+2)(a-2)}$$

The L.C.M. of the denominators is $(a+2)(a-2)$. Therefore the expression becomes

$$\frac{a(a+2)-4(a-2)-(a+6)}{(a+2)(a-2)}$$

$$=\frac{a^2+2a-4a+8-a-6}{(a+2)(a-2)}$$

$$=\frac{a^2-3a+2}{(a+2)(a-2)}=\frac{(a-2)(a-1)}{(a+2)(a-2)}=\frac{a-1}{a+2}$$

Exercise 3.11

Simplify the following

1. $\dfrac{a^2b}{ab}$
2. $\dfrac{abc}{b^2}$
3. $\dfrac{2x^2y}{16x}$
4. $\dfrac{3pqr}{15p^2r^2}$
5. $\dfrac{64abc^2}{8bc}$
6. $\dfrac{21pq}{14q^2r}$
7. $\dfrac{a}{b}\times\dfrac{2b^2}{a}$
8. $\dfrac{2c}{d}\times\dfrac{c^2}{d^3}$
9. $\dfrac{3xy}{2}\times\dfrac{4z^2}{9x}$
10. $\dfrac{pq}{9r}\times\dfrac{6r^2}{7q}$
11. $\dfrac{abc}{d}\div\dfrac{a}{d^2}$
12. $\dfrac{2p}{q}\div\dfrac{q}{2p}$
13. $\dfrac{x^2y}{z}\div\dfrac{xy}{z^2}$
14. $\dfrac{a}{b}\times\dfrac{c}{d}\div\dfrac{ac}{bd}$
15. $\dfrac{a}{b}\div\dfrac{c}{d}\times\dfrac{ac}{bd}$
16. $\dfrac{a+b}{c}\times\dfrac{5}{2(a+b)}$
17. $\dfrac{2(x-y)}{z}\div\dfrac{x-y}{3z}$
18. $\dfrac{a^2+ab}{b}\times\dfrac{c}{ac+bc}$
19. $\dfrac{x^2+2xy+y^2}{x}\times\dfrac{y}{x^2-y^2}$
20. $\dfrac{x^2-x-2}{x^2-2x-3}\div\dfrac{x^2-3x+2}{x^2-4x+3}$
21. $\dfrac{1}{a}+\dfrac{1}{b}$
22. $\dfrac{2}{c}-\dfrac{1}{d}$
23. $\dfrac{1}{2x}+\dfrac{2}{y}$
24. $\dfrac{1}{a+b}+\dfrac{1}{a-b}$
25. $\dfrac{3}{x-y}-\dfrac{2}{x+y}$
26. $\dfrac{x+y}{x-y}+\dfrac{x-y}{x+y}$
27. $\dfrac{a^2+ab}{a+b}+\dfrac{b^2+ab}{a+b}$
28. $\dfrac{1}{x^2+3x+2}+\dfrac{3}{x^2-x-2}$
29. $\dfrac{1}{a^2-ab}-\dfrac{2}{a^2-b^2}$
30. $\dfrac{1}{x^2-9}+\dfrac{1}{(x-3)^2}$
31. $\dfrac{a}{a-a^2}-\dfrac{bc}{ab-b}$
32. $\dfrac{x+1}{x^2+3x+2}-\dfrac{x-2}{x^2-5x+6}$
33. $\dfrac{a-b}{a(a^2-b^2)}+\dfrac{ab+b^2}{b(a+b)^2}$
34. $\dfrac{1}{x^2+3x+2}+\dfrac{1}{x^2+5x+6}+\dfrac{1}{x^2+7x+12}$
35. $\dfrac{a^2}{bc}+\dfrac{(a-b)^2}{b(b-c)}-\dfrac{(a-c)^2}{c(b-c)}$

3.12 Indices

a^3 means $a \times a \times a$ $\quad$ $4a^4$ means $4 \times a \times a \times a \times a$

Rule 1 $\quad a^m \times a^n = a^{m+n}$

e.g. $x^3 \times x^4 = x^{3+4} = x^7$

$4a^2 \times 3a^3 = (4 \times 3)a^{2+3} = 12a^5$

Rule 2 $\quad a^m \div a^n = a^{m-n}$

e.g. $x^6 \div x^5 = x^{6-5} = x^1$ or x

$8x^9 \div 2x^5 = (8 \div 2)x^{9-5} = 4x^4$

Rule 3 $\quad (a^m)^n = a^{m \times n} = a^{mn}$

e.g. $(a^2)^3 = a^{2 \times 3} = a^6$

$(4x^2)^3 = (4)^3 x^{2 \times 3} = 64x^6$

Because $x^{\frac{1}{2}} \times x^{\frac{1}{2}} = x^{\frac{1}{2}+\frac{1}{2}} = x^1$, then $x^{\frac{1}{2}} = \sqrt{x}$

In general $\quad \boxed{x^{\frac{1}{n}} = \sqrt[n]{x}}$

e.g. $9^{\frac{1}{2}} = \sqrt{9} = 3$; $\quad 16^{\frac{1}{4}} = \sqrt[4]{16} = 2$

Because $x^3 \div x^4 = \dfrac{x \times x \times x}{x \times x \times x \times x} = \dfrac{1}{x}$

and $x^3 \div x^4 = x^{3-4} = x^{-1}$, then $x^{-1} = \dfrac{1}{x}$

In general $\quad \boxed{x^{-n} = \dfrac{1}{x^n}}$

e.g. $4^{-1} = \dfrac{1}{4}$; $\quad 8^{-3} = \dfrac{1}{8^3} = \dfrac{1}{512}$

$4a^{-6} = \dfrac{4}{a^6}$; $\quad (2a)^{-3} = \dfrac{1}{(2a)^3} = \dfrac{1}{8a^3}$

$(\frac{2}{3})^{-3} = \dfrac{1}{(\frac{2}{3})^3} = \dfrac{1}{\frac{8}{27}} = \frac{27}{8} = 3\frac{3}{8}$

In general $\quad \boxed{a^{\frac{m}{n}} = \sqrt[n]{(a^m)}}$

e.g. $27^{\frac{2}{3}} = (\sqrt[3]{27})^2 = 3^2 = 9$

$(16x)^{1.5} = (16x)^{1\frac{1}{2}} = (16x)^{\frac{3}{2}} = \sqrt[2]{(16x)^3} = 4^3 x^{\frac{3}{2}} = 64x^{\frac{3}{2}}$

$64^{-\frac{5}{6}} = \dfrac{1}{64^{\frac{5}{6}}} = \dfrac{1}{(\sqrt[6]{64})^5} = \dfrac{1}{2^5} = \dfrac{1}{32}$

Because $x^2 \div x^2 = 1$

and $x^2 \div x^2 = x^2 \times x^{-2} = x^{2-2} = x^0$

then in general $\boxed{x^0 = 1}$

e.g.

$$8^0 = 1$$
$$27x^0 = 27 \times 1 = 27$$
$$(4x)^0 = 1$$

Exercise 3.12

Simplify

1. (a) $x^4 \times x^6$ (b) $x^8 \times x^5$ (c) $x^3 \times x^4 \times x^5$
(d) $\frac{1}{2}x \times \frac{1}{4}x^7 \times \frac{3}{4}x^2$

2. (a) $x^5 \div x^2$ (b) $x^{16} \div x^4$ (c) $x^{10} \div x^5$ (d) $x^3 \div x^7$

3. (a) $x^7 \times x^4 \div x^5$ (b) $x^6 \times x^5 \div x^8$ (c) $\dfrac{x^7}{5} \times \dfrac{x}{4}$ (d) $\dfrac{x^6 \times x^4 \times x^3}{x^2}$

4. (a) $(x^7)^2$ (b) $(x^4)^3$ (c) $(2x^2)^3$ (d) $(\frac{1}{2}x^3)^2$ (e) $\left(\dfrac{2}{x^2}\right)^3$

5. (a) $\sqrt{x^4}$ (b) $\sqrt[4]{x^{16}}$ (c) $\sqrt[3]{x^9}$ (d) $\sqrt{16x^{12}}$ (e) $\sqrt[5]{\dfrac{x^{25}}{32}}$

6. Express without $\sqrt{}$ signs (a) $\sqrt[4]{x}$ (b) $\sqrt[5]{x^2}$ (c) $\sqrt[3]{x^7}$ (d) $\sqrt{x^5}$

7. Express with $\sqrt{}$ signs (a) $x^{\frac{1}{2}}$ (b) $x^{\frac{3}{4}}$ (c) $x^{\frac{7}{8}}$ (d) $x^{\frac{3}{8}}$ (e) $x^{\frac{a}{b}}$

8. Express with positive indices (a) x^{-4} (b) x^{-5} (c) $\dfrac{x^3}{y^{-2}}$
(d) $\dfrac{x^{-2}}{x^3}$ (e) $x^{-\frac{1}{2}}$ (f) $\dfrac{(2x)^3}{x^{-1}}$ (g) $x^2 \times 4x^{-\frac{1}{2}}$ (h) $\sqrt[5]{x^4} \times \sqrt{x^{-2}}$
(i) $1 \div 4x^{-\frac{1}{2}}$ (j) $\sqrt[3]{x^{-4}} \times \dfrac{1}{x^{-3}} \div x^6$

9. Evaluate (a) $4^{-\frac{1}{2}}$ (b) $8^{\frac{2}{3}}$ (c) $25^{-\frac{3}{2}}$ (d) $4^{2.5}$
(e) $4^{-1.5}$ (f) $32^{\frac{3}{5}}$ (g) 6^0 (h) $81^{\frac{3}{4}}$ (i) $64^{\frac{2}{3}}$
(j) $125^{\frac{1}{3}}$ (k) $16^{1\frac{1}{4}}$

10. Evaluate (a) $2^{\frac{1}{2}} \times 2^{2\frac{1}{2}}$ (b) $(5^3)^{\frac{2}{3}}$
(c) $9^{\frac{1}{3}} \times 9^{-\frac{1}{3}}$ (d) $25^{\frac{3}{4}} \times 25^{-\frac{1}{4}}$

11. Evaluate (a) $8^{\frac{2}{3}} \times 81^{\frac{3}{4}}$ (b) $16^{\frac{3}{4}} \times 125^{\frac{1}{3}} \times 27^{-\frac{1}{3}}$
(c) $3^{1.4} \times \sqrt{3^{1.2}}$

12. Evaluate (a) $10^{2.1} \times \sqrt{10^{1.8}}$ (b) $9^{\frac{1}{2}} \times 16^{\frac{3}{4}} + 4^{-2.5} \div 16^{-1.5}$

13. Evaluate (a) $(\sqrt[5]{9})^3 \times (9^{\frac{9}{5}})^{\frac{1}{2}}$ (b) $\sqrt[3]{4^5} \div (4^{\frac{1}{6}})^7$ (c) $\sqrt{2^{1\frac{2}{3}}} \times \sqrt[3]{2^{3.5}}$

14. Evaluate (a) $(\sqrt{\frac{16}{25}})^3$ (b) $(3\frac{3}{8})^{\frac{2}{3}}$ (c) $(1\frac{13}{36})^{-1\frac{1}{2}}$ (d) $(\frac{8}{27})^{\frac{2}{3}}$
(e) $(\frac{1}{9})^{-\frac{1}{2}}$

3.13 Quadratic equations

An equation which contains a square as the highest power of the unknown is called a *quadratic equation.*

e.g. $x^2 + 3x + 2 = 0$

$4x^2 = 7x - 6$

These equations are usually written with one side equal to zero and the term containing the square positive.

e.g. $6 = 7x - 4x^2$ is written $4x^2 - 7x + 6 = 0$

Solution by factors

This method is based on the following:

(a) If $ab = 0$, then either $a = 0$ or $b = 0$

(b) If $(a + 2)(a + 3) = 0$, then either $(a + 2) = 0$ or $(a + 3) = 0$

(c) If $(2a - 5)(4a + 7) = 0$, then either $(2a - 5) = 0$ or $(4a + 7) = 0$.

Example 1 $x^2 - 4 = 0$

By factorizing the left-hand side of the equation, it becomes

$(x + 2)(x - 2) = 0$

Then either $(x + 2) = 0$,

or $(x - 2) = 0$, so $x = +2$ or $x = -2$.

Example 2 $x^2 - 3x = 0$

By factorizing the left-hand side of the equation, it becomes

$x(x - 3) = 0$

Then either $x = 0$

or $(x - 3) = 0$, so $x = 0$ or $x = 3$.

Example 3 $x^2 - 3x + 2 = 0$

By factorizing the left-hand side of the equation, it becomes

$(x - 2)(x - 1) = 0$

Then either $(x - 2) = 0$

or $(x - 1) = 0$, so $x = 1$ or $x = 2$.

Example 4 $6 + 7x = -2x^2$

The equation is rearranged to make $-2x^2$ positive, and then the left-hand side is factorized.

$$2x^2 + 7x + 6 = 0$$
$$(2x + 3)(x + 2) = 0$$

Then either $(2x + 3) = 0$

or $(x + 2) = 0$, so $x = -1\frac{1}{2}$ or $x = -2$.

Note. If $x^2 = 9$, then $x = \pm\sqrt{9}$, and $x = +3$ or $x = -3$ because $-3 \times -3 = 9$ and $+3 \times +3 = 9$.

Solution by formula

This method is used *only* when factorization is not possible.
If $ax^2 + bx + c = 0$, where a, b, and c are constants,

$$\text{then} \quad x = \frac{-b \pm \sqrt{(b^2 - 4ac)}}{2a}$$

Example 5

Solve the equation $5x^2 - 20x - 28 = 0$, giving each answer correct to 3 significant figures.
In this example, $a = 5$, $b = -20$, $c = -28$. Substituting these values in the above formula gives

$$x = \frac{--20 \pm \sqrt{((-20)^2 - (4 \times 5 \times -28))}}{2 \times 5}$$

$$= \frac{20 \pm \sqrt{(400 - (-560))}}{10}$$

$$= \frac{20 \pm \sqrt{(400 + 560)}}{10}$$

$$= \frac{20 \pm \sqrt{960}}{10}$$

$$= \frac{20 \pm 30{\cdot}98}{10} \quad \text{from square root tables}$$

$$= \frac{20 + 30{\cdot}98}{10} \quad \text{or} \quad \frac{20 - 30{\cdot}98}{10}$$

$$= \frac{50{\cdot}98}{10} \quad \text{or} \quad \frac{-10{\cdot}98}{10}$$

$$= 5{\cdot}098 \quad \text{or} \quad -1{\cdot}098$$

$$\therefore \quad x = 5{\cdot}10 \text{ or } x = -1{\cdot}10 \text{ (to 3 S.F.)}$$

Simultaneous equations

You may encounter a problem involving simultaneous equations in which one of the equations is quadratic. These are solved by a combination of the methods given on pages 72 and 84.

Example 6 Solve $2x^2 - 2y - 6 = 0$ (i)
$x + 2y = 0$ (ii)

From (ii), we know that $y = -\frac{x}{2}$

Substituting for y in (i)

$$2x^2 - 2\left(-\frac{x}{2}\right) - 6 = 0$$
$$2x^2 + x - 6 = 0$$
$$(2x - 3)(x + 2) = 0 \qquad \therefore x = 1\tfrac{1}{2} \text{ or } x = -2$$

Hence we obtain from (ii)

$$\text{when } x = 1\tfrac{1}{2},\ y = \tfrac{3}{4}$$
$$\text{and when } x = -2,\ y = 1$$

Note that each value of x has its own value of y.

Exercise 3.13a

Solve by factors

1. $x(x-3) = 0$
2. $2x(x-3) = 0$
3. $(x-2)(x-3) = 0$
4. $(x+\frac{1}{2})(x-4) = 0$
5. $(4x+12)(3x-9) = 0$
6. $x^2 - 9x = 0$
7. $x^2 - 3x = 0$
8. $2x^2 - 4x = 0$
9. $2x^2 + 17x = 0$
10. $3x^2 + 8x = 0$
11. $9x^2 + 12x = 0$
12. $x^2 - 9 = 0$
13. $x^2 - 121 = 0$
14. $12x^2 - 192 = 0$
15. $x^2 - 3x + 2 = 0$
16. $x^2 - x - 6 = 0$
17. $x^2 - 7x + 12 = 0$
18. $x^2 - 6x + 5 = 0$
19. $x^2 + 5x + 6 = 0$
20. $x^2 + x - 30 = 0$
21. $x^2 + 6x - 16 = 0$
22. $x^2 + 7x + 12 = 0$
23. $x^2 - 7x + 6 = 0$
24. $3x^2 - 8x + 4 = 0$
25. $2x^2 - x - 1 = 0$
26. $12x^2 - 11x + 2 = 0$
27. $4x^2 - 15x + 9 = 0$
28. $6x^2 - x - 2 = 0$
29. $4x^2 - x - 3 = 0$
30. $6x^2 - 7x - 3 = 0$
31. $5x^2 + 19x - 4 = 0$
32. $12x^2 + 97x + 8 = 0$
33. $12x^2 - 56x + 9 = 0$

Solve the following equations, giving answers correct to three significant figures.

34. $x^2 + 5x + 2 = 0$
35. $x^2 - 4x + 1 = 0$
36. $x^2 + 3x - 1 = 0$
37. $x^2 + 6x + 2 = 0$
38. $x^2 - 7x + 9 = 0$
39. $x^2 - 3x - 3 = 0$
40. $x^2 - 5x + 1 = 0$
41. $2x^2 + 3x - 1 = 0$
42. $2x^2 + 3x - 7 = 0$
43. $3x^2 + 8x + 2 = 0$
44. $4x^2 + 8x + 1 = 0$
45. $\frac{1}{2}x^2 + x + 3 = 0$

Solve the following pairs of simultaneous equations.

46. $x^2 - 5y + 16 = 0$, $x - y + 2 = 0$
47. $x^2 - 3y - 7 = 0$, $x = y + 1$
48. $6x^2 + y - 3 = 0$, $y = x + 1$
49. $2x^2 + y^2 - 2 = 0$, $y - x = 1$
50. $x^2 + 2xy + 27 = 0$, $x + y + 3 = 0$
51. $x^2 + xy + y^2 = 3$, $2x + y = 3$

52. $16y^2 - 16y + 99x = 23$
$2y + 3x = 1$

53. $2x^2 + y^2 + 6y + 5x + 10 = 0$
$2x + y + 3 = 0$

54. $4x^2 + 25y^2 - 80y - 3x + 62 = 0$
$4x + 5y = 8$

55. $\frac{1}{x} + \frac{1}{y} = 5;\ x + y = \frac{5}{6}$

Solution of problems

Problems which require quadratic equations to solve them are tackled in the same way as outlined in Section 3.6. Because the equation is quadratic, two answers will be found, and both will have to be considered.

Example

On a journey of 30 km, a cyclist calculated that, if he reduced his average speed by 2 km/h, he would take 30 minutes longer. Calculate his average speed.

Let the cyclist's average speed be x km/h, then the time taken on the journey is $\frac{30}{x}$ hours.

His reduced speed would be $(x - 2)$ km/h, and the time taken on the journey is then $\frac{30}{(x-2)}$ hours.

Equating the two times (in hours) of the journey,

$$\frac{30}{x-2} - \frac{1}{2} = \frac{30}{x}$$

Multiplying both sides of the equation by $2x(x - 2)$, the L.C.M.,

$$\begin{aligned} 30 \times 2x - x(x-2) &= 30(x-2) \times 2 \\ 60x - x^2 + 2x &= 60x - 120 \\ 0 &= x^2 - 2x - 120 \\ 0 &= (x-12)(x+10) \\ \therefore \quad (x-12) &= 0, \text{ so } x = 12 \\ \text{or} \quad (x+10) &= 0, \text{ so } x = -10 \end{aligned}$$

$\therefore$ the cyclist's average speed x is either 12 km/h or -10 km/h. But an average speed of -10 km/h would mean he was riding backwards.

$\therefore$ his average speed is 12 km/h.

Check:
At an average speed of 12 km/h, the time taken on the journey is $\frac{30}{12} = 2\frac{1}{2}$ hours.
At an average speed of 10 km/h, the time taken on the journey is $\frac{30}{10} = 3$ hours.

Exercise 3.13b

1. The perimeter of a rectangle is 48 cm. If one side is of length x cm, show that the area of the rectangle is $(24x-x^2)\text{ cm}^2$. If the area is 128 cm^2, find the length of the shorter side.
2. One number is 3 times as big as another number and the product of these two numbers is 27 times the smaller one. Find the two numbers.
3. The square of a number is decreased by the number to give the answer 6. Find the number.
4. A rectangle is two cm longer than it is wide. Its area is 35 cm^2. Find its length and breadth.
5. A right-angled triangle has one of the sides about the right angle 8 cm longer than the other. Its area is 64 cm^2. Find the length of those sides.
6. A right-angled isosceles triangle has its hypotenuse 4 cm longer than each of the other two sides. How long are the equal sides? (Answer correct to 3 significant figures).
7. A large open rectangular water tank is twice as long as it is wide. Its depth is 4 m less than its width and it is made of 1440 m^2 of steel plate. How deep is it?
8. On a journey of 10 kilometres, a walker calculated that, if he reduced his average speed by 1 kilometre per hour, the journey would take 30 minutes longer. Calculate his average speed.
9. When the price of a train ticket was increased by 50 pence, the number of tickets which could be bought for £100 was reduced by 10. What was the original price of a ticket?
10. Two wheels on a child's toy have diameters differing by 1 cm. The child notices that one wheel rotates 7 more times than the other one when the toy travels 24·2 m. Calculate the diameter of the larger wheel. (Take $\pi = \frac{22}{7}$).
11. A shopkeeper buys a quantity of sugar for £20. He sells all but 10 kg of it at 5p per kg more than he gave for it, thus making a profit of £2·50. How much did he buy and at what price?
12. A bath can be filled by either or both of two taps. Running alone one tap takes one minute more than the other to fill the bath. Running together they take 1 minute 12 seconds. How long does each take on its own?

Miscellaneous exercise 3

1. When $x = -\frac{1}{2}$, find the value of

   (a) x^2 (b) x^3 (c) $(2x)^2$ (d) $\dfrac{1}{3x}$

   (e) $\dfrac{1}{3x^{-2}}$ (f) $\left(\dfrac{x}{2}\right)^{-2}$ (g) $(-x)^{-1}$ (h) $(-8x)^{1\frac{1}{2}}$

   (i) $(2x^{-2})^{-3}$ (j) $\dfrac{x^{\frac{2}{3}}}{(27x)^{-\frac{1}{3}}}$

2. Simplify the following by removing brackets and collecting like terms.

   (a) $(x+3)(x-3)-(x+3)^2$ (b) $(x+2y)^2-2(x+2y)(x+3y)$
   (c) $(a+b)^2-(a-b)^2$ (d) $(x+2y)(x-y)-y(x-2y)-2x^2$
   (e) $6(a^2-b^2)-3(a-b)(2a-3b)$

3. Solve the following equations

   (a) $5-2(2x-1) = 3$ (b) $\dfrac{x}{2}-\dfrac{2x-5}{3} = 2$

   (c) $\dfrac{3(2x-1)}{4}-\dfrac{2(x+2)}{3} = 1$ (d) $\frac{2}{3}(x+4)+\frac{3}{5}(2x+1) = 0$

   (e) $\dfrac{3}{3x+7} = \dfrac{4}{x-1}$

4. (a) Find four consecutive even numbers whose sum is 1124.
   (b) Find four consecutive odd numbers whose sum is 1208.
   (c) Find four consecutive numbers whose sum is 1166.
5. In each of the following, rearrange the expression to make its subject the letter shown in the square brackets.
   (a) $A = 2\pi rh$ [h] (b) $V = \frac{4}{3}\pi r^3$ [r]
   (c) $B = 2b + \sqrt{b^2 + 6bu}$ [u] (d) $k^2 = \frac{2An}{bd}(1 - k)$ [k]
6. The two expressions $\frac{1}{6}h[a^2 + b^2 + (a + b)^2]$ and $\frac{1}{3}[b^2(h + x) - a^2x]$ are found by different methods for the volume of a certain solid. Show they are equivalent if
   $$\frac{b}{h + x} = \frac{a}{x}.$$
7. Solve the following equations, giving the answer correct to two decimal places where necessary.
   (a) $x^2 + 5x + 2 = 0$ (b) $x^2 - 6x + 5 = 0$ (c) $x^2 + 3x - 1 = 0$
   (d) $12x^2 - 11x + 2 = 0$ (e) $6x^2 - x - 2 = 0$ (f) $12x^2 + 97x + 8 = 0$
   (g) $4x^2 + 8x + 1 = 0$ (h) $3x^2 + x + 2 = 0$
8. When each edge of a cube is decreased by 1 cm, its volume is decreased by 61 cm^3. Find the surface area of the original cube.
9. A three-digit number is such that the sum of its digits is 12. The middle digit is half the sum of the other two and the last digit is three times the first one. Find the number.
10. Driving to the station each morning at 40 km/h, I usually pass at the same place a man walking at 5 km/h. One day, when I am 10 minutes late starting, I pass the man 500 metres beyond where I usually pass him. Is the man late or early and by how much?
11. Show that
    (a) $(x + y)^2 - (y + z)^2 + (x - z)^2 = 2(x + y)(x - z)$
    (b) if $a = \frac{1}{1 - x}$ and $x = \frac{1}{1 - y}$ then $y = \frac{1}{1 - a}$
12. If $x : y = 5 : 6$, find the value of $\frac{(3x - 4y)(2x + y)}{x^2 - y^2}$.
13. If $R = r + t$ and $V = \pi h(R^2 - r^2)$, find the value of r when $V = 66$, $h = 10$, $t = 0{\cdot}5$, $\pi = 3\frac{1}{7}$.
14. A square carpet has sides x m long and is placed in the middle of a square room of side y m. Find (a) the area of the floor not covered by the carpet
    (b) if this area is equal to half the area of the carpet, show that $y = \sqrt{\frac{3}{2}}x$.
15. Solve the equation
    $$\frac{2}{x + 3} + \frac{4}{x - 3} = \frac{1}{x + 5}$$ giving the roots correct to 2 D.P.

Part 4 Graphs

4.1 Plotting graphs

General rules for plotting graphs

(a) Draw 2 straight lines, intersecting at right angles to form the axes.
(b) Choose a suitable scale, which produces a graph to fill most of the graph paper. This scale should be easy to subdivide.
(c) Label each axis to indicate briefly what information is shown, e.g. cost in £'s.
(d) Plot the points either from the data given or from the table of values which has had to be constructed.
(e) If the points plotted appear to be on a curve, join them up with a continuous line so that the curve is smooth, i.e. contains no kinks. If they do not, join the points up by a series of straight lines. (In some cases bars or columns are used instead of straight lines.)
(f) Give the graph a title.

Statistical graphs

These are graphs of quantities which are usually independent of each other, and are mainly used for displaying data, e.g. annual rainfall; cost of living. The plotted points are joined by straight lines, and no reliable information can be found from the graph for any points which lie in between the points plotted from the table of values.

In this type of graph, the horizontal axis is used for fixed values (e.g. days of the week) and the vertical axis for the calculated or observed values (e.g. temperature in °C).

Example

The following table shows the number of hours of sunshine, recorded in a school, during the first ten days of June 1976.

Date	1	2	3	4	5	6	7	8	9	10
Number of hours	6	13	14	8	1	7	9	10	13	15

Represent this data graphically and from your graph state:

(a) on which day there was most sunshine
(b) on how many days there were more than 10 hours sunshine
(c) the mean number of hours of sunshine daily.

From the graph opposite:

(a) the sunniest day was the 10th
(b) on 4 days there were more than 10 hours of sunshine.
(c) the mean number of hours of sunshine was

$$\frac{6+13+14+8+1+7+9+10+13+15}{10} = \frac{96}{10} = 9{\cdot}6 \text{ hours.}$$

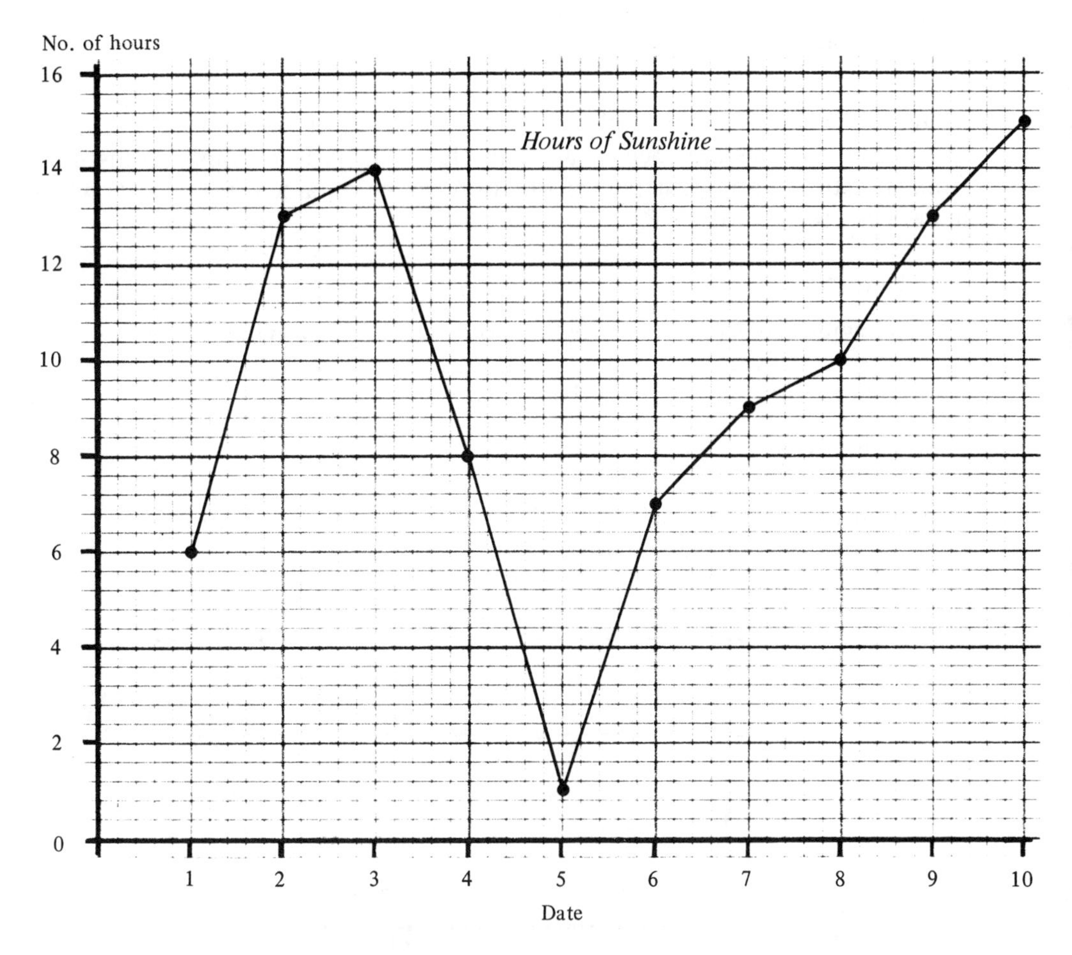

Exercise 4.1

1. The following chart shows maximum and minimum temperatures for the days of a certain week

	S	M	T	W	T	F	S
Max. temp. in °C	15	25	23	21	27	24	20
Min. temp. in °C	10	14	12	12	11	11	9

Draw a temperature chart which shows this data and from it answer the following questions *if you can*

(a) Which day had the highest temperature?
(b) Which day had the lowest temperature?
(c) Which day has the greatest variety of temperature?
(d) What was the temperature at 6 p.m. on Monday?

2. The following table shows the rainfall (monthly) for Bogchester last year.

	J	F	M	A	M	J	J	A	S	O	N	D
Rainfall in cm	12	11	16	18	8	4	5	6	10	9	12	13

Represent this data graphically and answer the following *if you can*

(a) Which months had the highest and lowest rainfall?
(b) How much rain fell in the second half of January?

4.2 Straight line graphs

Straight line graphs are examples of direct proportion. The distance travelled in a given time at a constant speed is an example of this type of graph. As distinct from statistical graphs, further information can be obtained from points which lie in between those plotted.

Example

The following table shows the cost of printing wedding invitation cards.

Number printed	5	10	15	25	30
Cost in pence	35	60	85	135	160

Represent this information graphically and from your graph estimate
(a) the cost of printing 20 cards
(b) the number of cards printed for £1.

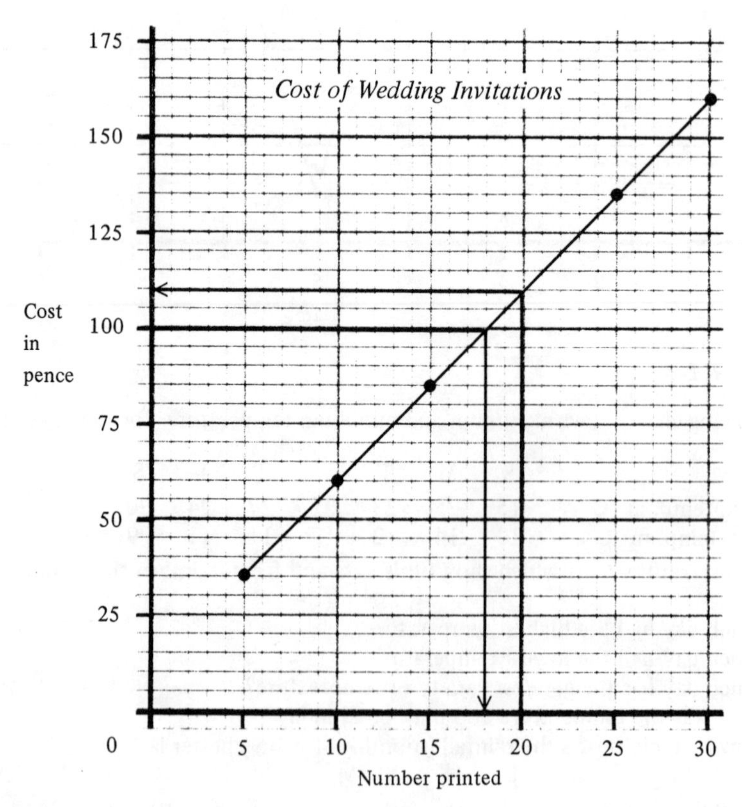

From the graph
(a) cost of printing 20 cards = 110 pence
(b) number of cards printed for £1 = 18.

Exercise 4.2a

In the following questions, draw a graph to illustrate the data given, and use the graph to answer the questions.

1.

Perimeter of square (cm)	4	8	20	40
Edge length of square (cm)	1	2	5	10

(a) Find the perimeter of a square of edge length
(i) 3 cm (ii) 4·5 cm (iii) 8·25 cm
(b) Find the edge length of a square with perimeter
(i) 30 cm (ii) 13 cm (iii) 32·5 cm

2.

Hours of work	1	5	10	20
Wages in £'s	2·10	10·50	21	42

(a) Find the wages for the following hours worked
(i) 35 (ii) 26 (iii) 38
(b) Find the hours worked for the following wages
(i) £52·50 (ii) £63 (iii) £68·25

3.

Kilometres	1	10	20
Miles	$\frac{5}{8}$	$6\frac{1}{4}$	$12\frac{1}{2}$

(a) Convert the following to miles
(i) 30 km (ii) 78 km (iii) 144 km
(b) Convert the following to kilometres
(i) 10 miles (ii) 72 miles (iii) 94 miles

4. The following data was obtained by suspending various weights from a spring

Weight (kg)	1	4	10	15
Length of spring (cm)	13·5	18	27	34·5

(a) Find the length of the spring with the following weights
(i) 3 kg (ii) $7\frac{1}{2}$ kg (iii) 12 kg
(b) Find the weight for the following length of spring
(i) 15 cm (ii) 20·25 cm (iii) 30·75 kg
(c) Find the length of the unstretched spring.

Distance time graphs at constant speed

These are examples of straight line graphs. The horizontal axis is used for the time taken and the vertical axis for the distance travelled.

distance travelled = speed × time

Make sure that the units correspond, e.g. *speed* in metres per second, means that *time* has to be measured in seconds.

Example

At 10.00 hours a man starts to cycle to a town 45 kilometres away at an average speed of 15 km/h. At 11.30 hours a motorist follows him in a car travelling at an average speed of 45 km/h. Where and when does the motorist overtake the cyclist?

(a) Draw suitable axes, with time on the horizontal axis, scaled from 10.00 hours and distance on the vertical axis scaled to 50 km.

(b) At 11.00 hours the cyclist is 15 km away from his starting point. At 12.00 hours he is 30 km away. Use this information to draw a straight line from 10.00 hours to show the cyclist's progress.

(c) In a similar way plot the progress of the motorist starting at 11.30 hours.

(d) The point of intersection of these two straight lines gives the time and place at which the motorist overtakes the cyclist. i.e. 12.15 hours, 34 km from the start.

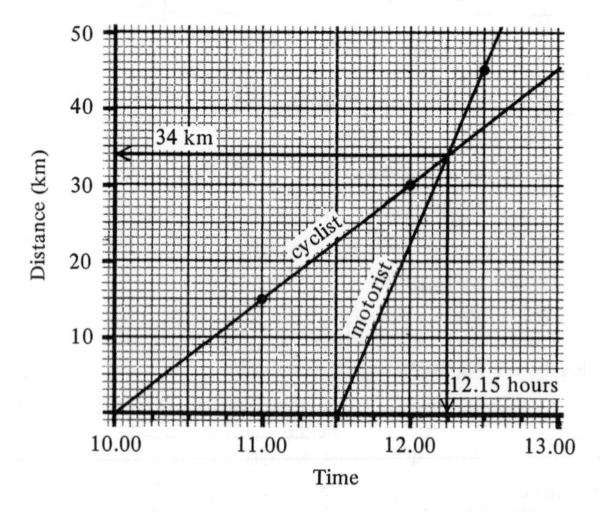

Exercise 4.2b

1. A cyclist sets out to ride from A to B, 100 km away. He rides at 20 km/h. An hour later another cyclist sets out from B to ride to A at 25 km/h. Draw a suitable graph to find when and where they meet.
2. A man sets out to walk from A at 6 km/h. He walks for 50 minutes and then rests for 10 minutes, keeping this up for four hours. Another man starts an hour later and walks without resting at 7 km/h. When and where does he overtake the first man?
3. A and B run a 100 m race. A starts from scratch and finishes in 40 seconds. B, with 5 m start, is then 20 m behind A at the winning post. When and where did A pass B?
4. C starts the race of question 3 five seconds late, but still runs a dead heat with A. When and where did he pass B?
5. In still water I can row at 6 km/h. On a particular journey I rowed upstream against a current of 2 km/h and then returned downstream to a point $\frac{1}{2}$ km short of my starting point. The whole trip took 1 hour. Find graphically how far upstream I went.
6. A cyclist starts to ride at 18 km/h but after a time he has to reduce this to 12 km/h. If he completes a 50 km journey in $3\frac{1}{2}$ hours, find graphically when and where he changed speed.

7. A motorist sets out from his home at 9.00 a.m. at 55 km/h. Half an hour later, his next door neighbour follows at 65 km/h along the same route. When are the two men 10 km apart?
8. A and B raced for 300 m. A ran at 5 m/s but B, after giving him 5 seconds start, passed him after he had run 100 m. Find graphically
   (a) how many seconds behind B was A in reaching the winning post?
   (b) how far was A from the winning post when B reached it?
   (c) what was B's speed in m/s?

Miscellaneous exercise 4a

1. The following table shows the monthly cost of living index for a certain year, the cost for June of the previous year being taken as 100.

Month	J	F	M	A	M	J	J	A	S	O	N	D
Index	112	116	117	120	122	125	127	126	124	128	130	132

   Represent this data graphically and state *if you can*
   (a) When was the cost of living increasing?
   (b) When was the cost of living falling?
   (c) What was the cost of living index for the third week in July.
2. The temperature taken every hour on a certain day was as follows

Time (a.m.)	1	2	3	4	3	6	7	8	9	10	11	12 noon
Temp. °C	12	10	11	$11\frac{1}{2}$	12	14	15	16	18	20	22	25

Time (p.m.)	1	2	3	4	5	6	7	8	9	10	11	12 midnight
Temp. °C	27	30	29	27	$24\frac{1}{2}$	23	22	18	16	$15\frac{1}{2}$	14	13

   Represent this data graphically and say (a) when the temperature was rising most rapidly and (b) when it was falling most rapidly.
3. The numbers of pupils admitted to a certain school over a ten-year period were as shown.

Year	1950	1951	1952	1953	1954	1955	1956	1957	1958
No. of pupils	100	120	140	180	185	192	200	198	180

Year	1959	1960
No. of pupils	174	170

   Represent this data graphically and state during which *two*-year period the growth in numbers was greatest.
4. A motorist sets out from A at 09.00 hours at 50 km/h and drives for three hours. He rests for an hour and then returns to A in two hours. Find his speed on the return journey. At 10.00 hours another motorist sets out from B at 60 km/h and drives towards A which is 200 km away. Find graphically when and where he meets the first motorist. If he does not stop, how much sooner than the first motorist does he reach A? (Give your answer correct to the nearest minute.)
5. Two motorists set out at the same time to go from A to B. One travels at 60 km/h and the other at 45 km/h. If the faster car arrives 24 minutes before the slower one, how far was the journey?

4.3 Intersection of graphs

Every straight line can be written as an equation of the form $y = mx + c$, where m and c are constants. Because every point which lies on this line must obey the equation of the line, then to plot this straight line graph:

(a) put the equation in the above form, e.g. $y - 3x = -2$ becomes $y = 3x - 2$.

(b) find sets of points which obey this relationship and display them on a table of values.

(c) plot the graph.

Example 1 Plot the graph $2y - 6x = -4$.

Step 1. $2y - 6x = -4$, becomes $2y = 6x - 4$ and then $y = 3x - 2$.

Step 2. Construct a table of values, using suitable values of x to produce corresponding values of y.

x	0	1	2
$y = 3x - 2$	-2	1	4

Step 3. Plot the graph with x values on the horizontal axis and y values on the vertical axis.

Note. Only 3 pairs of values of x and y are necessary for a straight line graph.

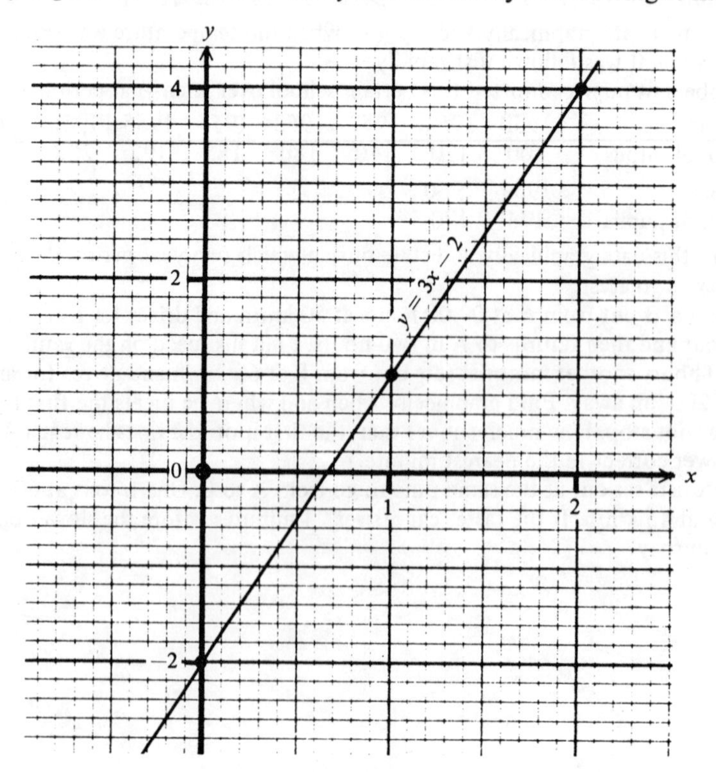

Example 2

Solve graphically the simultaneous equations

$$x + y = 7$$
$$2y - x = 10$$

Step 1. Rewrite the equations in the form $y = mx + c$.

Hence $x + y = 7$ becomes $y = 7 - x$

$2y - x = 10$ becomes $y = 5 + \frac{x}{2}$

Step 2. Draw up tables of values

x	0	1	2
$y = 7 - x$	7	6	5

x	0	1	2
$y = 5 + \frac{x}{2}$	5	$5\frac{1}{2}$	6

Step 3. Plot the graphs using the same axes.

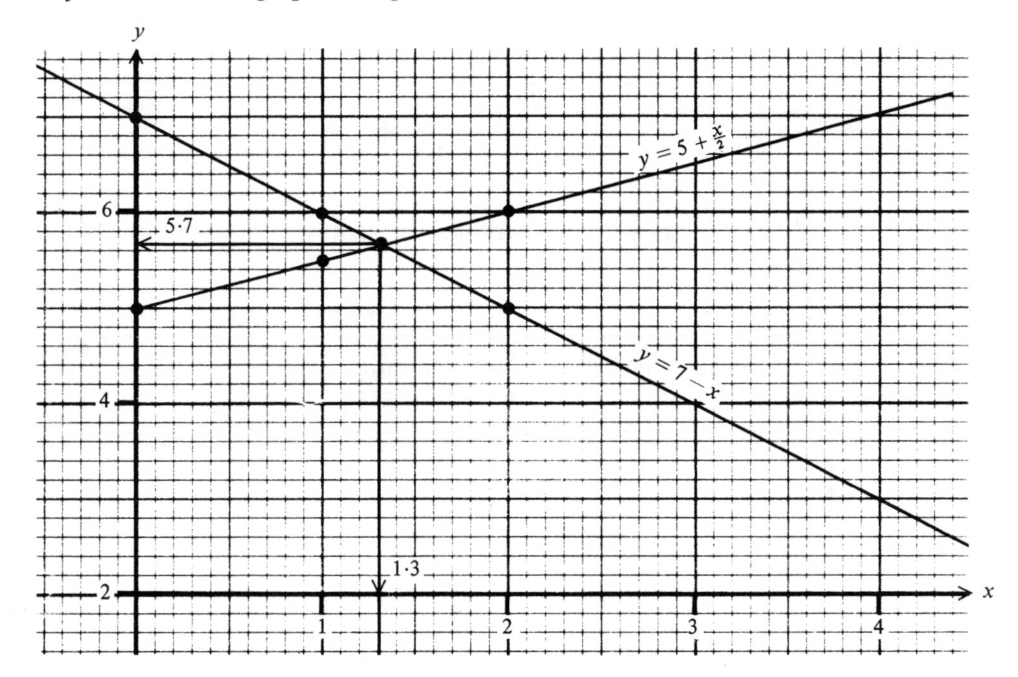

Step 4. The point of intersection of the straight lines is the point at which x and y satisfy both equations simultaneously

i.e. $x = 1{\cdot}3$; $y = 5{\cdot}7$ (both to 1 decimal place)

Exercise 4.3

1. Plot each straight line on a separate graph, and state the co-ordinates of the points where the graphs cut the x and y axis.
(a) $y = x + 2$ (b) $y = 2x - 1$ (c) $2y = 4x + 2$
(d) $2y = 3x + 1$ (e) $x + y = 4$ (f) $x - y = 6$
(g) $2x + y = 5$ (h) $x + 2y + 2 = 0$
2. Solve the following pairs of simultaneous equations graphically
(a) $x + y = 5$; $y = x + 1$ (b) $y = 4x$; $y = 2x + 2$
(c) $x + 5y = 5$; $y = 6x - 14\frac{1}{2}$ (d) $2x + 3y + 13 = 0$; $x = y + 1$

4.4 Linear laws from experimental data

Any straight line graph is of the form $y = mx + c$, where m is the gradient and c is the intercept on the y-axis. This equation can be used to find the relationship between two variables which are directly proportional to one another.

Example

The law connecting E (effort) and W (load) in an experiment with a machine is believed to be of the form $E = aW + b$. By plotting these results, find suitable values for a and b.

W	5	7·5	10	12·5	15	20
E	2·1	2·5	3	3·4	4	4·8

(a) Plot the points and, if they lie on or about a straight line, join them with the 'line of best fit'.

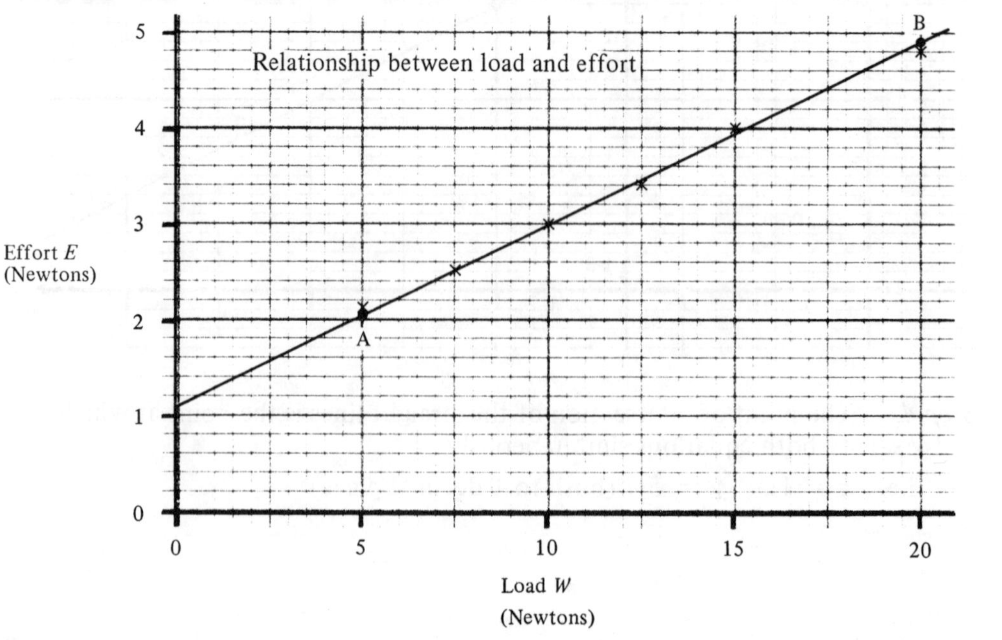

(b) Take two points A and B which lie on the line and are as far apart as possible. Read the co-ordinates of the points from the graph: A (5, 2·05); B (20, 4·9).

(c) As these points lie on the straight line, they satisfy a relationship of the form $y = mx + c$ which in this case is the equation $E = aW + b$.

$$\text{From point A } 2{\cdot}05 = 5a + b \quad \text{(i)}$$
$$\text{From point B } 4{\cdot}9 = 20a + b \quad \text{(ii)}$$
$$\text{Subtract (i) from (ii) } 2{\cdot}85 = 15a$$
$$0{\cdot}19 = a$$
$$\text{Replace } a \text{ by } 0{\cdot}19 \text{ in (i) } 2{\cdot}05 = 5 \times 0{\cdot}19 + b$$
$$2{\cdot}05 = 0{\cdot}95 + b$$
$$1{\cdot}1 = b$$

$\therefore$ equation is $E = 0{\cdot}19W + 1{\cdot}1$.

If the graph is drawn with the axes starting from the origin, then the equation can also be obtained by finding the gradient and the intercept on the y-axis and substituting in $y = mx + c$.

$$\text{From the graph: gradient is } \frac{\text{difference in } y \text{ values}}{\text{difference in } x \text{ values}}$$

$$\text{Taking 10 and 20 gradient is } \frac{4{\cdot}9 - 3{\cdot}0}{10} = 0{\cdot}19$$

Intercept on y-axis is 1·1

$\therefore$ equation is $y = 0{\cdot}19x + 1{\cdot}1$

$$E = 0{\cdot}19W + 1{\cdot}1.$$

Exercise 4.4

1. The following values of E (electromotive force) and R (resistance) are connected by a law of the form $R = a + bE$. Find the most likely values of a and b.

E (Volts)	1·0	1·75	2·2	2·85	3·6	4·1	5·55
R (ohms)	12·5	23·5	30·5	40	51·5	59	80·75

2. The law connecting E (effort) and W (load) in an experiment with a lifting machine is believed to be $E = a + bW$. Using the data below, check that this is true and find the most likely values of a and b.

W kg	10	20	30	40	50	60	70
E kg	6	7·1	8·2	8·9	9·8	11	12·1

3. A gas engine test gave the following relationship between indicated horse-power (I) and brake horse-power (B). Find the law of the form $B = a + bI$ connecting them.

B	0·6	3	7	11	15	26	39
I	2	5	10	15	20	30	50

4. In an experiment on a screw jack, the following results were obtained. Show that they are consistant with the law $W = a + bP$ and find the most likely values of a and b.

W (load in kg)	40	95	205	315	425	520
P (effort in kg)	5	10	20	30	40	50

4.5 Curved graphs

The graphs of quantities that do not vary in direct proportion are usually curves. To plot a curve, a more detailed table of values is necessary. When completing a table of values, be careful of signs, especially
(a) $-x^2$, which when $x = -3$ is $-(-3)^2 = -9$
(b) x^3, which when $x = -3$ is $-3 \times -3 \times -3 = -27$
(c) $2x^2$, which when $x = -3$ is $2 \times -3 \times -3 = 18$.

Example 1

Plot the graph of $y = x^2 - x - 6$ for values of x from -3 to $+4$.

Table of values

x	-3	-2	-1	0	1	2	3	4	$\frac{1}{2}$
x^2	9	4	1	0	1	4	9	16	$\frac{1}{4}$
$-x$	3	2	1	0	-1	-2	-3	-4	$-\frac{1}{2}$
-6	-6	-6	-6	-6	-6	-6	-6	-6	-6
y	6	0	-4	-6	-6	-4	0	6	$-6\frac{1}{4}$

Note. Because two adjacent values of y are the same, it is advisable to plot another point, in this case when $x = \frac{1}{2}$.

The graph opposite of $y = x^2 - x - 6$ can be used to solve equations.

Example 2

(a) Solve the equation $x^2 - x - 6 = 0$.
This equation is solved where the line $y = 0$ cuts this graph i.e. when $x = 3$ or -2.

(b) Solve the equation $x^2 - x - 6 = 3$.
This equation is solved when the line $y = 3$ cuts this graph, i.e. when $x = -2{\cdot}5$ or $3{\cdot}5$.

(c) Solve the equation $x^2 - x - 5 = 0$.
This equation is solved where the line $y = -1$ cuts the graph i.e. when $x = -1{\cdot}8$ or $2{\cdot}8$.

Note. At the point of intersection of two graphs, the values of y are the same. So, when $y = -1$ and $y = x^2 - x - 6$ intersect, $x^2 - x - 6 = -1$, giving the solution for x in $x^2 - x - 5 = 0$.

Many equations can be solved by drawing two intersecting graphs and reading off the values of x at the point of intersection.

Example 3

If the graphs of $y = x^3 + \dfrac{1}{x^2}$ and $y = \dfrac{x}{2} + 2$ are plotted, the values of y at the points of intersection are the same.

So $x^3 + \dfrac{1}{x^2} = \dfrac{x}{2} + 2$

which when simplified gives $2x^5 + 2 = x^3 + 4x^2$ or $2x^5 - x^3 - 4x^2 + 2 = 0$, and this is the equation which can be solved from the intersection of these two graphs.

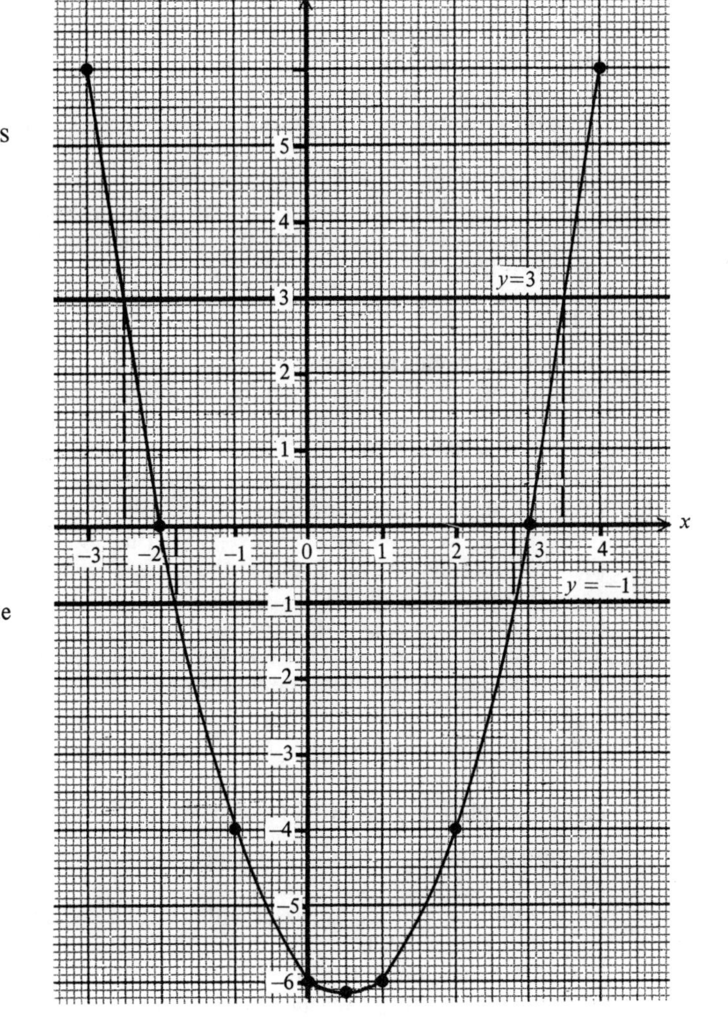

Exercise 4.5

1. Plot the curve $y = x^2 - 3x + 2$ taking values of x from -2 to $+6$. Hence solve the equation $x^2 - 3x + 2 = 0$. By drawing an appropriate straight line, solve also the equation $x^2 - 3x - 2 = 0$.
2. Plot the curve $y = x^2 - 4x + 1$ taking values of x from -2 to $+5$. By drawing any appropriate straight lines, use this graph to solve the following equations
   (a) $x^2 - 4x + 1 = 0$
   (b) $x^2 - 4x + 3 = 0$
   (c) $x^2 - 5x + 3 = 0$
   (d) $x^2 - 3x - 1 = 0$
3. Plot the curve $y = 7 + 2x - x^2$ taking values of x from -3 to $+5$. Hence solve the following equations
   (a) $7 + 2x - x^2 = 0$
   (b) $5 + 2x - x^2 = 0$
   (c) $6 + x - x^2 = 0$
   (d) $11 - 2x - 2x^2 = 0$
4. Using the same scales and axes, plot $3y = x^2 - 16$ and $y = x - 2$, taking values of x from -5 to $+5$. Find the co-ordinates of the points of intersection of the line and the curve and write down the equation of which the x co-ordinates are the roots.
5. Plot the graph of $y = \dfrac{1}{x+1}$ from $x = -\frac{3}{4}$ to $x = +3$. Let 5 cm represent 1 unit on the x-axis and also on the y-axis. Read off the value of y when $x = 0{\cdot}2$ and the value of x when $y = 1{\cdot}3$.
   Plot also the line $x + y = 3$ and read off the values of x between which $\dfrac{1}{x+1}$ is less than $3 - x$.

Miscellaneous exercise 4b

1. On the same scales and axes plot
   (a) $3x + 4y = 12$ (b) $3y = 4x + 9$
   (c) $4x = 3y + 16$ (d) $3x + 4y + 13 = 0$
   State the co-ordinates of the various crossing points and measure the distance between them.
2. Show that the line $3y + 3 = 6x$ passes through the point of intersection of the lines $3x + 4\frac{1}{2}y = 7\frac{1}{2}$ and $3x = 2 + y$. State the co-ordinates of this common point.
3. On the same scales and axes, plot the following straight lines
   (a) $y = 2x + 3$ (b) $2y = 4x + 8$ (c) $3y + 6x = 12$
   (d) $\frac{y}{2} - x - 1 = 0$
   What do you notice about these straight lines?
4. Plot each pair of straight lines on the same scales and axes.
   (a) $y = 2x + 4$ and $2y = 6 - x$ (b) $x + y = 5$ and $x = y$
   (c) $x = 6$ and $y = 6$ (d) $3x + y = 2$ and $3y - x = 2$
   What do you notice about each pair of straight lines?
5. (a) On the same scales and axes plot the following straight lines
   (i) $2y - x = 0$ (ii) $y + 2x = 5$ (iii) $2y + x = 10$
   (b) Measure the internal angles of the triangle formed by the points of intersection of these 3 straight lines.
   (c) Calculate the area of this triangle.
6. The relationship $C = a + bR$ exists between two quantities C and R. Find the most likely values of a and b from the following data.

R (cm)	1	2	4	6	8
C (cm)	6·28	12·56	25·1	37·7	50·24

7. Plot the graph of $y = x^3 + \frac{1}{x^2}$ for $x = \frac{1}{2}$ to $x = 2$ (taking values of x every $\frac{1}{4}$ unit). Plot also the line $y = \frac{1}{2}x + 2$ and hence find *two* of the solutions of the equation $2x^5 - x^3 - 4x^2 + 2 = 0$.
8. A stone thrown vertically upwards with a velocity of 80 m/s is y metres above its starting point after t seconds where $y = 80t - 10t^2$. Draw the graph of this equation for $t = 0$ to $t = 8$. From your graph find
   (a) the greatest height reached by the stone
   (b) when this occurred
   (c) when the stone was 40 m above its starting point.
9. Plot the semi-circle $x^2 + y^2 = 16$ from $x = 0$ to $x = 4$. Draw the line $x = 2$, a chord to the semi-circle, and find the length of the arc it cuts off.
10. Plot the graph of $y = x(x^2 - 16)$ for values of x from $x = -5$ to $x = +5$. By drawing another suitable line, find correct to one place of decimals the roots of the equation $x^3 - 16x - 15 = 0$.
11. Find a law connecting E the effort in kilograms exerted by a lifting machine and W the load in kilograms being lifted, using the following experimentally found values.

W	10	20	30	40	50	60	70	80
E	3·6	5·0	6·2	8·1	9·4	10·9	12·4	14·1

12. Plot the graph of $y = 3 + 2x - x^2$ for values of x from -3 to $+5$.
Using your graph, estimate
(a) the maximum value of y
(b) the solution of the equations (i) $3 + 2x - x^2 = 0$
(ii) $x^2 + x - 2 = 0$

13. (a) With the same axes, draw the graphs of $y = \dfrac{2}{x} - x$ and $y = x^2$ for values of x from $\frac{1}{2}$ to 4.
(b) Find and write down the equation which is solved at the point of intersection of these two graphs, and use the graph to estimate a root of this equation.

14. The following table gives the distance s metres travelled by a moving body in t seconds.

t	0	2	4	6	8	10	12	14	16
s	0	1	2·2	3·6	5·4	7·4	9·8	12·6	16·4

Draw a graph of s against t.
Estimate from the graph
(a) how far the body has travelled in 15 seconds
(b) how long it took to go 7 metres
(c) its speed at 10 and 16 seconds.

15. Plot the graph of $y = 4x^3 - 27x + 5$ for values of x from -3 to $+3$.
Using your graph estimate
(a) the values of x and y at the two turning points
(b) the two ranges of values of x for which y is negative
(c) the solution of the equations (i) $4x^3 - 27x + 5 = 0$
(ii) $4x^3 - 19x = 0$

Part 5 Geometry

5.1 Constructions

The following sketches are to remind you of the basic constructions which you should know.

1.

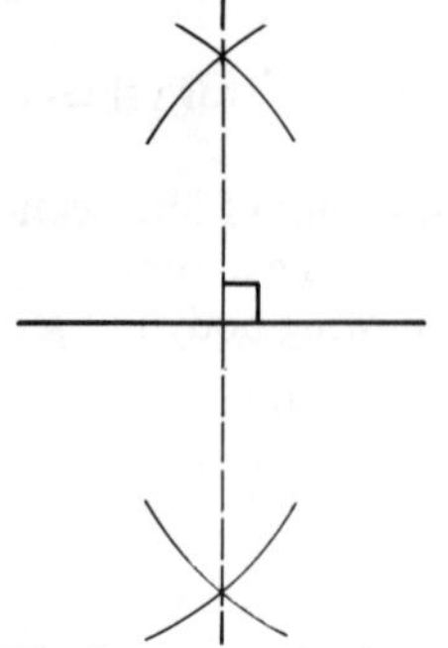

The bisector of a line

2.

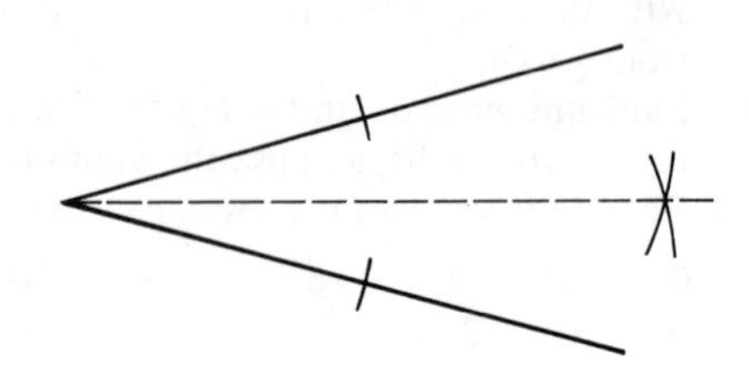

The bisector of an angle

3.

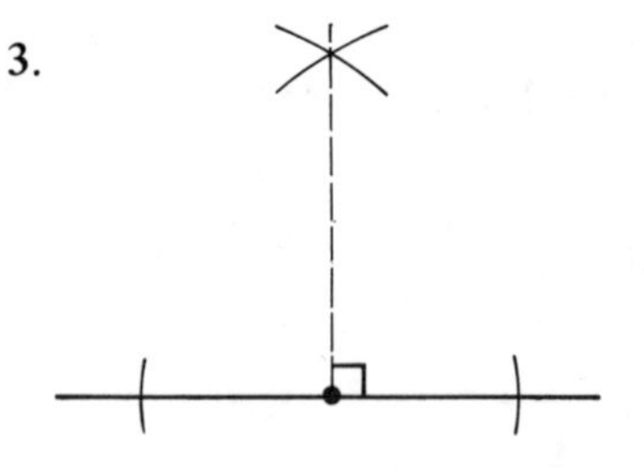

The perpendicular from a point on a line

4.

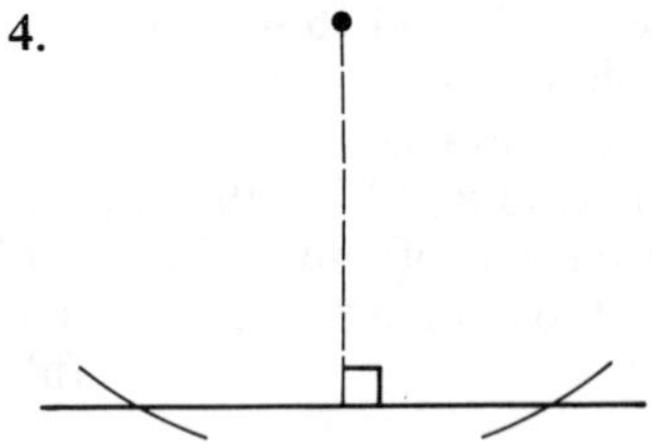

The perpendicular from a point to a line

5.

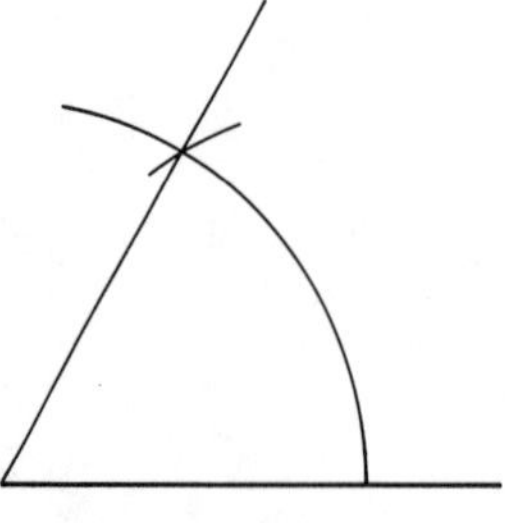

An angle of 60°

6.

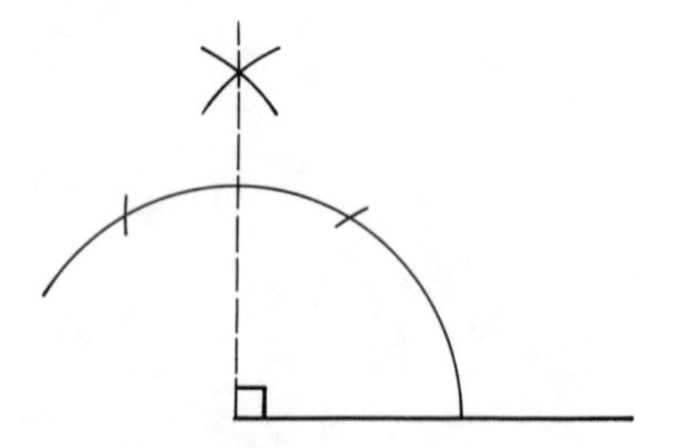

A right angle

7.

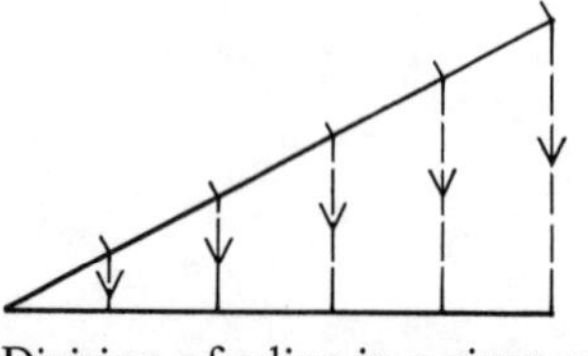

Division of a line in a given ratio

8.

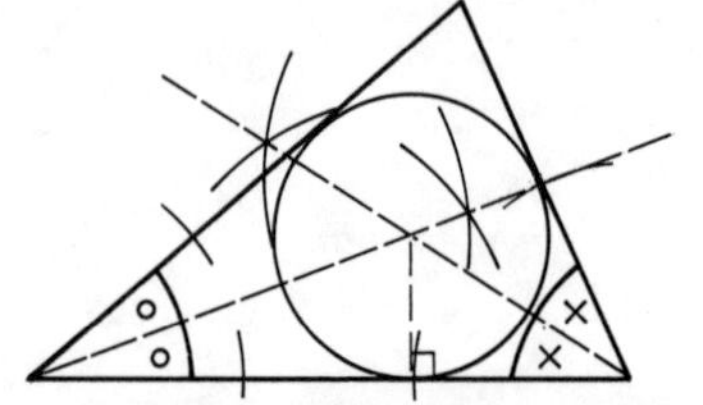

A circle inscribed in a triangle

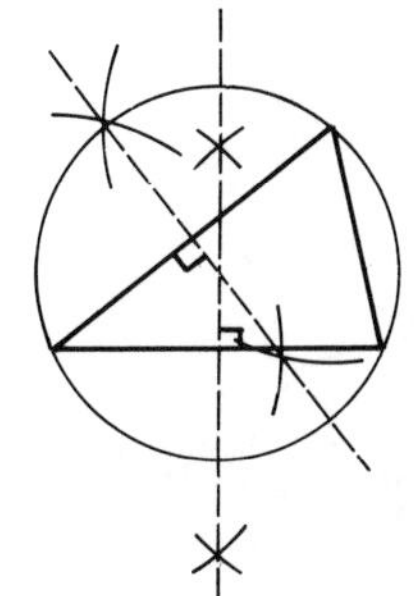

A circumscribed circle

10.

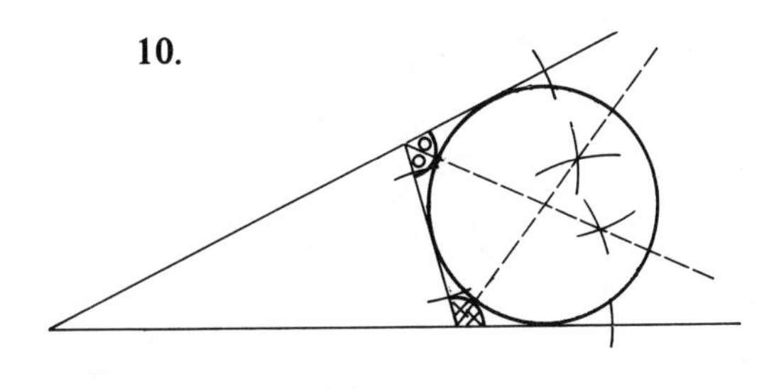

An escribed circle

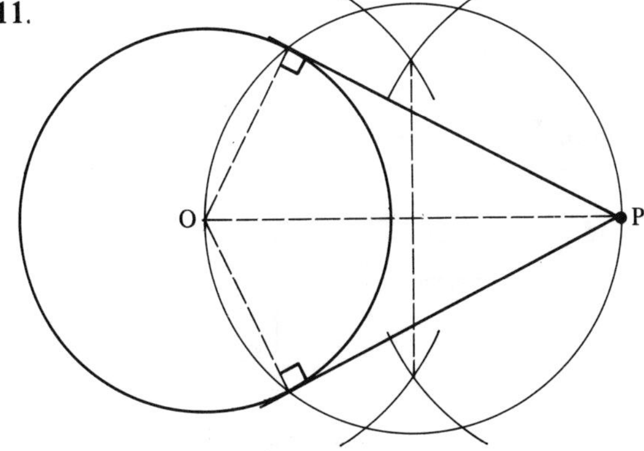

A pair of tangents from a point P

12.

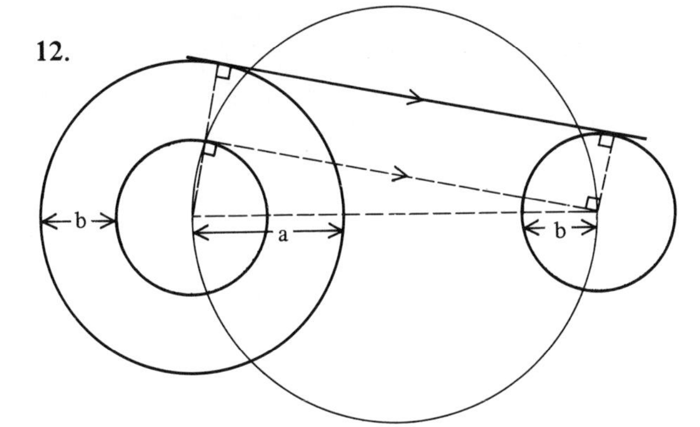

A common tangent to two circles

13.

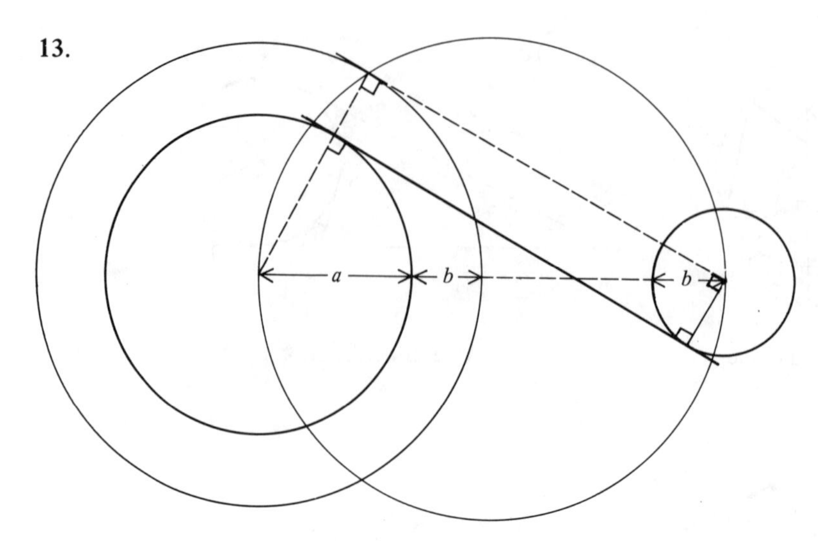

A transverse common tangent

14. **15.**

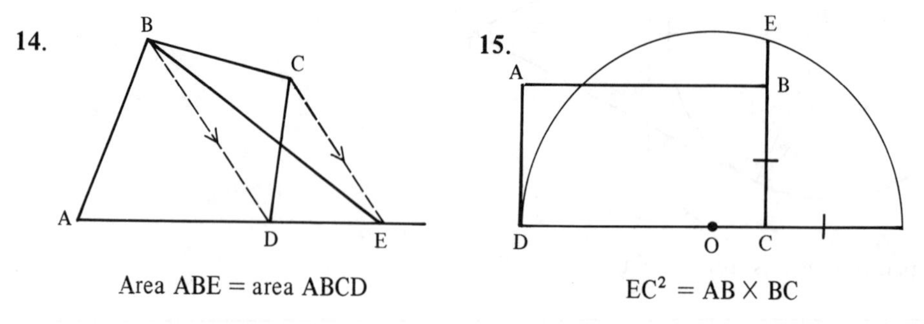

Area ABE = area ABCD

$EC^2 = AB \times BC$

16.

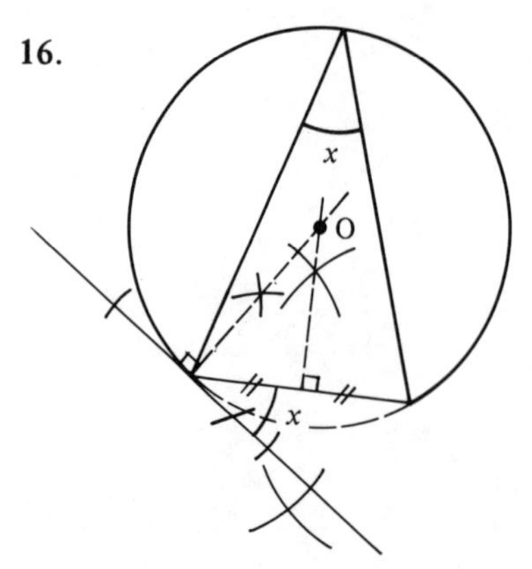

A segment of circle containing given angle x

Exercise 5.1a

All the constructions in the exercise below are to be carried out with pencil, ruler and compasses only. Lengths of lines and sizes of angles may only be measured if the question specifically says so.

1. Construct an angle of 90°.
2. Bisect the angle constructed in question **1**. Check with protractor.
3. Draw a straight line and mark on it two points near its ends. Bisect the distance between these points and then bisect one half again. Check your construction by measuring with a ruler.
4. Construct an angle of 60°. Check with a protractor.
5. Draw an angle of any reasonable size. Construct another angle of the same size alongside it.
6. Draw a straight line. Construct another line parallel to it and 5 cm away. (You may use a ruler to open your compasses to 5 cm).
7. Draw a straight line. Mark a point roughly 5 cm from it. Now draw a line parallel to the the first one through this point.
8. Draw a straight line. Mark a point roughly 5 cm from it. Now draw a line through this point and perpendicular to the first one.
9. Construct a triangle whose sides are 5, 9 and 10 cm long. (You may use a ruler to open your compasses to these distances.) Measure the size of the largest angle.

In the remaining questions you may use a ruler to open your compasses to the given distances as directed in question **9**.

10. Construct a triangle with sides 6 cm and 10 cm, the angle between those sides being 60°. Measure the length of the other side.
11. Construct a triangle of base 8 cm and with base angles of 45° and 60°. Measure the longer of the other two sides.
12. Construct a triangle of base 10 cm, altitude 5 cm and another side 8 cm.

Exercise 5.1b

In this exercise the word draw *means you can use any instrument you like, including a protractor. The word* construct *means use pencil, ruler and compasses only.*

1. Draw a triangle with sides 6, 8 and 10 cm. long. Construct its circumcircle and measure its radius.
2. Construct the in-circle of a triangle whose sides are 7, 9 and 10 cm long. Measure its diameter.
3. Draw a line 9 cm long. Divide it internally in the ratio 4 : 3. Measure each part.
4. Draw a line 6 cm long. Divide it externally in the ratio 7 : 4. How long is the whole line?
5. Construct a regular hexagon of side 4 cm. Reduce this to a triangle of equal area and find out what this area is.
6. Draw two circles of radii 5 and 3 cm respectively with their centres 10 cm apart. Construct both the direct and the transverse common tangents. Measure their lengths.
7. Draw a rectangle with sides 5 and 10 cm long. Construct a square of equal area and measures its diagonal.
8. Construct a major segment of a circle which stands on a chord of length 6 cm and contains an angle of 30°. Measure its radius.
9. Draw a line at roughly 45° to the edge of your piece of paper so that its end is within 1 cm of the edge. Erect a perpendicular to the line at this point.
10. Construct a triangle ABC such that AC = 10 cm, angle BAC = 30° and angle BCA = 45°. Now construct the circle which touches AB at B and passes through C. Measure its radius.

5.2 Bearings and angles

All bearings are measured in a *clockwise* direction from North and when written must contain 3 figures.

Example 1

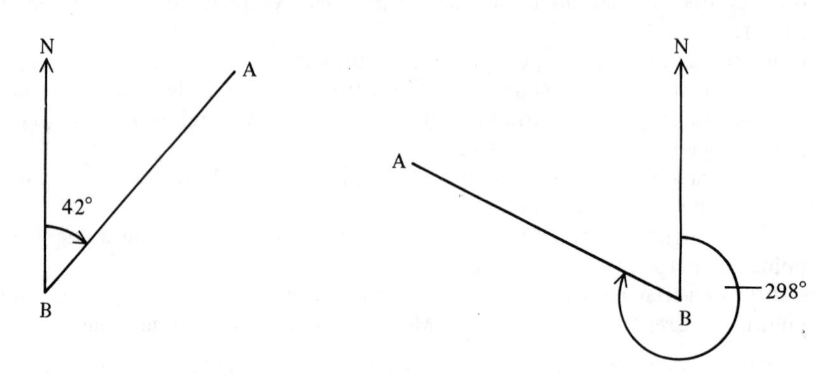

Bearing of A from B is 042° Bearing of A from B is 298°

The bearing of A from B is the direction of A measured in a clockwise direction from B.

Example 2

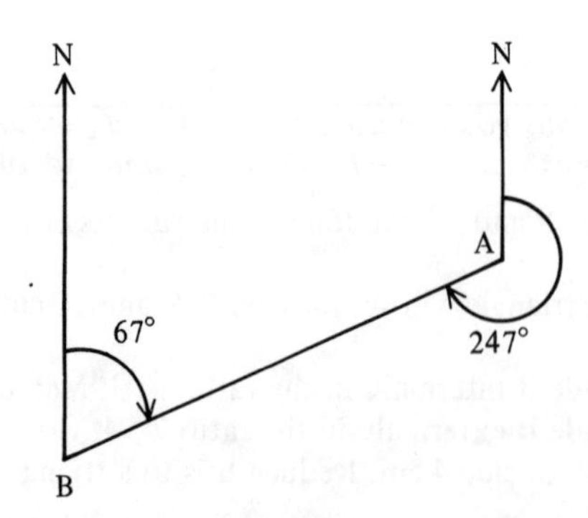

In the above diagram, the bearing of A from B is 067°. The bearing of B from A is known as the *reciprocal bearing* and is 67° + 180° or 247°.

Exercise 5.2a

1. Draw diagrams to illustrate the following
   (a) Bearing of A from B is
   (i) 026°, (i (ii) 132°, (iii) 264°, (iv) 348°
   (b) Bearing of C from D is
   (i) 178°, (ii) 269°, (iii) 359°, (iv) 089°

2. Find the acute angle between the following bearings
   (a) 012° and 064° (b) 078° and 144° (c) 297° and 351°
   (d) 310° and 022° (e) 275° and 004°
3. Find the obtuse angle between the following bearings
   (a) 026° and 130° (b) 097° and 300° (c) 218° and 344°
   (d) 200° and 022° (e) 090° and 269°
4. Find the reciprocal bearing for each of the following
   (a) B from A is 032° (b) D from C is 269° (c) E from F is 089°
   (d) A from B is 136° (e) R from P is 359°
5. Find the value of the angle $x°$ in each of the following diagrams

(a)

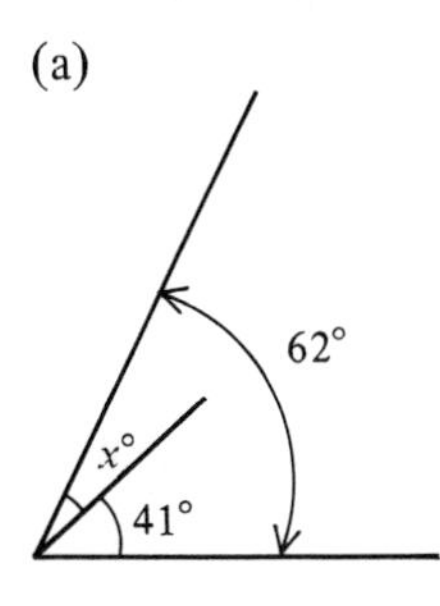

(b)

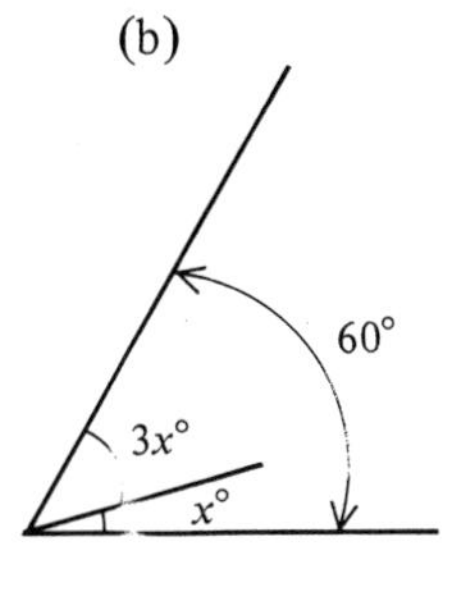

(c)

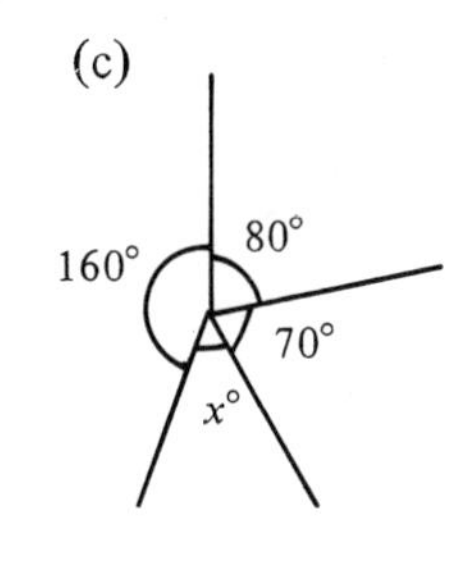

(d)

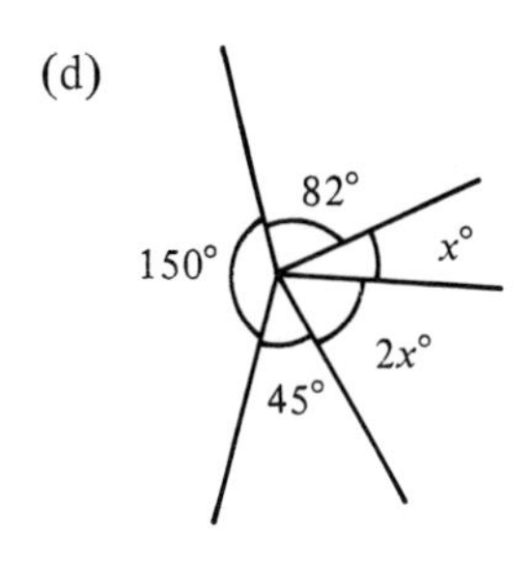

(e)

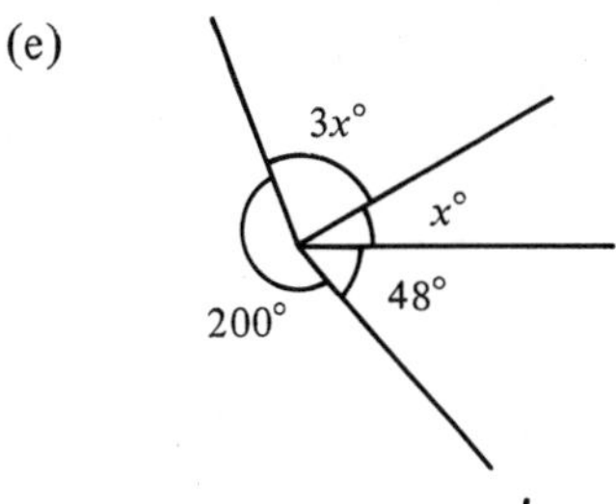

6. Using the diagram on the right:
   (a) Find a if $b = 80°, c = 90°$ and $d = 160°$
   (b) Find c if $b = d = 80°$ and $a = 40°$
   (c) Find a if $a = b, d = 120°$ and $c = 80°$
   (d) Find b if $a = 2x°, b = 3x°, c = 4x°$ and $d = 6x°$.

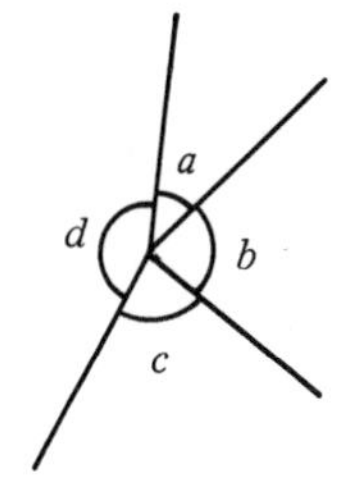

The sum of adjacent angles on a straight line is 180°. If the sum of two angles is 180°, they are called *supplementary angles.*

Example 1

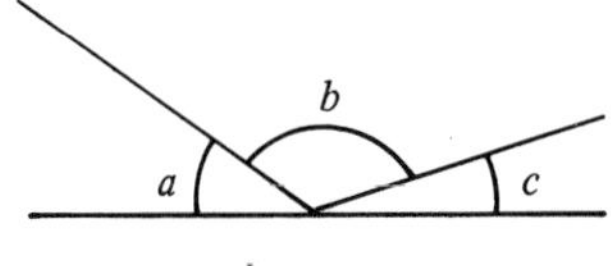

$\hat{a} + \hat{b} + \hat{c} = 180°$

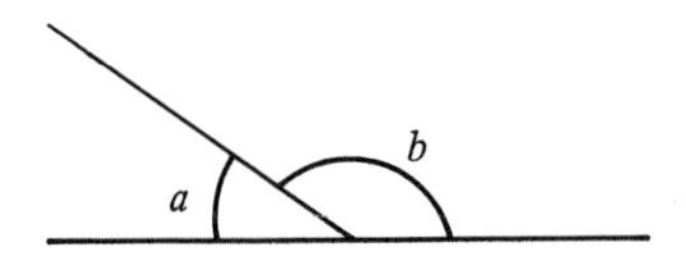

$\hat{a}$ and $\hat{b}$ are supplementary angles.

If the sum of two angles is 90°, they are called *complementary* angles.

$\therefore$ 40° and 50° are complementary angles.

When two straight lines intersect, the opposite angles are equal and are called *vertically opposite* angles.

Example 2

Find in the following diagram the sizes of angles a, b and c, giving reasons.

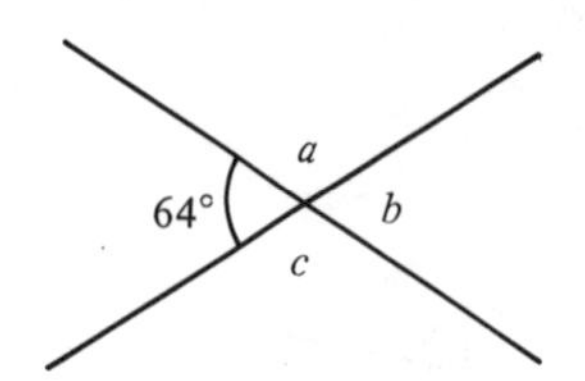

$\hat{a} = 116°$ (adjacent angles on a straight line)
$\hat{b} = 64°$ (vertically opposite 64°)
$\hat{c} = 116°$ (vertically opposite $\hat{a}$)

If two or more straight lines meet at a point the sum of all the angles is 360°.

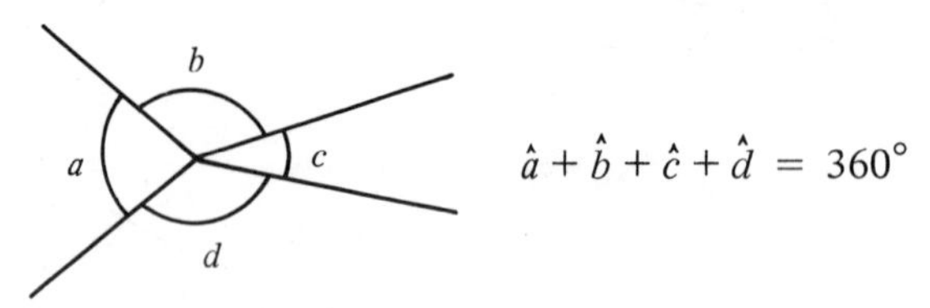

$\hat{a} + \hat{b} + \hat{c} + \hat{d} = 360°$

Example 3

Find the size of each angle, giving reasons.

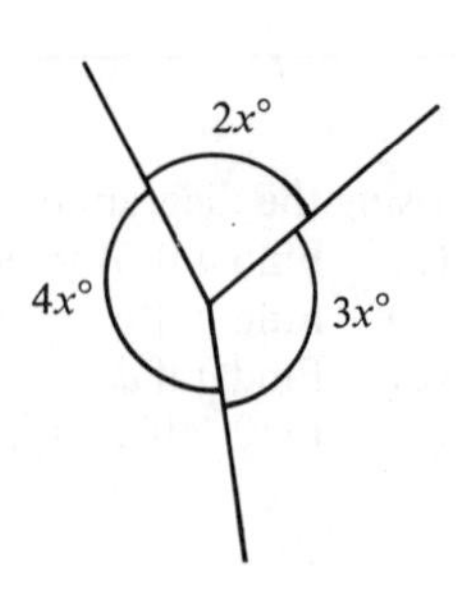

$$2x + 3x + 4x = 360 \text{ (sum of angles at a point)}$$
$$9x = 360$$
$$x = 40$$

$\therefore$ the angles are $2x = 2 \times 40° = 80°$
$3x = 3 \times 40° = 120°$
$4x = 4 \times 40° = 160°$

Exercise 5.2b

1. In the diagram on the right:
   (a) if $a = 120°$ find b
   (b) if $a = 72°$ find b
   (c) if $a = b$ find a
   (d) if $a = 3b$ find b

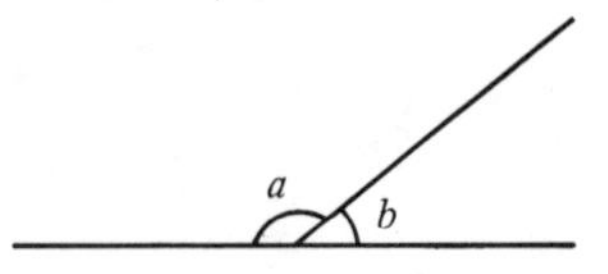

2. In the diagram on the right:
   (a) if $x = 80°$ and $y = 40°$ find z
   (b) if $x = 72°$ and $z = 36°$ find y
   (c) if $x = y = 68°$ find z

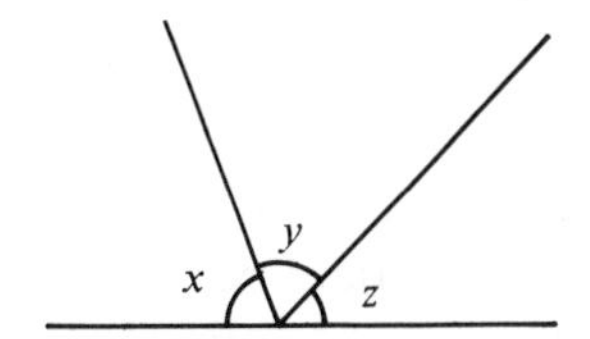

3. In the diagram on the right:
   (a) if $a = 130°$ find x and y
   (b) if $x = 56°$ find y
   (c) if $a + b = 220°$ find a
   (d) if $x = 2a$ find y

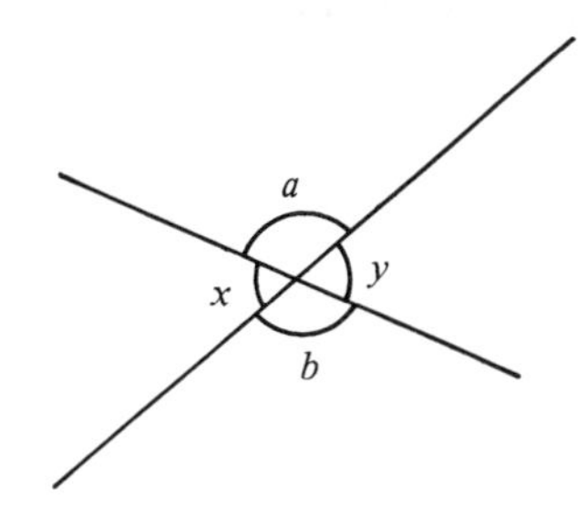

4. What is the supplement of
   (a) $45°$? (b) $96°$? (c) $162°$? (d) $112\frac{1}{2}°$? (e) $61\frac{1}{4}°$?
5. What is the complement of
   (a) $45°$? (b) $72°$? (c) $81°$? (d) $22\frac{1}{2}°$? (e) $31\frac{1}{4}°$?
6. Find x if the three angles $x°$, $2x°$ and $3x°$, when placed together form a straight line.
7. Find y if the three angles $y°$, $4y°$ and $5y°$, when placed together form a straight line.
8. In the diagram on the right, is DB *necessarily* a straight line? (Answer yes or no)
   (a) if $x = z$ and $w = y$
   (b) if $x = z$ and $w \neq y$
   (c) if $x = y = z$ and $w = 90°$
   (d) if $x + y = 180°$ and $w = y$
   (e) if $x + z = 180°$ and $w = y$

   What follows if
   (f) $x = z$ and $w = y$?
   (g) $w = x$ and $y = z$?
   (h) $y = 2x$ and $z = 2w$?
   (i) $w = y = 90°$?
   (j) $w + x = y + z$?

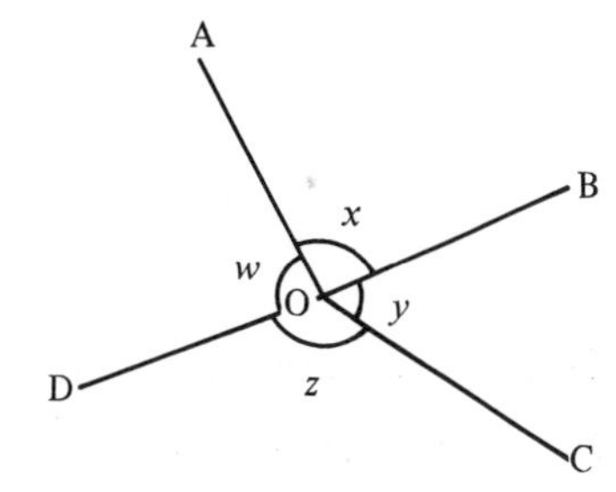

9. In the diagram
   (a) if $\hat{a} = \hat{d}$ and $\hat{b} + \hat{c} = \hat{e}$, is P$\hat{\text{O}}$S a straight line?
   (b) if $\hat{a} = \hat{b} = \hat{c} = 90°$, which line (if any) is straight?
   (c) if $\hat{b} = \hat{c}$ and $\hat{a} = \hat{d}$, what must follow (if anything)?
   (d) if $\hat{e} = 90°$ and $\hat{b} = \hat{c}$, is Q$\hat{\text{O}}$S a straight line?
   (e) if $\hat{e} = \hat{c}$ and $\hat{a} + \hat{b} = \hat{d}$,
      (i) is P$\hat{\text{O}}$S a straight line?
      (ii) is Q$\hat{\text{O}}$S a straight line?

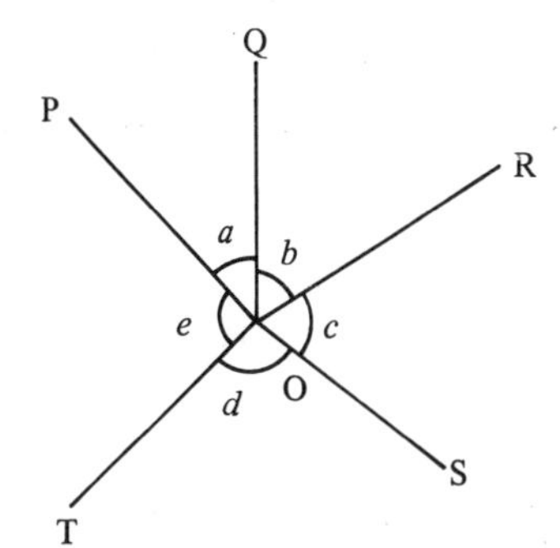

5.3 Parallel lines

Parallel lines are lines that are always the same distance apart.
When a pair of parallel lines are cut by a straight line, called a *transversal*, the angles formed have the following names and properties.

1. *Alternate* angles are equal

   $\hat{a} = \hat{b}$

   $\hat{c} = \hat{d}$

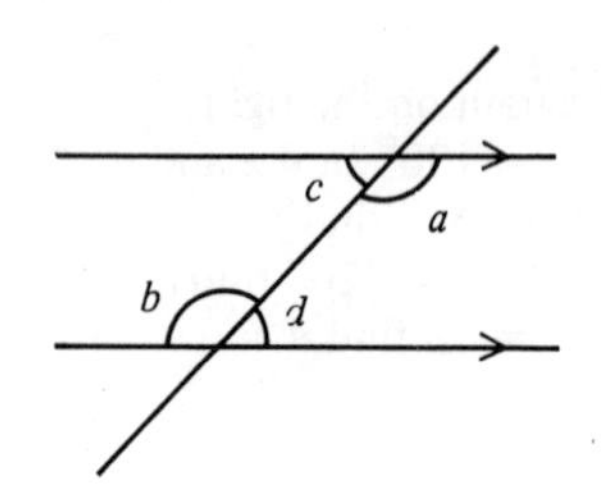

Example 1 Find $\hat{a}$ and $\hat{b}$ giving reasons.

$\hat{a} = 42°$ (alternate to 42°)

$\hat{b} = 63°$ (alternate to 63°)

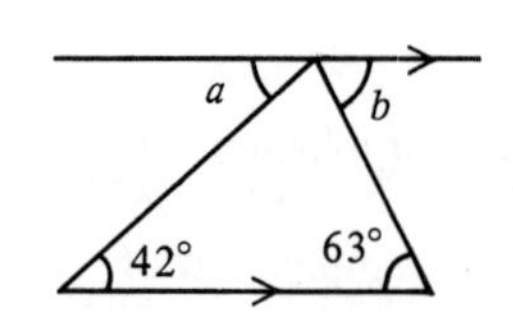

2. *Corresponding* angles are equal.

   $\hat{a} = \hat{b}$

   $\hat{c} = \hat{d}$

   $\hat{e} = \hat{f}$

   $\hat{g} = \hat{h}$

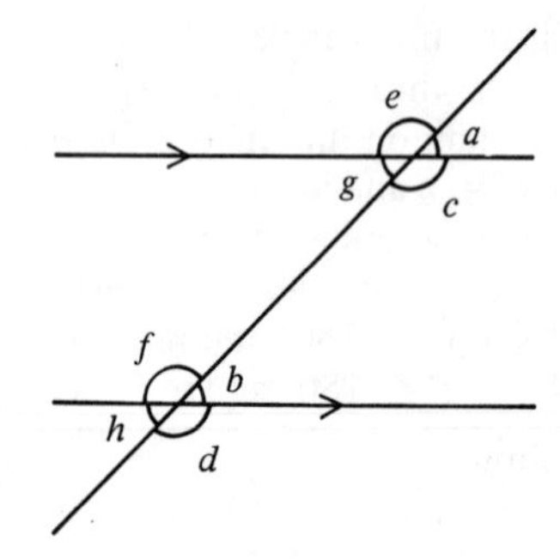

Example 2 Find angles a, b, c, giving reasons.

$\hat{a} = 60°$ (adjacent angles on a straight line)

$\hat{b} = 120°$ (corresponding to 120°)

$\hat{c} = 60°$ (corresponding to $\hat{a}$)

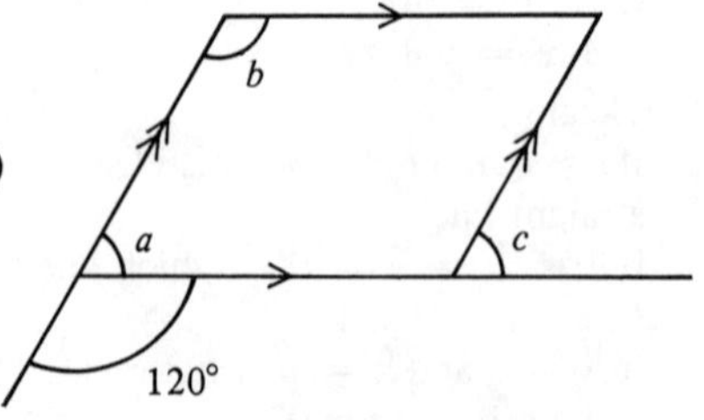

3. *Allied* angles (sometimes called *interior* angles) are supplementary.

   $\hat{a} + \hat{b} = 180°$

   $\hat{c} + \hat{d} = 180°$

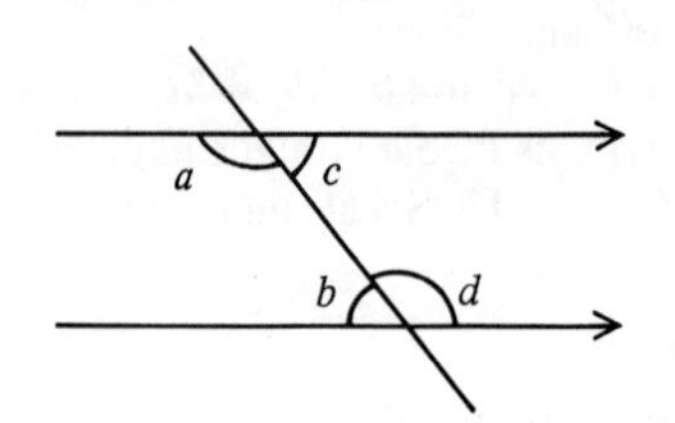

Example 3 Find $\hat{a}$, $\hat{b}$ and $\hat{c}$, giving reasons.

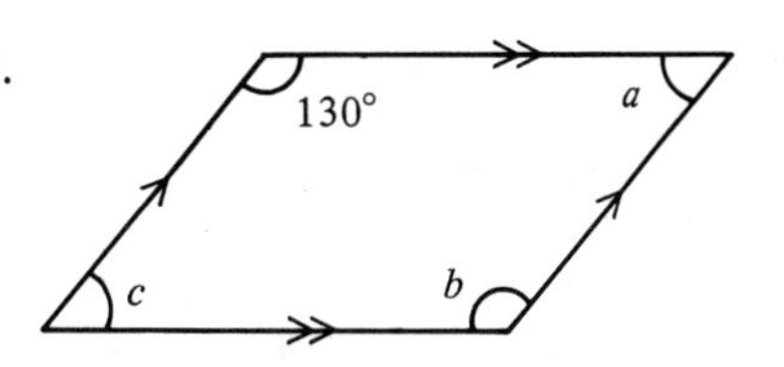

$\hat{a} = 50°$ (allied with 130°)

$\hat{b} = 130°$ (allied with $\hat{a}$)

$\hat{c} = 50°$ (allied with $\hat{b}$)

Questions on parallel lines may include other properties of straight lines and may require drawing in further lines and angles.

Example 4

Find the size of $\hat{x}$, giving reasons.

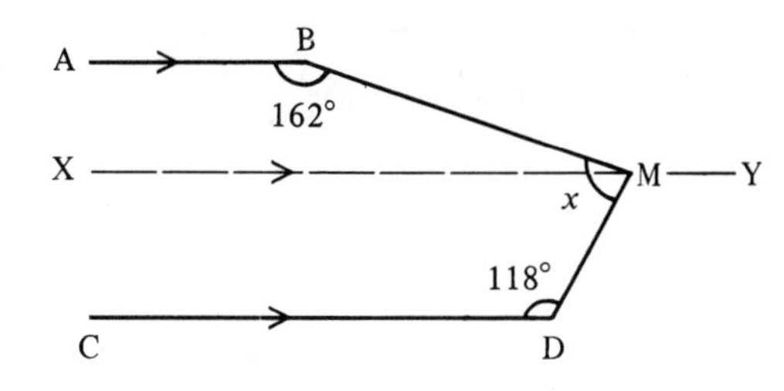

Draw a line, XMY through M, parallel to AB and CD.

$B\hat{M}X = 18°$ (allied with 162°)

$D\hat{M}X = 62°$ (allied with 118°)

$\therefore \quad \hat{x} = 80°$ ($B\hat{M}X + D\hat{M}X$)

Exercise 5.3

Find the unknown marked angles (following the alphabetical order). State the reasons clearly for each statement you make.

1.

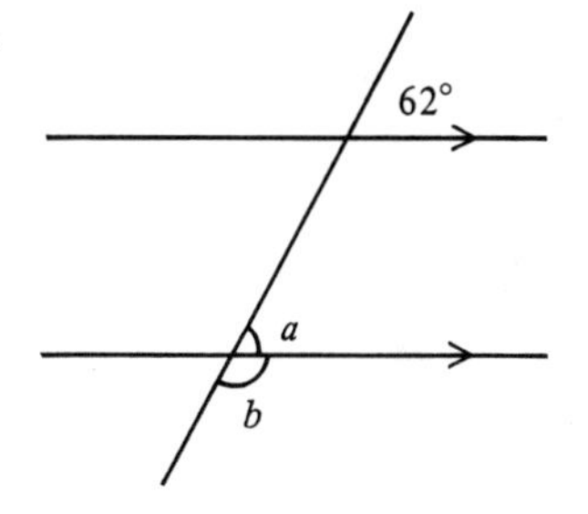

2.

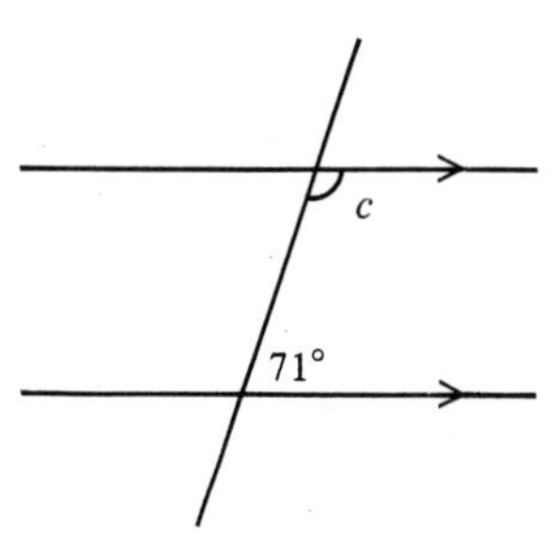

3.

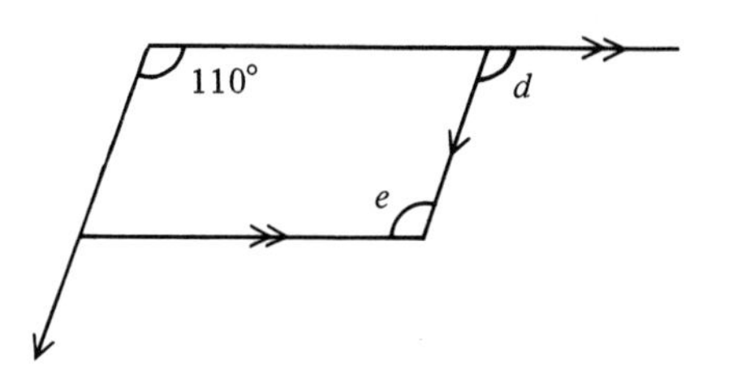

4.

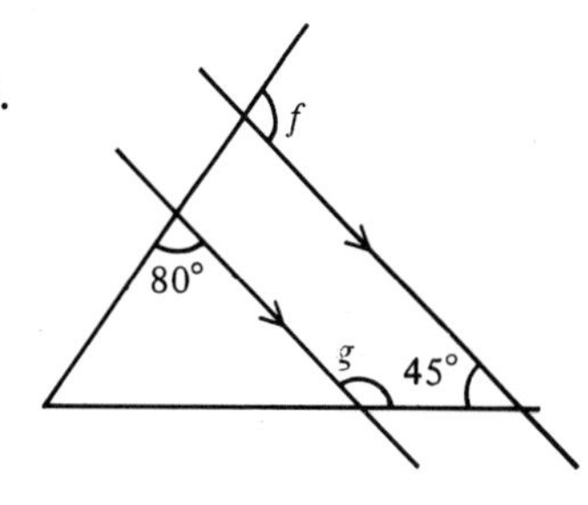

5.

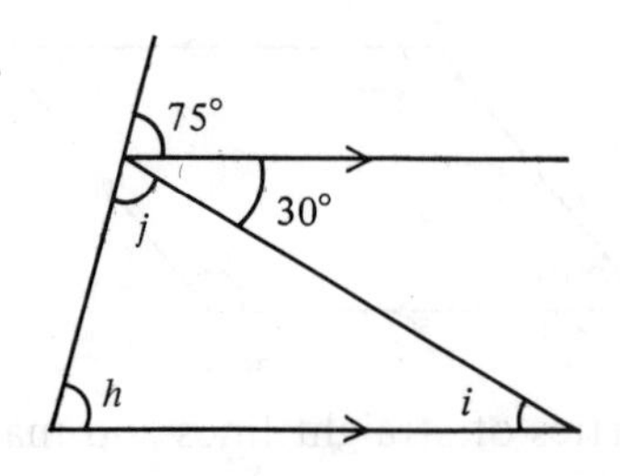

6.

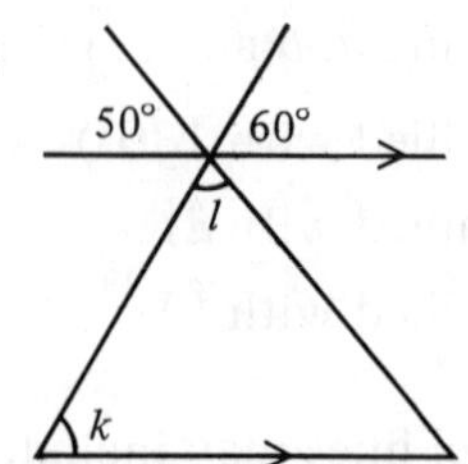

7.

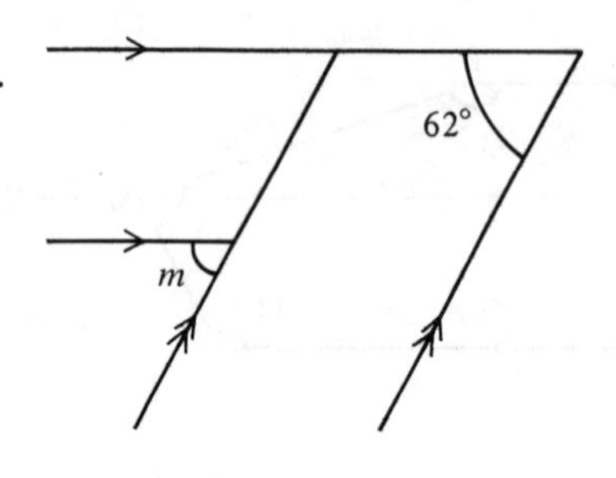

8.

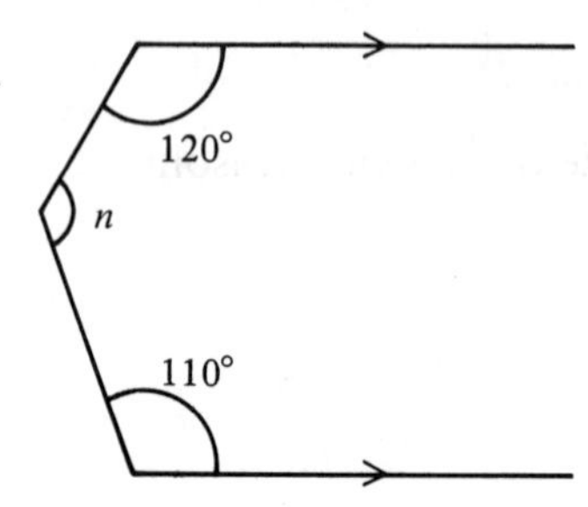

9.

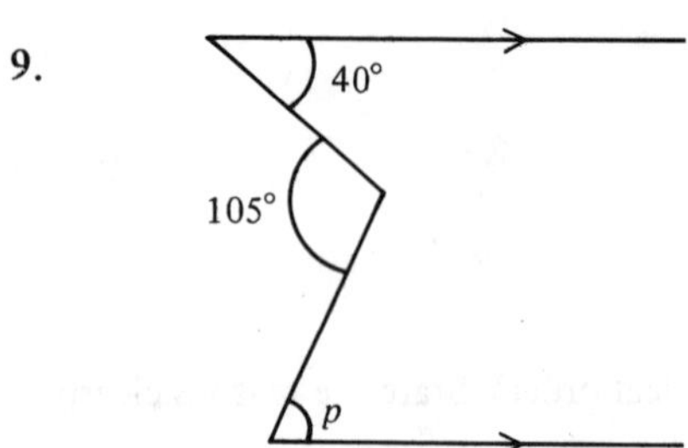

10.

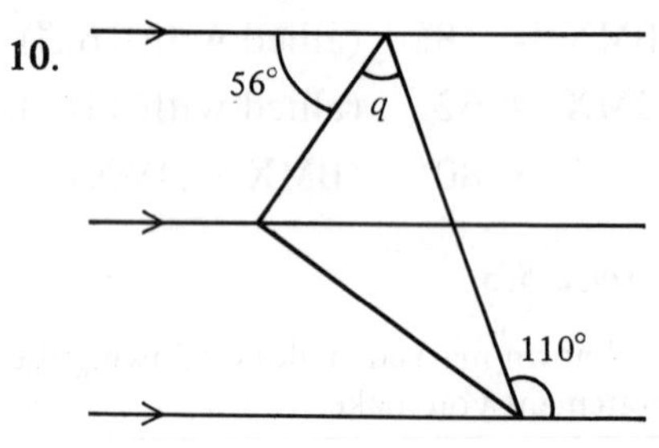

11.

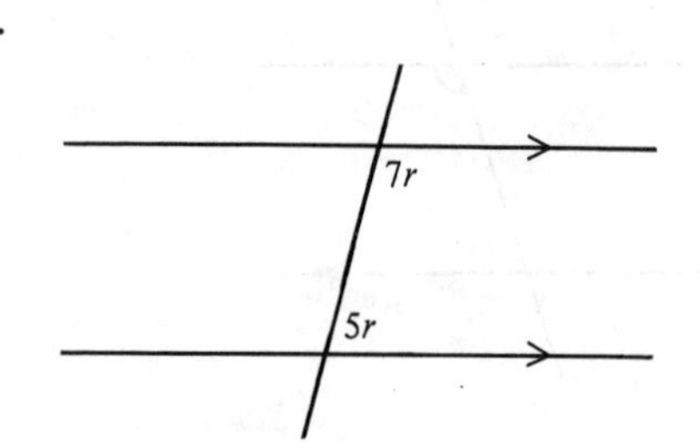

12.

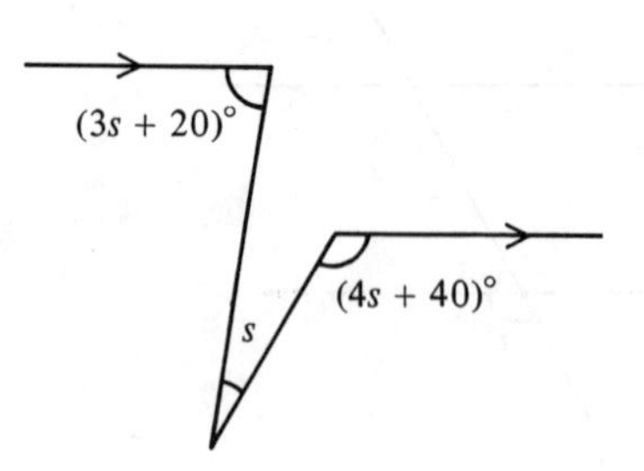

13.

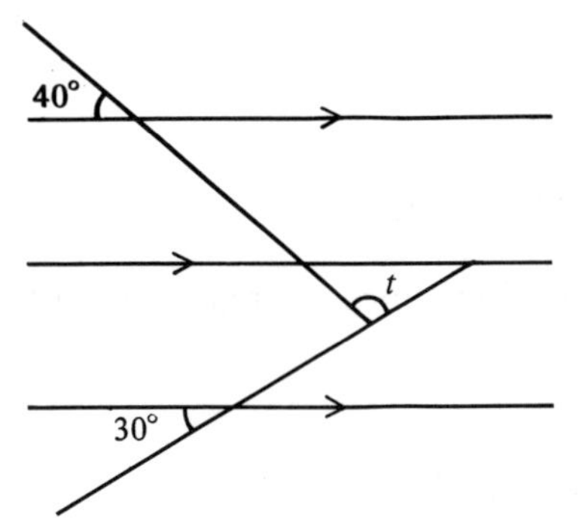

14.

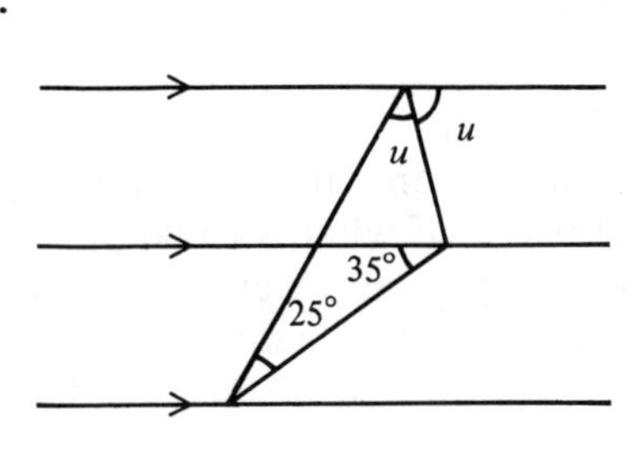

15.

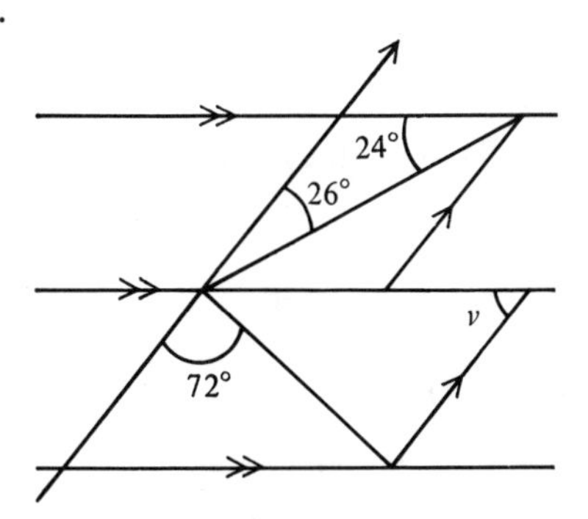

16.

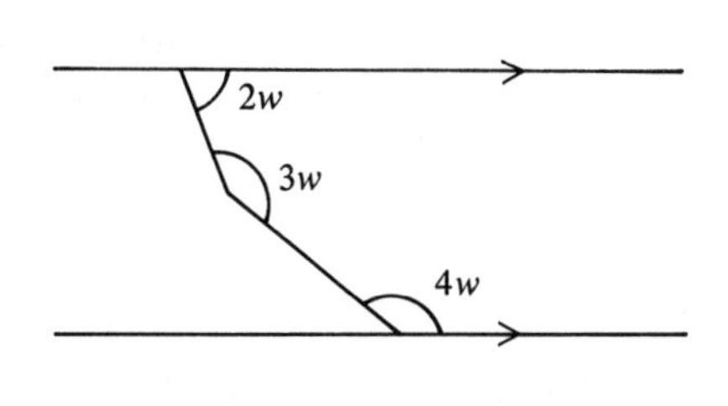

17.

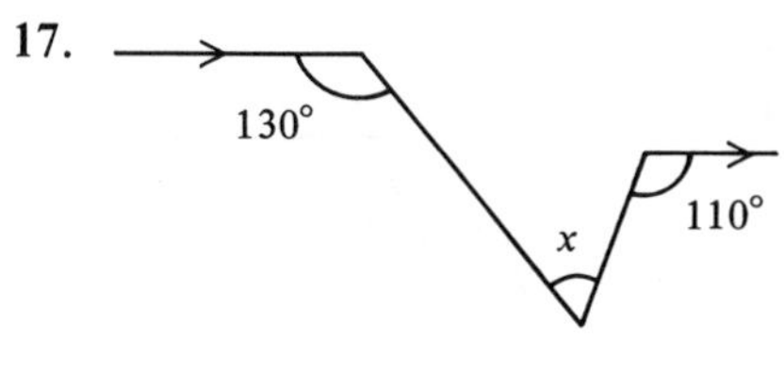

18. Which lines are parallel?

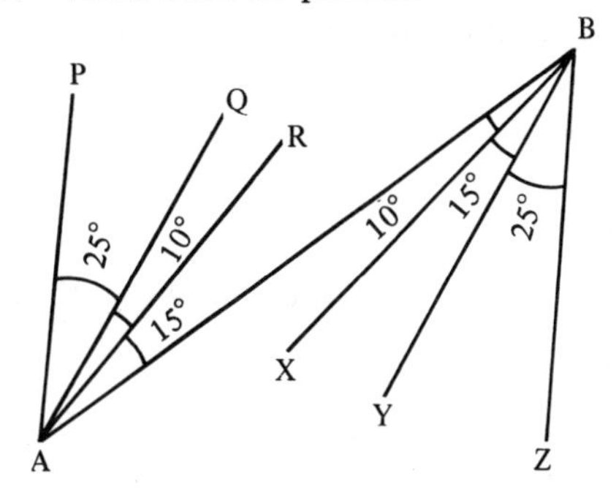

5.4 Simple proofs

Proofs should consist of:
(a) the diagram, drawn clearly and approximately to scale,
(b) a statement of what is to be proved,
(c) if necessary, a statement giving details of any extra lines or angles which have been added to the figure,
(d) the proof, with each step justified.

Example 1 In the following diagram, prove that $\hat{a} = \hat{b}$.

To prove $\hat{a} = \hat{b}$

In diagram insert $\hat{c}$ as shown

Proof $\hat{a} + \hat{c} = 180°$ (adjacent angles on a straight line)

$\hat{c} + \hat{b} = 180°$ (adjacent angles on a straight line)

$\therefore$ $\hat{a} = \hat{b}$.

Example 2

In the following diagram, prove that AB is parallel to CD.

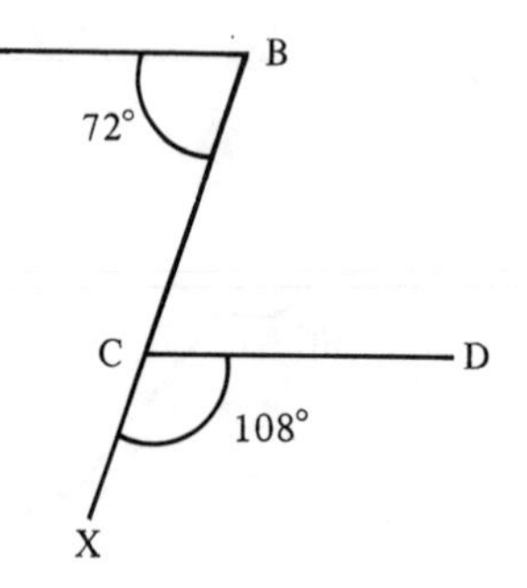

To prove AB is parallel to CD

Proof $\text{D}\hat{\text{C}}\text{B} = 72°$ (adjacent angles on a straight line)

$\therefore$ $\text{A}\hat{\text{B}}\text{C} = \text{B}\hat{\text{C}}\text{D}$ and as these are alternate angles and are equal, then AB is parallel to CD.

Example 3 In the following diagram, show that $\hat{a} = \hat{b}$.

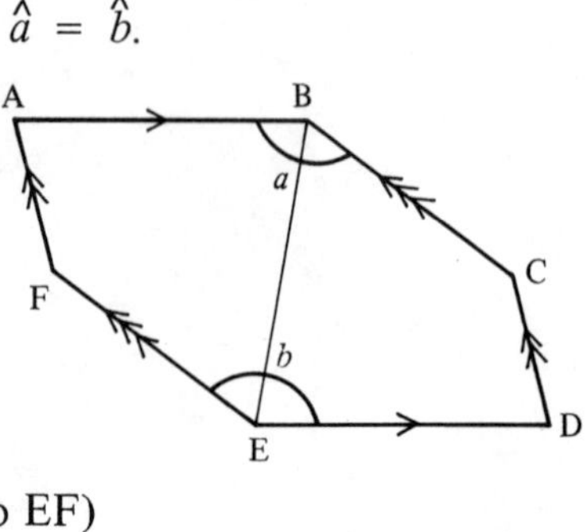

To prove $\hat{a} = \hat{b}$

In diagram letter A, B, C, D, E, F, as shown.
Draw line from B to E.

Proof $\text{A}\hat{\text{B}}\text{E} = \text{B}\hat{\text{E}}\text{D}$ (alternate angles: AB is parallel to ED)

$\text{C}\hat{\text{B}}\text{E} = \text{B}\hat{\text{E}}\text{F}$ (alternate angles: CB is parallel to EF)

But $\text{A}\hat{\text{B}}\text{E} + \text{C}\hat{\text{B}}\text{E} = \hat{a}$

and $\text{B}\hat{\text{E}}\text{D} + \text{B}\hat{\text{E}}\text{F} = \hat{b}$

$\therefore$ $\hat{a} = \hat{b}$.

Exercise 5.4

Draw your own diagrams. It may be necessary, in some cases, to draw an extra line or lines. Give brief reasons for any statements you make.

1.

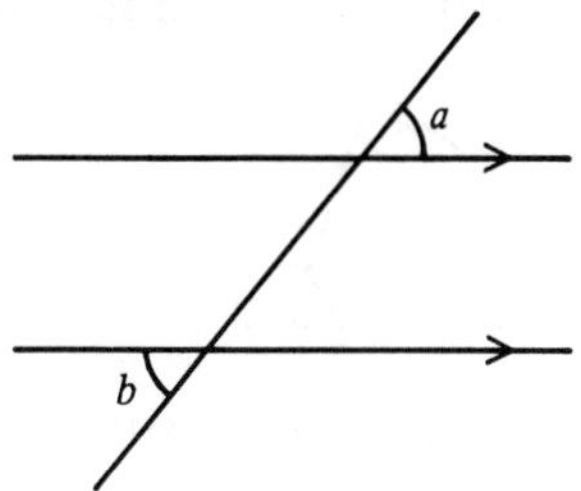

Prove $a = b$

2.

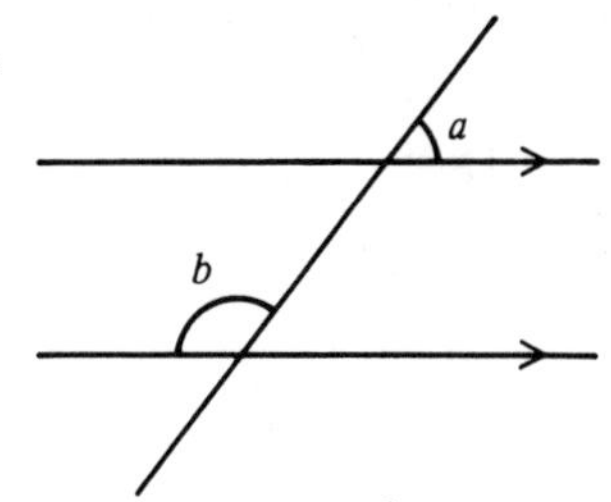

Prove $a = 180° - b$

3.

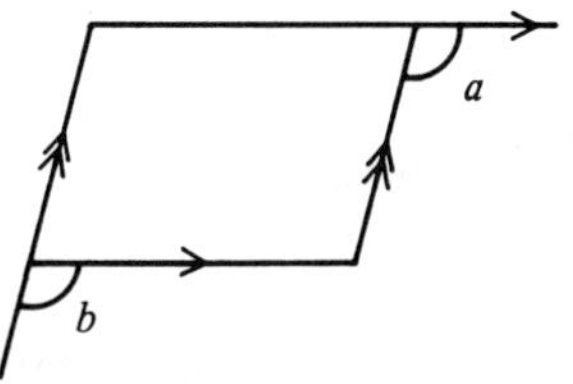

Prove $a = b$

4.

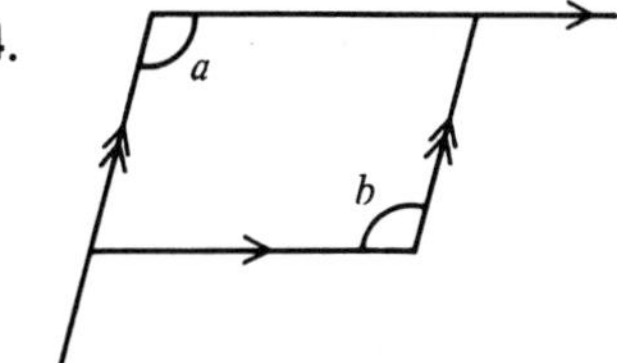

Prove $a = b$

5.

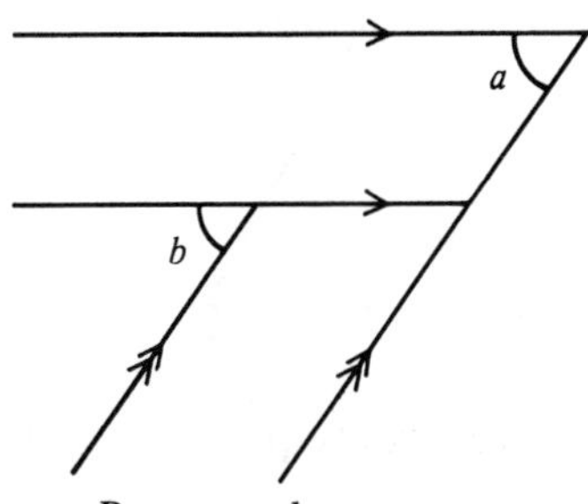

Prove $a = b$

6.

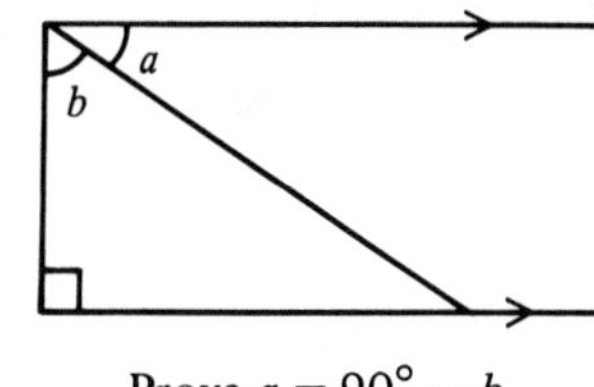

Prove $a = 90° - b$

7.

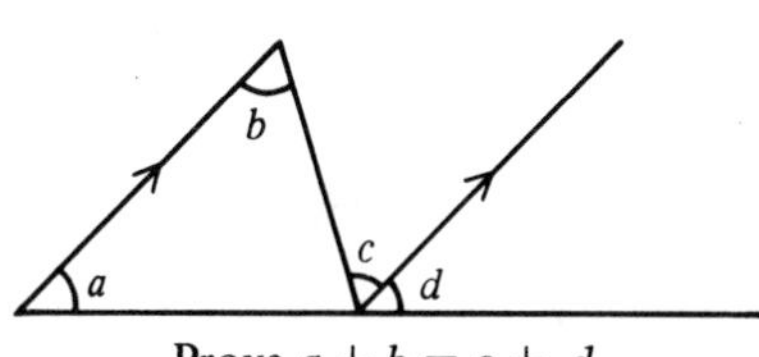

Prove $a + b = c + d$

8.

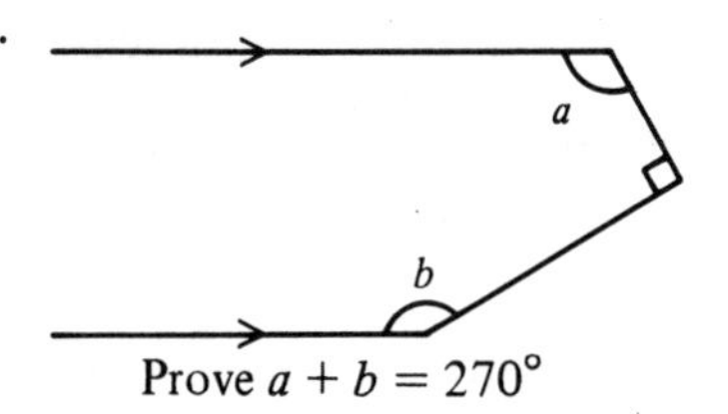

Prove $a + b = 270°$

9.

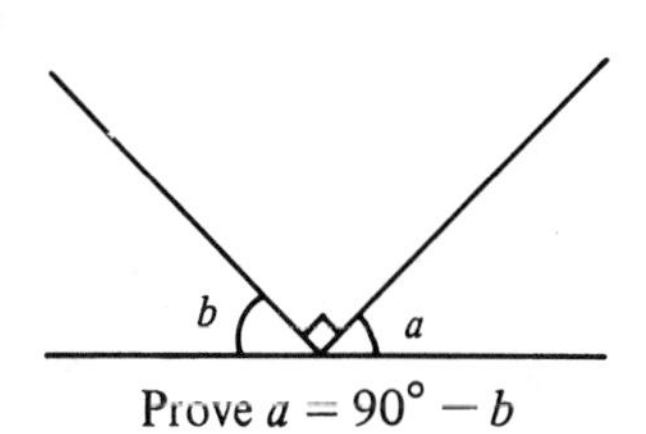

Prove $a = 90° - b$

10.

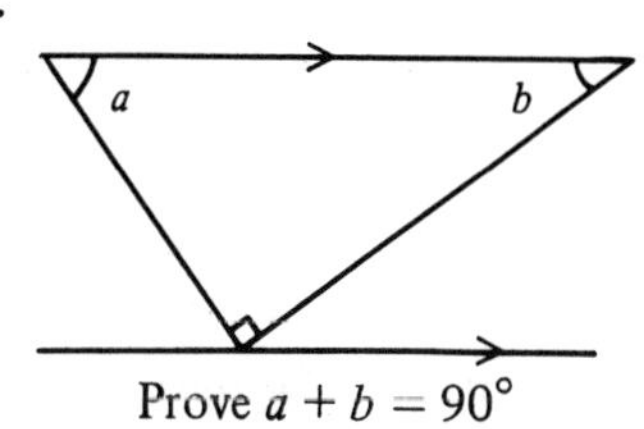

Prove $a + b = 90°$

5.5 Triangles

1. The sum of the interior angles of a triangle is 180°.
2. The exterior angle of a triangle is equal to the sum of the interior opposite angles.

$$\hat{a} + \hat{b} + \hat{c} = 180°$$
$$\hat{a} + \hat{b} = \hat{d}$$

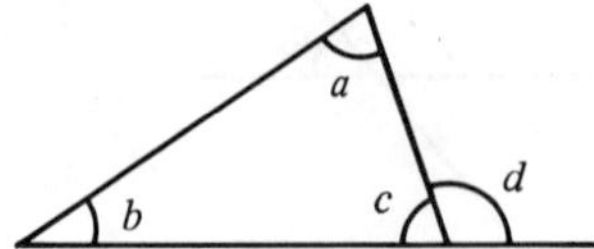

3. An isosceles triangle has 2 sides equal and the interior angles opposite to the equal sides are equal.

If $AB = BC$

then $B\hat{A}C = B\hat{C}A$

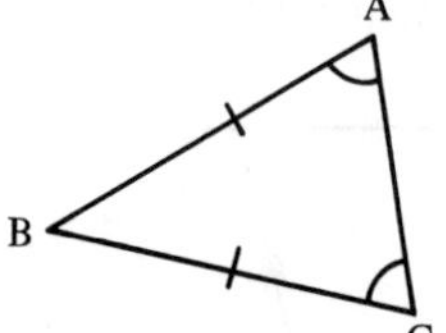

4. An equilateral triangle has all its sides equal and all its interior angles equal to 60°.

$AB = BC = CA$ and

$\hat{A} = \hat{B} = \hat{C} = 60°$

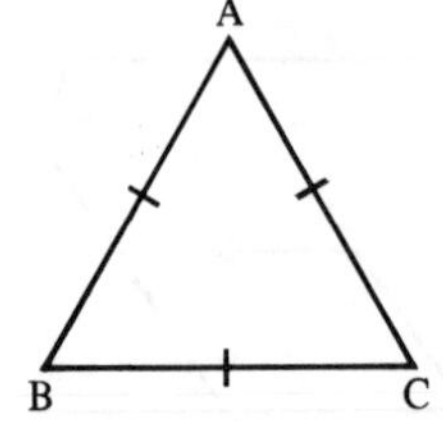

Note. Questions on the angle properties of triangles may also require use of the angle properties of straight lines and parallel lines.

Example 1 Find $\hat{a}$, giving reasons.

Put in $\hat{b}$ as shown

then $\hat{b} = 110°$ (40° + 70°, ext angle of a triangle)

$\hat{a} = 40°$ ($\hat{a} + \hat{b} + 30° = 180°$, sum of angles in a triangle)

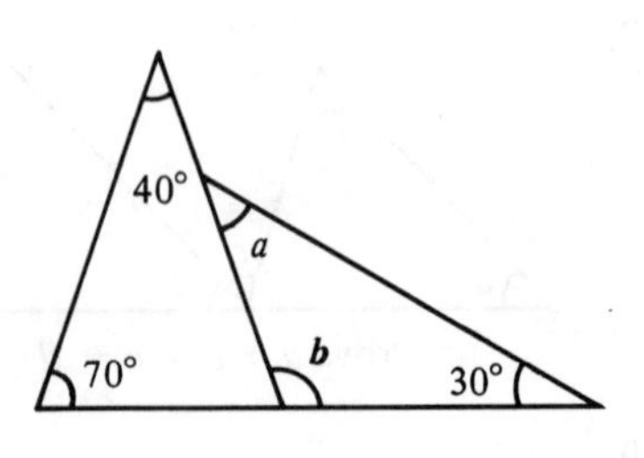

Example 2 Find $\hat{a}$, giving reasons.

Put in $\hat{b}$ and $\hat{c}$ as shown

then $\hat{b} = 100°$ (adjacent angles on a straight line)

$\hat{c} = 40°$ (equal angles in isosceles triangle, when non-equal angle is 100°)

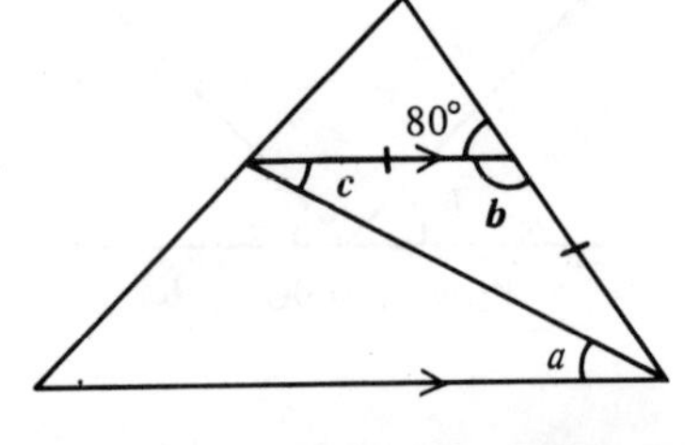

$\hat{a} = 40°$ (alternate with $\hat{c}$)

Example 3 Find $\hat{x}$, giving reasons.

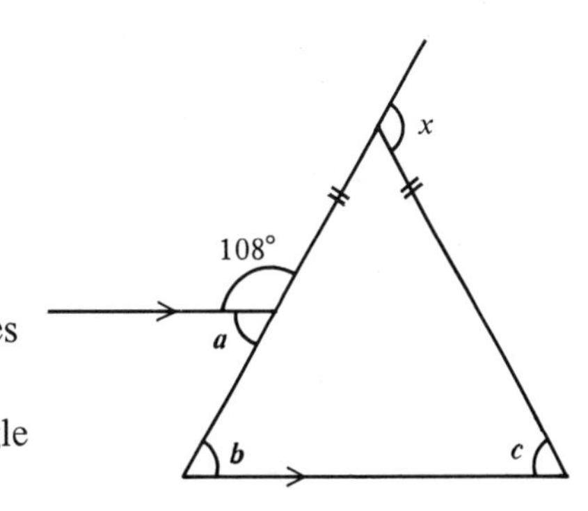

Put in $\hat{a}$, $\hat{b}$ and $\hat{c}$ as shown

then $\hat{a} = 72°$ (adjacent angles on a straight line)

$\hat{b} = 72°$ (alternate with $\hat{a}$)

$\hat{c} = 72°$ (equal angle in an isosceles triangle)

$\therefore$ $\hat{x} = 144°$ (exterior angle of a triangle equals the sum of the interior opposite angles)

Exercise 5.5a

Find the unknown marked angles (following the alphabetical order). State the reasons clearly for each statement you make.

1.

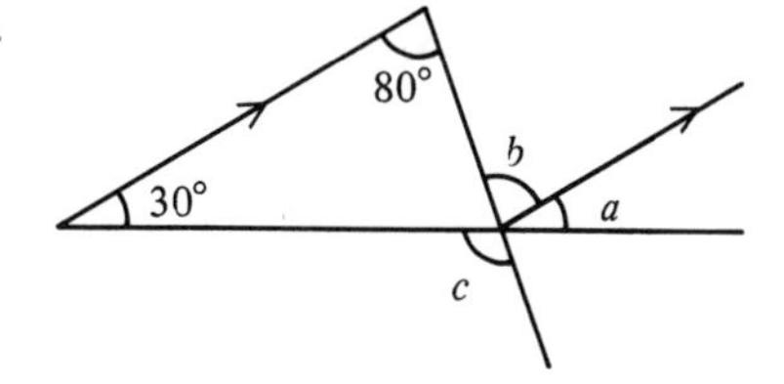

2.

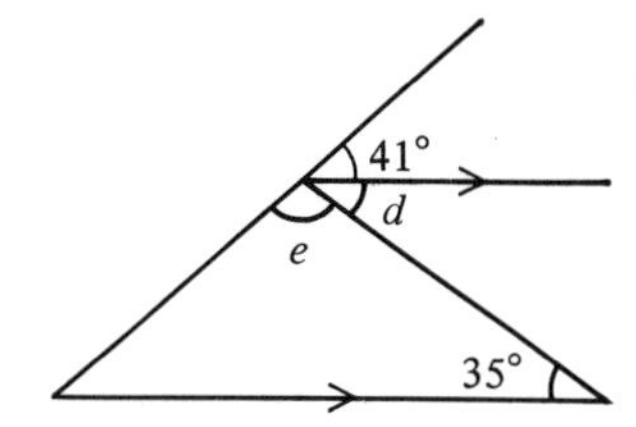

3.

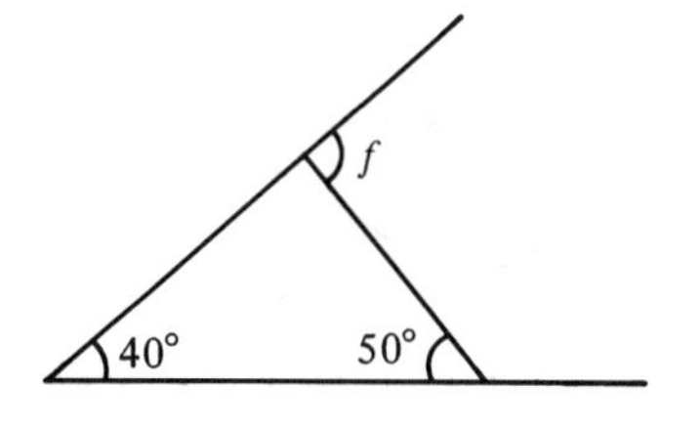

4.

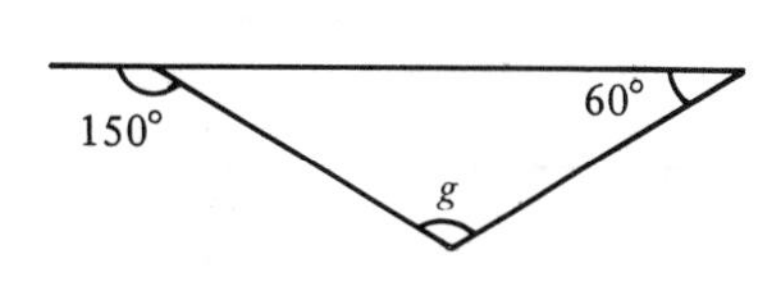

5.

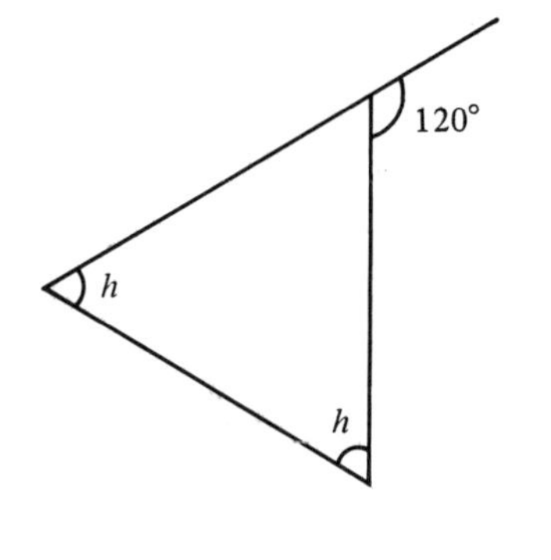

6.

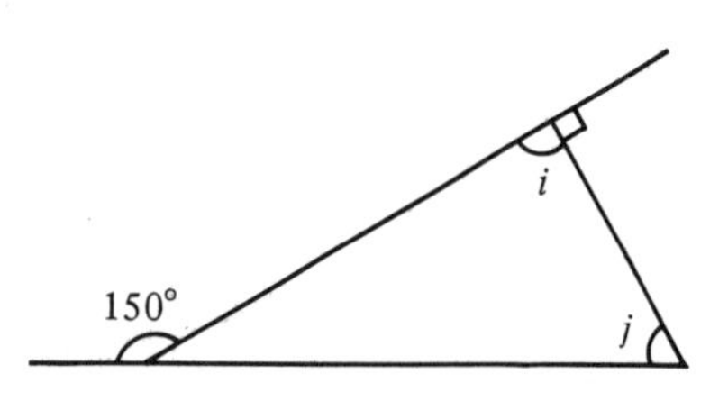

7.

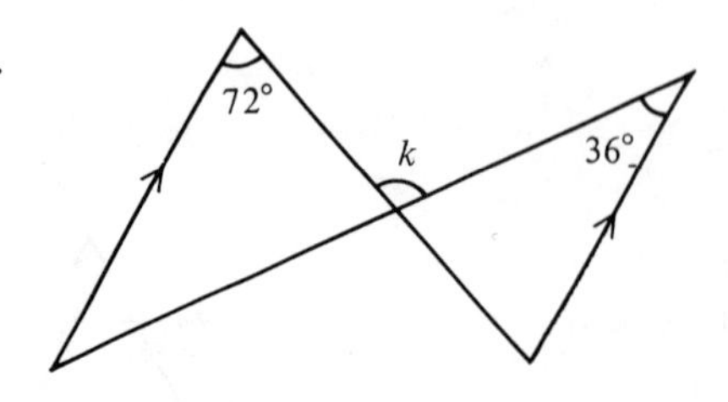

8.

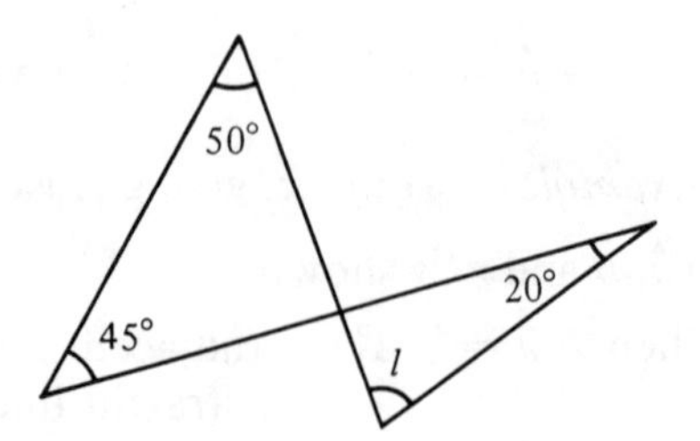

9.

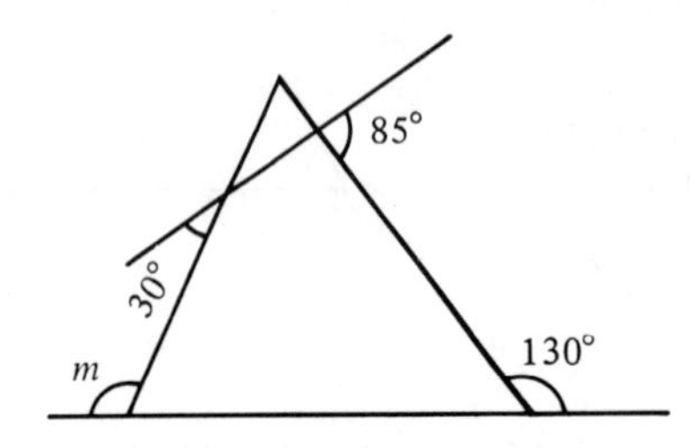

10.

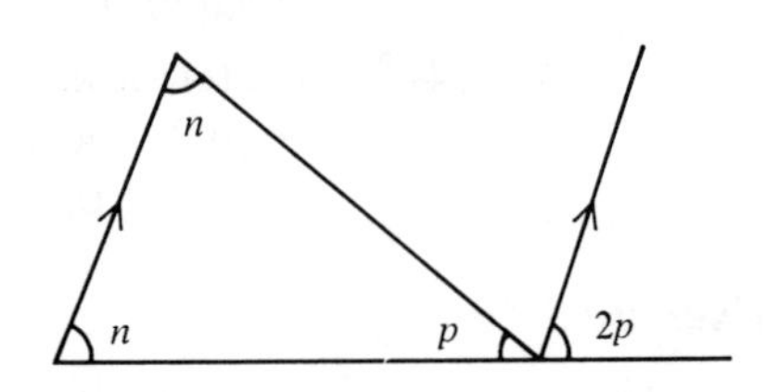

11.

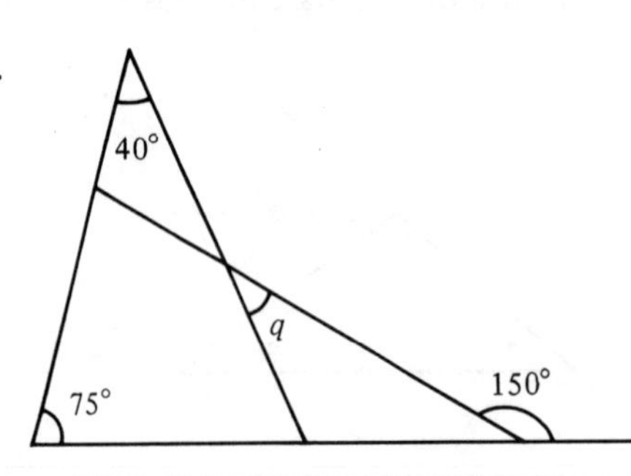

12.

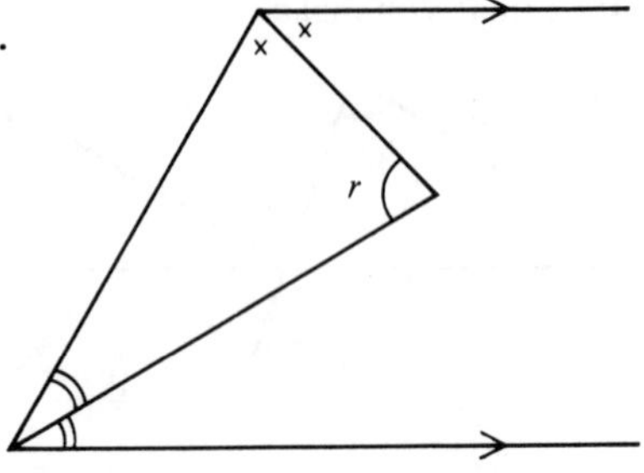

13.

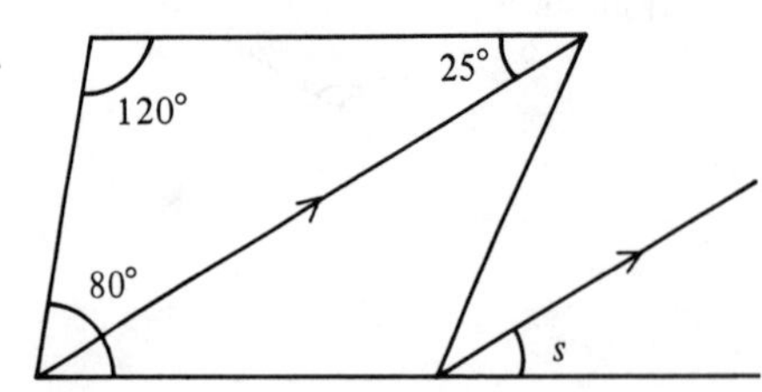

14.

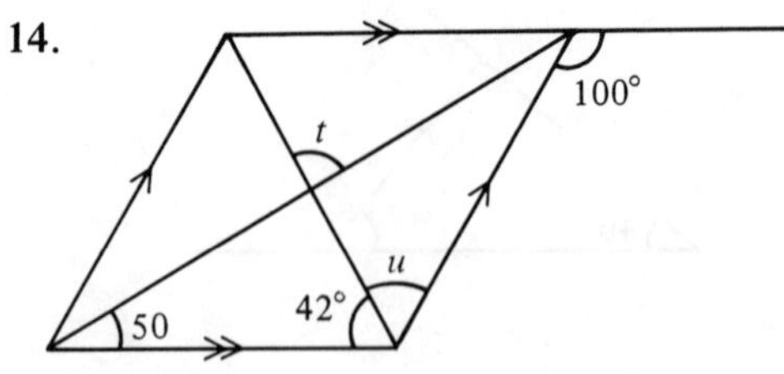

15.

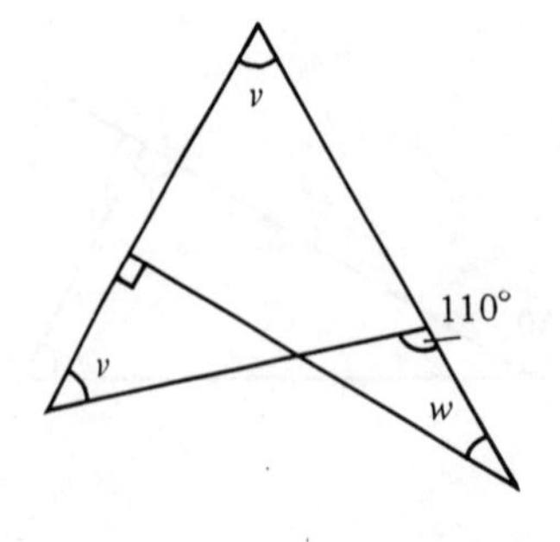

16.

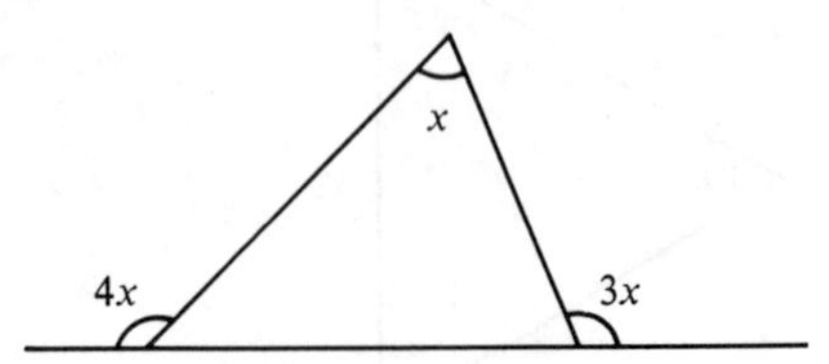

Exercise 5.5b

Find the unknown marked angles (following the alphabetical order). State the reasons clearly for each statement you make.

1.

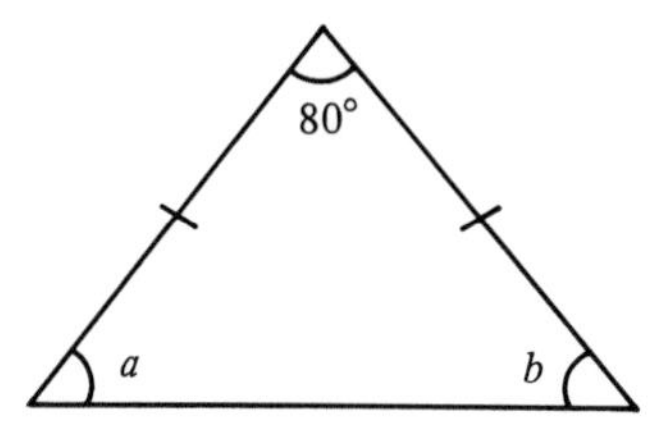

2.

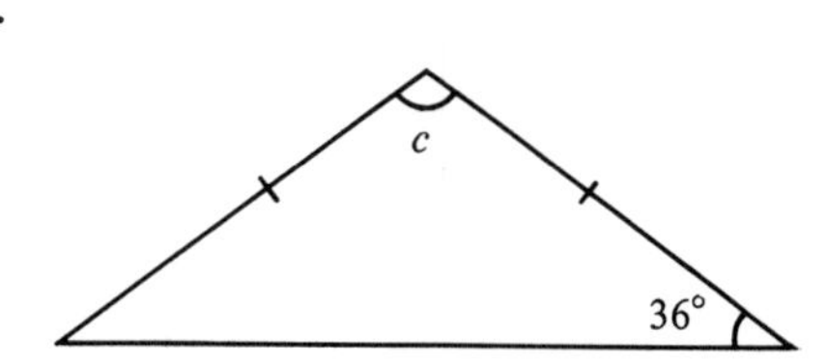

3.

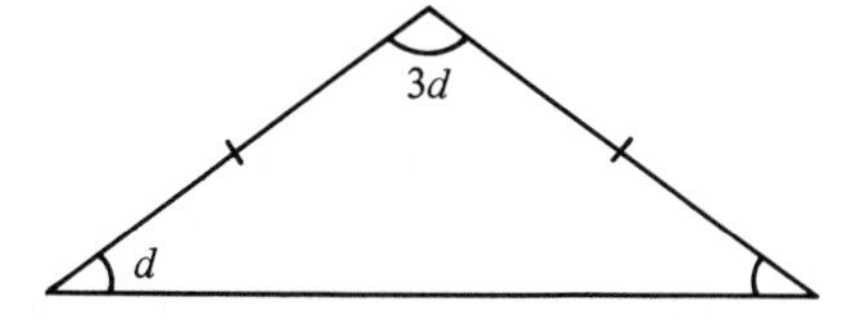

4.

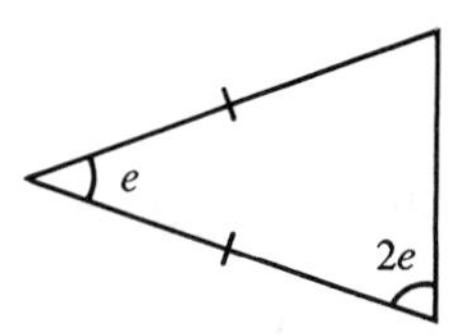

5.

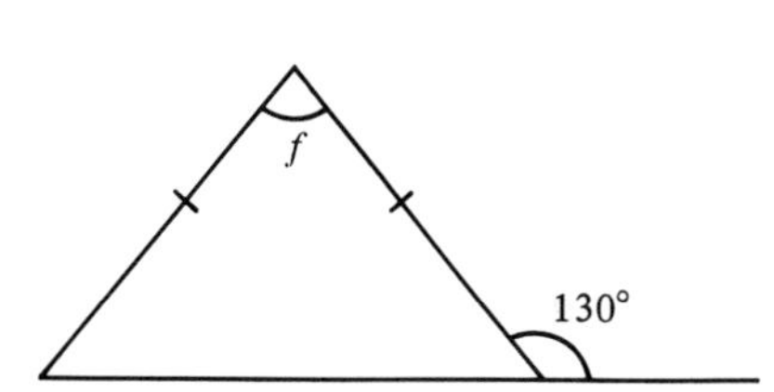

6.

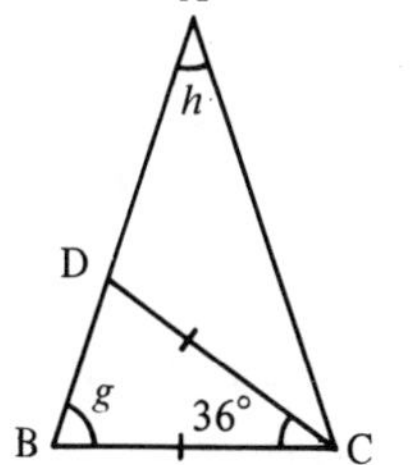

AB = AC
BC = CD

7.

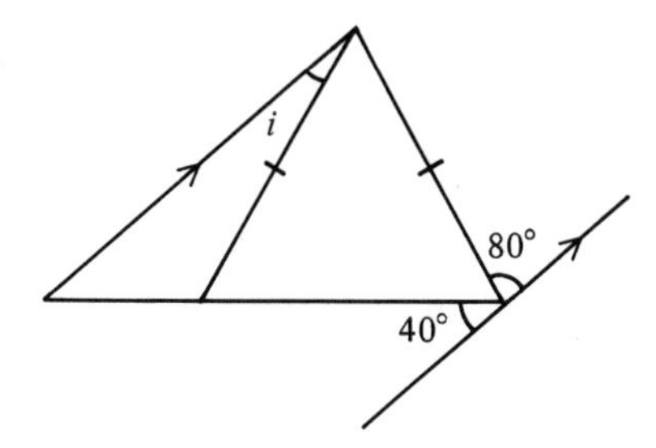

8.

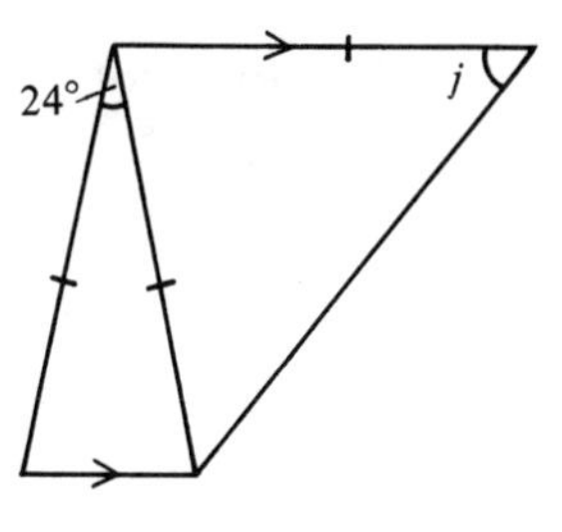

9.

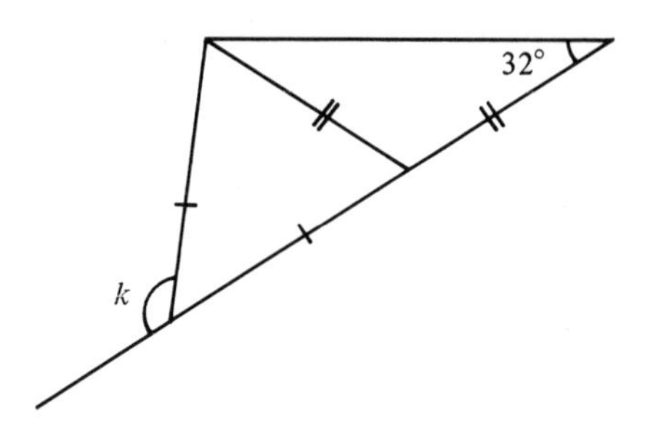

10.

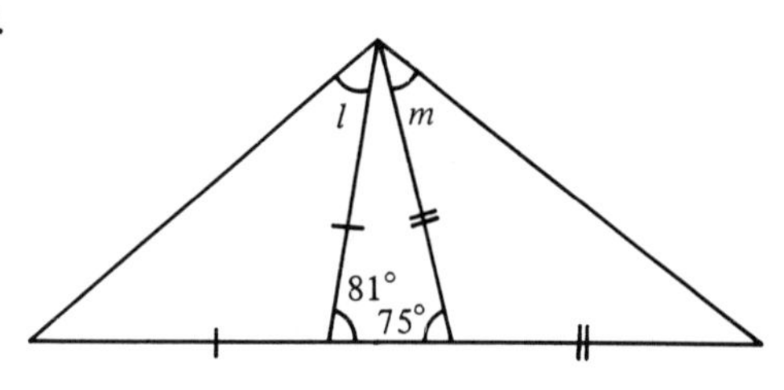

5.6 Polygons

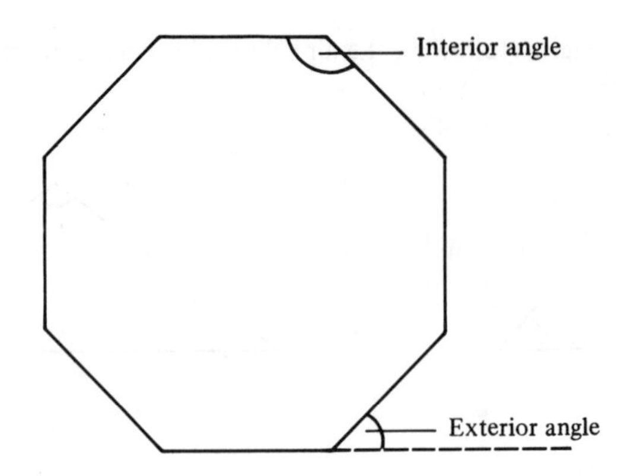

A *polygon* is a totally enclosed figure bounded by straight lines having as many angles as it has sides.
A *regular polygon* is a polygon which has all its sides equal and all its angles equal.
If N is the number of sides of a regular polygon, then the:

$$\textit{Exterior angle} = \frac{360°}{N}$$

Example 1

Find the exterior angle of a regular pentagon (a polygon with 5 sides).

$$\text{Exterior angle} = \frac{360}{5} = 72°$$

Interior angle = 180° – exterior angle.

Example 2

Find the interior angle of a regular octagon (a polygon with 8 sides).

$$\text{Exterior angle} = \frac{360°}{8} = 45°$$

$$\therefore \text{Interior angle} = 180° - 45° = 135°.$$

If a polygon has N sides, then the sum of the interior angles is $(2N - 4)$ right angles.

Example 3

Find the sum of the interior angles of a decagon (a 10-sided polygon).

$$\text{Sum of interior angles} = (20 - 4) \times 90°$$
$$= 16 \times 90° = 1440°.$$

Example 4

One interior angle of a polygon is 100°. The other interior angles are all equal to 110°. How many sides has the polygon?

Let the polygon have N sides. If one angle is 100°, then there are $(N - 1)$ angles, each of 110°.

$$\therefore\ 100° + (N-1) \times 110° = (2N-4) \times 90°$$
$$100 + 110N - 110 = 180N - 360$$
$$350 = 70N$$
$$5 = N$$

$\therefore$ the polygon has 5 sides.

Exercise 5.6

1. Find the size of each interior angle of
   (a) a regular pentagon (b) a regular hexagon
   (c) a regular octagon (d) a regular 15-sided figure
2. Find the size of each exterior angle of
   (a) a regular 7-sided figure (b) a regular 9-sided figure
3. Can a regular polygon have an exterior angle of
   (a) 10°? (b) 40°? (c) 32°?
   If the answer is yes, state the number of sides.
4. Can a regular polygon have an interior angle of
   (a) 160°? (b) 169°? (c) 150°?
   If the answer is yes, state the number of sides.
5. An octagon has angles of 120°, 140°, 170° and 165°. The other angles are all equal. Find them.
6. The angles of a hexagon are $4x°$, $5x°$, $6x°$, $7x°$, $8x°$ and $9x°$. Calculate the size of the largest angle.
7. Two sides of a regular pentagon are produced to meet. Calculate the size of the new angle formed.
8. The angles of a pentagon are $x°$, $(x + 20)°$, $(x - 15)°$, $2x°$ and $(1\frac{1}{2}x + 30)°$. Find x.
9. ABCDE is a regular pentagon. Find the angles of the triangles ADE and ADC.
10. P, Q, R, S and T are five adjacent corners of a regular 10-sided polygon. PQ produced meets SR produced in U, and TS produced in V. Calculate the angles of the triangle SUV.
11. With the data of question **10**, calculate the angles of triangle SQU.
12. ABCDEF is a regular hexagon. AFEG is a rhombus inscribed in it. Find the sum of the interior angles of ABCDEG.
13. ABCDEFGH is a regular octagon. AHI is an equilateral triangle inscribed in it. Find the sum of the interior angles of ABCDEFGHI.
14. ABCDEFGHI is a regular 9-sided figure with an equilateral triangle AIJ inscribed in it. Find the sum of the interior angles of ABCDEFGHIJ.
15. ABCDEF is a regular hexagon. A square ABXY is drawn outside the hexagon. Find the angles in triangle BFY.

5.7 Congruent triangles

Triangles are said to be *congruent* if they are alike in every possible way.

Two triangles can be proved to be congruent if:
(a) 3 sides of one are respectively equal to 3 sides of the other.
(b) 2 sides of one are respectively equal to 2 sides of the other and the angles included by each pair of sides are equal.
(c) 2 angles of one are respectively equal to 2 angles of the other, and a pair of corresponding sides is equal.
(d) the triangles are right-angled, their hypotenuses are equal and another pair of sides are equal.

These may be summarised as follows:
(a) 3 sides (S.S.S.)
(b) 2 sides and the included angle (S.A.S.)
(c) 2 angles and the corresponding side (A.A.S.)
(d) Right angle, hypotenuse, side (R.H.S.)

Proofs must be set out as follows:
(i) the diagram, drawn clearly and approximately to scale,
(ii) a resumé of the facts given,
(iii) what is to be proved,
(iv) if necessary, state any extra lines that have to be added to the figure,
(v) set out the proof, justifying each statement made.

Example 1

ABCD is a square and PCD is an equilateral triangle drawn inside the square. Prove that BP = AP.

Given ABCD is a square, with equilateral triangle PCD drawn inside.

To prove BP = AP

Proof In triangles APD and BPC

AD = BC (sides of square ABCD)

PD = PC (sides of equilateral triangle PDC)

$A\hat{D}P = B\hat{C}P$ (each is $90° - 60°$)

$\therefore$ Δ APD $\equiv$ Δ BPC (S.A.S.)

Hence AP = BP.

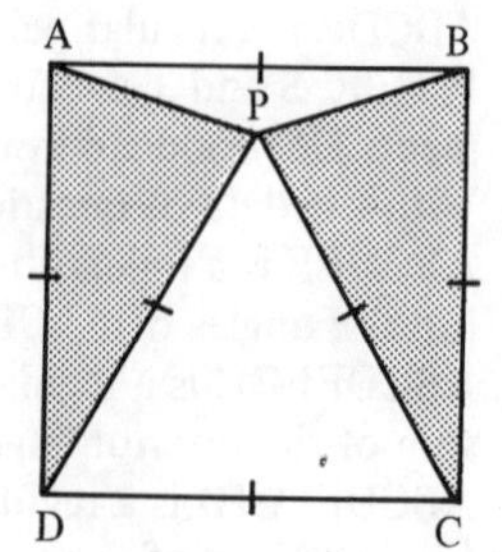

Example 2

ABCD is a quadrilateral in which AB = DC and AB is parallel to DC. Prove that ABCD is a parallelogram.

Given ABCD is a quadrilateral; AB = DC; AB is parallel to DC.

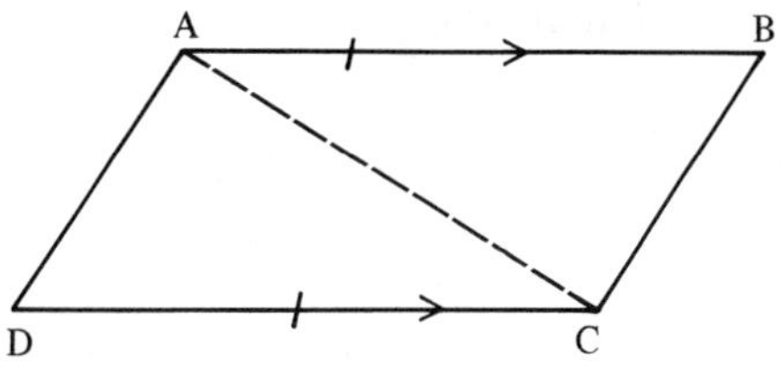

To prove ABCD is a parallelogram.

Construction Join A to C.

Proof In triangles ABC and CDA

AB = DC (given)

AC is common to both triangles.

$B\hat{A}C = D\hat{C}A$ (alternate angles, AB is parallel to DC)

∴ triangles ABC and CDA are congruent (S.A.S.).

Hence $B\hat{C}A = D\hat{A}C$

But these are alternate angles

∴ BC is parallel to AD

i.e. both pairs of opposite sides of quadrilateral ABCD are parallel

∴ ABCD is a parallelogram.

Exercise 5.7

1. AB and CD are two straight lines which bisect each other at O. Prove AC = BD.
2. ABCD is a square. E is the mid-point of AB.
   Prove: (a) ED = EC (b) angle EDC = angle ECD.
3. E and F are the mid-points of sides AB and BC of square ABCD.
   Prove angle BAF = angle ADE.
4. AB is the chord of a circle, centre O. If C is a point on the chord such that OC is perpendicular to AB, prove AC = CB.
5. ABPQ and ACRS are two squares on opposite sides of the straight line ACB.
   Prove QC = BS.
6. ABCD is a square and P a point on the diagonal BD. Prove angle APB = angle BPC.
7. The diagonal AC of quadrilateral ABCD bisects the angles at A and C.
   Prove angle D = angle B.
8. ABC is an isosceles triangle. D is a point on the base BC such that DA bisects angle A.
   Prove: (a) BD = DC (b) BD is perpendicular to DA.
9. ABC and DBC are two isosceles triangles lying on the same side of base BC.
   Prove angle DAB = angle DAC.
10. P is a point on the line which bisects angle BAC. Prove that the perpendiculars from P onto AB and AC are equal in length.
11. M is the mid-point of side AB of rectangle ABCD. An arc centre M cuts AD and BC at Q and R. Prove AQ = BR and then that BQ = AR.
12. AB and CD are equal chords of a circle, centre O. Prove angle OAB = angle OCD.
13. Two circles have a common centre O. ABCD is a straight line that cuts the larger circle at A and D and the smaller one at B and C. Prove AB = CD.
14. Triangle ABC has two squares ABLM and ACNP drawn externally on its sides AB and AC.
    Prove MC = PB.
15. D is the mid-point of base BC of an isosceles triangle ABC. DM and DN are the perpendiculars from D to AB and AC respectively. Prove DM = DN.

5.8 Similar triangles

1. Triangles are similar if all the angles in one are equal to corresponding angles in the other.

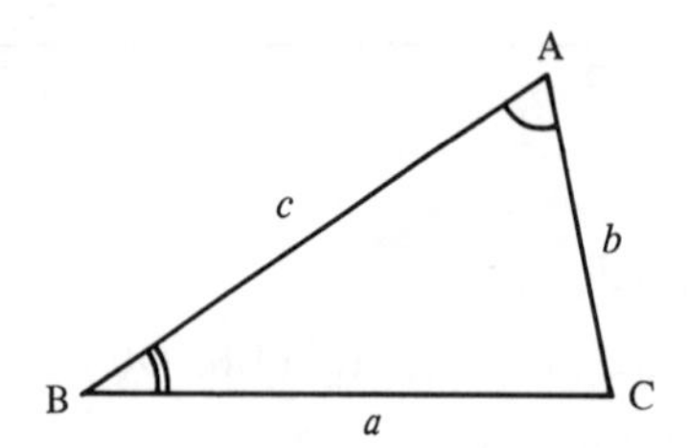

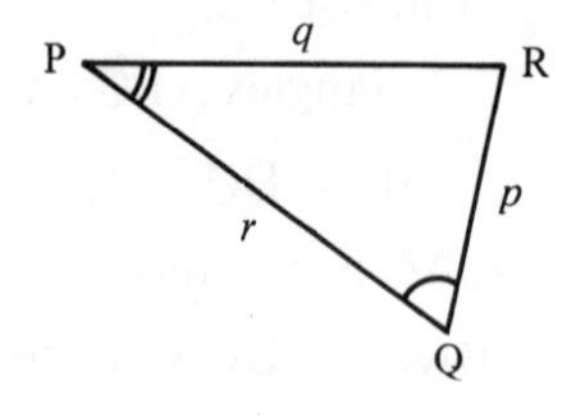

Triangle ABC is similar to triangle QPR because $\hat{A} = \hat{Q}$, $\hat{B} = \hat{P}$ and $\hat{C} = \hat{R}$.

2. If triangles are similar, then the sides opposite to the equal angles are in the same ratio.

   ∴ in the above diagram

   $$\frac{BC}{PR} = \frac{AC}{RQ} = \frac{AB}{PQ} \text{ or } \frac{a}{q} = \frac{b}{p} = \frac{c}{r}$$

3. If triangles are similar, then their areas are proportional to the squares of corresponding sides.

   ∴ (area of triangle ABC) : (area of triangle PQR) $= BC^2 : PR^2$

4. To prove that two triangles are similar, it is only necessary to prove that two angles in one are equal to two angles in the other. Proofs are set out in the same way as obtained for congruency in section 5.7 on page 124.

Example 1

In the following diagram, prove that triangle ADE is similar to triangle ABC and calculate the length of EC.

Given Triangle ABC as shown.

To prove (i) triangle ABC is similar to triangle ADE.

(ii) to find the length of EC.

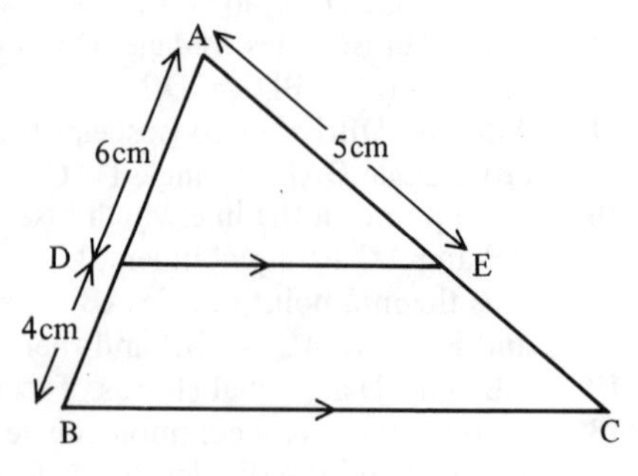

Proof In triangles ADE and ABC,

$\hat{A}$ is common

$A\hat{D}E = A\hat{B}C$ (DE is parallel to BC, corresponding angles)

$A\hat{E}D = A\hat{C}D$ (third angles in the triangle)

∴ triangle ADE is similar to triangle ABC

Hence $$\frac{AD}{AB} = \frac{AE}{AC}$$

$$\frac{6}{10} = \frac{5}{(5 + EC)}$$

$$6\,(5 + EC) = 5 \times 10$$

$$30 + 6EC = 50$$

$$6EC = 20$$

$$EC = 3\tfrac{1}{3} \text{ cm}$$

Exercise 5.8a

Find the unknown marked lengths (following the alphabetical order). Equal angles are marked with one arc or two arcs. The lengths may be taken as centimetres.

1.

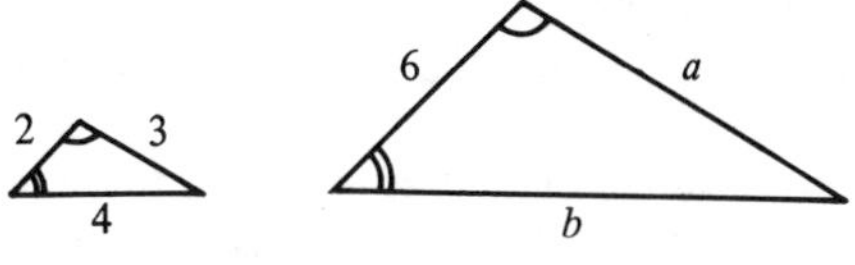

2.

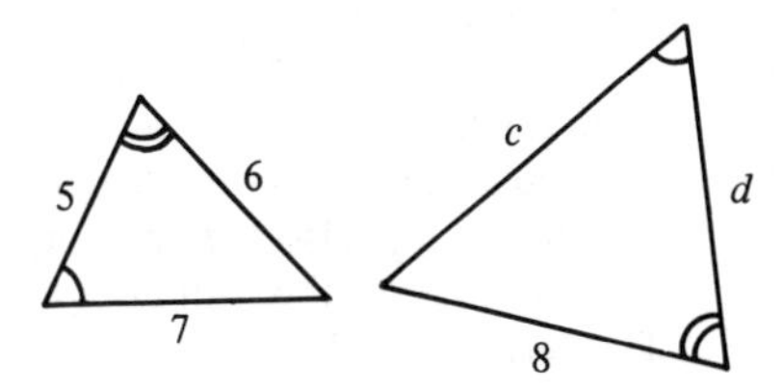

3.

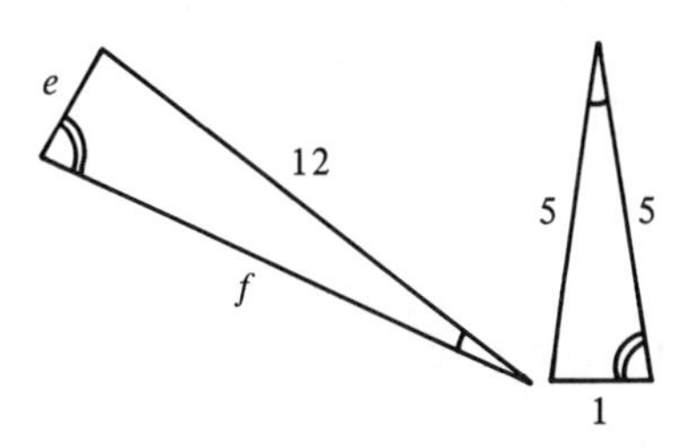

4.

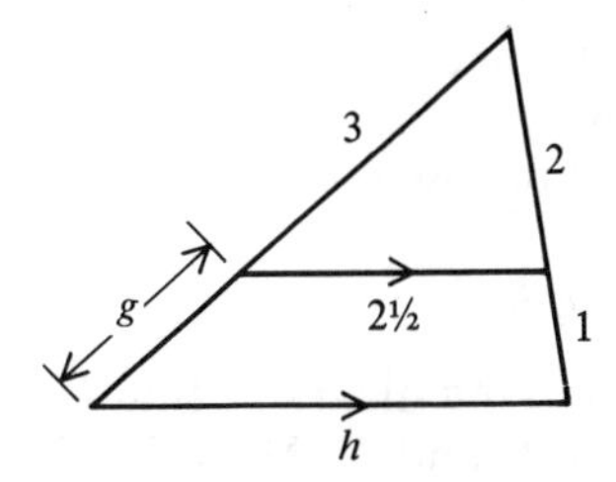

5.

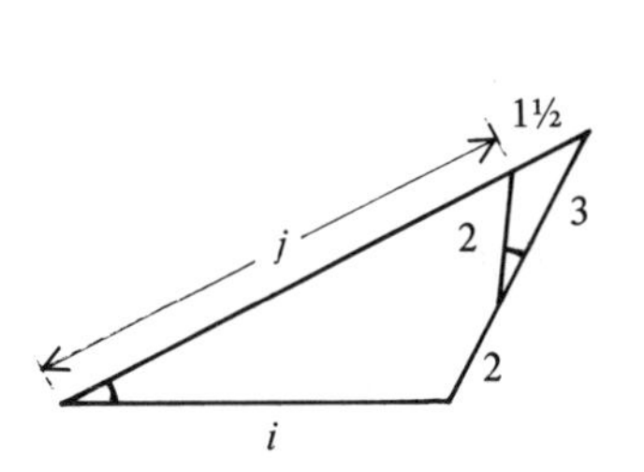

6.

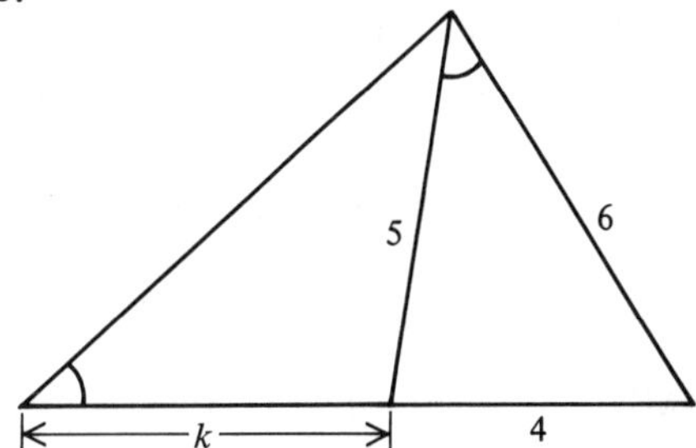

7.

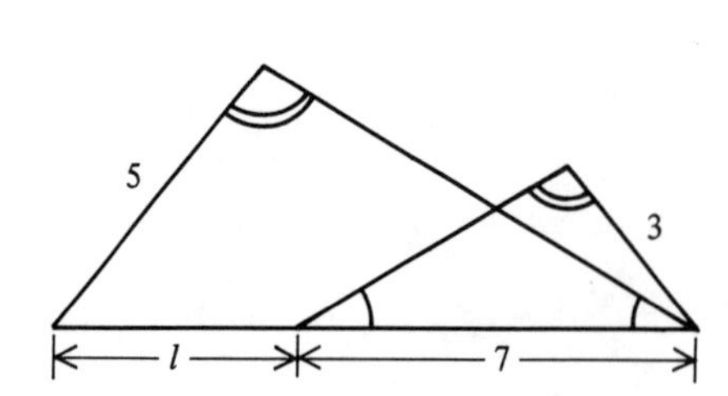

8.

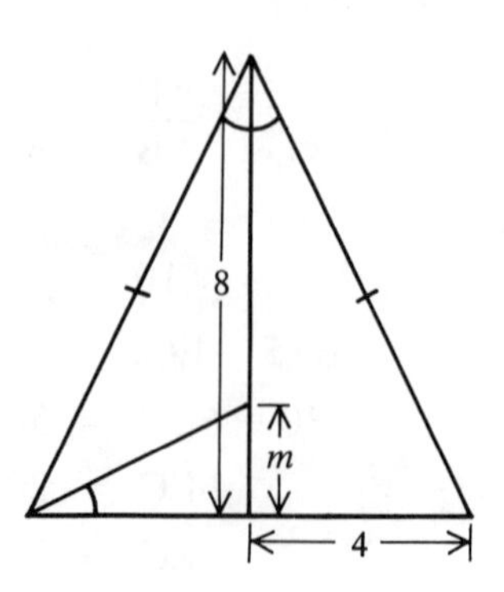

9. A projector throws a 30 cm wide picture when it is 50 cm from a screen. How wide is the picture when the projector is moved back 20 cm?

10. A lampshade has top and bottom diameters 12 cm and 19 cm and is 10 cm high. Find the height of the cone of which this could be the lower half.

11. A pole of height 2 m casts a shadow 1·5 m long. Find the height of a tree whose shadow is 25 m long.

12. A cubic box of side 1 m stands closely against a wall. A ladder is placed to touch the wall, the ground and also the edge of the box. If the foot of the ladder is then 50 cm from the box, how far up the wall does it reach?

13. The vertical height of a pair of steps is 2·5 m when the feet are 60 cm apart. Find the length of a piece of cord which holds the steps together if it is 20 cm from the floor.

14. Find the width of a building 20 m away if a 30 cm ruler held 50 cm from an observer's eye just hides it.

15. If a poor marksman misses a target which is 30 m away by 5 cm by how much may he expect to miss a target which is 50 m away?

Example 2

In the following diagram, find (i) the length AD, (ii) the ratio of the areas of the triangles DEC and AEM. (Δ DEC : Δ AEM)

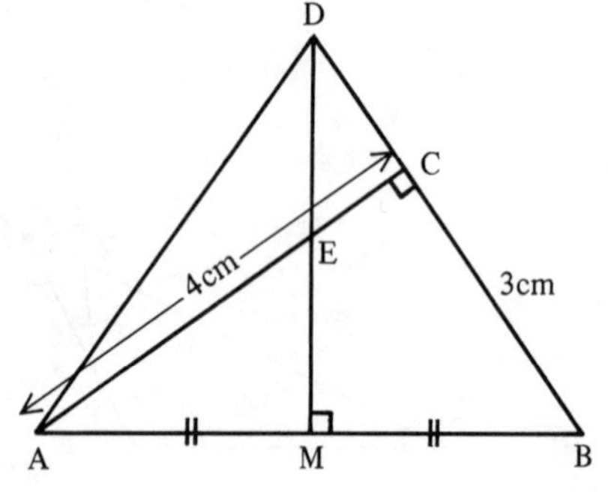

Given The diagram as drawn.

To find (i) the length AD
(ii) the ratio ΔDEC : ΔAEM.

Proof

(i) In triangles MDB and CAB, $\hat{B}$ is common and

$D\hat{M}B = A\hat{C}B$ (90° given)

$M\hat{D}B = C\hat{A}B$ (third angles in the triangle)

$\therefore$ triangle MDB is similar to triangle CAB

Hence $\dfrac{DB}{AB} = \dfrac{DM}{AC} = \dfrac{MB}{CB}$

In the right-angled triangle ABC:

$$AB^2 = AC^2 + BC^2 = 3^2 + 4^2 = 25$$

$$\therefore \quad AB = \sqrt{25} = 5 \text{ cm}$$

$$\therefore \quad MB = 2{\cdot}5 \text{ cm} \qquad (AM = MB, \text{ given})$$

$$\therefore \quad \frac{DB}{5} = \frac{2{\cdot}5}{3}$$

and $3DB = 5 \times 2{\cdot}5$

$$DB = \frac{5 \times 2{\cdot}5}{3} = 4\tfrac{1}{6} \text{ cm.}$$

Because DM is perpendicular to AB, and AM = MB, triangle DAB is isosceles and AD = DB

$\therefore$ AD = $4\frac{1}{6}$ cm.

(ii) In triangles DEC and AEM,

$D\hat{C}E = A\hat{M}E$ (each 90°)

$D\hat{E}C = A\hat{E}M$ (vertically opposite angles)

$E\hat{D}C = E\hat{A}M$ (third angles in the triangle)

$\therefore$ triangle DEC is similar to triangle AEM, and their areas are proportional to the squares of corresponding sides.

or $\Delta DEC : \Delta AEM = DC^2 : AM^2$.

$AM = 2{\cdot}5$ cm; $DC = 4\frac{1}{6} - 3 = 1\frac{1}{6}$ cm

$$\therefore \quad \Delta DEC : \Delta AEM = (1\tfrac{1}{6})^2 : (2\tfrac{1}{2})^2$$

$$= \tfrac{49}{36} : \tfrac{25}{4} = 49 : 225$$

Exercise 5.8b

All lengths marked are in cm.

1.

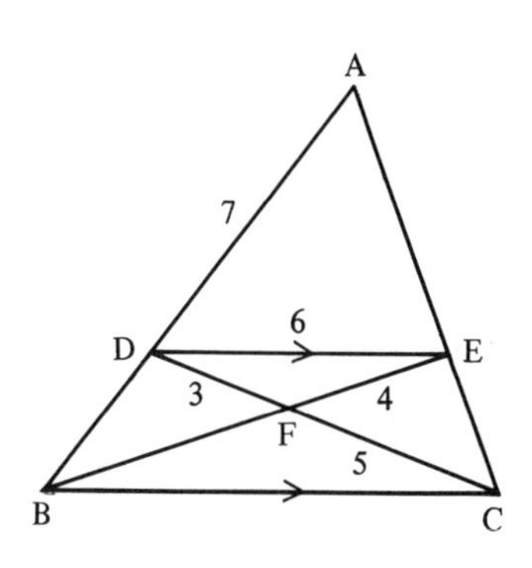

Find BD and BF, and the ratio ΔADE : ΔABC

2.

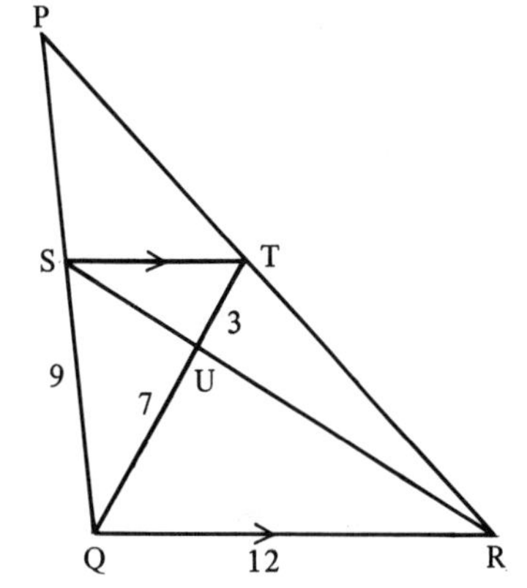

Find PS and ST, and the ratio (area of PST) : (area of STRQ)

3.

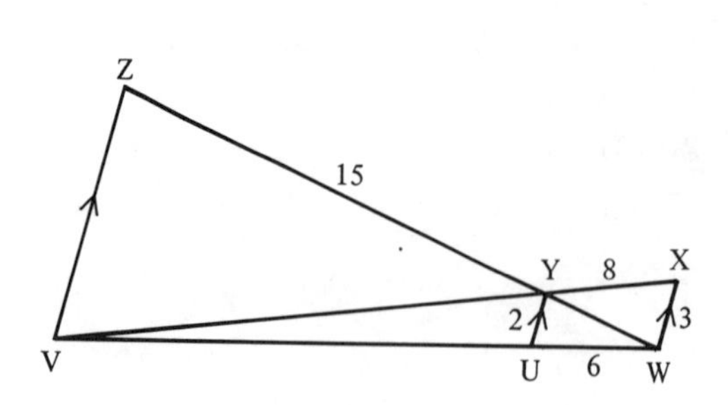

Find UV, VZ and VY, and the ratio
$\Delta UVY : \Delta UYW$

4.

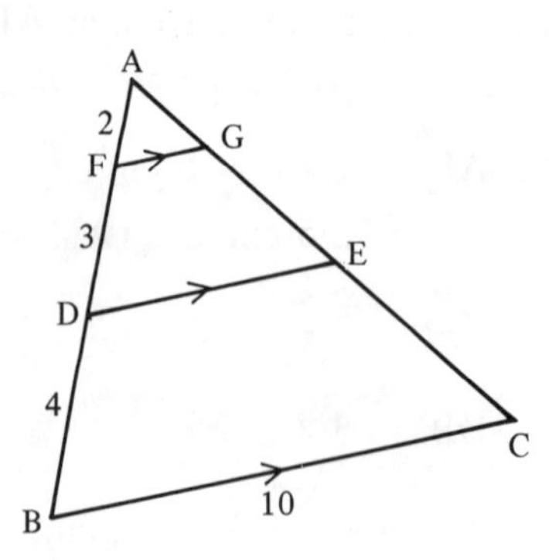

Find DE and FG and ratio
(area FGED) : (area DECB)

5.

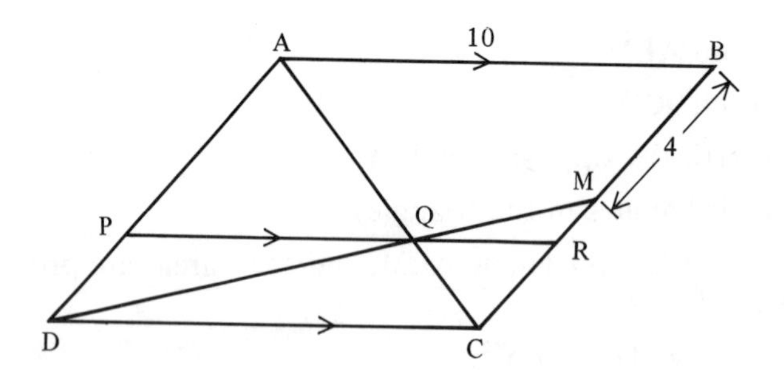

ABCD is a parallelogram with AB = 10 cm and BC = 8 cm. M is the mid-point of BC.
Find PQ, MR, and the ratios $\Delta DPQ : \Delta QRM$, and $\Delta DPQ : \Delta QRC$.

6. In question 5, if M had been a point such that the ratio BM : MC = 2 : 1, find the ratios DQ : QM, PR : RQ and $\Delta QRM : \Delta PQD$.

7.

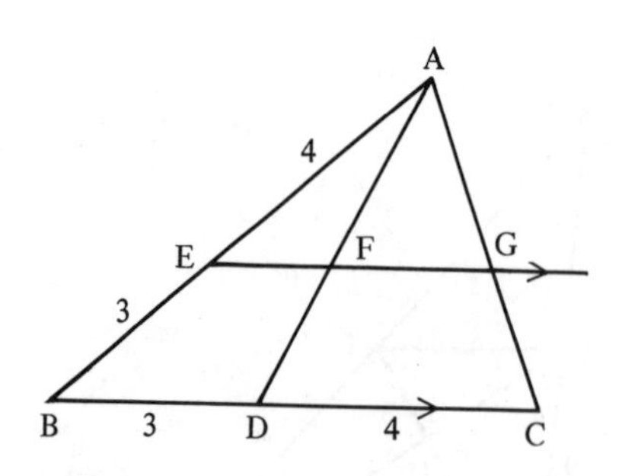

Find EF, FG, and the ratio
$\Delta AEF : \Delta AFG$

8.

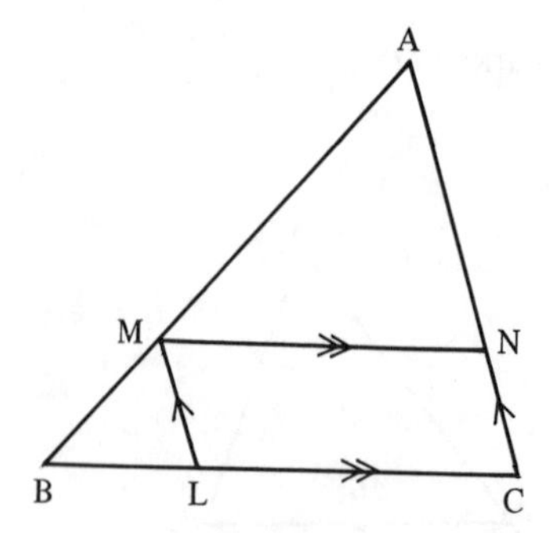

If the ratio $\Delta AMN : \Delta BML = 9 : 4$, find the ratio (area ABC) : (area MNCL)

Miscellaneous exercise 5a

1. Construct a triangle with sides 6 cm and 8 cm and altitude 5 cm. (N.B. the base is the side whose length is *not* given.)
2. Construct a square of side 7 cm. Measure its diagonals.
3. Construct a square whose diagonals are 10 cm. Measure its sides.
4. Construct a rectangle whose sides are 6 cm and 8 cm. Measure its diagonals.
5. Construct a rectangle whose diagonals are 12 cm long with an angle of 60° between them. Measure the shorter side.
6. Construct a quadrilateral ABCD with AB = 6 cm, BC = 3·4 cm, CD = 5 cm, DA = 5·6 cm and BD = 5·2 cm. Measure AC.
7. Draw a triangle of sides 6, 9 and 10 cm. On the 10 cm base BC construct another triangle DBC of half the area of triangle ABC but so that angle D = angle A. Measure DB.
8. Draw two circles of radii 2 cm and 3 cm respectively with their centres 7 cm apart. Construct a circle of radius 3·5 cm to touch both circles externally. How far is its centre from the other centres? Now construct another circle of radius 5 cm to touch the 3 cm circle externally and the 2 cm circle internally. How far is its centre from that of the 3·5 cm circle?

9.

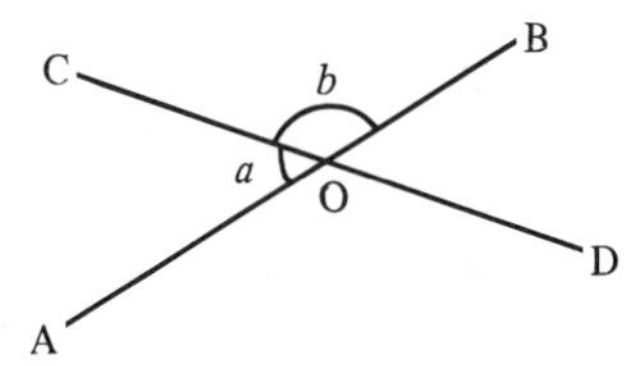

If $C\hat{O}A = B\hat{O}D$ and $a + b = 180^\circ$, prove that COD is a straight line.

10.

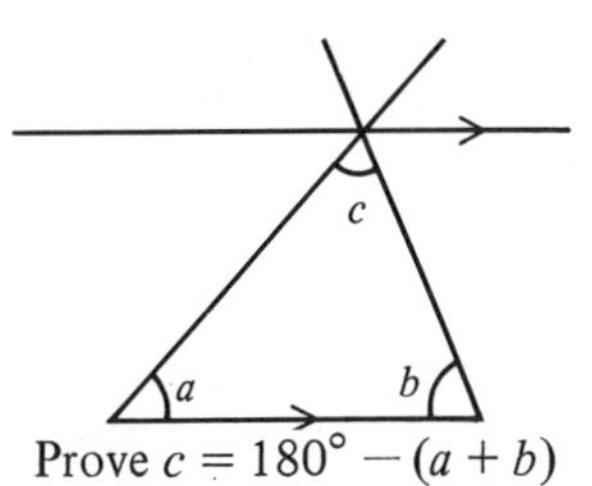

Prove $c = 180^\circ - (a + b)$

11. Find n.

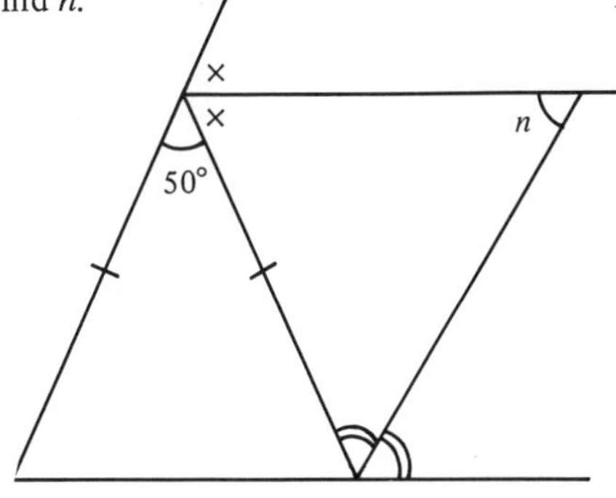

12. Find p and q.

13. ABCD is a square. An arc centre A cuts BC at M and CD at N. Prove CM = CN.
14. Two circles, centres O and P, cut at A and B. OP cuts the common chord AB at N. Prove angle AON = angle NOB and that AN = NB.
15. L, M, and N are the mid-points of sides AB, BC, and CD of square ABCD. Prove angle AML = angle DMN.
16. ABCD is a square. The side AB is produced to P and the side BC is produced to Q so that BP = CQ. DP cuts BC at L and AQ cuts DC at M. Prove BL = CM.
17. ABCD is a quadrilateral. AD = BC and AC = BD. If AC and BD cut at P prove PD = PC.

5.9 Quadrilaterals

A quadrilateral is a plane figure bounded by four straight lines. The sum of its interior angles is 360°.
Special quadrilaterals are:

1. A *parallelogram* is a quadrilateral with its opposite sides equal and parallel. Its opposite angles are equal. The diagonals bisect each other, but are not equal.

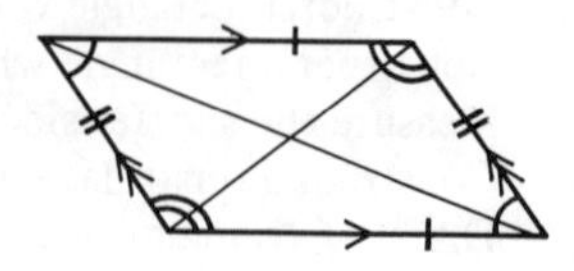

2. A *rhombus* is a parallelogram with all its sides equal. Its diagonals bisect one another at right angles, but are not equal.

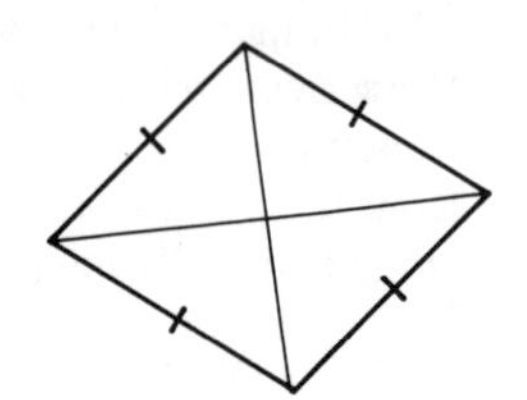

3. A *rectangle* is a parallelogram, with all its angles right angles. Its diagonals are equal and bisect one another.

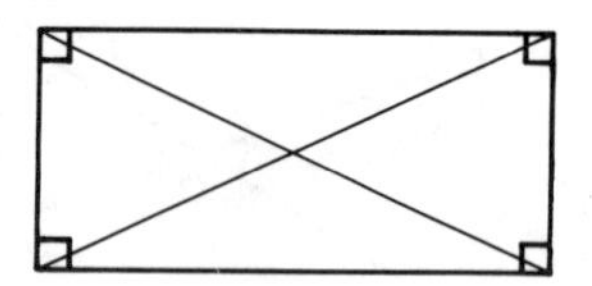

4. A *square* is a parallelogram with all its sides equal and all its angles right angles. Its diagonals bisect each other at right angles and are equal in length.

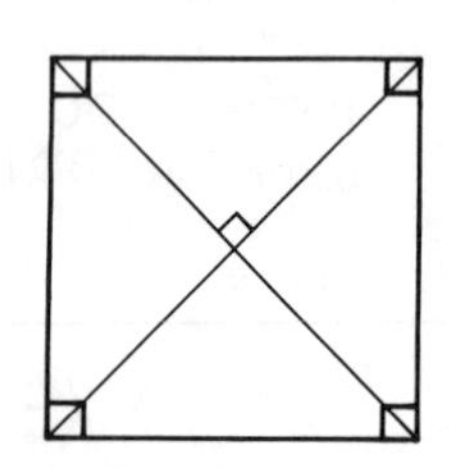

5. A *trapezium* is a quadrilateral with one pair of opposite sides parallel. An *isosceles* trapezium has its non-parallel sides equal.

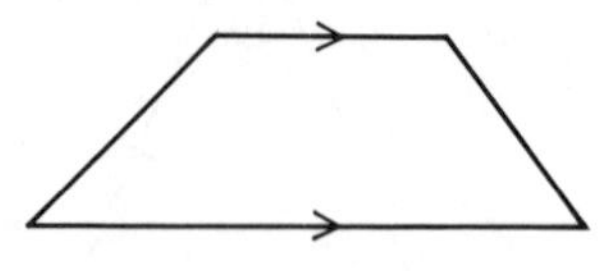

6. A *kite* is a quadrilateral consisting of two isosceles triangles on the opposite sides of the same base. The diagonals are perpendicular to each other, but are unequal in length; one diagonal is bisected by the other.

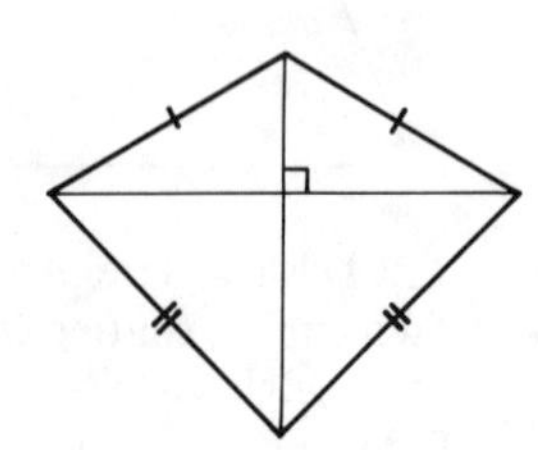

Example 1

In the following diagram, ABCD is a rectangle in which the diagonals intersect at X. If $D\hat{B}C = 37°$, find $A\hat{X}B$, giving reasons.

Calculation

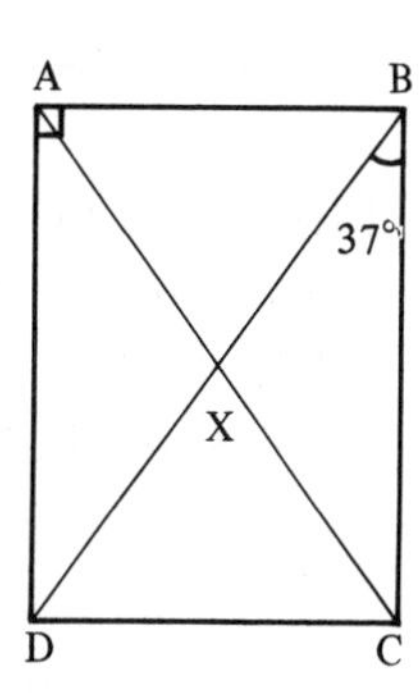

$A\hat{B}D = 53°$ (90° − 37°, ABCD is a rectangle)

$B\hat{A}X = 53°$ (diagonals of a rectangle are equal, and bisect each other, so AX = BX)

$\therefore A\hat{X}B = 74°$ (sum of angles in Δ AXB)

Example 2

ABCD is a parallelogram in which $A\hat{B}C = 43°$. A line through A meets CD at E and $A\hat{E}D = 68°$. Calculate, with reasons, (i) $D\hat{A}E$ (ii) $B\hat{C}D$.

Calculation

(i) $A\hat{D}E = 43°$ (opposite to $A\hat{B}C$ in parallelogram ABCD)

$\therefore D\hat{A}E = 69°$ (sum of angles in triangle ADE)

(ii) $B\hat{C}D = 137°$ (AB is parallel to DC: allied angles)

Exercise 5.9

1. In the rectangle ABCD, the diagonals intersect at E. If $A\hat{D}E = 60°$, find $E\hat{C}B$ and $A\hat{E}B$.
2. In the parallelogram ABCD, $B\hat{D}C = 30°$. Find $A\hat{B}D$.
3. In the rhombus ABCD, $B\hat{A}D = 140°$. Find the $A\hat{B}D$ and $A\hat{D}C$.
4. In the rhombus PQRS, $Q\hat{S}R = 29°$. Find $P\hat{S}Q$.
5. ABCD and ABPQ are parallelograms on opposite sides of AB. If $B\hat{A}D = 110°$ and angle $P\hat{Q}A = 70°$, find $P\hat{B}C$.
6. ABCD is a parallelogram and E is a point on DC such that AD = DE. If $D\hat{A}E = 36°$, find $A\hat{B}C$.
7. ABCD is a rhombus and M is the mid-point of DC. BD and AM intersect at N. If $D\hat{B}C = 30°$ and $D\hat{A}M = 40°$, find $B\hat{N}M$ and $A\hat{M}C$.
8. Find the angles of a parallelogram in which one angle is three times the other.
9. ABCD is a rhombus and ABPQ a square outside it. If $A\hat{B}C = 100°$, find $D\hat{A}Q$ and $A\hat{Q}D$.
10. ABCD is a square. A line through A cuts BD at M and BC at N. If $M\hat{A}C = 10°$ find the size of the angles of triangle AMD and of angle ANC.
11. ABCD is a parallelogram whose diagonals intersect at E. $D\hat{A}C = 50°$, $A\hat{B}D = 45°$, and $D\hat{E}C = 80°$. Find $A\hat{C}D$ and the exterior angle at D.
12. ABCD is a parallelogram and ADE is an equilateral triangle inscribed in it. AB = AE and $D\hat{E}B$ (reflex) is 250°. Find $B\hat{C}D$.
13. ABCD is a square. The bisector of $B\hat{A}C$ cuts BD at L, BC at M and DC produced at N. Find $A\hat{M}C$, $A\hat{L}D$, and $A\hat{N}C$.

5.10 Pythagoras' Theorem

The theorem of Pythagoras states that:
In any right-angled triangle, the square on the hypotenuse is equal to the sum of the squares on the other two sides.

So in this diagram

$$BC^2 = AB^2 + AC^2$$
or $$AB^2 = BC^2 - AC^2$$
or $$AC^2 = BC^2 - AB^2$$

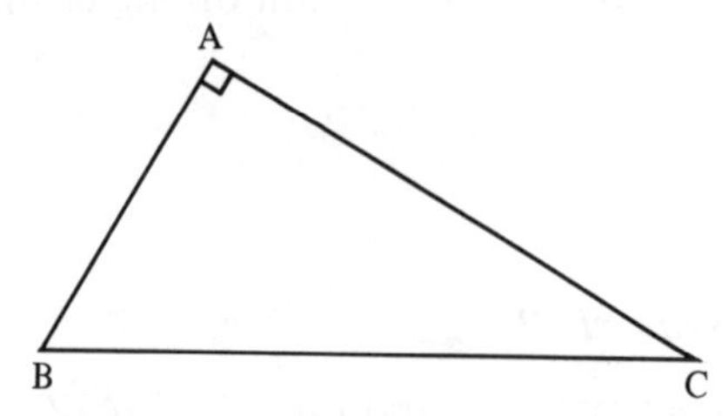

One of the chief uses of this theorem is in the calculation of sides and diagonals in plane and solid figures as the following examples illustrate.

Example 1

In triangle ABC, right-angled at A, AB = 7 cm, AC = 40 cm. Calculate the length of BC, correct to 1 decimal place.

Using the theorem of Pythagoras:

$$BC^2 = AB^2 + AC^2$$
$$BC^2 = 7^2 + 40^2$$
$$BC^2 = 49 + 1600$$
$$BC = \sqrt{1649}$$

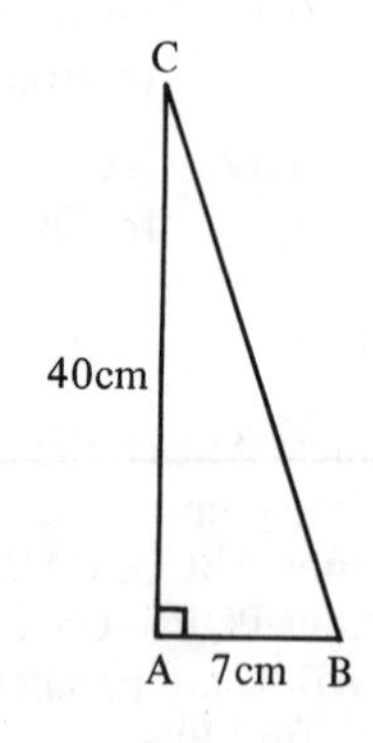

and using square root tables

$$BC = 40{\cdot}61$$
$$= 40{\cdot}6 \quad \text{(to 1 D.P.)}$$

Example 2

ABCD is a rectangle, in which AC = 12·5 cm, and AB = 7·5 cm. Calculate the length of BC. Hence find the area of rectangle ABCD.

Using right-angled triangle ABC and the theorem of Pythagoras:

$$AC^2 = AB^2 + BC^2$$
$$12{\cdot}5^2 = 7{\cdot}5^2 + BC^2$$
$$12{\cdot}5^2 - 7{\cdot}5^2 = BC^2$$
$$156{\cdot}25 - 56{\cdot}25 = BC^2$$
$$\therefore \quad BC = \sqrt{100} = 10 \text{ cm}$$
$$\therefore \quad \text{Area of ABCD} = AB \times BC = 7{\cdot}5 \times 10$$
$$= 75 \text{ cm}^2$$

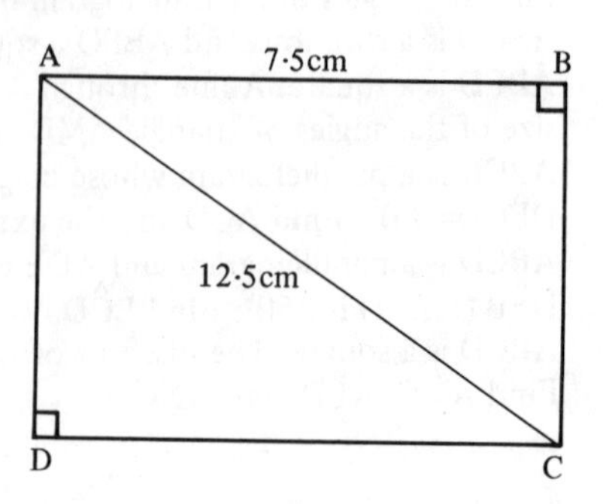

Example 3

In the following diagram, calculate the length of the diagonal EC.

(a) Using right-angled triangle ABC, calculate the length of AC.

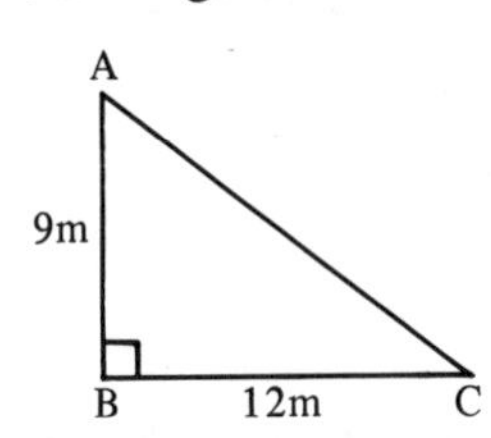

$$AC^2 = AB^2 + BC^2$$
$$AC^2 = 9^2 + 12^2$$
$$AC^2 = 81 + 144$$
$$AC = \sqrt{225}$$
$$AC = 15 \text{ m.}$$

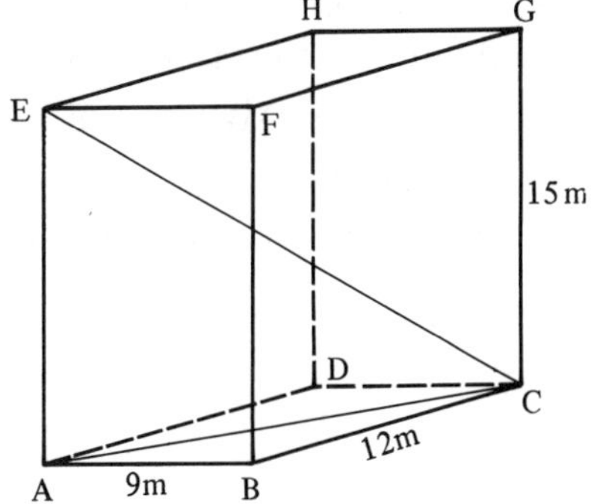

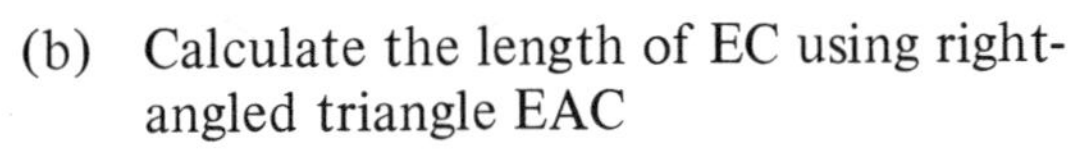
(b) Calculate the length of EC using right-angled triangle EAC

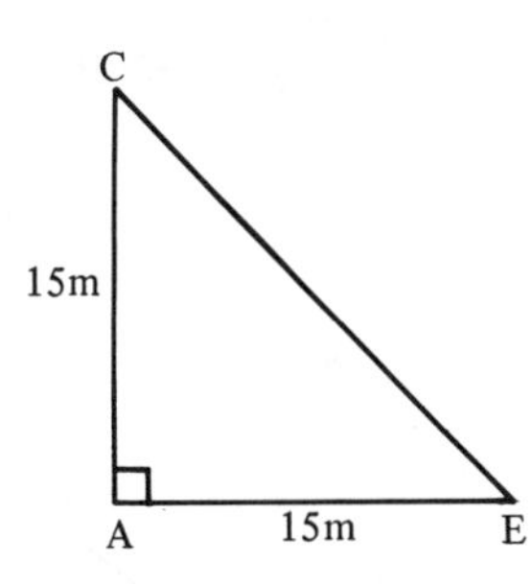

$$EC^2 = AC^2 + AE^2$$
$$EC^2 = 15^2 + 15^2$$
$$EC^2 = 225 + 225$$
$$EC = \sqrt{450}$$
$$EC = 21{\cdot}21 \text{ m} = 21{\cdot}2 \text{ m (to 1 D.P.)}$$

Exercise 5.10

1. Find the hypotenuse of each of the following right-angled triangles whose sides are
   (a) 5 cm; 12 cm (b) 7 cm; 24 cm (c) 9 cm; 10 cm
   (d) 47 cm; 50 cm (e) 2·146 cm; 3·922 cm
2. Find the third side of each of the following right-angled triangles whose hypotenuse and one side are
   (a) 10 cm; 8 cm (b) 9 cm; 7 cm (c) 12·4 cm; 11 cm
   (d) 92 cm; 81 cm (e) 4·182 cm; 3·604 cm
3. A 5 m ladder is placed with its foot 2 m from a wall. How high up the wall will it reach?
4. The mast of a ship is 11 m high and the width of the deck is 4 m. How long is the rope securing the top of the mast to the side of the deck?
5. Find the altitude of an equilateral triangle of side 6 cm.
6. Find the length of the diagonal of a square of side 6 cm.
7. Find the slant height of a cone of base radius 10 cm and perpendicular height 20 cm.
8. Find the width of a rectangle of length 24 cm and diagonal 28 cm.
9. A rhombus of side 5 cm has one diagonal 8 cm long. Find the length of the other diagonal and the area of the rhombus.
10. Find the length of the longest thin stick that can be fitted into a rectangular box 32 cm long by 16 cm high and 8 cm wide.
11. The foot of the ladder in question **3** is now pulled out from the wall a further 50 cm. How far down the wall does its top slide?
12. A pendulum is 1 m long and is swinging so that the distance between the extreme positions of the weight is 20 cm. How high does the weight rise by the time it gets to the end of its swing?

5.11 Chords

A chord of a circle is a straight line joining any two points on the circumference.

1. The line joining the centre of a circle to the mid-point of a chord, is perpendicular to that chord
   $\therefore\ O\hat{M}A = O\hat{M}B = 90°$
   Conversely, the line drawn from the centre of a circle perpendicular to a chord bisects that chord.

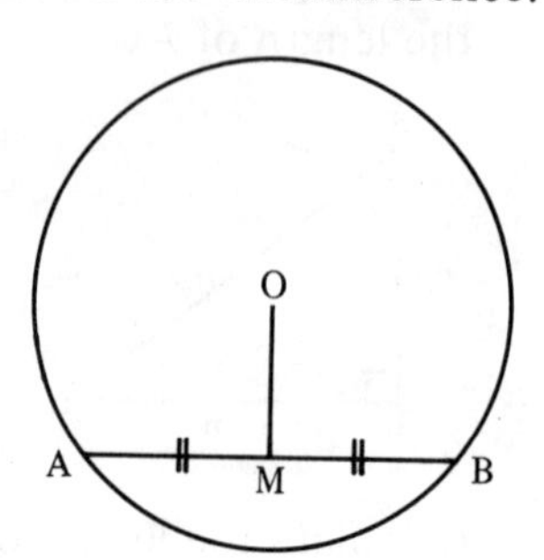

2. Equal chords are the same distance from the centre. Thus if X is the mid-point of AB and Y is the mid-point of CD, then OX = OY.

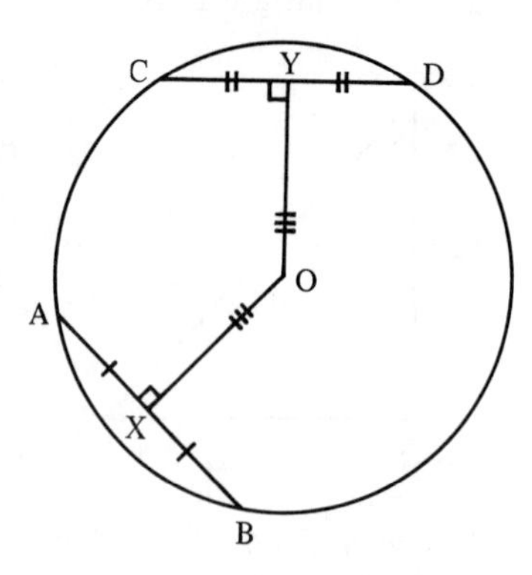

Example 1

In a circle of radius 7 cm, calculate the distance from the centre of a chord 6 cm long.

Let AB be the chord, with mid-point M and the centre of the circle is O.

Then triangle AOM is right-angled at M.
Using the theorem of Pythagoras,

$$MA^2 + MO^2 = OA^2$$
$$3^2 + MO^2 = 7^2$$
$$MO^2 = 7^2 - 3^2$$
$$MO = \sqrt{40} = 6{\cdot}33 \text{ cm (to 3 S.F.)}$$

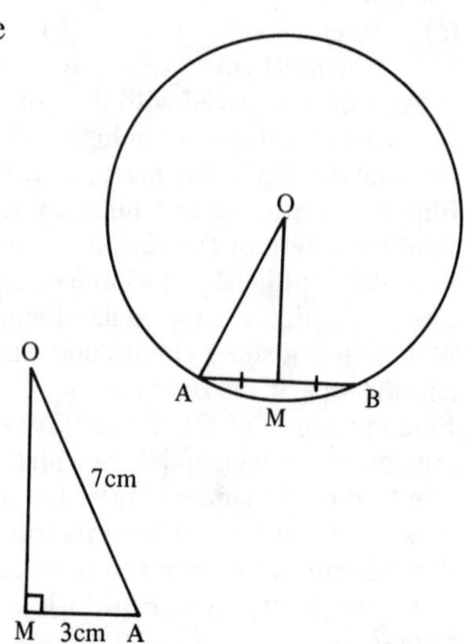

Example 2

A bowl in the shape of a hemisphere has an internal diameter of 24 cm and is partly filled with water so that the diameter of the surface of the water is 20 cm. How far from the top of the bowl is the surface of the water?

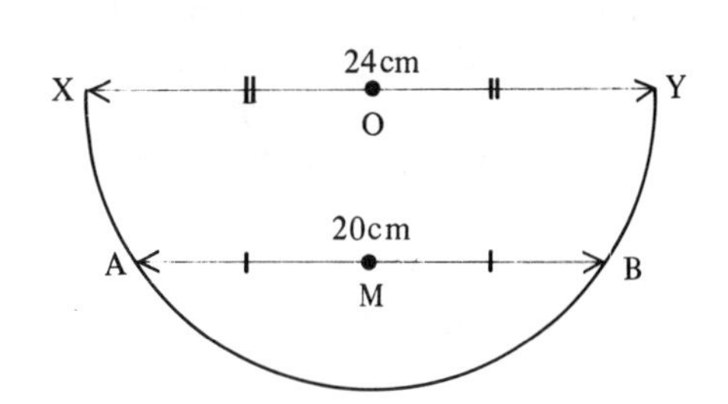

Let the mid-point of the diameter of the bowl be O, and the mid-point of the diameter of the surface of the water be M. Then OM is the required depth, and $O\hat{M}B = 90°$.

By Pythagoras' theorem in triangle OMB:

$$OM^2 + MB^2 = OB^2$$
$$OM^2 + 10^2 = 12^2$$
$$OM^2 = 12^2 - 10^2$$
$$OM = \sqrt{44}$$
$$OM = 6{\cdot}633 \text{ cm}$$
$$= 6{\cdot}63 \text{ cm (to 3 s.f.)}$$

∴ the water is 6·63 cm from the top of the bowl.

Exercise 5.11

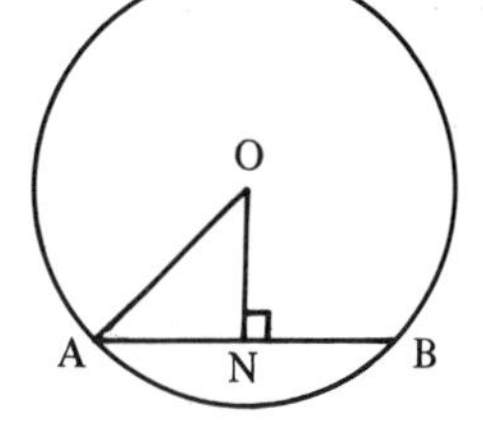

1. In the diagram on the right, O is the centre of the circle.
   (a) If AN = 6 cm, find AB
   (b) If ON = 3 cm, and AB = 8 cm, find AO
   (c) If OA = 13 cm and AB = 24 cm, find ON
   (d) If ON = 2 cm and OA = 7 cm, find AB
   (e) If AB = 16 cm and ON = 5 cm, what is the diameter of the circle?
2. PQ and XY are parallel chords of a circle of radius 10 cm. Their lengths are 19 cm and 5 cm respectively. How far apart are PQ and XY if
   (a) they are on the same side of the centre?
   (b) if they are on opposite sides of the centre?
3. A circle circumscribes a rectangle of sides 6 cm and 4 cm. What is the length of its radius?
4. A circle circumscribes a square of area 150 cm^2. What is its radius?
5. Find the area of an isosceles triangle of base 20 cm and circumscribed by a circle of radius 15 cm.
6. Find the distance between the opposite sides of a regular hexagon which is inscribed in a circle of radius 18 cm.
7. Two equal circles intersect so that the length of their common chord is 10 cm. Their centres are 19 cm apart. Find their radii.
8. Two circles of radii 8 cm and 15 cm intersect. Their common chord is 12 cm long. How far apart are their centres?
9. AB and CD are perpendicular chords of a circle centre O and radius 6 cm. They intersect at X. If AB = 10 cm and CD = 8 cm, find the length of OX.
10. AB and AC are perpendicular chords of a circle centre O and radius 12 cm. If AB = 10 cm, how long is AC?

5.12 Angles in a circle

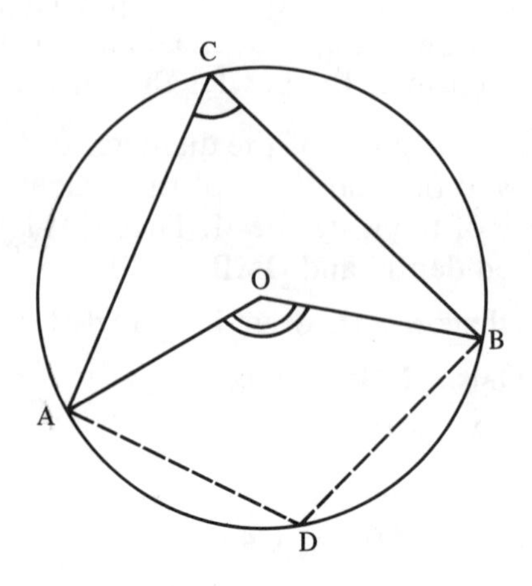

If AB is an arc or a chord of a circle, centre O, then the angle AOB is called the angle subtended at the *centre* by AB.
Similarly the angle ACB is called the angle subtended at the *circumference* by AB.
The following angle properties should be known.

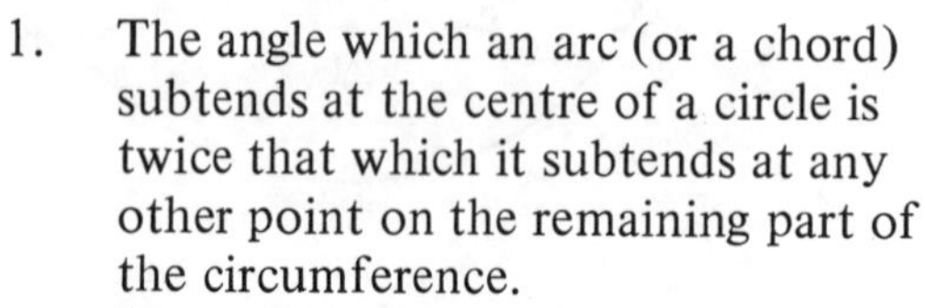

1. The angle which an arc (or a chord) subtends at the centre of a circle is twice that which it subtends at any other point on the remaining part of the circumference.
   Hence from the above diagram

$$A\hat{O}B = 2\,A\hat{C}B$$

and reflex $A\hat{O}B = 2\,A\hat{D}B$

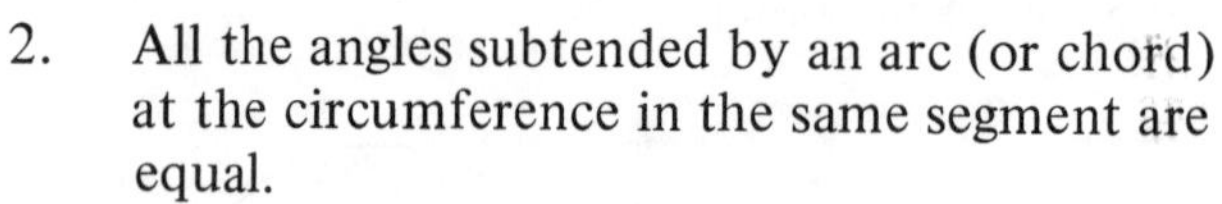

2. All the angles subtended by an arc (or chord) at the circumference in the same segment are equal.
   Hence $A\hat{C}B = A\hat{D}B = A\hat{E}B$.

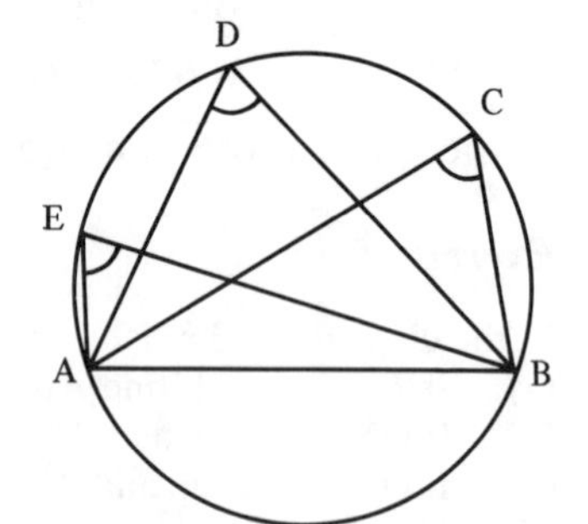

3. Equal chords (or arcs) subtend equal angles at the circumference.
   Hence $A\hat{Y}B = C\hat{X}D$

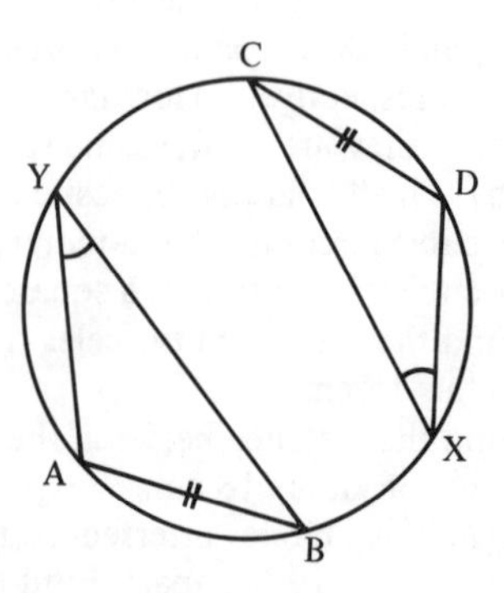

4. The angle subtended at the circumference by a diameter of a circle is 90°.
   Hence $A\hat{D}B = A\hat{C}B = 90°$

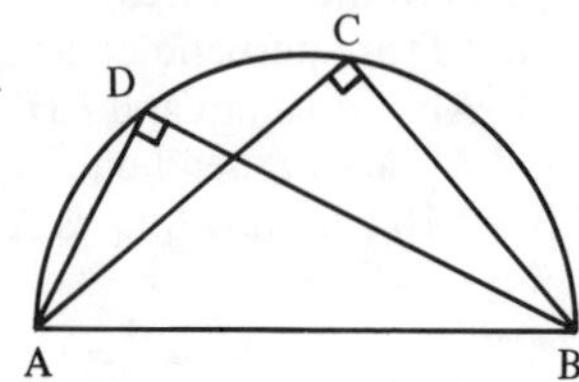

Note. Many questions on the circle will require knowledge of the four properties above of angles in a circle.

Example

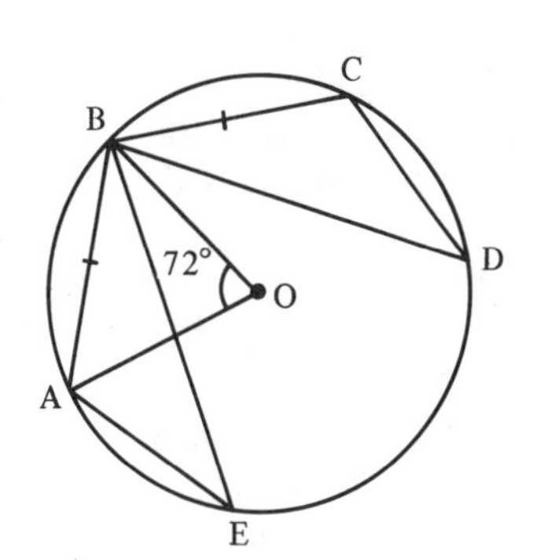

A, B, C, D, E, are five points in order on the circumference of a circle, centre O.
If AB = BC, and $A\hat{O}B = 72°$, find, giving reasons,
(a) $A\hat{E}B$, (b) $B\hat{D}C$.

$B\hat{E}A = 36°$ ($B\hat{O}A = 2\,B\hat{E}A$)

$B\hat{D}C = 36°$ (equal chords, AB and BC subtend equal angles)

Exercise 5.12

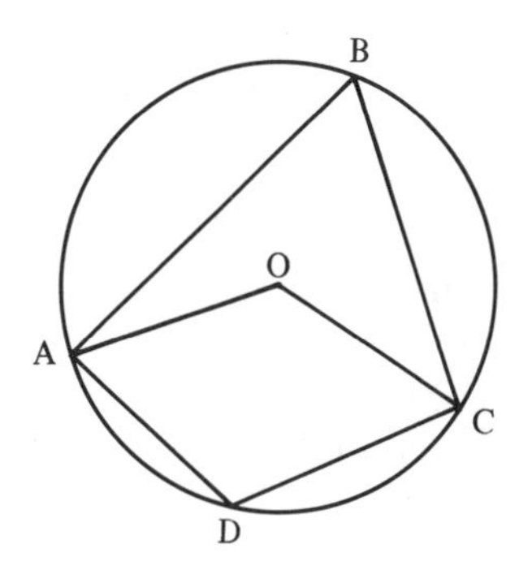

1. In the diagram on the right
   (a) If $A\hat{O}C = 140°$, find $A\hat{B}C$ and $A\hat{D}C$
   (b) If $A\hat{B}C = 60°$, find $A\hat{O}C$ and $A\hat{D}C$
   (c) If $A\hat{O}C$ reflex $= 200°$, find $A\hat{B}C$
   (d) If $A\hat{B}C = 80°$, find $O\hat{A}C$
   (e) If $O\hat{C}A = 20°$, find $A\hat{D}C$.

2. In the diagram on the right
   (a) If $A\hat{E}B = 40°$, find $A\hat{C}B$ and $A\hat{B}O$
   (b) If $A\hat{E}B = 50°$ and $B\hat{E}C = 45°$, find $C\hat{A}O$
   (c) If AD = BD, $A\hat{D}B = 40°$ and $A\hat{O}B = 120°$, find $B\hat{A}O$, $O\hat{A}D$ and $A\hat{C}E$.
   (d) If $A\hat{O}B = 110°$ and $A\hat{D}B = 40°$, find $D\hat{A}C$ and $A\hat{P}B$
   (e) If AD = BD, $E\hat{P}C = 90°$ and $E\hat{D}C = 46°$, find $A\hat{O}B$.
3. A, B, C and D are points on the circumference of a circle. $D\hat{C}B = 80°$ and $D\hat{B}C = 50°$. Find $B\hat{A}C$ and $B\hat{D}C$.
4. AB and CD are two perpendicular chords of a circle. If $A\hat{B}D = 40°$, find $C\hat{A}B$.
5. A diameter AB and a chord CD of a circle are produced to meet in E. If $A\hat{E}C = 30°$ and $D\hat{A}C = 20°$, find $B\hat{A}D$.
6. A chord SR is parallel to the diameter PQ of a circle. RP bisects $S\hat{P}Q$. Find $S\hat{Q}P$ and $S\hat{P}Q$.
7. AB is the diameter of a circle and C and D are two points on the circumference on the same side of AB. AD = DC. If $D\hat{A}B = 70°$, find the size of $A\hat{D}C$.
8. A, B and C, are points on the circumference of a circle centre O such that OABC is a parallelogram. Find $C\hat{O}A$.
9. ABCD is a quadrilateral inscribed in a circle. BC = CD. AB is parallel to DC and $D\hat{B}C = 50°$. Find $A\hat{D}B$.
10. ABCDE is a pentagon inscribed in a circle. AE = ED. $A\hat{E}B = 20°$, $C\hat{E}D = 40°$ and $B\hat{E}C = 60°$. Calculate the angles of the pentagon.

5.13 Cyclic quadrilaterals

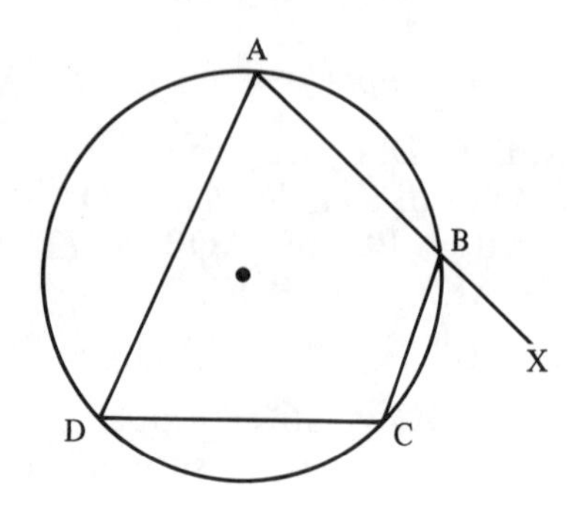

Points which lie on the circumference of the same circle are called cyclic (or concyclic) points.
A cyclic quadrilateral is a quadrilateral with all its four corners on the circumference of the same circle.
In any cyclic quadrilateral:

(a) the opposite interior angles are supplementary
(b) the exterior angle is equal to the opposite interior angle.

Thus, in the above figure, ABCD is a cyclic quadrilateral.

So: $D\hat{A}B + D\hat{C}B = 180°$

$A\hat{D}C + A\hat{B}C = 180°$

and the exterior angle $C\hat{B}X = A\hat{D}C$

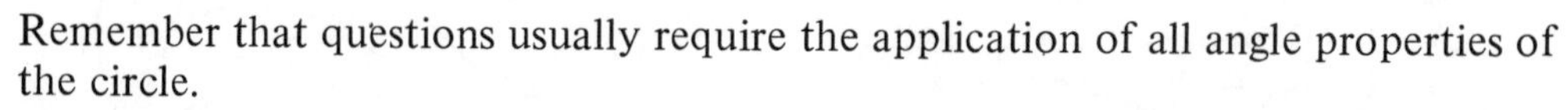

Remember that questions usually require the application of all angle properties of the circle.

Example

If O is the centre of the circle on the right, find the size of $\hat{e}$, giving reasons.
Letter the diagram ABCD as shown, then

$A\hat{C}D = 90°$ (angle subtended at circumference by the diameter AOD)

$B\hat{A}C = B\hat{C}A = \hat{e}$ (equal chords, BC, AB, and CD, subtend equal angles at the circumference).

$B\hat{A}D + B\hat{C}D = 180°$ (opposite angles in the cyclic quadrilateral ABCD)

But $B\hat{A}D = B\hat{A}C + C\hat{A}D = \hat{e} + \hat{e} = 2\hat{e}$

and $B\hat{C}D = B\hat{C}A + A\hat{C}D = \hat{e} + 90°$

$\therefore\ 2\hat{e} + \hat{e} + 90° = 180°$ ($B\hat{A}D + B\hat{C}D = 180°$)

$3\hat{e} = 90°$

$\therefore\ \hat{e} = 30°$

Exercise 5.13

Find the unknown marked angles (following the alphabetical order). State the reasons clearly for each statement you make. Any point marked O is the centre of a circle.

1.

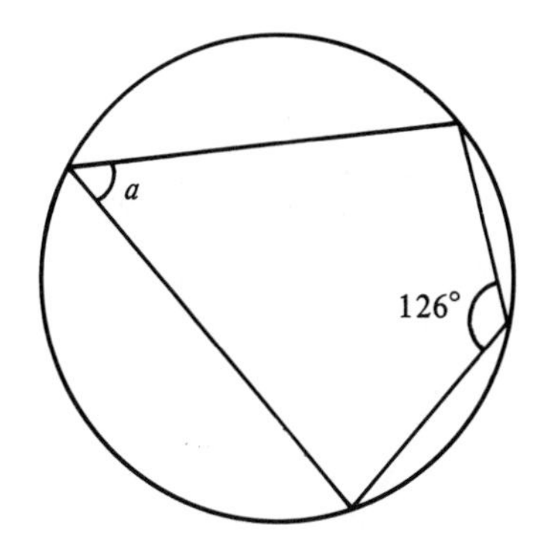

2.

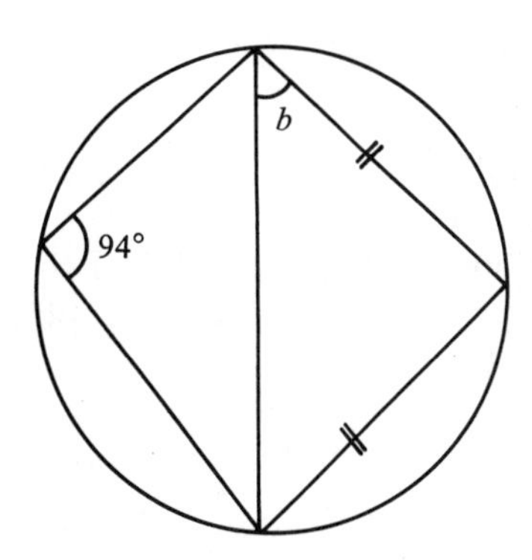

3.

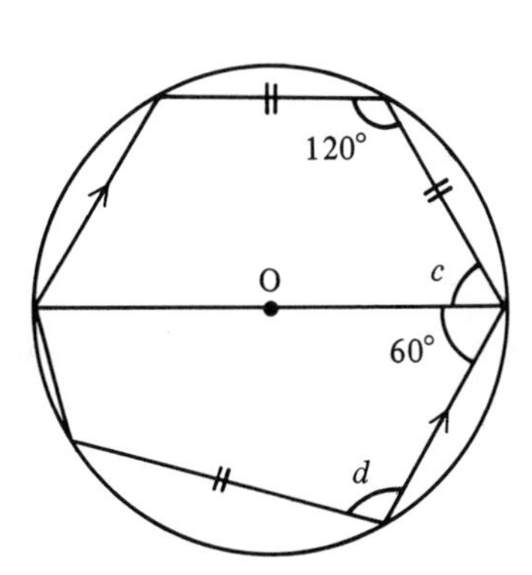

4.

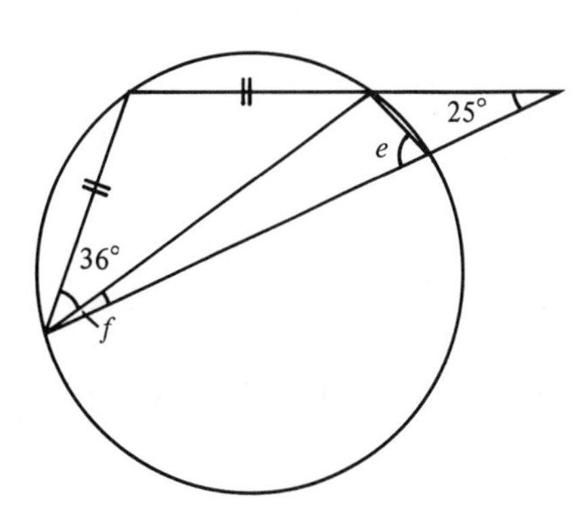

5.

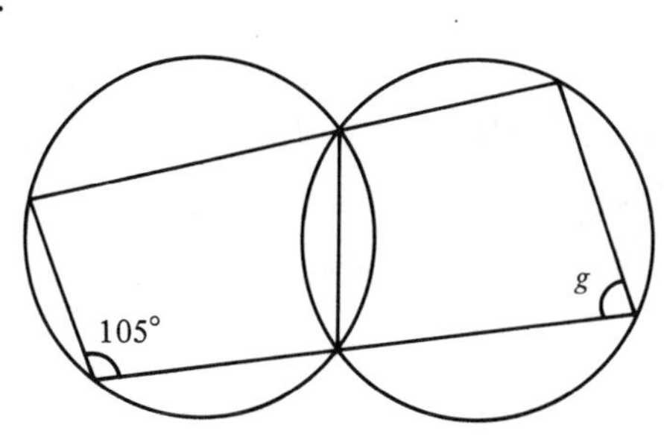

6.

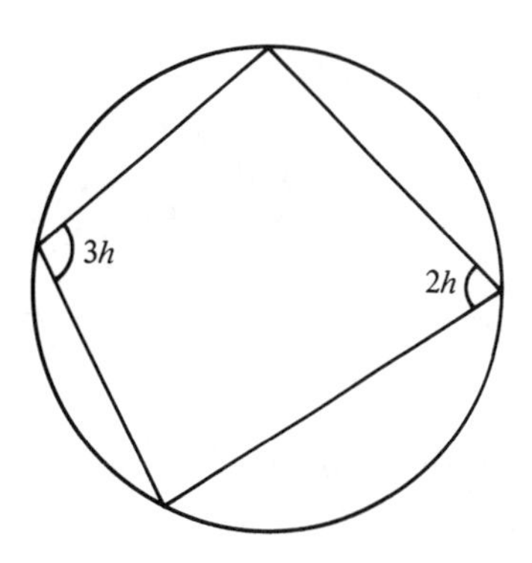

7.

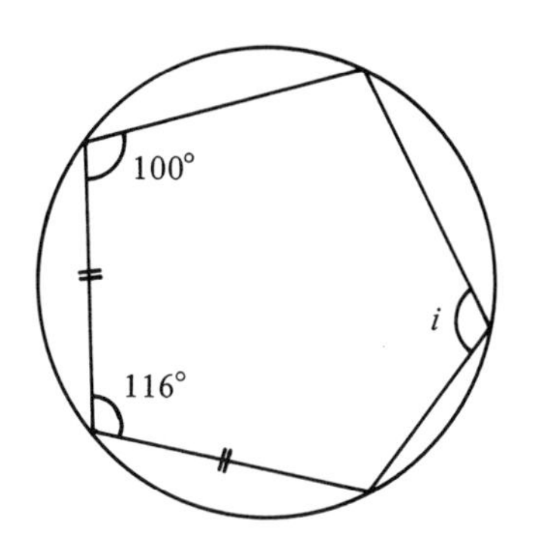

8.

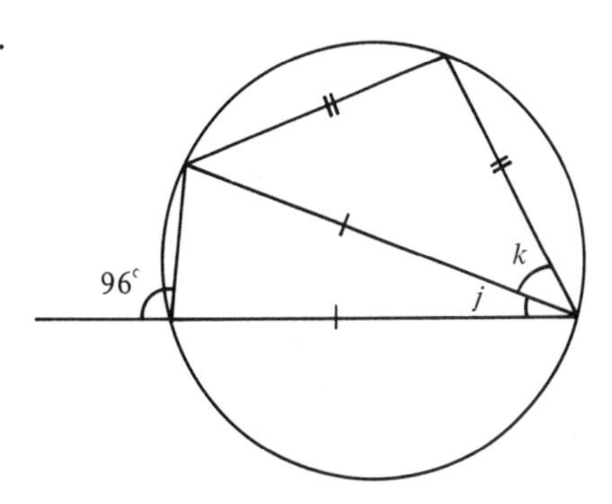

5.14 Tangents

1. A tangent is a straight line which touches the circumference of a circle at one point only and is at right angles to the radius at this point of contact.
2. Two and only two tangents can be drawn to a circle from a point outside the circle. These tangents are equal in length.

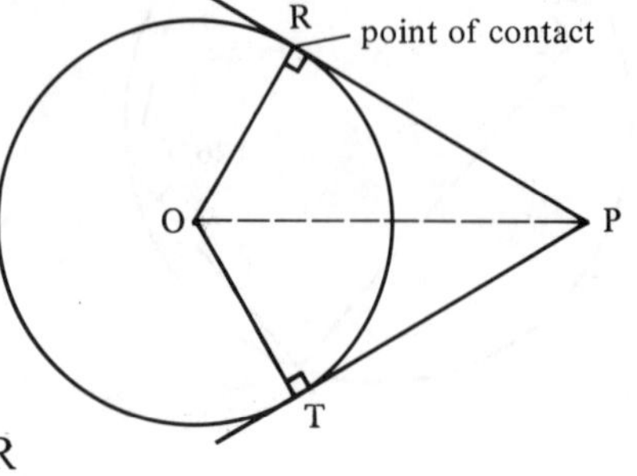

From the above figure $PT = PR$

and $R\hat{O}T + R\hat{P}T = 180°$

If OP is joined, then

$R\hat{P}O = T\hat{P}O$

and $R\hat{O}P = T\hat{O}P$.

Note. Questions involve either calculation of angles using the above angle properties together with other angle properties of the circle, or calculations of length using the theorem of Pythagoras or trigonometric ratios.

Example 1

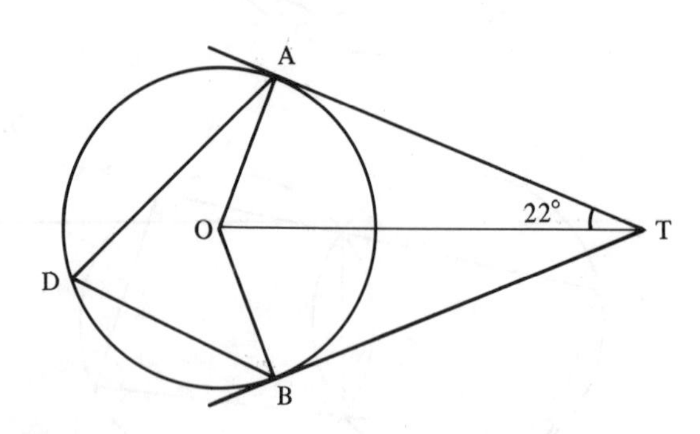

Calculate with reasons (a) $O\hat{A}T$ (b) $A\hat{O}B$ (obtuse) (c) $A\hat{D}B$

(a) $O\hat{A}T = 90°$ (angle between radius and tangent at the point of contact)

(b) $B\hat{T}O = 22°$ (OT bisects $A\hat{T}B$)

$A\hat{T}B = 44°$ ($B\hat{T}O + A\hat{T}O$)

∴ $A\hat{O}B$ (obtuse) $= 136°$ ($A\hat{T}B + A\hat{O}B = 180°$)

(c) $A\hat{D}B = 68°$ ($A\hat{O}B = 2\ A\hat{D}B$).

Example 2

From a point T two tangents are drawn to a circle centre O, touching the circle at A and B respectively. If OA = 10 cm and AT = 24 cm calculate, (a) the length of OT (b) the size of AOB (to the nearest degree).

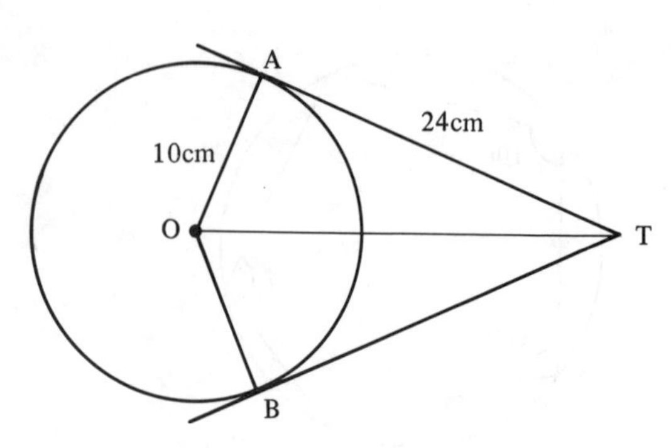

(a) Because OA is a radius and AT is a tangent, then $O\hat{A}T = 90°$.

Using the theorem of Pythagoras

$OT^2 = AT^2 + AO^2 = 24^2 + 10^2 = 576 + 100$

$OT = \sqrt{676} = 26$ cm.

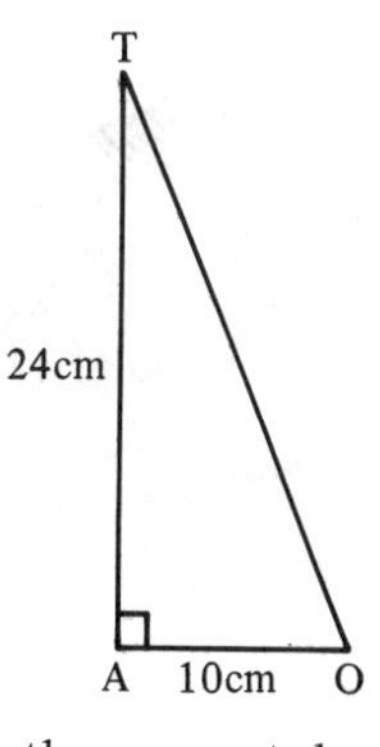

(b) Also in this triangle

$\tan T\hat{O}A = \frac{TA}{AO} = \frac{24}{10} = 2{\cdot}4$

$\therefore \quad T\hat{O}A = 67°\,23'$

But $\quad T\hat{O}A = B\hat{O}T \quad$ and $A\hat{O}B = T\hat{O}A + B\hat{O}T$

$\therefore \quad A\hat{O}B = 67°\,23' \times 2 = 134°\,46' = 135°$ (to the nearest degree).

Exercise 5.14

1. In the diagram on the right
   (a) If OA = 3 cm and AT = 4 cm, find OT.
   (b) If $A\hat{T}B = 70°$ find $A\hat{O}T$.
   (c) If AT = 9 cm and PT = 5 cm, find OA.
   (d) If $A\hat{P}T = 130°$, find $A\hat{T}O$.
   (e) If OA = 6 cm and AT = 12 cm, find PT.
   (f) If $A\hat{P}O = 50°$, find $P\hat{A}T$ and $P\hat{T}A$.
   (g) If OA = 4 cm and PT = 4 cm, find $A\hat{T}O$.
   (h) If $O\hat{T}A = 30°$ and OA = 7 cm, find AP.
   (i) If OA = 7 cm and AT = 24 cm, find AB.
   (j) If AB = $4\frac{4}{5}$ cm and AT = 4 cm, find OA.
2. A circle touches the sides of a quadrilateral ABCD at W, X, Y and Z. If the angles of ABCD are 60°, 80°, 100° and x, find x and the angles of WXYZ.
3. A circle touches the sides AB, AC, and BC of a triangle ABC at P, Q, and R. If AP = 4 cm, CQ = 3 cm and BR = 2 cm, find the lengths of the sides of the triangle.
4. The sides AB and AC of triangle ABC are produced. An escribed circle, centre O, touches AB produced and AC produced internally and BC externally. If $\hat{A} = 50°$ and $A\hat{C}B = 66°$, find $B\hat{O}C$.
5. If in question **4**, $B\hat{O}C$ now equals 80° and BO = OC, find $\hat{A}$.
6. AB is a tangent to a circle centre O, touching the circle at B. If the radius of the circle is 5 cm and AO is 10 cm, find the radius of another circle centre O with tangent AB′, such that the area of triangle AB′O equals the area of triangle ABO.

5.15 The alternate segment

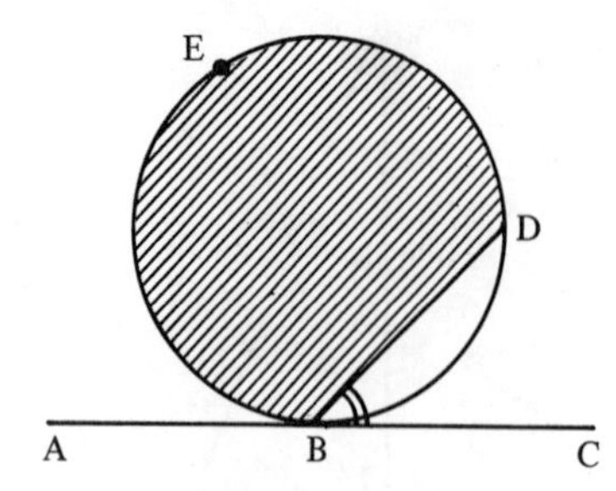

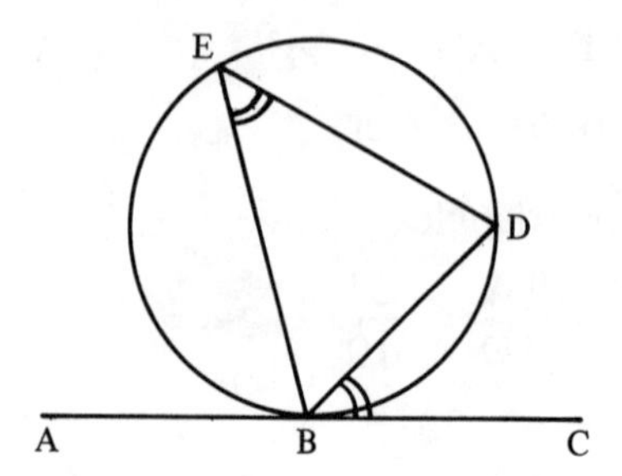

In the above diagrams,

(a) the shaded segment BED is called the *alternate segment* to the angle CBD.

(b) the angle between a tangent to a circle and a chord drawn through the point of contact is equal to any angle subtended by the chord at the circumference in the alternate segment.

Hence $C\hat{B}D = B\hat{E}D$

Note. Questions on angle properties of the circle usually require knowledge of more than one angle property.

Example 1

Find with reasons (a) $A\hat{B}C$, (b) $A\hat{D}C$, (c) $P\hat{A}B$.

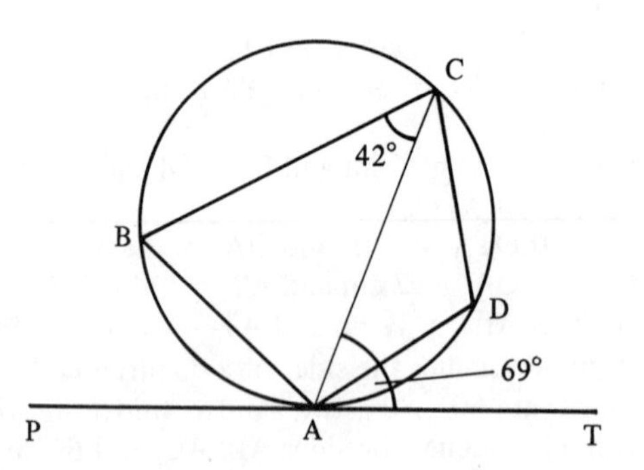

(a) $A\hat{B}C = 69°$ (in the alternate segment)

(b) $A\hat{D}C = 111°$ (ABCD is a cyclic quadrilateral)

(c) $P\hat{A}B = 42°$ (in the alternate segment)

Example 2

AB is the diameter of a circle, and C is on the circumference so that $B\hat{A}C = 35°$. If the tangent at C meets AB produced at T, calculate (a) $A\hat{C}B$, (b) $B\hat{C}T$, (c) $C\hat{T}A$, giving reasons.

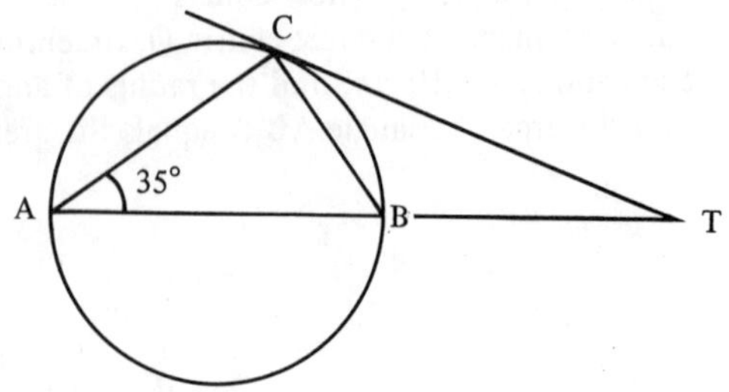

(a) $A\hat{C}B = 90°$ (AB is a diameter)

(b) $B\hat{C}T = 35°$ (alternate segment)

(c) $A\hat{C}T = 125°$ ($A\hat{C}B + B\hat{C}T$)

$\therefore$ $C\hat{T}A = 20°$ (sum of angles in triangle ACT)

Example 3

AB and AC are tangents to a circle, and CD is a chord parallel to AB. If $B\hat{A}C = 42°$, calculate, with reasons, (a) $B\hat{C}D$, (b) $B\hat{D}C$.

(a) $A\hat{B}C = 69°$ (AB = AC)
$B\hat{C}D = 69°$ (alternate angles because AB is parallel to CD)

(b) $B\hat{D}C = 69°$ (alternate segment)

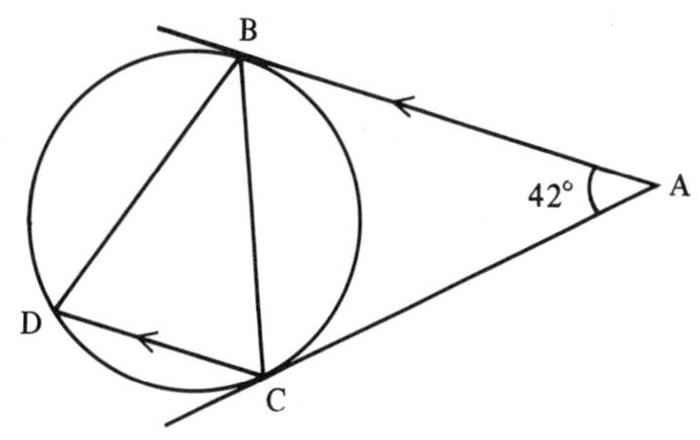

Exercise 5.15

1. In the diagram on the right
   (a) If angle $u = 85°$ and angle $v = 30°$, find the other angles of the triangle TDC.
   (b) If angle $y = 40°$ and angle $v = 77°$, find angles u and w.
   (c) If angle $x = 68°$ and angle $y = 31°$, find angles u, v and w.
   (d) If DT = DC and angle $y = 44°$, find angle u.
   (e) If DT = TC and angle $v = 72°$, find angle w.

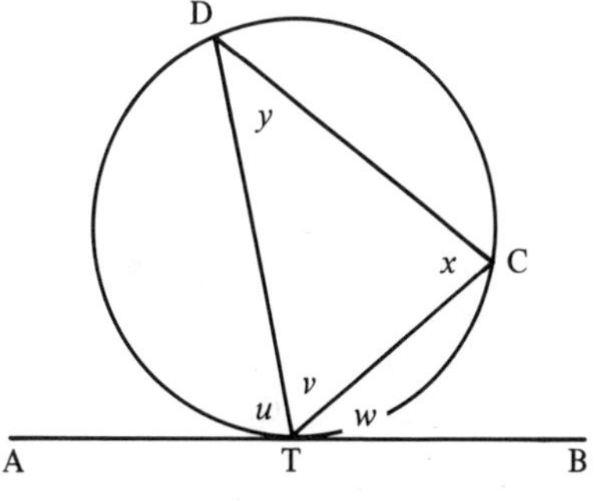

2. A, B and C are three points on the circumference of a circle. The tangents at A and B meet in T. If $A\hat{T}B = 84°$, find $A\hat{C}B$. (Give both possible answers.)
3. The angles of a triangle are 50°, 60° and 70°. Its inscribed circle touches its sides in A, B and C. Find the angles of the triangle ABC.
4. PT is a tangent to a circle PQRS. If PQ = QR and angle PRQ = 24°, find $T\hat{P}R$ and $P\hat{S}R$.
5. XPY is the tangent to the circumcircle of quadrilateral PQRS. If SP bisects $X\hat{P}R$ and QP bisects $Y\hat{P}R$ and $P\hat{Q}R = 80°$, find $P\hat{R}Q$ and $P\hat{S}R$.
6. The tangent at C to the circumcircle of triangle ABC meets AB produced at T. If $\hat{A} = 40°$ and $A\hat{C}T = 124°$, find the angles of triangle BCT.
7. AB and AC are tangents to a circle. CD is a chord parallel to AB. If $B\hat{A}C = 56°$, find the angles of triangle BCD.
8. AB and DC are two parallel chords of a circle. The tangent at A meets CD produced at T. If $D\hat{A}C = 47°$ and $C\hat{A}B = 36°$, find $A\hat{T}C$.
9. Two circles touch internally at T and ATB is their common tangent. RWV is a straight line such that RT and VT are chords of the larger circle which cut the smaller circle at S and U respectively, and WT is a chord of the smaller circle.
   (a) If $A\hat{T}R = 70°$, $B\hat{T}V = 45°$, and $U\hat{T}W = 20°$, find $T\hat{S}W$ and the angles of the triangle SWR.
   (b) If $U\hat{W}V = U\hat{V}W = 35°$, find the new size of $T\hat{S}W$. Find also $S\hat{W}T$.
   (c) If STUW is now a square of side 14 cm, find the length of SR.
10. Two circles intersect at A and B. From P, a point on one circle lines PAD and PBC are drawn to meet the other circle in D and C. If $A\hat{P}B = 40°$ and the tangent at P makes an angle of 50° with AP, find the angles of the quadrilateral ABCD.

5.16 Intersecting chords

1. If two chords of a circle AB and CD intersect at a point X inside the circle, then XA.XB = XC.XD.

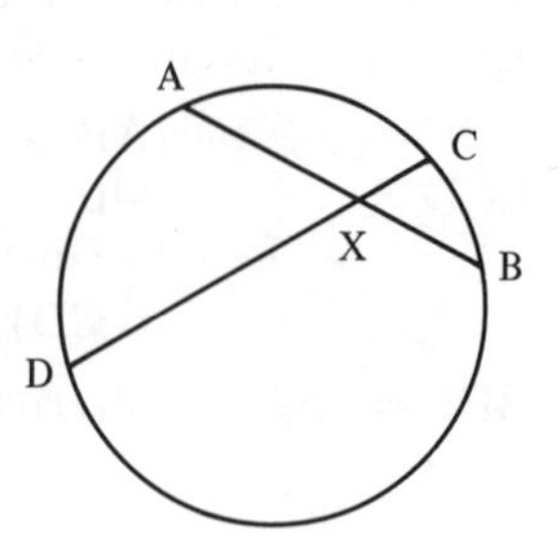

2. If two chords of a circle AB and CD intersect at a point X outside the circle, then XA.XB = XC.XD.

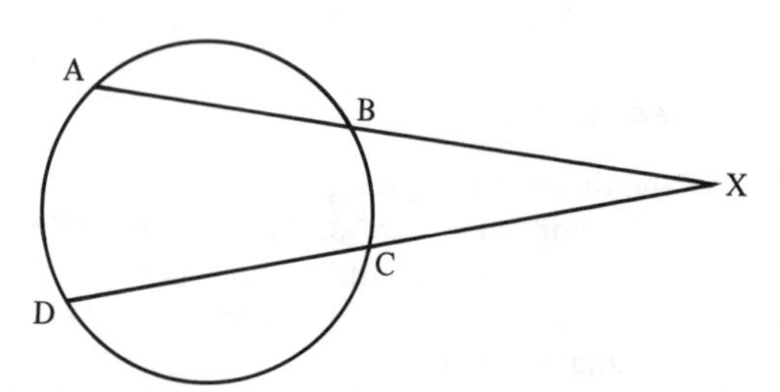

3. If the points B and A become closer together, they will eventually coincide at the point T, and ABX will become the tangent TX. Then

$$XT.XT = XC.XD$$

or

$$XT^2 = XC.XD.$$

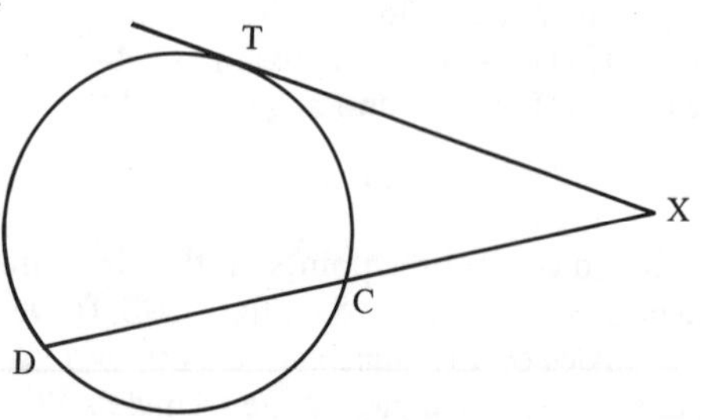

Example 1

The chords AB and CD of a circle meet at a point X inside the circle. If AX = 2·4 cm, XB = 5 cm, and CX = 8 cm, calculate the length of DX.

Hence $XA.XB = XC.XD$

so $2{\cdot}4 \times 5 = 8\ XD$

$12 = 8.XD$

$\dfrac{12}{8} = XD$

$XD = 1{\cdot}5$ cm.

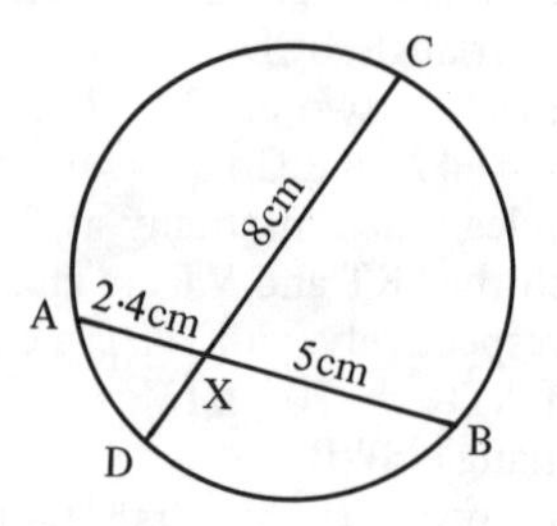

Example 2

The chords AB and CD of a circle when produced meet at a point X outside the circle. If AX = 7·2 cm, BX = 5 cm, and XD = 12 cm, calculate the length of XC.

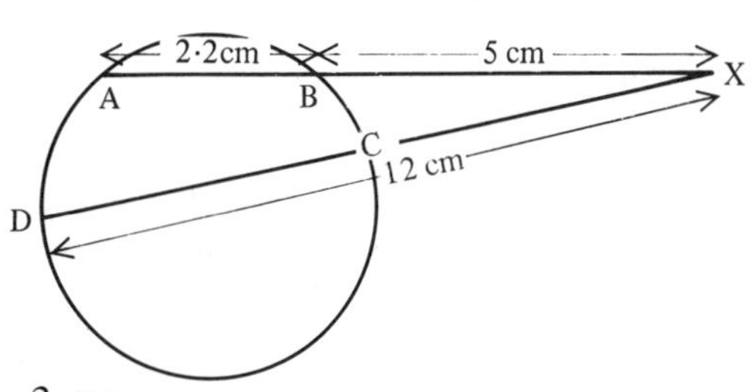

$$XA.XB = XC.XD$$
$$7{\cdot}2 \times 5 = (12 - CD) \times 12$$
$$36 = 144 - 12\,CD$$
$$12CD = 108$$
$$CD = 9 \text{ cm}$$
$$\therefore \quad XC = XD - CD = 12 - 9 = 3 \text{ cm.}$$

Example 3

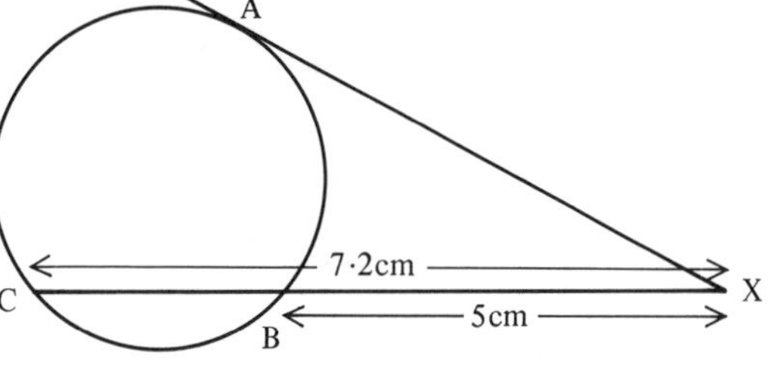

From a point X outside a circle, a tangent XA is drawn touching the circle at A, and a line XBC is drawn from X cutting the circle at B and C. If XC = 7·2 cm and XB = 5 cm, calculate the length of XA.

$$XA^2 = XB.XC$$
$$= 5 \times 7{\cdot}2 = 36$$
$$XA = 6 \text{ cm.}$$

Exercise 5.16

1. In the figure on the right
   (a) If AX = 2 cm, BX = 7 cm and CX = 3 cm, find DX.
   (b) If CX = 4 cm, DX = 5 cm and AX = 10 cm, find BX.
   (c) If AB = 11 cm, AX = 6 cm and XD = 2 cm, find CD.
   (d) If CX = 2 cm, XD = 8 cm and AX = XB, find AB.
   (e) If AX = XB = 6 cm and CX = 4XD, find CD.
   (f) If CD is a diameter and CD is perpendicular to AB, find (i) the radius of the circle when AB = 8 cm and XD = 2 cm,
   (ii) the length of AB when CX = 25 cm and XD = 4 cm.
2. In the figure on the right
   (a) If PX = 10 cm, QX = 3 cm and RX = 15 cm, find SX.
   (b) If PQ = 7 cm, QX = 3 cm and SX = 5 cm, find RS.
   (c) If PX = 8 cm, and QX = 2 cm, find XT.
   (d) If TX = 6 cm and PX = 9 cm, find QX.
   (e) If TX = 5 cm and QX = 2 cm, find PQ.

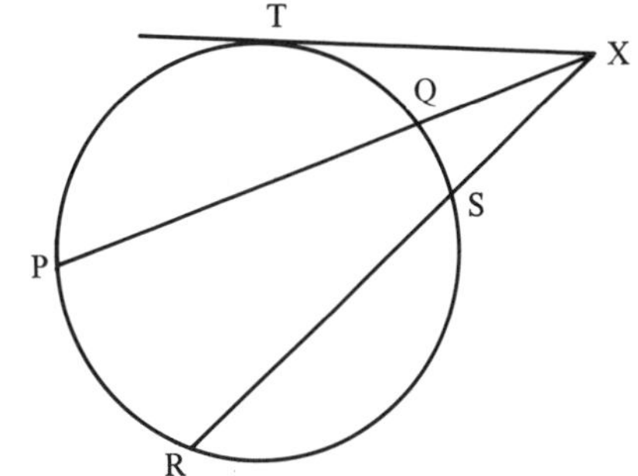

3. Two circles intersect at P and Q. A straight line cuts one circle at A and B, the other circle at C and D, and PQ at X. If AC = 10 cm, CX = 1 cm, XB = 2 cm and XQ = 5 cm, find PX and BD.

5.17 Angle bisector

The line which bisects an angle of a triangle internally divides the side opposite the angle in the ratio of the sides containing the angle.
Similarly, the bisector of the exterior angle divides the opposite side externally.

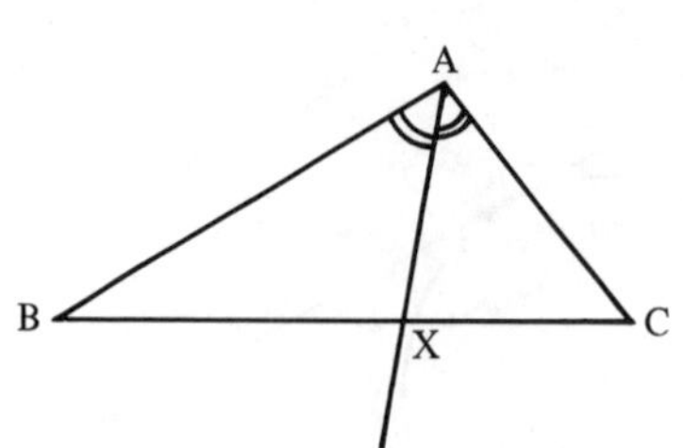

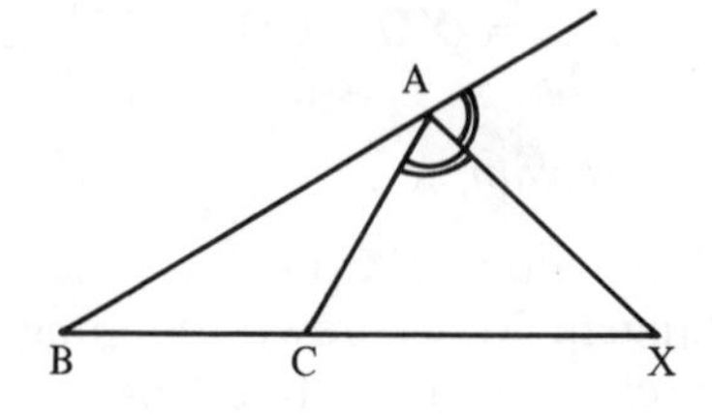

Hence AB : AC = XB : XC.

Example 1

ABC is a triangle right-angled at B. M is a point on AC so that BM bisects angle B. BN is the perpendicular from B to AC. If BC = 3 cm and AB = 4 cm, find the length of MN.
As $\hat{B}$ is bisected, then

$$AB : BC = MA : MC$$

$$4 : 3 = MA : MC$$

But $$AC = 5 \text{ cm}, (3^2 + 4^2 = AC^2)$$

$$\therefore \quad MC = \frac{3}{7} \text{ of } 5$$

$$= \frac{15}{7} \text{ cm}$$

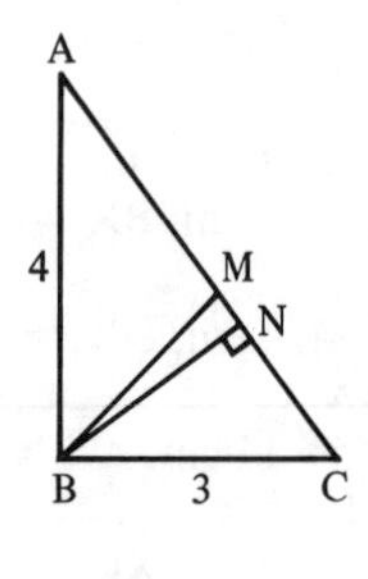

Triangle BNC is similar to triangle ABC.

$$\therefore \frac{NC}{BC} = \frac{BC}{AC}$$

$$\therefore \frac{NC}{3} = \frac{3}{5}$$

$$\therefore NC = \frac{9}{5} \text{ cm}$$

$$\therefore MN = MC - NC$$

$$= \frac{15}{7} - \frac{9}{5} = \frac{12}{35} \text{ cm.}$$

Example 2

In triangle ABC, D is on AC and BD bisects $A\hat{B}C$; E is on BC produced and BE bisects the external angle at B. If AD = 5, DC = 3, find AE.

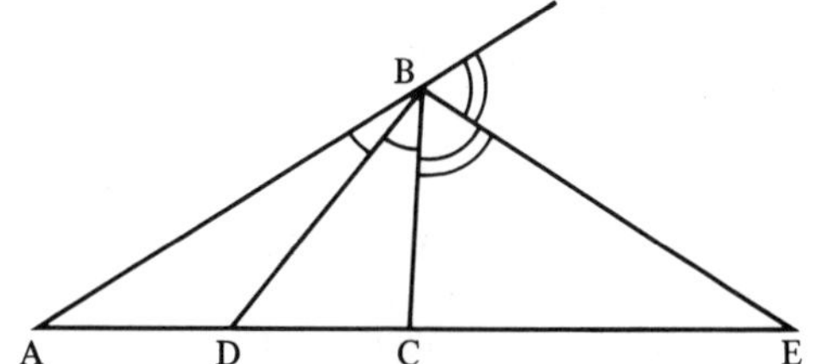

Because the angles at B are bisected,

AB : DC = AD : DC = AE : CE

∴ 5 : 3 = AE : CE

But CE = AE − (5 + 3)

∴ 5 : 3 = AE : (AE − 8)

5AE − 40 = 3AE ∴ AE = 20

Exercise 5.17

Questions 1 to 12 refer to the diagram. BD and BE are the internal and external bisectors of the angle B. Lengths may be taken as cm. Note that $D\hat{B}E$ is always a right angle.

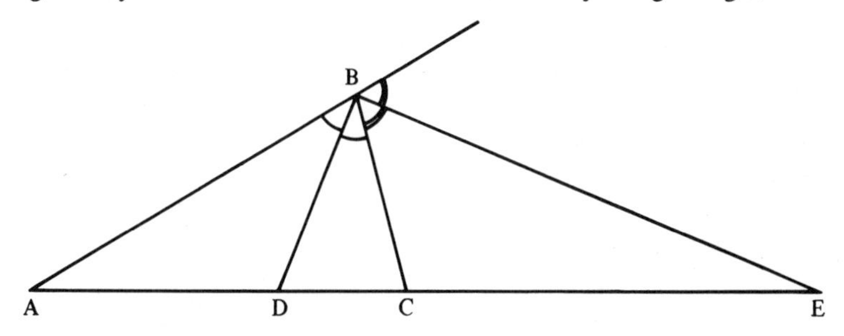

1. If AB = 8, BC = 2, and AD = 5, find DC.
2. If AD = 4, DC = 5, and BC = 6, find AB.
3. If AB = 6, BC = 4, and AE = 10, find CE.
4. If AB = 6, BC = 4, and CE = 8, find AC.
5. If AB = 8, BC = 3, and AC = 9, find CE.
6. If AB = 9, BC = 4, and AD = 6, find DE.
7. If DC = 2, CE = 15, and BC = 7, find AD and AB.
8. If AB = 7, BC = 5, and DE = 10, find AE.
9. If AB = 8, and AD = 2DC, find BC and the ratio DC : CE.
10. If AB = 5, BC = 4, BD = 2·7, and AD = 4, find DC and BE.
11. If AD = 6, and DC = 4, find CE.
12. If AB = $3\frac{1}{2}$, BC = 1, AC = 4, and M is the mid-point of AE, find DM.
13. I is the in-centre of triangle ABC. AC = 6, AB = 8, and BC = 9. AI, BI and CI are produced to meet the opposite sides in L, M, and N. Find the ratio BL : AM.
14. ABCD is a cyclic quadrilateral with DC = BC. Its diagonals intersect at X, so that DX = 4, AX = 6, and XC = 2. If AD = 5, find AB.
15. The angle B of triangle ABC is bisected by BP, P being a point on AC. M is the mid-point of BC and AM intersects BP at Q. If AP : PC = 4 : 3, find the ratio AQ : QM.
16. In quadrilateral ABCD, AB = 12 cm, BC = 9 cm, CD = 15 cm, and AD = 20 cm. The bisectors of angles B and D meet AC in L and M respectively. Find the length of ML.

5.18 Loci

The locus of a point is the path traced out by the point when it moves under certain conditions. All points which lie on the locus satisfy the condition.

Example 1

The locus of a point which moves on a plane at a given distance from a fixed point O, is a circle with centre O and the given distance its radius.

Example 2

The locus of a point on a plane, equidistant from two given intersecting straight lines MAN and XAY, is the pair of lines which bisect the angles between the lines.

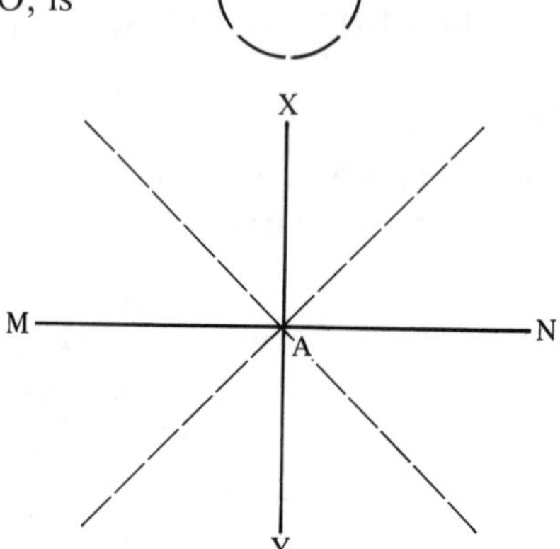

Example 3

The locus of a point P which moves on one side only of a straight line XY, so that the angle XPY is constant, is an arc of a circle passing through X and Y.

Note. If the angle is a right angle, the locus is a semicircle.

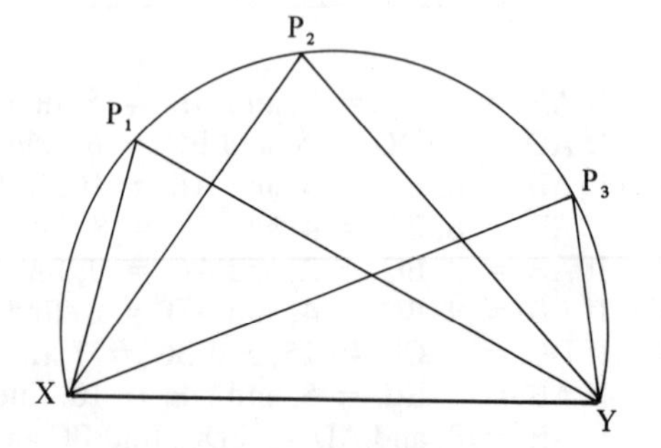

Exercise 5.18

Sketch and describe the following loci

1. The hub of a railway wheel running along a straight, horizontal railway line.
2. The nose of a donkey tethered to a peg if it keeps the rope taut.
3. The head of a small boy sliding down a flight of stairs on a tea tray.
4. The head of a dog secured to a chain which can slide along a straight wire.
5. The centre of a penny which rolls round the circumference of a five penny piece.
6. A monkey climbs half way up a ladder which is leaning against a wall. At this point the foot of the ladder slips away from the wall. Make a careful drawing of the locus of the monkey.
7. The centres of all circles that pass through two given points.
8. The centre of a circle that always passes through one given point.
9. A point that moves so that it is always equidistant from two given points.
10. A point that moves so that it is always equidistant from two parallel lines.
11. A point that moves so that it is always equidistant from two intersecting straight lines.
12. The centres of all circles that touch a given line at a given point.
13. The centres of all circles that touch a pair of intersecting straight lines.
14. The vertices of all triangles on a given base AB of length 10 cm and of area 50 cm^2.
15. The vertices of all right angled triangles of hypotenuse 10 cm.
16. A triangle has a base 20 cm long and is 400 cm^2 in area. If the vertex is fixed, find the locus of the foot of the perpendicular upon the base.
17. A straight line AB of length 20 cm moves so that its ends always lie on each of two perpendicular straight lines OX and OY (see question **6**). Perpendiculars are drawn to OX and OY from each position of A and B and intersect at C. Find the locus of C.
18. ABCD is a parallelogram made of rods of fixed length but loosely jointed at the corners. If AB is fixed, find the locus of the mid-point of CD.
19. Make an accurate drawing of an equilateral traingle ABC of side 10 cm. Find a point P which is equidistant from AB and AC and is 7 cm from B.
20. AB is a straight line and C a point 5 cm from it. Find the position of a point P which is 4 cm from AB and 6 cm from C.
21. ABC is a triangle right-angled at B. AB = 8 cm and BC = 12 cm in length. Find accurately the position of a point P which is equidistant from AB and AC and also equidistant from B and C.
22. Find the position of a point that is equidistant from all three sides of a triangle whose sides are 7, 8, and 10 cm long.
23. Find the position of a point that is equidistant from all three vertices of the triangle in question **22**.
24. X and Y are two fixed points in a plane and P is a variable point such that the area of triangle XYP is constant. Find the locus of P.

Miscellaneous exercise 5b

1. Draw a circle centre O radius 5 cm. Mark a point P which is 8 cm from O. Construct a line from P which cuts the circle at A and B where AB = 8 cm long. Measure its perpendicular distance from O.
2. Draw a circle of radius 5 cm. Inscribe in it a triangle whose angles are 45°, 60° and 75°. Measure its sides.
3. Construct two circles of radii 6 cm and 8 cm respectively whose common chord is 7 cm long. From one end of the common chord construct another chord of the smaller circle which is bisected by the larger one. Measure its length.
4.

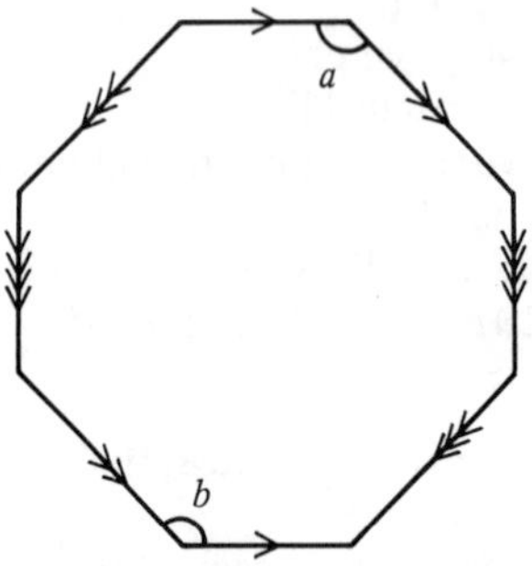

Prove $a = b$

5.

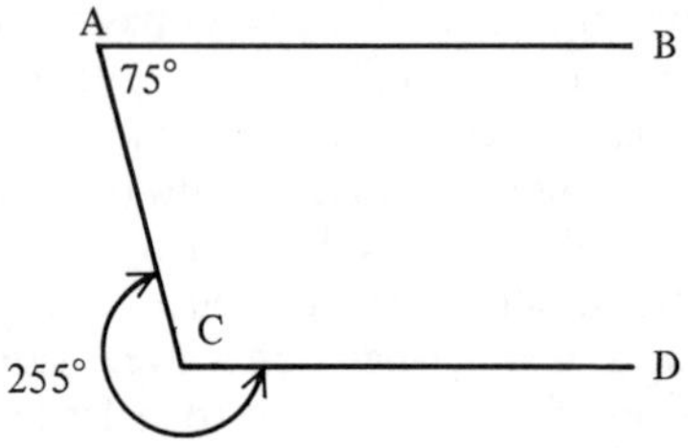

Prove AB and CD are parallel

6. Find t.

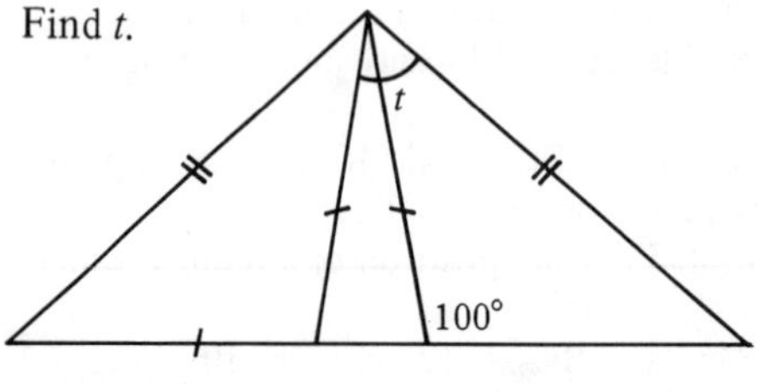

7. Find u.

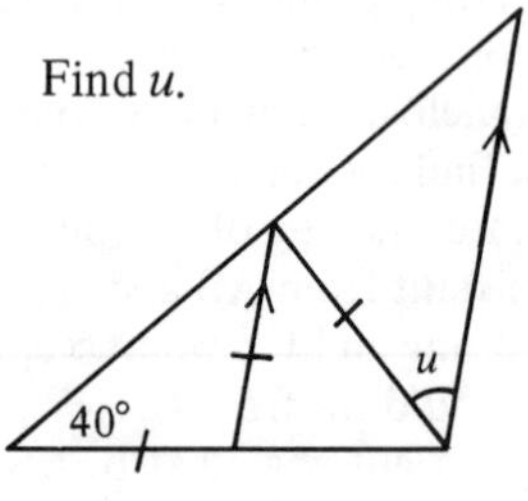

8.

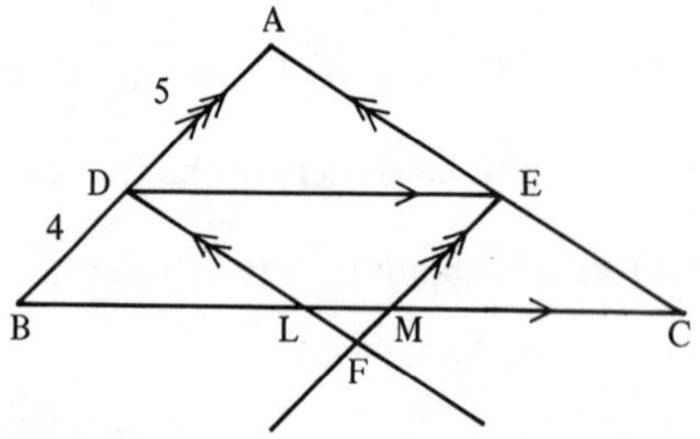

Find the ratios
(area AED) : (area ABC) : (area DECL) : (area EMC) : (area DEML) : (area LMF).

9. ABCD is a square whose diagonals intersect at L. M is a point on AB such that AL = AM. ML produced cuts DC at N. Find $D\hat{L}N$ and $L\hat{N}C$.
10. ABCD is a parallelogram whose diagonals intersect at S. P is a point on AB such that triangle APS is equilateral. $A\hat{D}C = 60°$. Find $P\hat{S}B$.
11. ABCD is a parallelogram with $\hat{C} = 110°$. P is the mid-point of DC. $D\hat{A}P = 40°$ and $A\hat{P}B = 55°$. Find the angle between AD produced and BP produced.

12. A rectangular block 3 cm by 4 cm by 5 cm fits exactly into a sphere. What is its radius?
13. In a test on the hardness of a certain metal, a small steel sphere of diameter 5 mm is pressed into a plate of the sample of metal and leaves a circular depression of diameter 2 mm. Calculate the depth of the depression.
14. VW and XY are two equal perpendicular chords of a circle, centre O. They intersect at Z.
    (a) If VW = 10 cm and the radius = 6 cm, find the length of OZ.
    (b) If OZ = 4 cm and the radius = 6 cm, find the length of VW.
    (c) If OZ = 4 cm and VW = 10 cm, find the radius of the circle.
15. AB and AC are two chords, each of length 18 cm, of a circle of radius 10 cm. Find the length of BC.
16. Find the length of the diagonal of a rectangular solid whose dimensions are a, $2a$ and $3a$ units long.
17. What is the length of the diagonal of a rectangle of sides $(a + b)$ and $(2a + b)$ units long?
18. What is the area of a rhombus of side a cm when one diagonal is of length b cm?
19. The area of a square field is 12 000 m^2. How long is its diagonal?
20. The length of a rectangular field is twice its breadth and its diagonal is 200 m long. Find its area and perimeter.
21. In the figure on the right, PH is a tangent to the circle centre O.
    (a) Show that $PA^2 + 2.OA.AP - PH^2 = 0$.
    (b) If PA is very small compared with OA, it can be assumed that $PH^2 = 2OA.AP$. Taking the radius of the earth as 6400 km, show that a man on a cliff h m high can see a distance of $\sqrt{12{\cdot}8h}$ km approximately out to sea.
    (c) How high must a cliff be for a man to be able to see 15 km out to sea?
    (d) How far can a man see from the top of a 2000 m high mountain?

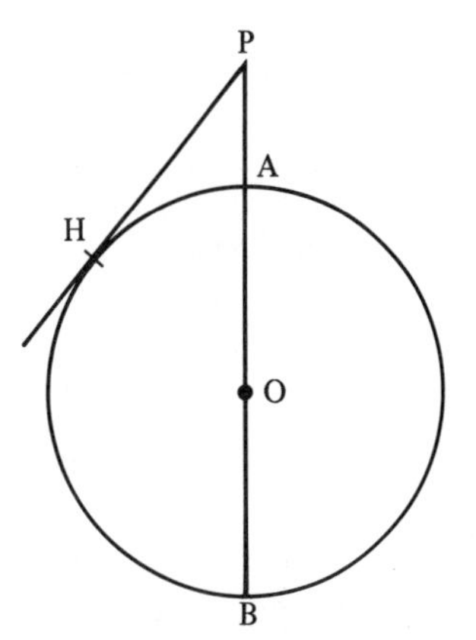

22. Two circles intersect at P and Q. The tangent to one at T cuts the other circle at A and B. PQ produced cuts TA at R. If QR = 2 cm, RT = 4 cm and AB = 6 cm, find the length of PQ and AR.
23. TA and TB are tangents to a circle centre O. If C is a point on the minor arc such that arc AC : arc CB = 4 : 5 and ATB = 72°, find AOC and CAT.
24. Repeat question **23** if C is a point on the major arc.
25. A sphere of radius 4 cm rests inside a cone (vertex downwards) so that the circle of contact between it and the cone is 9 cm from the vertex. How far is the centre of the sphere from the vertex? If the cone is 10 cm high how far does the sphere protrude above it?
26. The point of contact of a wheel and the ground is 30 cm from a step which it just touches. The step is 18 cm high. Find the radius of the wheel.

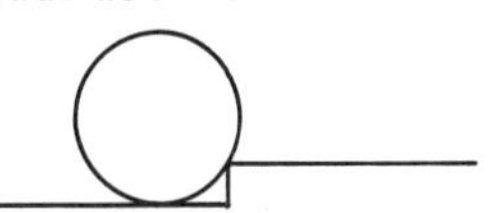

27. Taking the radius of the earth as 6400 km find, correct to the nearest km, the distance of the horizon seen from the top of a mountain 6 km high.
28. Two circles, radii 5 cm and 9 cm, have their centres 20 cm apart. Calculate the length of
    (a) the direct common tangent (b) the transverse common tangent
29. Two circles, centres O and P, touch internally at T. A is a point on their common tangent such that AT = 10 cm, AO = 11 cm, and AP = 14 cm. Find the length of OP.
30. Taking the radius of the earth to be 6400 km, calculate the height of a space ship whose pilot can see the horizon 900 km away.

Part 6 Trigonometry

6.1 Use of tables

An angle of one degree is divided into 60 smaller parts called *minutes*.

$1° = 60'$

Trigonometric tables, as illustrated below, consist of three main columns, A, B, and C.
Column A lists the angles from 0° to 90°.
Column B shows the division of the degree at 6-minute intervals from 0′ to 54′.
Column C is called the *mean difference* column.

Example 1

Find the sine of an angle 45° 46′ (i.e. 45° 42′ + 4′).

Table of natural sines

A	B										C				
	0′	6′	12′	18′	24′	30′	36′	42′	48′	54′	1′	2′	3′	4′	5′
→ 45°	·7071	7083	7096	7108	7120	7133	7145	[7157]	7169	7181	2	4	6	[8]	10 ←
46°	·7193	7206	7218	7230	7242	7254	7266	7278	7290	7302	2	4	6	8	10
47°	·7314	7325	7337	7349	7361	7373	7385	7396	7408	7420	2	4	6	8	10
48°	·7431	7443	7455	7466	7478	7490	7501	7513	7524	7536	2	4	6	8	10

(a) Find 45° in column A of the table of natural sines.
(b) On the same row as 45°, find the number under 42′ in column B, i.e. 0·7157.
(c) Again on the same row, find the number under 4′ in column C, i.e. 0·0008.
(d) The required ratio is 0·7157 + 0·0008 = 0·7165.

Tangent tables are used in a similar way. Remember that above 45°, the value of the tangent is greater than 1.

Example 2

Find the angle whose tangent is 1·1053.

Table of natural tangents

A	B										C				
	0′	6′	12′	18′	24′	30′	36′	42′	48′	54′	1′	2′	3′	4′	5′
45°	1·000	0035	0070	0105	0141	0176	0212	0247	0283	0319	6	12	18	24	30
46°	1·0355	0392	0428	0464	0501	0538	0575	0612	0649	0686	6	12	18	25	31
→ 47°	1·0724	0761	0799	0837	0875	0913	0951	0990	[1028]	1067	6	13	19	[25]	32 ←
48°	1·1106	1145	1184	1224	1263	1303	1343	1383	1423	1463	7	13	20	26	33

(a) In column B, find either the exact tangent value or the nearest number below it, in this case 1·1028 which is the tangent of 47° 48′.
(b) 1·1028 is 0·0025 less than 1·1053 and this difference corresponds to 4′ in column C
(c) The required angle is 47° 48′ + 4′ = 47° 52′.

Example 3

Find (i) the cosine of 50° 41′, (ii) the angle whose cosine is 0·6980.

Table of natural cosines

A	B										C SUBTRACT				
	0′	6′	12′	18′	24′	30′	36′	42′	48′	54′	1′	2′	3′	4′	5′
→ 45°	·7071	7059	7046	7034	7022	7009	6997	6984	6972	6959	2	4	6	8	10 ←
46°	·6947	6934	6921	6909	6896	6884	6871	6858	6845	6833	2	4	6	8	11
47°	·6820	6807	6794	6782	6769	6756	6743	6730	6717	6704	2	4	6	9	11
48°	·6691	6678	6665	6652	6639	6626	6613	6600	6587	6574	2	4	7	9	11
49°	·6561	6547	6534	6521	6508	6494	6481	6468	6455	6441	2	4	7	9	11
→ 50°	·6428	6414	6401	6388	6374	6361	6347	6334	6320	6307	2	4	7	9	11 ←

In cosine tables, the numbers in column C are *subtracted* because the cosine ratio gets smaller as the angle gets larger.

(i) cosine 50° 41′ = cosine (50° 36′ + 5′)
   (a) Find 50° in column A of the table for natural cosines.
   (b) On the same row as 50°, find the number under 36′ in column B, i.e. 0·6347.
   (c) Again on the same row, find the number under 5′ in column C, i.e. 0·0011
   (d) The required ratio is 0·6347 − 0·0011 = 0·6336.

(ii) the angle whose cosine is 0·6980
   (a) Because the ratio gets smaller as the angle gets larger, find the nearest number *above* the required ratio in column B, i.e. 0·6984 which is the cosine of 45° 42′ (the dotted square).
   (b) 0·6984 is 0·0004 more than 0·6980 and this is equivalent to 2′ in column C.
   (c) The required angle is 45° 42′ + 2′ = 45° 44′.

Log tangent, log sine and log cosine tables are used in a similar way to that outlined above.

Exercise 6.1

1. Write down the sine of the following angles

(a) 23°	(b) 68°	(c) 25° 12′	(d) 77° 48′
(e) 35° 36′	(f) 81° 18′	(g) 19° 5′	(h) 27° 26′
(i) 75° 27′	(j) 34° 59′	(k) 59° 50′	(l) 81° 45′

2. Write down the cosine of the following angles

(a) 47°	(b) 73°	(c) 59° 24′	(d) 65° 48′
(e) 38° 24′	(f) 39° 54′	(g) 37° 3′	(h) 81° 45′
(i) 17° 31′	(j) 74° 55′	(k) 55° 21′	(l) 29° 35′

3. Write down the tangent of the following angles

(a) 16°	(b) 77°	(c) 86°	(d) 18° 6′
(e) 45° 18′	(f) 55° 36′	(g) 71° 54′	(h) 39° 22′
(i) 88° 12′	(j) 21° 19′	(k) 36° 55′	(l) 73° 39′

4. Write down the angle of the following sines

(a) ·3907	(b) ·8829	(c) ·9466	(d) ·4131
(e) ·2890	(f) ·8758	(g) ·2362	(h) ·7578
(i) ·7780	(j) ·1124	(k) ·9392	(l) ·8620

5. Write down the angle of the following cosines

(a) ·9703	(b) ·5446	(c) ·3007	(d) ·8862
(e) ·9573	(f) ·2904	(g) ·3856	(h) ·9830
(i) ·9141	(j) ·5676	(k) ·9687	(l) ·8515

6. Write down the angle of the following tangents

(a) ·2679	(b) 1·0724	(c) ·3719	(d) 2·4023
(e) 1·6909	(f) 2·0794	(g) ·1929	(h) 1·3343
(i) ·2428	(j) 2·3127	(k) 3·9566	(l) 10·39

7. Write down the log sine of the following angles

(a) 58° 37′	(b) 27° 47′	(c) 79° 52′	(d) 47° 31′

8. Write down the log cosine of the following angles

(a) 18° 47′	(b) 36° 23′	(c) 49° 39′	(d) 81° 50′

9. Write down the log tangent of the following angles

(a) 36° 39′	(b) 69° 44′	(c) 84° 59′	(d) 80° 38′

10. Write down the angle of the following log sines

(a) $\bar{1}$·0261	(b) $\bar{2}$·7857	(c) $\bar{2}$·9242	(d) $\bar{1}$·3872

11. Write down the angle of the following log cosines

(a) $\bar{2}$·1450	(b) $\bar{1}$·7790	(c) $\bar{1}$·9546	(d) $\bar{1}$·5850

12. Write down the angle of the following log tangents

(a) 1·2806	(b) 0·1140	(c) $\bar{1}$·9045	(d) $\bar{2}$·9433

6.2 Sines

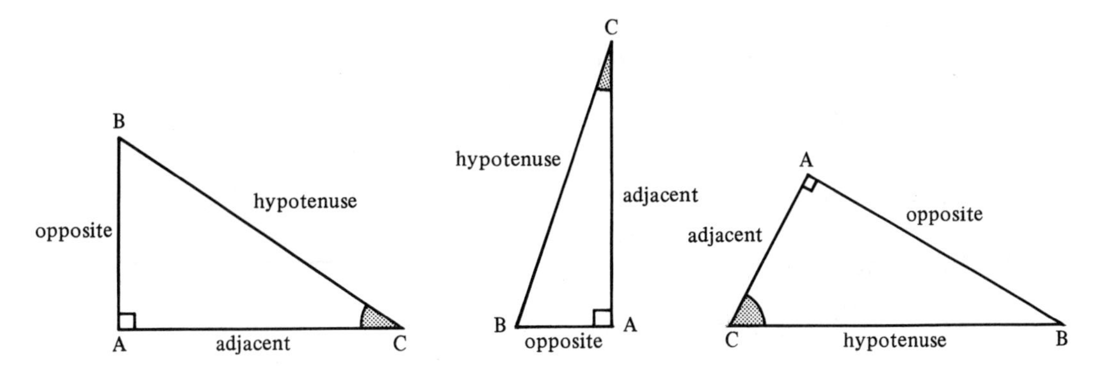

If ABC is a right-angled triangle, then
the side opposite the given angle C is called the *opposite* side,
the side next to the given angle C is called the *adjacent* side,
and the side opposite the right angle A is called the *hypotenuse.*

The ratio $\frac{\text{opposite side}}{\text{hypotenuse}}$ is called the *sine* of the angle.

In the above diagrams, $\sin \hat{C} = \frac{AB}{BC}$.

Below are given methods of using the sine ratio to solve right-angled triangles.

1. Given one side and one angle

(a) From the given angle (or right angle), name the unknown side either opposite, or adjacent, or hypotenuse, and repeat for the known side.
(b) Choose the appropriate ratio, and write down an equation connecting the given angle and this ratio.
(c) Solve this equation.

Example 1

In the diagram on the right, find the length AB.

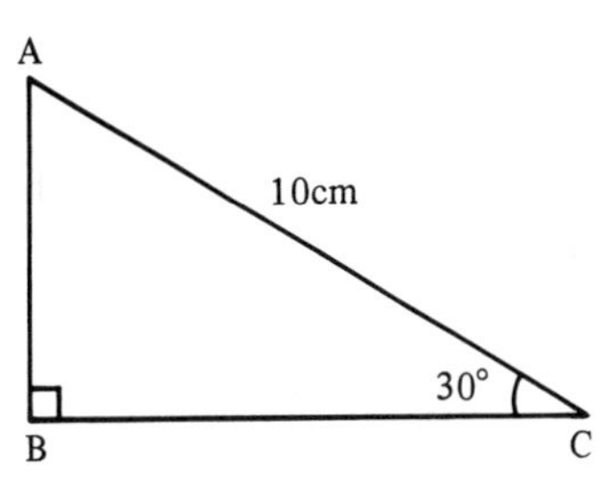

(a) AB is the opposite side; AC is the hypotenuse.

(b) $\frac{AB}{AC} = \sin \hat{C}$.

(c) $\frac{AB}{10} = \sin 30°$.

$\therefore \quad AB = 10 \sin 30° = 10 \times 0{\cdot}5$ (from natural sine tables)

$= 5$ cm.

Example 2

In the diagram on the right, find the length AC.

(a) AC is the hypotenuse; AB is the opposite side.

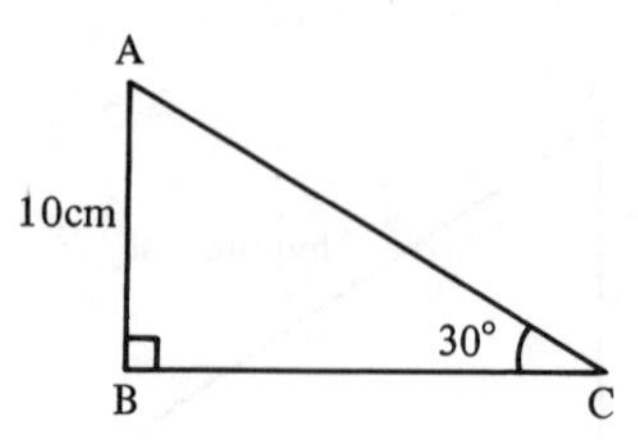

(b) $\dfrac{AB}{AC} = \sin \hat{C}$.

(c) $\dfrac{10}{AC} = \sin 30°$.

$10 = AC \times \sin 30°$

$\therefore \quad AC = \dfrac{10}{\sin 30°} = \dfrac{10}{0{\cdot}5} = 20$ cm.

Example 3

In the diagram on the right, find BC.
When the length of sides is large, it is more convenient to use logs to simplify calculations.

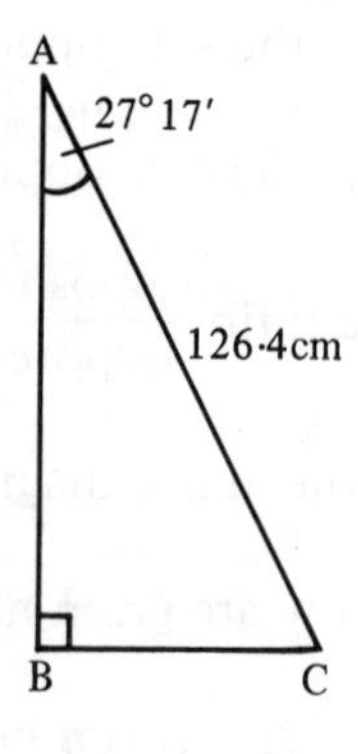

(a) BC is the opposite side; AC is the hypotenuse.

(b) $\dfrac{BC}{AC} = \sin \hat{A}$.

(c) $\dfrac{BC}{126{\cdot}4} = \sin 27°\,17'$.

$\therefore \quad BC = 126{\cdot}4 \times \sin 27°\,17'$

$= 57{\cdot}9$ cm (to 3 S.F.).

	No.	Log.	
×	126·4	2·1018	+
	log sin 27° 17′	$\bar{1}{\cdot}6612$	
	57·94	1·7630	

2. *Given two sides*

(a) Express the ratio of the given sides as a fraction corresponding to a trigonometric ratio.
(b) Change this fraction into a decimal fraction.
(c) Find the size of this angle from the appropriate tables.

Example 1

In the diagram on the right, find $\hat{C}$.

(a) AB is the opposite side; AC is the hypotenuse.

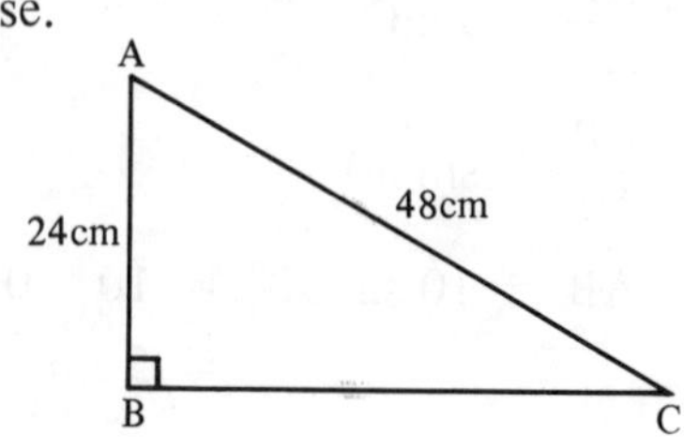

$\dfrac{AB}{AC} = \sin \hat{C}$

(b) $\sin \hat{C} = \dfrac{24}{48} = 0{\cdot}5$

(c) $\hat{C} = 30°$ (using natural sine tables).

Example 2

In the diagram on the right, find $\hat{A}$.
Here the fraction cannot be easily converted to decimals, so it is more convenient to use logs.

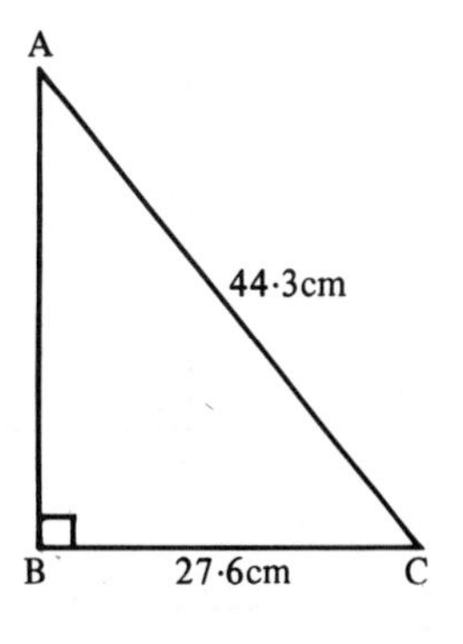

(a) BC is the opposite side, AC is the hypotenuse.

$$\frac{BC}{AC} = \sin \hat{A}$$

(b) $$\frac{27{\cdot}6}{44{\cdot}3} = \sin \hat{A}$$

	No.	Log.	
÷	27·6	1·4409	−
	44·3	1·6464	
	38° 32′	$\bar{1}$·7945	

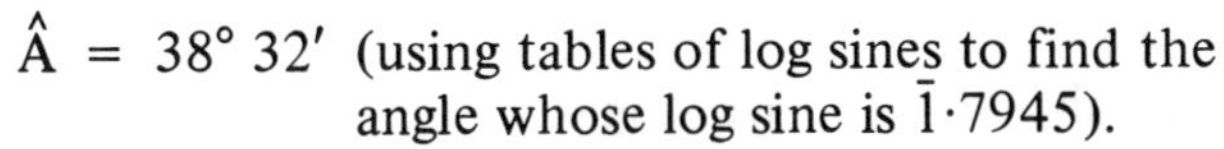
$\hat{A} = 38° 32'$ (using tables of log sines to find the angle whose log sine is $\bar{1}{\cdot}7945$).

Exercise 6.2

In all questions in this exercise, triangle ABC is right-angled at C, triangle LMN is right-angled at N, triangle PQR is right-angled at R, and triangle XYZ is right-angled at Z.

1. In triangle ABC, AB = 5 cm, $\hat{A}$ = 20°, find BC.
2. In triangle LMN, LM = 7 cm, $\hat{L}$ = 72°, find MN.
3. In triangle XYZ, XY = 5 cm, $\hat{X}$ = 26° 12′, find YZ.
4. In triangle PQR, PQ = 32 cm, $\hat{P}$ = 60° 35′, find QR.
5. In triangle LMN, LM = 12 cm, $\hat{L}$ = 63° 2′, find MN.
6. In triangle XYZ, XY = 15 cm, $\hat{X}$ = 34° 10′, find YZ.
7. In triangle ABC, AB = 25 cm, $\hat{A}$ = 71° 50′, find BC.
8. In triangle LMN, LM = 105 cm, $\hat{L}$ = 18° 26′, find MN.
9. In triangle XYZ, XY = 92 cm, $\hat{X}$ = 47° 4′, find YZ.
10. In triangle ABC, AB = 16 cm, $\hat{A}$ = 38° 38′, find BC.

11. In triangle ABC, BC = 5 cm, $\hat{A}$ = 24°, find AB.
12. In triangle LMN, MN = 16 cm, $\hat{L}$ = 38°, find LM.
13. In triangle XYZ, YZ = 502 cm, $\hat{X}$ = 83° 24′, find XY.
14. In triangle ABC, BC = 6·28 cm, $\hat{A}$ = 19° 54′, find AB.
15. In triangle PQR, QR = 18·4 cm, $\hat{P}$ = 26° 17′, find PQ.
16. In triangle LMN, MN = 9·2 cm, $\hat{L}$ = 51° 14′, find LM.
17. In triangle ABC, BC = 627 cm, $\hat{A}$ = 18° 9′, find AB.
18. In triangle XYZ, YZ = 84·6 cm, $\hat{X}$ = 38° 21′, find XY.
19. In triangle PQR, QR = 19·1 cm, $\hat{P}$ = 81° 41′, find PQ.
20. In triangle LMN, MN = 46·2 cm, $\hat{L}$ = 15° 56′, find LM.

21. In triangle ABC, AB = 10 cm, BC = 8 cm, find $\hat{A}$.
22. In triangle LMN, LM = 15 cm, MN = 7 cm, find $\hat{L}$.
23. In triangle XYZ, XY = 12 cm, YZ = 11 cm, find $\hat{X}$.
24. In triangle ABC, AB = 14 cm, BC = 12 cm, find $\hat{A}$.
25. In triangle PQR, PQ = 18 cm, QR = 6 cm, find $\hat{P}$.
26. In triangle LMN, LM = 9 cm, MN = 4·5 cm, find $\hat{L}$.
27. In triangle ABC, AB = 13·8 cm, BC = 8·74 cm, find $\hat{A}$.
28. In triangle PQR, PQ = 8·2 cm, QR = 7·15 cm, find $\hat{P}$.

6.3 Cosines

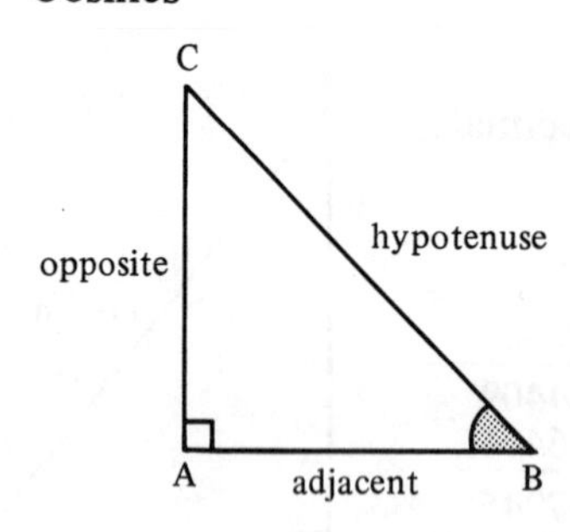

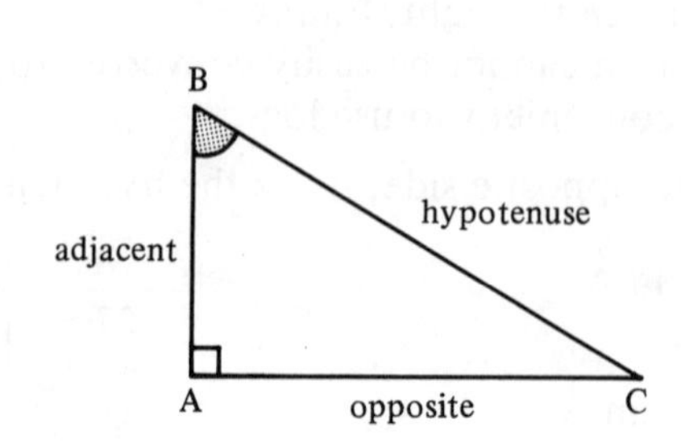

The ratio $\frac{\text{adjacent side}}{\text{hypotenuse}}$ is called the *cosine* of the angle.

In the above diagrams, $\cos \hat{B} = \frac{AB}{BC}$.

Example 1

In the diagram on the right, find the length AC.

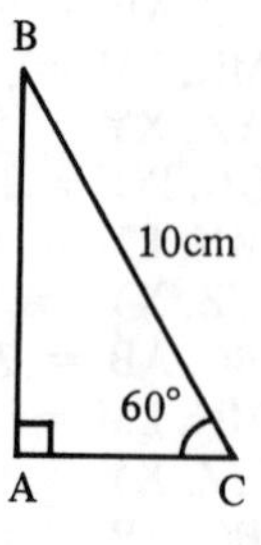

(a) AC is the adjacent side, BC is the hypotenuse.

(b) $\frac{AC}{BC} = \cos \hat{C}$

(c) $\frac{AC}{10} = \cos 60°$

$\therefore$ $AC = 10 \times \cos 60°$

$= 10 \times 0{\cdot}5 = 5$ cm.

Example 2

In the diagram on the right, find BC.

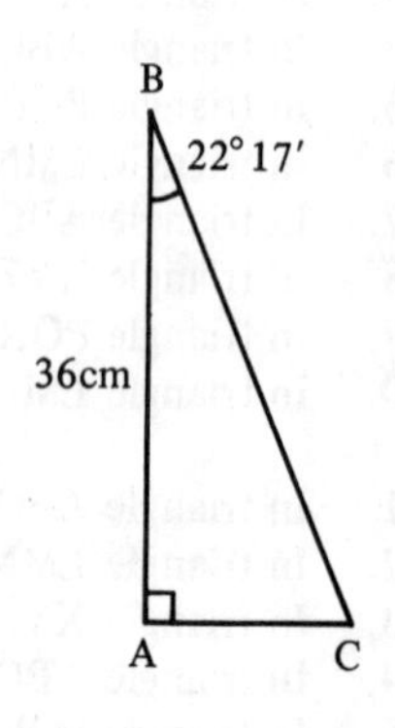

(a) AB is the adjacent side, BC is the hypotenuse.

(b) $\frac{AB}{BC} = \cos \hat{B}$

(c) $\frac{36}{BC} = \cos 22° \, 17'$

$36 = BC \times \cos 22° \, 17'$

$BC = \frac{36}{\cos 22° \, 17'}$

$\therefore$ BC = 38·9 cm (to 3 S.F.)

No.	Log.
36	1·5563
÷ log cos 22° 17′	$\bar{1}$·9663
38·90	1·5900

Example 3

In the diagram on the right, find $\hat{B}$.

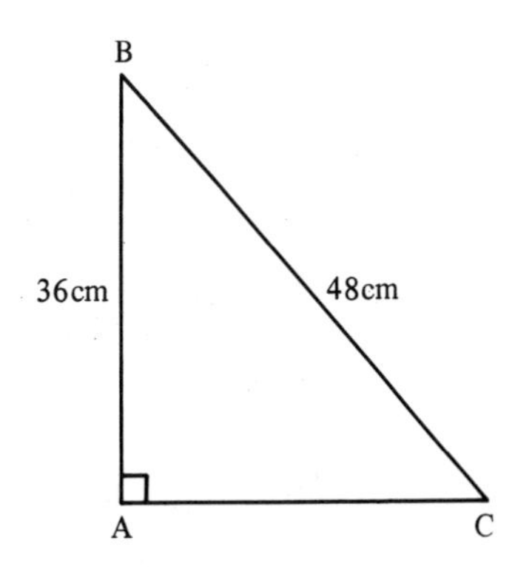

(a) AB is the adjacent side, BC is the hypotenuse.

(b) $\cos \hat{B} = \dfrac{AB}{BC}$

(c) $\cos \hat{B} = \dfrac{36}{48}$

$= 0{\cdot}75$

$\therefore \quad \hat{B} = 41^\circ 24'$.

Exercise 6.3

In all questions in this exercise, triangle ABC is right-angled at C, triangle LMN is right-angled at N, triangle PQR is right-angled at R, and triangle XYZ is right-angled at Z.

1. In triangle ABC, AB = 5 cm, $\hat{A} = 36^\circ$, find AC.
2. In triangle LMN, LM = 12 cm, $\hat{L} = 42^\circ$, find LN.
3. In triangle PQR, PQ = 64 cm, $\hat{P} = 39^\circ 12'$, find PR.
4. In triangle XYZ, XY = 49 cm, $\hat{X} = 58^\circ 36'$, find XZ.
5. In triangle LMN, LM = 103 cm, $\hat{L} = 47^\circ 54'$, find LN.
6. In triangle XYZ, XY = 136 cm, $\hat{X} = 28^\circ 30'$, find XZ.
7. In triangle PQR, PQ = 12·5 cm, $\hat{P} = 37^\circ 14'$, find PR.
8. In triangle ABC, AB = 73·6 cm, $\hat{A} = 56^\circ 39'$, find AC.
9. In triangle PQR, PQ = 22·36 cm, $\hat{P} = 72^\circ 53'$, find PR.
10. In triangle XYZ, XY = 1079 cm, $\hat{X} = 45^\circ 46'$, find XZ.

11. In triangle ABC, AC = 8 cm, $\hat{A} = 37^\circ$, find AB.
12. In triangle XYZ, XZ = 14 cm, $\hat{X} = 75^\circ$, find XY.
13. In triangle LMN, LN = 34·6 cm, $\hat{L} = 27^\circ 36'$, find LM.
14. In triangle PQR, PR = 83·45 cm, $\hat{P} = 27^\circ 39'$, find PQ.
15. In triangle XYZ, XZ = 9·264 cm, $\hat{X} = 74^\circ 41'$, find XY.
16. In triangle ABC, AC = 4862 cm, $\hat{A} = 48^\circ 17'$, find AB.
17. In triangle LMN, LN = 0·9863 cm, $\hat{L} = 39^\circ 59'$, find LM.
18. In triangle PQR, PR = 18·33 cm, $\hat{P} = 14^\circ 39'$, find PQ.
19. In triangle XYZ, XZ = 264·9 cm, $\hat{X} = 23^\circ 56'$, find XY.
20. In triangle ABC, AC = 286·4 cm, $\hat{A} = 81^\circ 34'$, find AB.

21. In triangle LMN, LM = 18 cm, LN = 13 cm, find $\hat{L}$.
22. In triangle ABC, AB = 45 cm, AC = 23 cm, find $\hat{A}$.
23. In triangle XYZ, XY = 378 cm, XZ = 245·6 cm, find $\hat{X}$.
24. In triangle PQR, PQ = 34·56 cm, PR = 28·45 cm, find $\hat{P}$.
25. In triangle ABC, AB = 49·55 cm, AC = 37·56 cm, find $\hat{A}$.
26. In triangle LMN, LM = 3·479 cm, LN = 2·496 cm, find $\hat{L}$.
27. In triangle PQR, PQ = 1200 cm, PR = 937·5 cm, find $\hat{P}$.
28. In triangle ABC, AB = 18·66 cm, AC = 16·45 cm, find $\hat{A}$.
29. In triangle XYZ, XY = 2·367 cm, XZ = 1·983 cm, find $\hat{X}$.
30. In triangle ABC, AB = 0·0452 cm, AC = 0·0245 cm, find $\hat{A}$.

6.4 Tangents

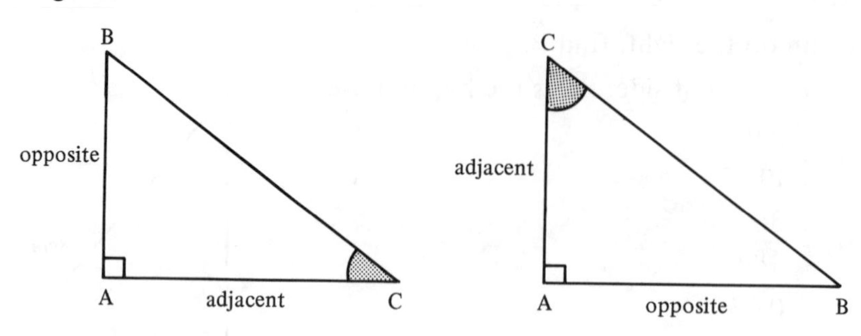

The ratio $\dfrac{\text{opposite side}}{\text{adjacent side}}$ is called the *tangent* of the angle.

In the above diagram, $\tan \hat{C} = \dfrac{AB}{AC}$.

Note. When using tables of tangents, remember that for angles greater than 45° the tangent ratio is greater than 1.

Example 1

In the diagram on the right, find the length AB.

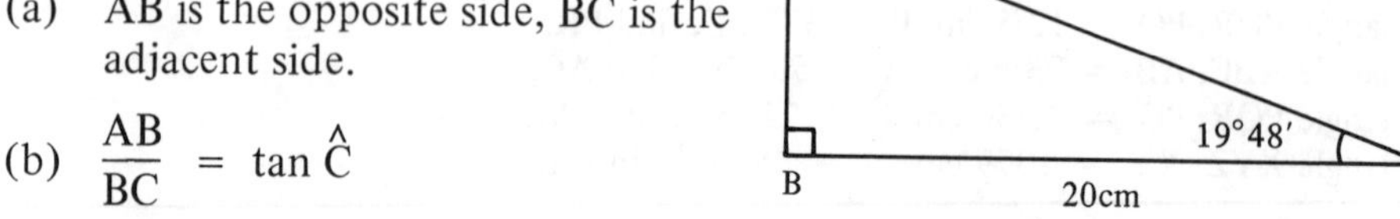

(a) AB is the opposite side, BC is the adjacent side.

(b) $\dfrac{AB}{BC} = \tan \hat{C}$

(c) $\dfrac{AB}{20} = \tan 19°\,48'$

$AB = 20 \times \tan 19°\,48'$

$= 20 \times 0{\cdot}36$

$= 7{\cdot}2$ cm.

Example 2

In the diagram on the right, find BC.

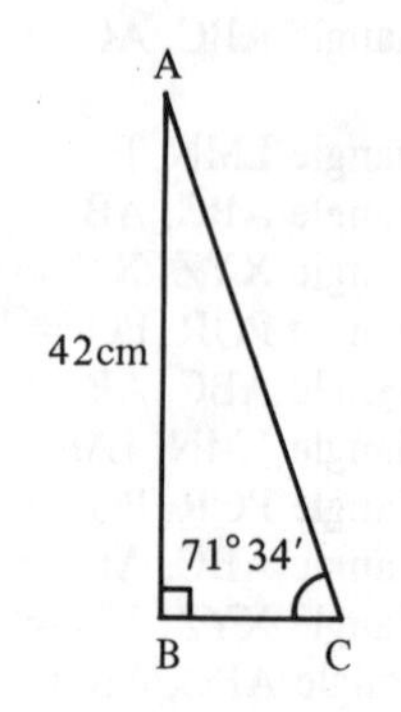

(a) AB is the opposite side, BC is the adjacent side.

(b) $\dfrac{AB}{BC} = \tan \hat{C}$

(c) $\dfrac{42}{BC} = \tan 71°\,34'$

$42 = BC \times \tan 71°\,34'$

$$BC = \frac{42}{\tan 71^\circ 34'} = \frac{42}{3} = 14 \text{ cm.}$$

Note. To avoid division when using the tangent ratio (especially when the numbers are awkward), the following alternative method can be employed in Example 2.

$$\hat{C} = 71^\circ 34' \quad \therefore A = 90^\circ - 71^\circ 34' = 18^\circ 26'$$

then BC is the opposite side and AB is the adjacent side.

so
$$\tan \hat{A} = \frac{BC}{AB}$$

$$\tan 18^\circ 26' = \frac{BC}{42}$$

$$42 \times \tan 18^\circ 26' = BC$$

$$42 \times 0{\cdot}3333 = BC$$

$$BC = 14 \text{ cm.}$$

Exercise 6.4

In all questions in this exercise, triangle ABC is right-angled at C, triangle LMN is right-angled at N, triangle PQR is right-angled at R, and triangle XYZ is right-angled at Z.

1. In triangle PQR, PR = 45 cm, $\hat{P}$ = 47°, find QR.
2. In triangle XYZ, XZ = 14 cm, $\hat{X}$ = 68°, find YZ.
3. In triangle ABC, AC = 23 cm, $\hat{A}$ = 37° 45′, find BC.
4. In triangle LMN, LN = 17·55 cm, $\hat{L}$ = 75° 48′, find MN.
5. In triangle ABC, AC = 22·93 cm, $\hat{A}$ = 37° 45′, find BC.
6. In triangle PQR, PR = 36·32 cm, $\hat{P}$ = 55° 41′, find QR.
7. In triangle LMN, LN = 37·65 cm, $\hat{L}$ = 26° 37′, find MN.
8. In triangle XYZ, XZ = 9·45 cm, $\hat{X}$ = 25° 35′, find YZ.
9. In triangle PQR, PR = 0·02375 cm, $\hat{P}$ = 23° 44′, find QR.
10. In triangle ABC, AC = 65·33 cm, $\hat{A}$ = 45°, find BC.

11. In triangle ABC, BC = 45 cm, $\hat{A}$ = 65°, find AC.
12. In triangle PQR, QR = 38 cm, $\hat{P}$ = 75°, find PR.
13. In triangle LMN, MN = 43·6 cm, $\hat{L}$ = 49° 42′, find LN.
14. In triangle XYZ, YZ = 7344 cm, $\hat{X}$ = 29° 48′, find XZ.
15. In triangle PQR, QR = 2·365 cm, $\hat{P}$ = 43° 58′, find PR.
16. In triangle ABC, BC = 0·1674 cm, $\hat{A}$ = 82° 36′, find AC.
17. In triangle LMN, MN = 90·88 cm, $\hat{L}$ = 62° 33′, find LN.
18. In triangle PQR, QR = 1·234 cm, $\hat{P}$ = 85° 48′, find PR.
19. In triangle LMN, MN = 1469 cm, $\hat{L}$ = 6° 53′, find LN.
20. In triangle ABC, BC = 8·933 cm, $\hat{A}$ = 89° 6′, find AC.

21. In triangle ABC, BC = 34 cm, AC = 27 cm, find $\hat{A}$.
22. In triangle LMN, LN = 35 cm, MN = 34 cm, find $\hat{L}$.
23. In triangle PQR, QR = 45 cm, PR = 87 cm, find $\hat{P}$.
24. In triangle XYZ, YZ = 12·3 cm, XZ = 3·67 cm, find $\hat{X}$.
25. In triangle ABC, BC = 25·45 cm, AC = 67·23 cm, find $\hat{B}$.

6.5 Simple plane problems

Problems which require the use of trigonometric ratios should be tackled in the following way.

1. Draw a clear diagram, approximately to scale.
2. Pick out a suitable right-angled triangle and name the vertices when necessary.
3. Choose the appropriate trigonometric ratio, build up an equation, and solve it.
4. Give the answer in the required form, e.g. distance of ship from port is 27 km.

In some problems the use of the theorem of Pythagoras may also be necessary.

When solving problems the following terms will often be used.

Angle of elevation

The angle of elevation of the top of the tree B, observed from a point A is the angle which the line AB makes with the horizontal at A.

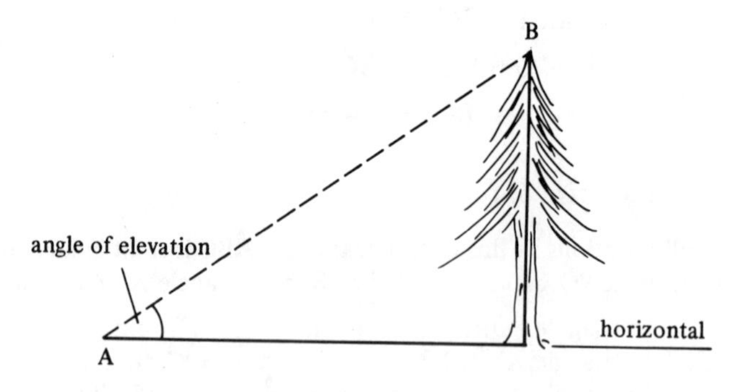

Angle of depression

The angle of depression of the boat B, observed from the top of the cliff A is the angle which the line AB makes with the horizontal at A.

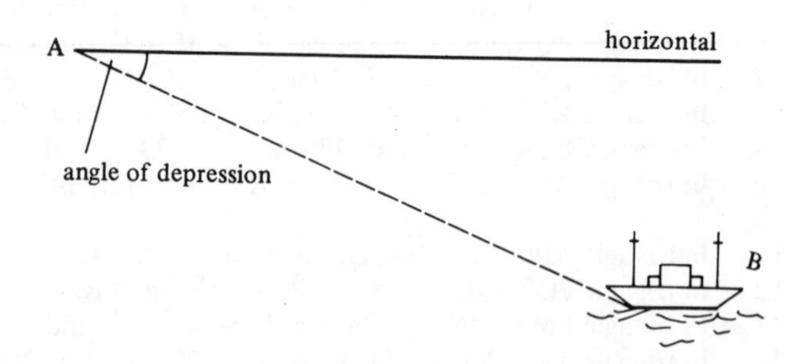

Bearings (see section 5.2)

All bearings are measured in a clockwise direction from N.
The bearing of B from A is 072° and the bearing of A from B is 252°.

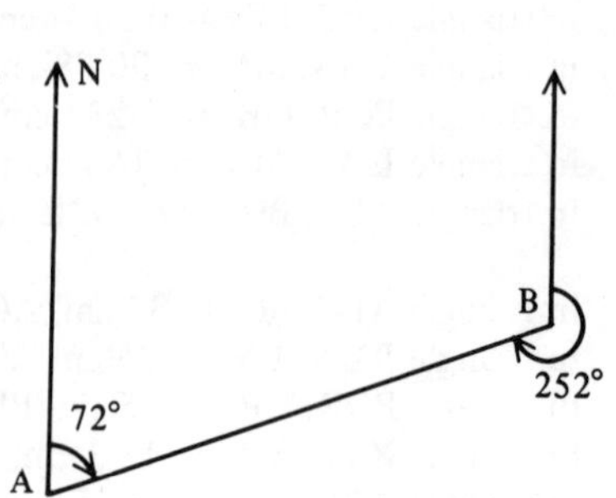

Gradients

In this section the gradient of a slope is the sine of the angle the line of slope makes with the horizontal. This is the gradient measured by a surveyor. In the diagram on the right, the gradient is $\frac{1}{3}$, or the angle whose sine is $0{\cdot}\dot{3}$.

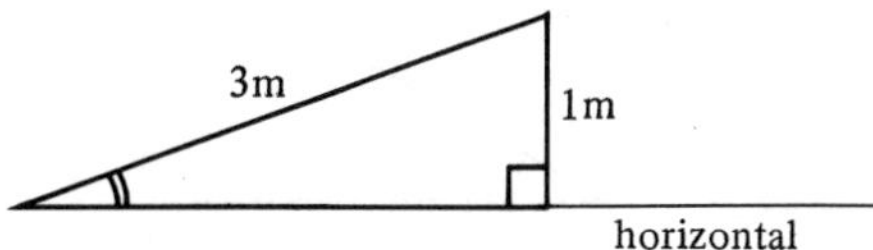

Example 1

A ship steams from a port A for 27 km due North, to B, then changes direction and steams 36 km on a bearing 090° to C. Find (a) the shortest distance from A to C, (b) the bearing of C from A.

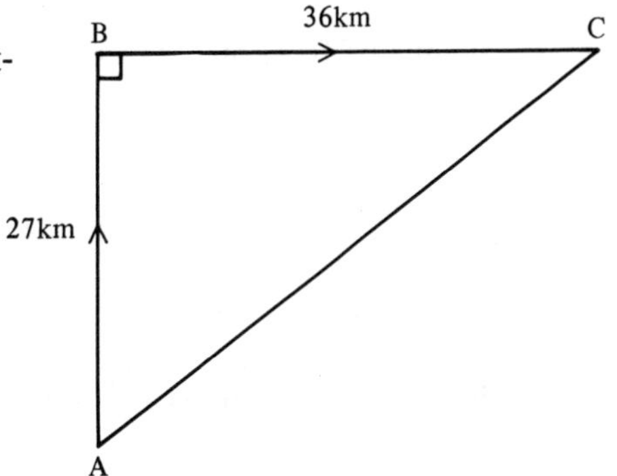

(a) The shortest distance is AC, in the right-angled triangle ABC.
Using the theorem of Pythagoras

$$\begin{aligned} AC^2 &= AB^2 + BC^2 \\ &= 27^2 + 36^2 \\ &= 729 + 1296 \\ &= 2025 \end{aligned}$$

$$\therefore \quad AC = \sqrt{2025} = 45 \text{ km.}$$

(b) The angle which gives the bearing of C from A is $B\hat{A}C$. In triangle ABC, BC is the opposite side and AB the adjacent side.

$$\therefore \quad \frac{BC}{AB} = \tan B\hat{A}C$$

$$\tan B\hat{A}C = \frac{36}{27} = 1{\cdot}3333$$

$$\therefore \quad \hat{C} = 53°\,8'.$$

Hence, the shortest distance is 45 km and the bearing of C from A is 053° 8′.

Example 2

An observer stands 120 m from the foot of a tower. The angle of elevation of the top of the tower is 28° and the angle of elevation of the top of a flagpole which stands on the top of the tower is 29°. How high is the flagpole?

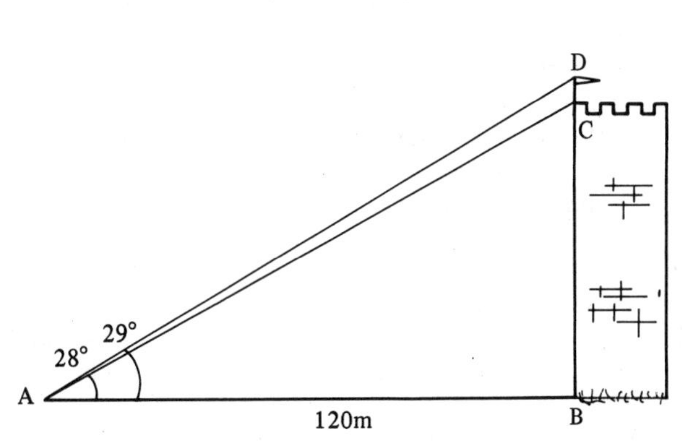

Letter the diagram ABCD as shown. Using the right-angled triangles ABC and ABD:

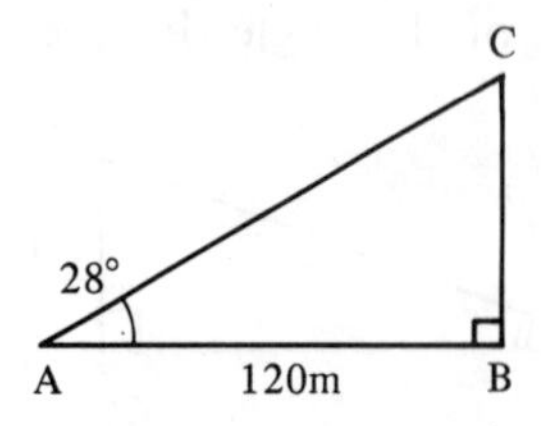

$$\frac{BC}{120} = \tan 28° \qquad \frac{BD}{120} = \tan 29°$$

$$BC = 120 \times \tan 28° \qquad BD = 120 \times \tan 29°$$

$$\begin{aligned}\therefore \text{ height of flagpole CD} &= BD - BC \\ &= 120 \tan 29° - 120 \tan 28° \\ &= 120 (\tan 29° - \tan 28°) \\ &= 120 (0{\cdot}5543 - 0{\cdot}5317) \\ &= 120 \times 0{\cdot}0226 \\ &= 2{\cdot}712 \text{ m}\end{aligned}$$

∴ height of flagpole is 2·7 m (to 1 D.P.).

Exercise 6.5

1. Find the radius of the circle which circumscribes a square of side 20 cm.
2. A ladder of length 6 m stands with its foot 1 m from a wall against which it is leaning. At what angle is it inclined to the vertical?
3. A ladder stands with its foot 1 m from a wall and it is inclined at 25° to the vertical. How high up the wall does it reach?
4. Find the area of an equilateral triangle of side 15 cm.
5. A ladder 5 m long stands in a passage with vertical walls. Its foot is 2 m from one wall and 1 m from the other. The ladder is rotated from the position in which its top rests against one wall to the position in which it rests against the other. Through what angle has the ladder been turned?
6. An aeroplane is flying at a height of 2000 m and its angle of elevation from a point P is 57°. What would be the angle of elevation of a second aeroplane flying at the same height but twice as far away?
7. In question **6**, another aeroplane is flying immediately above the first one but 1000 m higher. What is its angle of elevation from P?
8. A ship steams 25 km on a bearing of 072° and then 20 km on a bearing of 048°. Find its distance and bearing from its starting point.
9. A ship steams on a bearing of 050° for 5 km and then on a bearing of 130° for 7 km. Find its distance and bearing from its starting point.
10. A man stands on the top of a cliff 120 m high. He observes two boats in line with him at angles of depression of 45° and 69°. How far apart are they?
11. A tower stands on the side of a hill of gradient 1 in 20 (sine). A man walks 200 m downhill from the foot of the tower and observes that the angle of elevation of its top is 26°. How high is the tower?

12. A rectangular table top 3 m by 2 m stands in a vertical plane with one corner on the floor and the longer side inclined at 50° to the horizontal. How high above the floor is the top corner?
13. A rhombus of side 12 cm has one of its angles 49°. Find the lengths of its diagonals.
14. From an observer in an aeroplane flying at 3000 m a ship is seen due South at an angle of depression of 50° and a port is seen due North at an angle of depression of 12°. How far is the ship from the port?
15. Two corridors, one of width 2 m and one of width 1 m meet at right angles. A workman attempting to take a ladder round the corner gets it stuck when it is at 45° to each wall as shown in the diagram. How long is the ladder? How much longer would it have to be if it had got stuck when it made an angle of 60° with the wall of the narrower corridor?

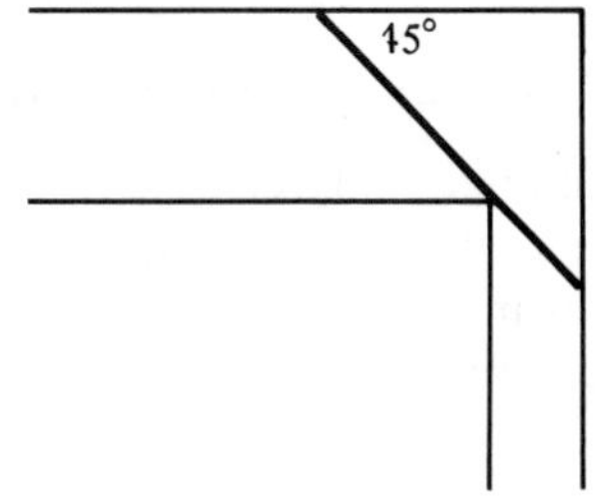

16. The top and bottom of a 4 m flagstaff which stands on the top of a tower have angles of elevation of 34° and 26° from a point level with the base of the tower. How high is the tower?
17. An engineer wishes to bridge a river which he cannot at first cross. He observes, however, that the angle of elevation of the top of a tree on the far bank is 27° from a point on the near bank and 14° from a point 30 m further back. How wide was the river?
18. From the figure on the right, calculate
    (a) the length of AD
    (b) the area of the trapezium ABCD.

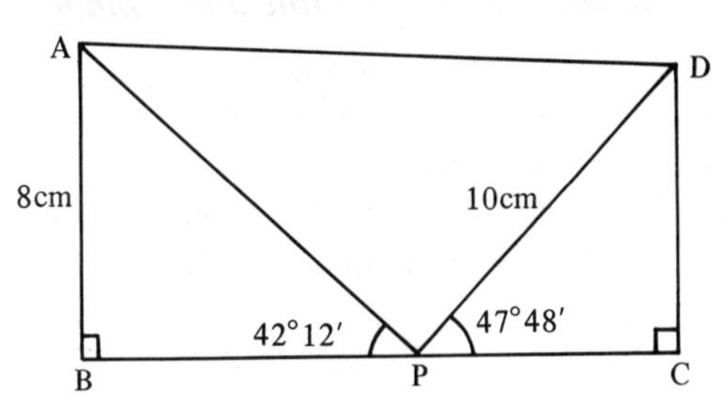

19. From the top of a vertical cliff 50 m high, the angles of depression of two boats at sea are 2° 33′ and 4° 30′ respectively. Calculate the distance between the two boats.
20. In the figure on the right, not drawn to scale, O is the centre of the inscribed circle of triangle ABC. If B = 40°, C = 50°, and the radius of the inscribed circle is 2 cm, calculate
    (a) the length of BC
    (b) the length of AB
    (c) the length of AC.

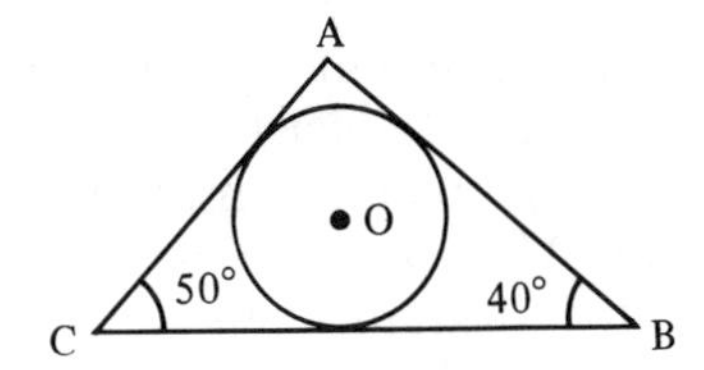

6.6 Simple 3-D problems

The solution of simple problems based on solids requires the drawing of a clear diagram. This should show the right-angled triangles which are used to solve the problem.
In these problems, the following items may have to be found.

1. The angle between two planes

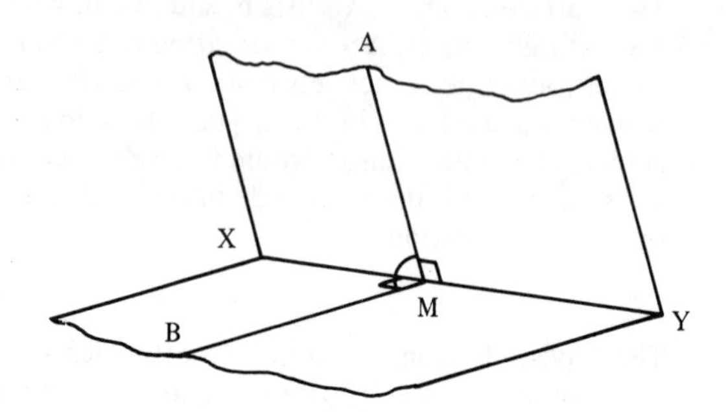

The angle between two planes is the angle at a point where two lines meet, one on each plane, that are perpendicular to the line of intersection of the planes.

In the diagram, XY is the line of intersection of the planes. If both BM and AM are perpendicular to XY, then the angle between the two planes is $A\hat{M}B$.

2. The angle between a line and a plane

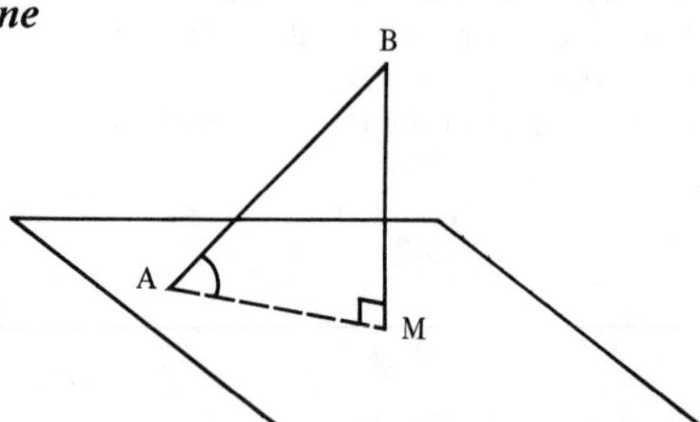

In the diagram, the line AB meets a plane at the point A. If BM is the perpendicular drawn to the plane from the point B, the angle between the line AB and the plane is BAM.

3. The perpendicular to a plane

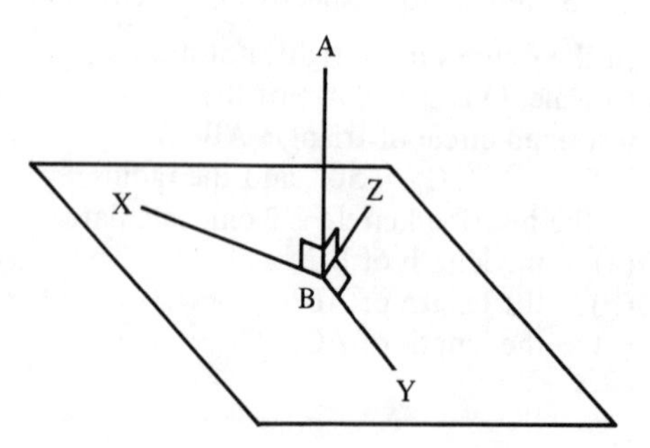

Any line in the plane that is drawn to the foot of a perpendicular to that plane meets the perpendicular at 90°.

Hence, if AB is perpendicular to the plane in the diagram, then
$Y\hat{B}A = Z\hat{B}A = X\hat{B}A = 90°$.

Example 1

In the diagram on the page opposite, X, Y, and Z are three points on horizontal ground, such that XY = 6 m, XZ = 10 m. At X stands a vertical flagpole XP; the angle of elevation of the top of the flagpole P from Y is 27°.

Calculate
(a) the height of the flagpole,
(b) the angle of elevation of the top of the flagpole from Z.

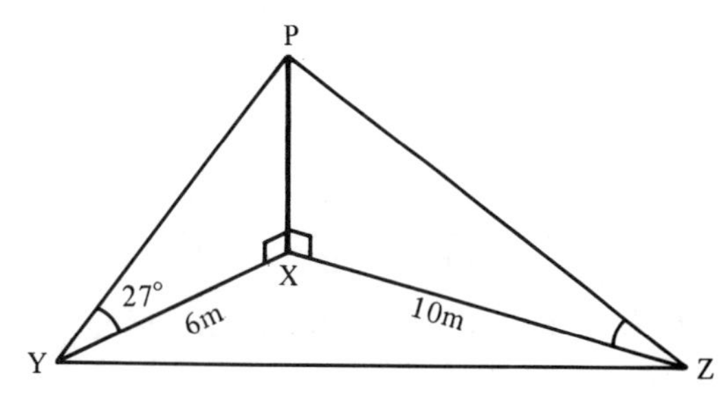

(a) Using the right-angled triangle XPY to find PX:

$$\tan 27° = \frac{PX}{6}$$

$$\therefore \quad PX = 6 \times \tan 27°$$
$$= 6 \times 0{\cdot}5095$$
$$= 3{\cdot}057 \text{ m.}$$

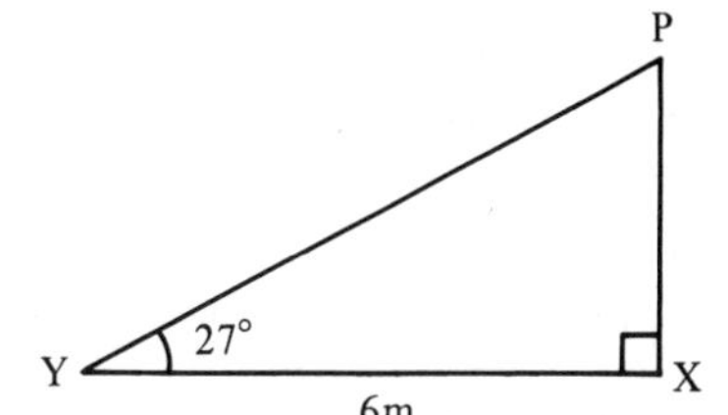

(b) Using the right-angled triangle $P\hat{X}Z$ to find the angle of elevation $P\hat{Z}X$

$$\tan P\hat{Z}X = \frac{3{\cdot}057}{10} = 0{\cdot}3057$$

$$\therefore \quad P\hat{Z}X = 17°$$

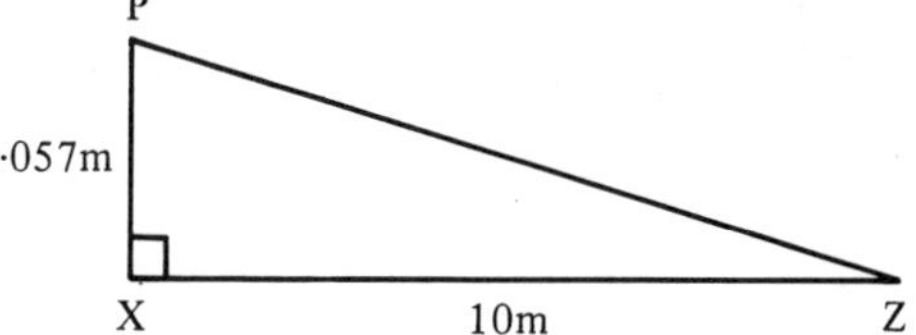

∴ height of flagpole is 3·06 m (to 3 S.F.) and the angle of elevation from Z is 17°.

Exercise 6.6

1. Find the angles which the diagonals of a cube make with (a) an edge and (b) a face passing through one end of the diagonal.
2. A tree stands at the corner of a square field of side 100 m. If the tree is 10 m high what angles does it subtend at each corner of the field and at its centre?
3. A wireless mast is due West of A and 100 m away. At B, due North of A on level ground it subtends an angle of 32° and its bearing is 220°. Find its height.
4. The plane face of a hill slopes at 15° to the horizontal and a path 150 m long makes an angle of 40° with the line of greatest slope. How far is the top of the path vertically above the bottom?
5. Another path on the same hillside as question **4** rises 40 m when sited at an angle of 50° to the line of greatest slope. How long is it?
6. The top of a desk is inclined at 10° to the horizontal. Find the angle which a line on the desk drawn at 30° to the bottom edge makes with the horizontal.
7. A pyramid stands on a square base of side 24 cm and has a vertical height of 18 cm. Find the angle between a slant edge and the base.
8. A man in an observation balloon 500 m high observes the angles of depression of two points on the ground, one due South of him and one due West to be 30° and 20° respectively. How far apart are the two points?

6.7 The sine rule

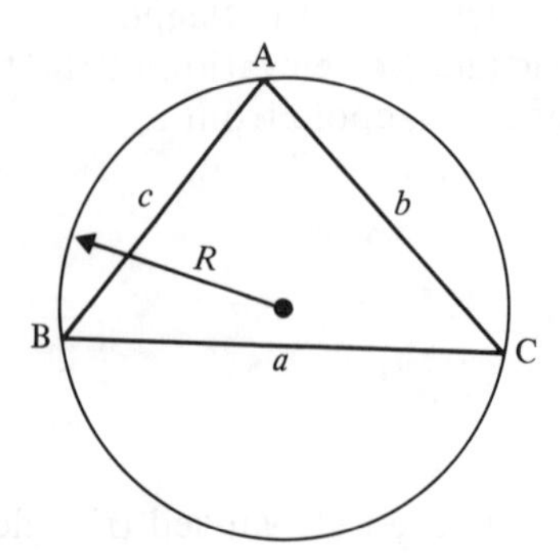

In any triangle,

$$\frac{a}{\sin \hat{A}} = \frac{b}{\sin \hat{B}} = \frac{c}{\sin \hat{C}} = 2R$$

where R is the radius of the circumcircle.

This is known as the *sine rule* and is used in the following cases.

(a) given the size of any two angles and the length of any side.
(b) given the length of any two sides and the size of the angle opposite one of these sides.

Example 1

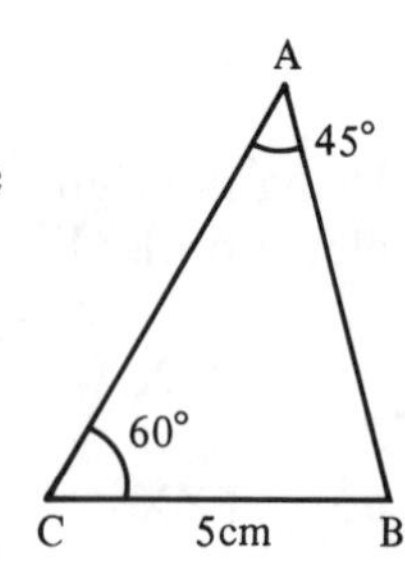

In the diagram on the right, find
(a) the length of AB, (b) the radius R of the circumcircle

From triangle ABC

$a = 5$ cm, AB $= c$, $\hat{A} = 45°$ and $\hat{C} = 60°$.

Hence $\dfrac{a}{\sin \hat{A}} = \dfrac{c}{\sin \hat{C}}$

$$\frac{5}{\sin 45°} = \frac{c}{\sin 60°} \qquad \therefore \ c = \frac{5 \sin 60°}{\sin 45°}$$

$$= 6.12 \text{ cm (to 3 S.F.)}.$$

Also $2R = \dfrac{a}{\sin \hat{A}} = \dfrac{5}{\sin 45°} = 7.071 \qquad \therefore \ R = 3.54$ (to 3 S.F.).

Example 2

In the diagram on the right, find the size of angle ABC.
From triangle ABC,

AB $= c$, AC $= b$ and $\hat{C} = 60°$.

Hence $\dfrac{\sin \hat{B}}{b} = \dfrac{\sin \hat{C}}{c}$

$$\frac{\sin \hat{B}}{7} = \frac{\sin 60°}{8} \qquad \therefore \ \sin \hat{B} = \frac{7 \sin 60}{8} = 0.7578$$

$$\hat{B} = 49°16'.$$

The area A of a triangle is given by the formula

$$A = \tfrac{1}{2}ab \sin \hat{c}$$

Example 3

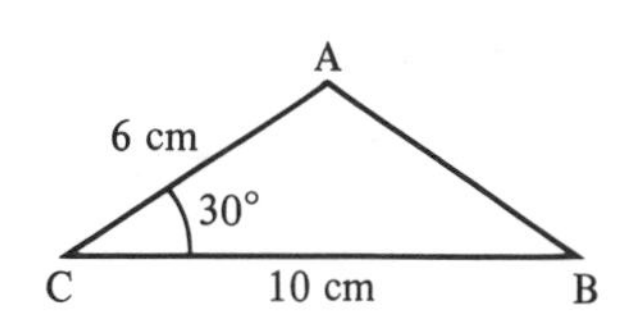

Find the area of triangle ABC

$$A = \tfrac{1}{2} \times 10 \times 6 \times \sin 30^\circ = 15 \text{ cm}^2$$

Exercise 6.7

Questions 1 to 10 refer to triangle ABC. Capital letters are used to denote angles and the corresponding small letters to denote the length of the side opposite.

1. If $\hat{A} = 40^\circ$, $\hat{B} = 60^\circ$ and $b = 6$ cm, find a.
2. If $\hat{A} = 50^\circ$, $\hat{C} = 30^\circ$ and $a = 8$ cm, find c.
3. If $\hat{B} = 70^\circ$, $\hat{C} = 40^\circ$ and $b = 14$ cm, find c.
4. If $\hat{C} = 20^\circ$, $\hat{A} = 80^\circ$ and $c = 9{\cdot}5$ cm, find a.
5. If $\hat{A} = 36^\circ 12'$, $\hat{B} = 72^\circ 48'$ and $b = 8{\cdot}1$ cm, find a.
6. If $\hat{A} = 81^\circ 3'$, $\hat{C} = 15^\circ 17'$ and $a = 3{\cdot}14$ cm, find c.
7. If $\hat{C} = 74^\circ 8'$, $\hat{A} = 37^\circ 19'$ and $c = 82{\cdot}1$ cm, find a.
8. If $\hat{B} = 52^\circ 38'$, $\hat{C} = 47^\circ 21'$ and $b = 74{\cdot}6$ cm, find c.
9. If $\hat{A} = 27^\circ 35'$, $\hat{C} = 86^\circ 17'$ and $a = 19{\cdot}6$ cm, find b.
10. If $\hat{C} = 72^\circ 8'$, $\hat{A} = 41^\circ 19'$ and $b = 14{\cdot}1$ cm, find a.
11. A door of width 75 cm stands open at an angle of 40°. Find the distance between the edge of the door and the door post.
12. A skylight of length 1·5 m is propped open by a stick 0·5 m long. Through what angle does the skylight open?
13. A surveyor wishes to find the distance to a mountain peak X. He marks out a base line AB on the ground 1000 m long and measures the angles XAB and XBA. They are 85° and 78° respectively. How far is X from A?
14. A ship calls up two wireless stations A and B to help find his position. The ship finds the bearing of A is 045° and of B is 110°. A is 12 km due North of B. How far is the ship from B?
15. The angles of elevation of the top of a tower from two points A and B 100 m apart and in line with the tower are 50° and 20° respectively. Owing to the presence of a moat, the base of the tower cannot be reached, but how high is it?
16. An engineer wishes to float a pontoon bridge across a river but he cannot measure its width. However, he observes that the angle of elevation of the top of a tree on the far bank from a point on his bank is 12°. On going 20 m away from the river the angle becomes 10°. How wide is the river?
17. C is at the foot of a tower. From the ends A and B of a horizontal base line 600 m in length, it is found that the angles CAB and CBA are 67° 30′ and 49° 15′ respectively. From A the angle of elevation of the top of the tower is 8° 17′. Find its height.
18. The triangle ABC has angles 40°, 60° and 80°. Its perimeter is 100 cm. Find the longest side.
19. Two houses A and B are 100 m apart and B is due East of A. The bearing of a church C from A is 145° and from B is 225°. Which is nearer to the church and by how much?
20. In questions **1** to **10**, find (a) the radius of the circumcircle
(b) the area of each triangle.

6.8 The cosine rule

In any triangle ABC

$$a^2 = (b^2 + c^2) - (2\,bc \cos \hat{A}) \quad ①$$

$$\cos \hat{A} = \frac{b^2 + c^2 - a^2}{2\,bc} \quad ②$$

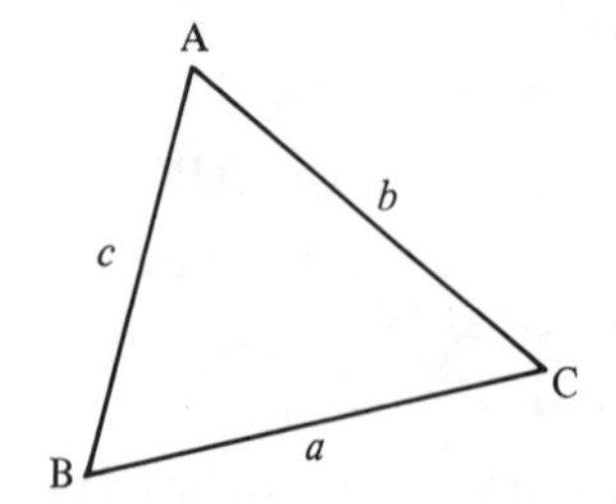

These are two versions of the *cosine rule.* It is used in the following circumstances.
(a) Use equation ① to find the length of a side in a triangle, given the length of two sides and the size o fthe angle included between these two sides.
(b) Use equation ② to find the size of an angle, given the length of all three sides of the triangle.

Note. The symbols of the two formulas must be adjusted to suit the triangle.
In any triangle, the smallest angle is found opposite the shortest side.
The smallest angle should always be found first. The sine rule is then used to find the next smallest angle.

Example 1

In the triangle on the right, find the length of BC.
In triangle ABC,

$c = 5$ cm, $b = 6$ cm, and $\hat{A} = 55°$

Hence $a^2 = (6^2 + 5^2) - (2 \times 6 \times 5 \times \cos 55°)$
$= (36 + 25) - (60 \times 0{\cdot}5736)$
$= 61 - 34{\cdot}416$
$= 26{\cdot}584$

$\therefore\ a = \sqrt{26{\cdot}584} = 5{\cdot}16$

$\therefore$ BC is 5·16 cm long (to 3 S.F.).

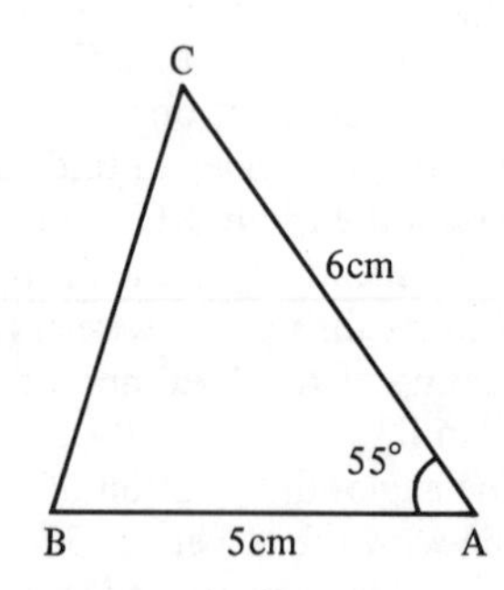

Example 2

In the triangle on the right, find the size of B$\hat{A}$C.
In triangle ABC,

$a = 5, b = 6, c = 6{\cdot}5$

Hence $\cos \hat{A} = \dfrac{6^2 + 6{\cdot}5^2 - 5^2}{2 \times 6 \times 6{\cdot}5}$

$= \dfrac{36 + 42{\cdot}25 - 25}{78}$

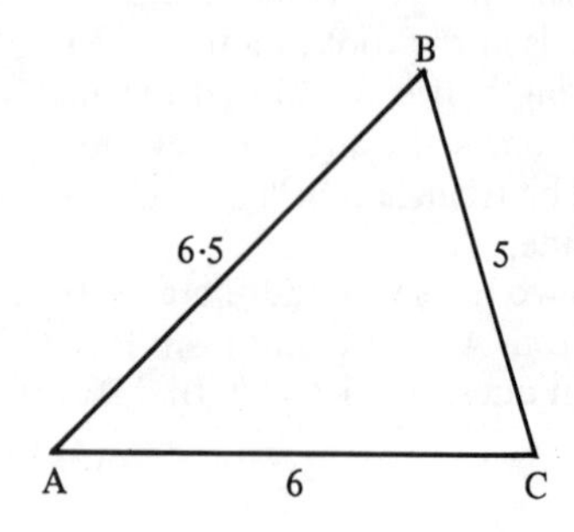

$$= \frac{78{\cdot}25 - 25}{78}$$

$$= \frac{53{\cdot}25}{78}$$

	No.	Log.
	53·25	1·7263
÷	78	1·8921
	46° 57′	$\bar{1}$·8342

$\therefore$ log cos $\hat{A} = \bar{1}{\cdot}8342 \qquad \hat{A} = 46° \, 57'$.

In any triangle ABC, if the length of all three sides is given, then its area A may be found by using the formula

$$A = \sqrt{s(s-a)(s-b)(s-c)} \text{ where } s = \frac{a+b+c}{2}$$

Example 3

Find the area of triangle ABC.

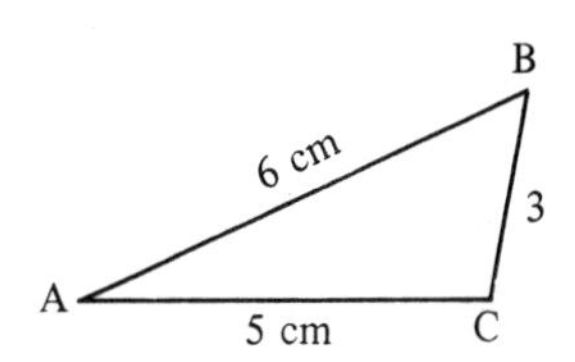

$$s = \frac{3+5+6}{2} = 7$$

$$A = \sqrt{7(7-3)(7-5)(7-6)}$$

$$= \sqrt{7 \times 4 \times 2 \times 1} = \sqrt{56} = 7{\cdot}48 \text{ cm}^2 \text{ (to 3 S.F.)}.$$

Exercise 6.8

In questions 1 to 10, calculate the length of the side opposite the given angle.

1. A = 34°, b = 4 cm, c = 5 cm.
2. B = 51°, a = 3 cm, c = 6 cm.
3. C = 18°, a = 5 cm, b = 12 cm.
4. A = 44° 12′, b = 19 cm, c = 31 cm.
5. B = 72° 6′, a = 6 cm, c = 16 cm.
6. C = 81° 54′, a = 8 cm, b = 5 cm.
7. A = 47° 33′, b = 9 cm, c = 11 cm.
8. B = 51° 47′, a = 8·4 cm, c = 9·1 cm.
9. C = 66° 17′, a = 7·66 cm, b = 8·12 cm.
10. A = 37° 4′, b = 3·54 cm, c = 4·81 cm.

In questions 11 to 20, find the smallest angle

11. a = 3 cm, b = 4 cm, c = 6 cm.
12. a = 4 cm, b = 5 cm, c = 8 cm.
13. a = 10 cm, b = 4 cm, c = 7 cm.
14. a = 12 cm, b = 11 cm, c = 16 cm.
15. a = 11 cm, b = 9 cm, c = 7 cm.
16. a = 8·1 cm, b = 9·2 cm, c = 10·3 cm.
17. a = 7·6 cm, b = 8·7 cm, c = 9·3 cm.
18. a = 3·7 cm, b = 2·1 cm, c = 4·7 cm.
19. a = 16·8 cm, b = 13·2 cm, c = 14·9 cm.
20. a = 10·6 cm, b = 12·4 cm, c = 9·8 cm.

21. A ship sails for 5 km on a bearing of 060° and then for 4 km on a bearing of 300°. What is her distance and bearing from her starting point?
22. From a lighthouse on a quay one buoy is 5 km away on a bearing of 050° and another 2 km away on a bearing of 030°. How far apart are the buoys?
23. A golfer is playing a 100 m hole. He hits his ball at 40° to the correct line and it travels 60 m. How far is the ball from the hole?
24. Two cricketers are 5 m apart in the outfield. The batsman is 12 m from one and 10 m from the other. Within what angle must he hit the ball if it is to pass between the two fielders?
25. An astronomer observes that he has to swing his telescope through 10° to view first one star and then another. If the two stars are respectively 50 and 80 light years away, how far apart are they?
26. Find the area of the triangles in Questions 11 to 15.

6.9 Ratios of angles > 90°

The diagram on the right shows the ratio which is positive for angles between 0° and 360°.

For example, between 180° and 270°, the tangent is positive and the sine and the cosine are negative.

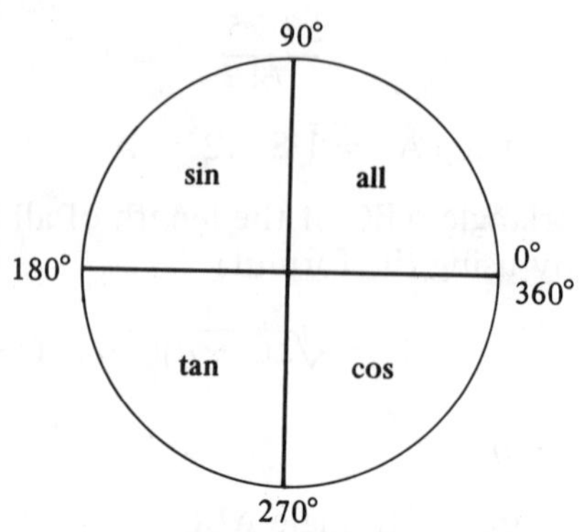

To find from tables the numerical value of the ratio of any angle θ:

(a) $90° < \theta < 180°$

Obtain the sign; then use the value of the ratio for $180° - \theta$.

Example $\tan 153° = -\tan(180° - 153°) = -\tan 27° = -0{\cdot}5095$

(b) $180° < \theta < 270°$

Obtain the sign; then use the value of the ratio for $\theta - 180°$.

Example $\sin 220° = -\sin(220° - 180°) = -\sin 40° = -0{\cdot}6428$

(c) $270° < \theta < 360°$

Obtain the sign; then use the value of the ratio for $360° - \theta$.

Example $\cos 339° = +\cos(360° - 339°) = \cos 21° = 0{\cdot}9336$

Remember that between 0° and 360°, there may be two angles with the same value for a trigonometric ratio.

Example $\cos^{-1}(-0{\cdot}8660)$ is 150° or 210°

Exercise 6.9

Using tables, find the value of

1. sin 120°
2. cos 120°
3. tan 120°
4. sin 135°
5. cos 135°
6. tan 135°
7. cos 150°
8. tan 100°
9. sin 95°
10. sin 150°
11. cos 100°
12. tan 150°
13. sin 175°
14. sin 130°
15. tan 95°
16. cos 110°
17. tan 156°
18. sin 145°
19. tan 155°
20. cos 136°
21. sin 255°
22. sin (−103)°
23. cos (−200)°
24. cos 253°
25. sin 316°
26. tan 328°
27. tan (−300)°
28. cos 294°
29. sin 564°
30. cos 667°

Using tables, find the angles in the range $0°$ to $360°$ which satisfy the following

31. $\sin^{-1}(-0{\cdot}5)$
32. $\cos^{-1}(-0{\cdot}5)$
33. $\tan^{-1}(-0{\cdot}5)$
34. $\tan^{-1} 1$
35. $\sin^{-1} 0{\cdot}866$
36. $\cos^{-1} 0{\cdot}866$
37. $\tan^{-1}(-1)$
38. $\cos^{-1}(-0{\cdot}7771)$
39. $\sin^{-1}(-0{\cdot}866)$
40. $\cos^{-1} 0$
41. $\sin^{-1}(-0{\cdot}6667)$
42. $\cos^{-1} 0{\cdot}625$
43. $\tan^{-1}(-1{\cdot}54)$
44. $\cos 3\theta = 0$
45. $\sin 2\theta = -1$
46. $\sin 3\theta = 0{\cdot}809$
47. $\sin\theta = 0{\cdot}53$
48. $\cos\theta = -0{\cdot}82$
49. $\tan\theta = 0{\cdot}76$
50. $\tan 4x = -0{\cdot}404$

Express the following ratios as the same ratio of an acute angle

51. $\sin 190°$
52. $\cos 350°$
53. $\sin 110°$
54. $\cos 250°$
55. $\sin 325°$
56. $\cos 145°$
57. $\tan 220°$
58. $\tan 125°$
59. $\tan 315°$
60. $\sin 570°$
61. $\tan 550°$
62. $\cos 660°$

63. If $\cos\hat{A} = -\frac{3}{5}$ and $\hat{A}$ is obtuse find $\sin\hat{A}$ and $\tan\hat{A}$.

64. If $\tan\hat{A} = -\frac{11}{60}$ and $\hat{A}$ is obtuse find $\sin\hat{A}$ and $\cos\hat{A}$.

65. If $\sin\hat{X} = 0{\cdot}9511$ and $\hat{X}$ is acute find $\tan\hat{X}$ and $\tan 2\hat{X}$.
66. When $\hat{A}$ is obtuse, $\sin\hat{A} = \frac{12}{15}$. Find the value of $(\tan\hat{A} - \cos\hat{A})$.
67. Find all the angles between $360°$ and $720°$ whose tangent is $0{\cdot}75$.
68. If $\sin\hat{A} = \frac{5}{13}$, find the value of
(a) $\sin^2\hat{A} + \cos^2\hat{A}$
(b) $\dfrac{\sin\hat{A}}{\cos\hat{A}}$

69. If $\operatorname{cosec}\hat{X} = -2$, find all possible values of $\hat{X}$ between $0°$ and $720°$.
70. If $\cos\hat{A} = \frac{8}{17}$ find the value of $\tan\hat{A} + \sin\hat{A}$
(a) when $\hat{A}$ is acute
(b) when $\hat{A}$ lies between $270°$ and $360°$
Show that $1 + \tan^2 A = \sec^2 A$.

6.10 Sine and cosine rule for angles > 90°

Note from section 6.9:

$$\sin 110^\circ = +\sin(180 - 110)^\circ$$
$$= +\sin 70^\circ$$
$$\cos 110^\circ = -\cos(180 - 110)^\circ$$
$$= -\cos 70.$$

Example 1

In triangle ABC on the right, $\hat{A} = 110^\circ$, $a = 8$ cm and $c = 5$ cm; find $\hat{C}$.

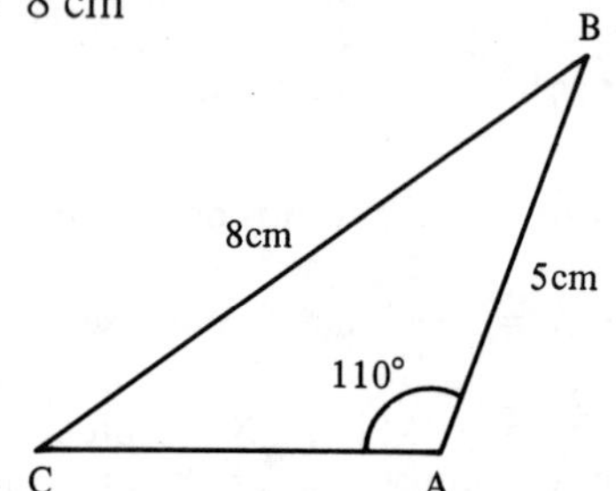

Using the sine rule,

$$\frac{\sin \hat{A}}{a} = \frac{\sin \hat{C}}{c}$$

$$\frac{\sin 110^\circ}{8} = \frac{\sin \hat{C}}{5}$$

$$\therefore \quad 8 \sin \hat{C} = 5 \times \sin 110^\circ$$

$$\sin \hat{C} = \frac{5 \times \sin 70}{8}$$

$$= \frac{5 \times 0{\cdot}9397}{8}$$

$$= \frac{4{\cdot}6985}{8} = 0{\cdot}5873$$

$$\hat{C} = 35^\circ 58'.$$

Example 2

Find the length of the side opposite the given angle in triangle ABC, when $\hat{A} = 108^\circ$, $b = 4$ cm and $c = 9$ cm.

Using the cosine rule,

$$a^2 = (b^2 + c^2) - (2 \times b \times c \times \cos \hat{A})$$
$$= (4^2 + 9^2) - (2 \times 4 \times 9 \times \cos 108^\circ)$$

but $\cos 108^\circ = -\cos(180 - 108^\circ) = -\cos 72^\circ = -0{\cdot}3090$

$$\therefore a^2 = (16 + 81) - 72 \times (-0{\cdot}3090)$$
$$= 97 - (-22{\cdot}248)$$
$$= 97 + 22{\cdot}248$$
$$= 119{\cdot}25 \text{ (to 2 D.P.)}$$

$\therefore \quad a = \sqrt{119{\cdot}25} = 10{\cdot}92$

$\therefore$ length of the side opposite the given angle is 10·9 cm (to 3 S.F.).

Example 3

Find the largest angle in triangle ABC in which $a = 6$ cm, $b = 5$ cm and $c = 9$ cm.

As the largest angle is opposite to the largest side, the required angle is $\hat{C}$.

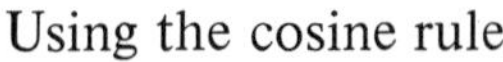

Using the cosine rule

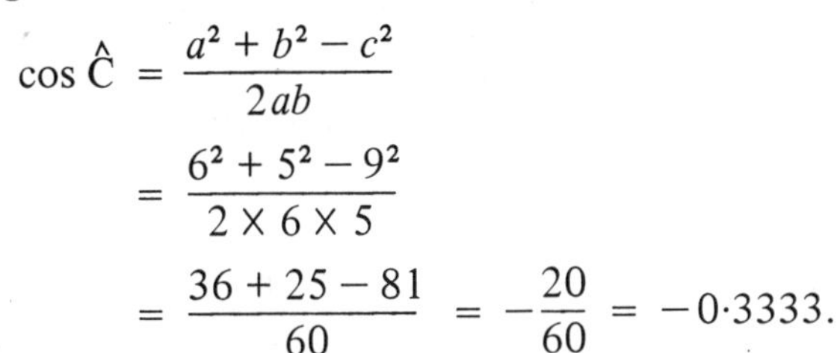

$$\cos \hat{C} = \frac{a^2 + b^2 - c^2}{2ab}$$

$$= \frac{6^2 + 5^2 - 9^2}{2 \times 6 \times 5}$$

$$= \frac{36 + 25 - 81}{60} = -\frac{20}{60} = -0{\cdot}3333.$$

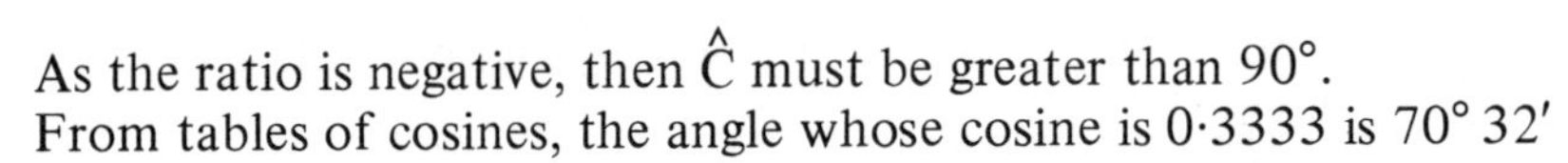

As the ratio is negative, then $\hat{C}$ must be greater than 90°.
From tables of cosines, the angle whose cosine is 0·3333 is 70° 32′

$\therefore$ the required angle is $180° - 70°\,32' = 109°\,28'$.

Exercise 6.10

1. If $\hat{A} = 120°$, $a = 10$ cm, $b = 8$ cm, find $\hat{B}$.
2. If $\hat{A} = 95°$, $a = 6$ cm, $c = 4$ cm, find $\hat{C}$.
3. If $\hat{B} = 105°$, $b = 12$ cm, $c = 9$ cm, find $\hat{C}$.
4. If $\hat{C} = 126°$, $c = 8$ cm, $a = 7$ cm, find $\hat{A}$.
5. If $\hat{B} = 114°$, $b = 17$ cm, $a = 12$ cm, find $\hat{A}$.
6. If $\hat{A} = 108°\,6'$, $a = 19{\cdot}5$ cm, $b = 15{\cdot}1$ cm, find $\hat{B}$.
7. If $\hat{C} = 144°\,36'$, $c = 6{\cdot}7$ cm, $b = 4{\cdot}4$ cm, find $\hat{B}$.
8. If $\hat{A} = 92°\,17'$, $a = 4{\cdot}32$ cm, $c = 2{\cdot}26$ cm, find $\hat{C}$.
9. If $\hat{C} = 121°\,35'$, $c = 5{\cdot}816$ cm, $a = 4{\cdot}772$ cm, find $\hat{A}$.
10. If $\hat{B} = 104°\,14'$, $b = 6{\cdot}922$ cm, $a = 3{\cdot}041$ cm, find $\hat{A}$.

Find the largest angle in the following triangles whose sides are given below. The units may be taken as cm.

11. 4, 6, 9 **12.** 3, 4, 6 **13.** 4, 5, 8 **14.** 5, 7, 11
15. 5, 8, 12 **16.** 5, 6, 8 **17.** 9, 10, 15 **18.** 8, 11, 16
19. 3·1, 4·6, 7·2 **20.** 4·9, 5·1, 9·5

In questions **21** to **28**, calculate the side opposite the given angle.

21. $\hat{A} = 100°$, $b = 3$ cm, $c = 6$ cm.
22. $\hat{B} = 120°$, $a = 4$ cm, $c = 7$ cm.
23. $\hat{C} = 98°$, $a = 9$ cm, $b = 6$ cm.
24. $\hat{B} = 145°$, $a = 8$ cm, $c = 17$ cm.
25. $\hat{A} = 160°$, $b = 14$ cm, $c = 15$ cm.
26. $\hat{C} = 112°\,6'$, $a = 19$ cm, $b = 21$ cm.
27. $\hat{A} = 94°\,18'$, $b = 8{\cdot}6$ cm, $c = 9{\cdot}4$ cm.
28. $\hat{B} = 103°\,27'$, $a = 9{\cdot}2$ cm, $c = 8{\cdot}1$ cm.

6.11 Triangle of velocities

If an object has two component velocities which can be represented by the sides of a triangle AB and BC, then the resultant velocity is that represented by the side AC.

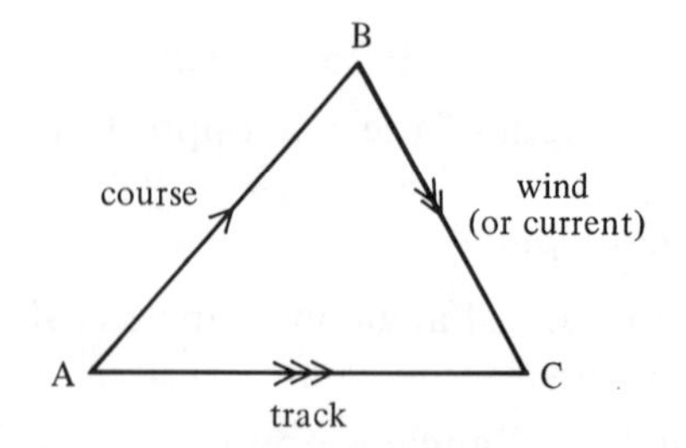

The *course* is the direction in which the object is heading. It is measured clockwise from North, and is represented by one arrow.

The *track* is the direction actually travelled, and is represented by three arrows.

The *wind* is the direction *from* which it blows. The direction to which the wind blows is represented by two arrows. e.g. a north-westerly wind blows from a direction 315°.

The *current* is the direction in which the current flows and is represented by two arrows.

Note. In a triangle of velocities, the number of arrows clockwise should equal the number of arrows anticlockwise.

The drift is the angle between the course and the track. The direction of the wind (or current) is always from course to track.

course
track

Problems are solved either by scale drawing or by calculation using trigonometric methods.
To solve a problem

(a) Draw a rough sketch, and put in the direction arrows carefully.
(b) If a scale drawing solution is used, decide upon a suitable scale, draw the figure accurately, and read off the required answer.
(c) If a trigonometric solution is attempted, label the diagram clearly, put in all given lengths and angles, and then carry out the necessary calculations.

Example

An aeroplane requires to follow a track of 060°. If its airspeed is 300 knots, and the wind velocity is 30 knots from 140°, find
(a) the course and (b) the ground-speed.

Sketch

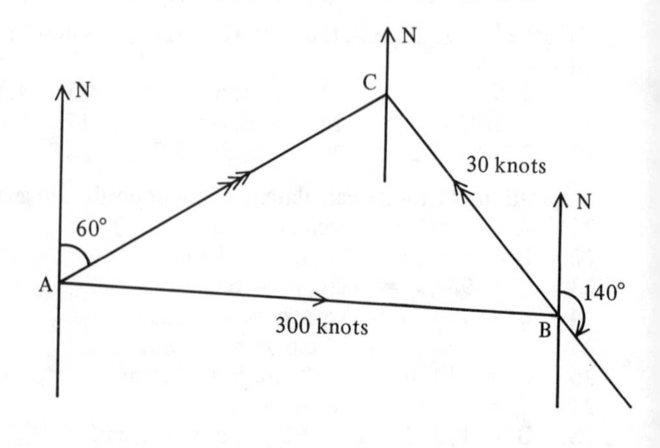

Let AC represent the track, AB the course, and BC the wind.

Then in triangle ABC, $A\hat{C}B = 100°$ or $(360 - 140 - 120)°$, angle $(C\hat{A}B + 60°)$ will be the required course, and AC will be the groundspeed.

(a) To find $C\hat{A}B$, use the sine rule: $a = 30$, $c = 300$, $\hat{C} = 100°$

$$\frac{\sin 100°}{300} = \frac{\sin C\hat{A}B}{30} \qquad \sin C\hat{A}B = \frac{30 \sin 100°}{300}$$

But $\quad \sin 100° = \sin(180 - 100)° = \sin 80°$

$$\therefore \ \sin C\hat{A}B = \frac{30 \sin 80°}{300} = \frac{\sin 80°}{10} = \frac{0{\cdot}9848}{10} = 0{\cdot}098\,48$$

$\therefore \quad C\hat{A}B = 5°\,39'$ and course required is $060° + 5°\,39' = 065°\,39'$.

(b) To find AC, use the sine rule: $A\hat{B}C = (180° - 100° - 5°\,39') = 74°\,21'$, $a = 30$, $c = 300$, and $A\hat{C}B = 100°$

$$\frac{AC}{\sin 74°\,21'} = \frac{300}{\sin 100°}$$

$$\therefore \ AC = \frac{300 \sin 74°\,21'}{\sin 100°} = \frac{300 \times 0{\cdot}9629}{0{\cdot}9848} = 293{\cdot}3$$

$\therefore$ the groundspeed is 293 knots (to 3 S.F.).

The solution to this example by scale drawing is shown by the diagram on the right.

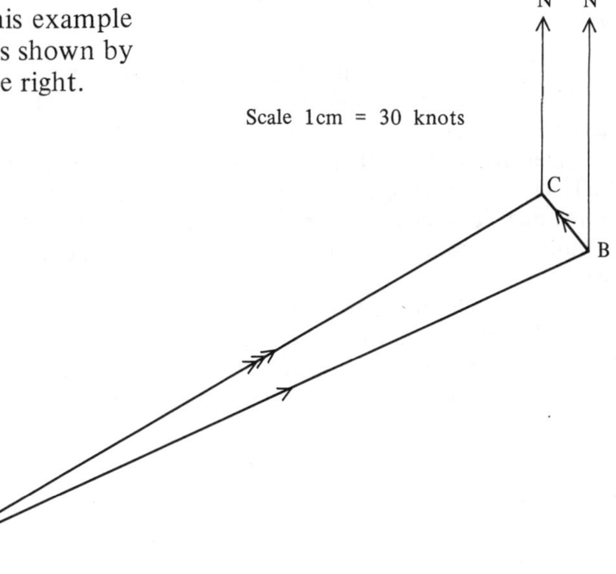

Method:

(a) Draw BC 1 cm long to represent the wind from 140°; mark with 2 arrows.
(b) Through C draw a line to represent the track coming to C.
(c) With centre B and radius 10 cm to represent the airspeed, cut the track at at A.

Then AB is the course 066°. AC is the groundspeed $= 9{\cdot}75 \times 30 = 292{\cdot}5$ knots.

Exercise 6.11

In questions 1 to 5, R is the resultant of velocities P and Q which are at right angles (shown in the diagram).

1. If P = 3 km/h and Q = 4 km/h, find R and θ.
2. If P = 5 km/h and Q = 7km/h, find R and θ.
3. If Q = 8 km/h and R = 12 km/h, find P and θ.
4. If P = 9 km/h and R = 14 km/h, find Q and θ.
5. If R = 10 km/h and θ = 42°, find P and Q.

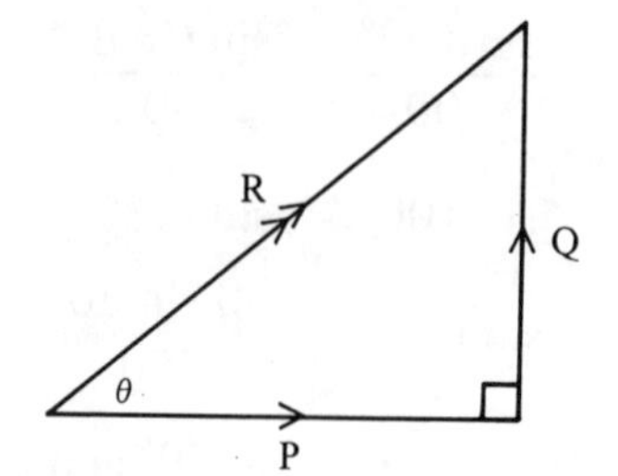

Questions 6 to 10 may be solved by calculation or by accurate drawing.

6. If P = 5 km/h, Q = 4 km/h and ϕ = 60°, find R and θ.
7. If P = 10 km/h, Q = 7 km/h and ϕ = 30°, find R and θ.
8. If Q = 50 km/h, θ = 30° and ϕ = 45°, find P and R.
9. If R = 70 km/h, θ = 40° and ϕ = 50°, find P and Q.
10. If R = 50 km/h, Q = 40 km/h and θ = 50°, find P and ϕ.

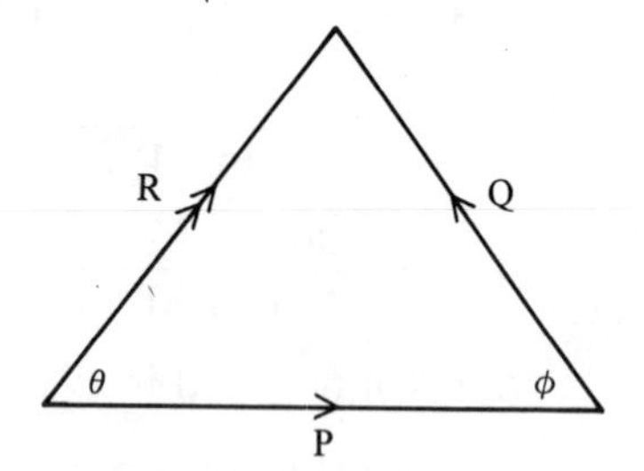

11. A pilot wishes to fly from A to a point B, due North of him. He can fly at 450 km/h in still air but faces a 60 km/h wind blowing from the north-east. In what direction should he steer his aeroplane and what is his groundspeed?
12. A boat is being steered North at 10 knots but is in a 2 knot current flowing from a bearing of 060°. On what bearing is the boat actually moving and at what speed?
13. A boat is steered due North and is moving through the water at 12 knots but is actually moving at 8 knots on a bearing of 350°. What is the speed and direction of the current in which it is sailing?
14. How long will it take a pilot to fly from A to B, 500 km due East of A, if he can fly at 800 km/h in still air but is faced with a south-easterly gale of 50 km/h?
15. An observer on the ground sees an aeroplane flying on a course of 060° and he estimates its speed to be 400 km/h. If there is a 20 km/h wind blowing from due South, what is the aeroplane's air speed?

Miscellaneous exercise 6

1. In the following triangles
   (a) find c if $\hat{C}$ = 141°13′, a = 13·4 cm, b = 15·8 cm.
   (b) find a if $\hat{A}$ = 162°55′, b = 16·22 cm, c = 18·31 cm.
2. A ship which can steam at 30 knots in still water is in a south-westerly current flowing at 10 knots. Find
   (a) in what direction and at what speed the ship will travel if it is steered due North
   (b) on what bearing it must be steered in order to travel due West and how long it will take to cover a distance of 100 nautical miles.

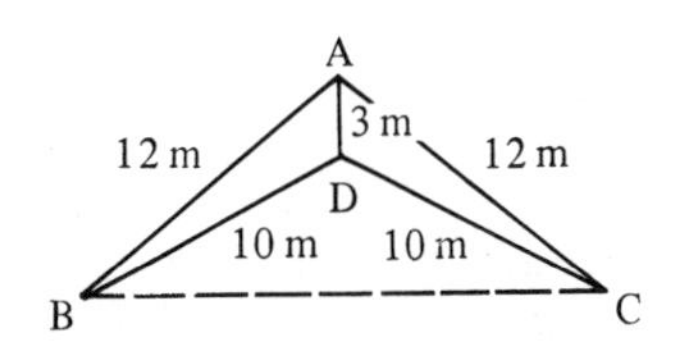

3. The diagram shows a symmetrical roof truss in which BD = DC = 10 m, AB = AC = 12 m, and AD = 3 m. Find $A\hat{B}D$ and the height of A above BC.
4. VABCDE is a right pyramid, vertex V, on a regular pentagonal base ABCDE. If it is 8 cm high and each side of the base is 5 cm, calculate (a) the length of edge VA (b) the angle between face VAB and the base (c) the angle between face VAB and edge DV.
5. Three circles centres A, B, and C, and radii 4, 5, and 6 cm touch each other. Find the area of triangle ABC and the size of $C\hat{B}A$.
6. ABC is a triangle on horizontal ground. AC = 50 m, AB = 70 m, and $A\hat{C}B = 60°$. At C stands a tower DC. The angle of elevation of D from A is 48°. Find the height of the tower and its angle of elevation from M, the mid-point of BC.
7. In triangle XYZ, $\hat{Z} = 90°$, XY = 2·367 cm, XZ = 1·983 cm. Find $\hat{X}$.
8. In triangle ABC, $\hat{C} = 90°$, AB = 0·0452 cm, AC = 0·0245 cm. Find $\hat{A}$.
9. At noon when the sun is at an angle of elevation of 60° a man is standing due East of a tower. He notices that the end of the shadow of the tower is 50 m from him in a north-westerly direction. How high is the tower?
10. ABC is a horizontal equilateral triangle and VA is the perpendicular to the plane ABC through A. If the angle of elevation of V from the mid-point of the base BC of the triangle is 62°, what is the angle of elevation from B?
11. A man on one bank of a river observes that the angle of elevation of a tree directly opposite to him on the other bank is 36°. On walking 100 m along the bank it is 18°. How high is the tree and how wide the river?
12. The elevation of the top of a tower from a point due North is 60° and from a point due East is 50°. If the two points are 100 m apart find the height of the tower.
13. In triangle PQR, $\hat{R} = 90°$, PR = 0·5698 cm, QR = 2·432 cm, find $\hat{Q}$.
14. A pilot, flying above thick cloud, believes himself to be flying due West at 500 km/h. In fact he is making a groundspeed of 540 km/h on a bearing of 260°. What is the speed and direction of the wind which is blowing him off course?
15. ABCD is a quadrilateral in which AB = 8 cm, AD = 15 cm, $A\hat{B}C = 110°$, $A\hat{D}C = 60°$, and $B\hat{A}D = 90°$. Calculate
    (a) the length of BD
    (b) the size of $A\hat{D}B$
    (c) the length of BC.
16. VABCD is a pyramid on a square base of side 10 cm. VA = VB = VC = VD = 15 cm. Calculate
    (a) the length of AC, the diagonal of the base
    (b) the vertical height VM of the pyramid
    (c) the angle between the edge VA and the base
    (d) the angle between the face VAD and the base.
17. The bearing of town B from A is 063°, and town C is due East of A. If the distance of A to B is 42 km and $A\hat{B}C = 110°$, calculate
    (a) the bearing of B from C
    (b) the distance AC
    (c) the area of triangle ABC.
18. A triangle of area 100 cm^2 has two of its sides 15 cm and 17 cm long. Find the angle between them.
19. In triangle ABC, $c = 9$ cm, $b = 8$ cm and angle C = 70°. Find its area.

Part 7 Calculus

7.1 Gradients by drawing

In this and later sections of this book, we shall use the mathematician's definition of gradient. The gradient of a line is the tangent of the angle which the line makes with the horizontal.

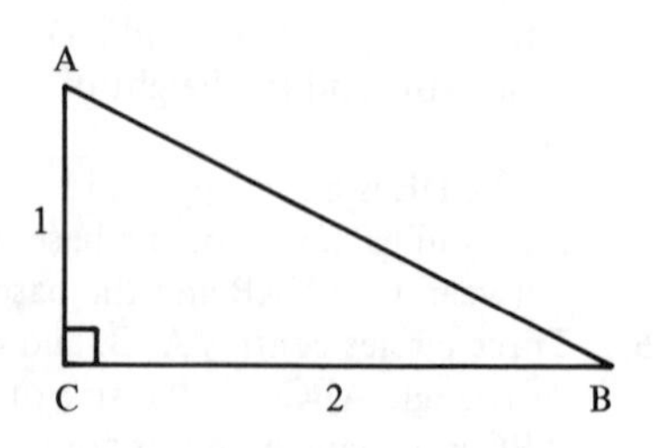

In the diagram, the gradient of AB is $\frac{1}{2}$ or

$\tan A\hat{B}C = 0{\cdot}5$.

The gradient of a curve at a given point is the gradient of the tangent to the curve at this point.

Example

If $y = x^2$, then the gradient of the curve when $x = 2$ is 4.
The gradient of the tangent at this point is $\frac{AB}{AC} = \frac{8}{2} = 4$.

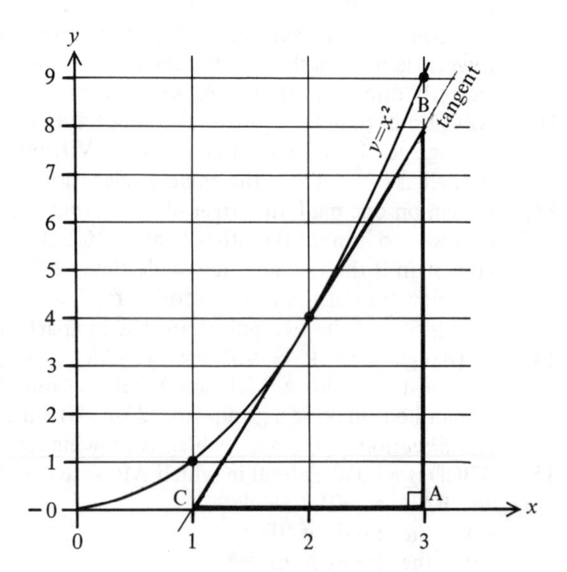

Exercise 7.1

1. A ball rolls down an inclined plane. It travels s centimetres in t seconds and s and t are connected by the equation $s = 2t^2$.
   Draw a graph representing this motion and from it answer the following questions.
   (a) How far has the ball travelled in the first second?
   (b) How far has it travelled in the fourth second?
   (c) What is its average speed in the first six seconds?
   (d) What is its average speed during the third second?
   (e) What is its speed at the end of the fourth second?
2. Draw the graph of $y = x^2 + 2$. Mark on it the points P, where $x = 2$, and Q where $x = 4$.
   (a) What is the gradient of the line PQ?
   (b) Mark the point R on the curve where $x = 3$. What is the gradient of the line PR?
   (c) Draw as accurately as you can the tangents to the curve at P, Q, and R. What are their gradients?

3. The distance d metres fallen by a stone in t seconds is given by the equation $d = 5t^2$.
   (a) How far has it travelled in 4 seconds?
   (b) What is its average speed for the first two seconds?
   (c) What is its average speed during the fifth second?
   (d) What is its speed when $t = 6$ seconds?
   (e) What is its speed when $t = 8$ seconds?
4. Find the gradient of $y = \frac{1}{x}$ at the point where $x = 2$.
5. Find the gradient of $y = 4x + 1$ at the points where $x = 0$ and 4.
6. Find the gradient of $y = 2 - x^2$ at the points where $x = 3$ and -3.
7. The distance s metres travelled in t seconds by a body moving in a straight line is given by the equation $s = 128t - 10t^2$.
   What is its speed when $t = 0, 4$, and 8 seconds?
   Can you explain what is meant by the third answer?
8. The distance y metres travelled in x seconds by a moving body is given by the equation
   $y = x + \frac{1}{x}$.
   Find its speed when $x = 1, 2$ and 3 seconds.
9. With the same data as question 8, find the speed at $\frac{1}{4}$ second and $\frac{1}{2}$ second.
10. Find the gradient of the curve $y = x^3$ at points where $x = 1, -1$ and $\frac{1}{4}$.
11. (a) Show that the curve $y = x^2 - 3x + 2$ cuts the x-axis at the point X (2, 0).
    (b) The curve also cuts the x-axis at the point Y. What are the co-ordinates of the point Y?
    (c) Find the gradient of the curve at the points X and Y.
12. Find the gradient of the curve $y = 3x - x^2$ at the points where
    (a) $x = 2$ (b) $x = 3$ (c) $x = 0$ (d) $x = 1{\cdot}5$.

7.2 Differentiation by rule

The following gives the procedures for differentiation.

(a) Simplify the expression:

e.g. $$\frac{x^2 - 4}{x + 2} = \frac{(x + 2)(x - 2)}{x + 2} = x - 2$$

(b) Put all terms in index form:

e.g. $$\frac{1}{\sqrt{x^3}} = x^{-\frac{3}{2}}$$

(c) If $y = ax^n$ where a is a constant, then $\frac{dy}{dx} = nax^{n-1}$. This is known as differentiation of y with respect to x.

(d) Give the answer in its simplest form, that is, without negative or fractional indices.

Example

Differentiate with respect to x, $\frac{x^4 - 2x^3 - 5}{x^2}$.

$$\text{Let } y = \frac{x^4 - 2x^3 - 5}{x^2} = \frac{x^4}{x^2} - \frac{2x^3}{x^2} - \frac{5}{x^2}$$

$$= x^2 - 2x - 5x^{-2}$$

$$\therefore \quad \frac{dy}{dx} = 2x - 2 - -2.5x^{-3}$$

$$= 2x - 2 + 10x^{-3}$$

$$= 2x - 2 + \frac{10}{x^3}$$

Note. If $y = x^4$, then $\frac{dy}{dx} = 4x^3$,

and $$\frac{d}{dx}\left(\frac{dy}{dx}\right) = \frac{d^2y}{dx^2} = 12x^2.$$

$\frac{dy}{dx}$ is known as the first derivative and $\frac{d^2y}{dx^2}$ is the second derivative of y with respect to x.

Exercise 7.2

Differentiate with respect to x the expressions in questions 1 to 30.

1. x^4
2. x^7
3. $10x^2$
4. $\frac{1}{x^2}$
5. $x + \frac{1}{x}$
6. $4x^2 - 6x$
7. 4
8. $\frac{1}{3}x^3 - 2$
9. $x^2 \times x^4$
10. $(2x)^4$
11. $(x + 1)^2$
12. x^n
13. $\sqrt{x}$
14. $\sqrt{4x^3}$
15. $x^{3\frac{1}{2}}$
16. $\frac{1}{\sqrt{x}}$
17. x^0
18. $x^{-\frac{1}{4}}$
19. $\sqrt[5]{x}$
20. $3x^2 + 6x - 7$
21. $x^{\frac{1}{2}n}$
22. $(x + 1)(x + 2)$
23. $(x - 3)(x + 4)$
24. $(2x + 1)(x - 1)$
25. $(x - 1)^2$
26. $\frac{x^2 + 3x - 4}{x - 1}$
27. $\frac{x^2 - 5x + 6}{x - 3}$
28. $\left(x + \frac{1}{x}\right)^2$
29. $\sqrt[b]{x}$
30. $\sqrt{x^b}$
31. If $y = 3x^2 + 5$, find $\frac{dy}{dx}$ when $x = 2$.
32. If $y = (x - 1)^2$, find $\frac{dy}{dx}$ when $x = 3$.
33. If $y = x^2 + 2x - 6$, find the value of x when $\frac{dy}{dx} = 0$.
34. If $y = \frac{1}{3}x^3 - 1\frac{1}{2}x^2 + 2x + 5$, find the values of x when $\frac{dy}{dx} = 0$.
35. If $y = \frac{1}{3}x^3 + 2\frac{1}{2}x^2 + 6x - 5$, find the values of x when $\frac{dy}{dx} = 0$.
36. If $y = 8x^2$, find $\frac{d^2y}{dx^2}$.
37. If $y = x^3 + 6x^2 + 2$, find $\frac{d^2y}{dx^2}$.
38. If $y = 6x^2$, prove that $x\frac{dy}{dx} = 2y$.
39. If $y = x(1 - x)$, prove that $1 + \frac{dy}{dx} = \frac{2y}{x}$.
40. If $y = x^3$, prove that $\frac{dy}{dx} \cdot \frac{d^2y}{dx^2} = 18y$.
41. If $y = 50x - 16x^2$, find $\frac{dy}{dx}$ and $\frac{d^2y}{dx^2}$ when $x = 0, 1$, and 2.
42. If $y = 2x^2 + 3x^3$, find $\frac{dy}{dx}$ and $\frac{d^2y}{dx^2}$ when $x = 1$ and 4.
43. If $pv = c$ where c is a constant, prove $\frac{dp}{dv} = -\frac{p}{v}$.
44. If $s = ut + \frac{1}{2}at^2$ where u and a are constants, prove that $\frac{d^2s}{dt^2}$ is constant.

7.3 Gradients by calculation

The gradient of a curve at the point (x, y) is called its derived function. It is found by differentiating y with respect to x.

Example 1

Find the gradient of the curve $y = 3x^2 - 2x + 3$ at the point (3, 24).

$$y = 3x^2 - 2x + 3$$

$$\therefore \frac{dy}{dx} = 6x - 2 \quad \text{which gives the gradient.}$$

The gradient at the point (3, 24), i.e. where $x = 3$ is equal to $(6 \times 3) - 2 = 18 - 2 = 16$.

Example 2

If $y = x^2 - 3x + 2$, find the value of x at the point on the curve where the tangent makes an angle of 16° 42′ with the x-axis.

$$y = x^2 - 3x + 2$$

$$\therefore \frac{dy}{dx} = 2x - 3 \quad \text{which gives the gradient.}$$

But the required gradient is the angle whose tangent is 16° 42′, i.e. 0·3.

$$\therefore 2x - 3 = 0{\cdot}3$$

$$2x = 3{\cdot}3$$

$$x = 1{\cdot}65$$

$\therefore x = 1{\cdot}65$ is the x co-ordinate of the required point on the curve.

Example 3

Find the equation of the tangent to the curve $y = x^2$ at the point (2, 4).

$$y = x^2$$

$$\therefore \frac{dy}{dx} = 2x \text{ which gives the gradient.}$$

The gradient at the point (2, 4), i.e. where $x = 2$ is equal to $(2 \times 2) = 4$.

$\therefore$ the required line is one with a gradient of 4, and it passes through the point (2, 4).

If $y = mx + c$, where m is the gradient,

then $y = 4x + c$.

As the point (2, 4) lies on this line

$$4 = (4 \times 2) + c$$

$$4 = 8 + c$$
$$c = -4$$

$\therefore$ the equation of the tangent is $y = 4x - 4$.

Exercise 7.3

1. Find the gradient of the following curves at the points indicated:
   (a) $y = 2x^2 + 3$ (1, 5) (b) $y = x^2 - 6$ (3, 3)
   (c) $y = \frac{8}{x^2}$ (2, 2) (d) $y = x^3 - 2x^2$ (0, 0)
   (e) $y = 2x^3 + x + 6$ (2, 24) (f) $y^2 = 4x^3$ (4, 16)
   (g) $xy = 12$ (3, 4) (h) $y = x(1-x)$ (1, 0)
   (i) $y = 2x + 7$ at any point (j) $y = 2x - 19$ at any point
2. Find the co-ordinates of the points indicated on the following curves.
   (a) $y = x^3 - 4x^2 - 2x + 8$ where the tangent is at 45° to the x-axis
   (b) $y = x^3 - 2x^2 - 5x + 10$ where the tangent is at 135° to the x-axis
   (c) $y = 2x^3 - 3x^2 + 1$ where the slope is 12
   (d) $xy = 12$ where the gradient is $-\frac{4}{3}$
   (e) $y = \frac{x^2}{5} + 2x$ where the tangent is inclined at 21° 48′ to the x-axis
3. Find the equations of the tangents to the following curves.
   (a) $y^2 = 4x$ at point (1, 2) (b) $y = 9 - \frac{1}{4}x^2$ at point (2, 8)
   (c) $5y = x^2 + 1$ at point (−2, 1) (d) $y^3 = 8x^2$ at point (−1, 2)
   (e) $xy = 9$ at point (3, 3)
4. P is the point (2, 12) on the curve $y = 3x^2$. If the tangent at P cuts the x-axis at T, find the length of OT.
5. P is the point (2, 2) on the curve $y = \frac{8}{x^2}$. If the tangent at P cuts the x-axis at T, find the length of OT.
6. P is the point (1, 1) on the curve $y = x^3$. PT is the tangent at P and PN is the perpendicular to the x-axis.
   Prove OT $= \frac{2}{3}$ ON.
7. P is the point $(2, \frac{1}{2})$ on the curve $y = \frac{1}{x}$. The tangent at P meets Ox at T and PN is the perpendicular from P to Ox. Find the slope of the curve at P and prove that ON = NT.
8. Sketch the graph of $y = \frac{1}{4}x^2 - 5$.
   Find the equation of the tangent at (6, 4).
   If this tangent cuts the axes at A and B, find the area of triangle AOB.
9. Find the co-ordinates of the points of intersection of the curves $y = 4x^2$ and $y = (x-1)^2$ and the equation of the tangents at these points.
10. Find the co-ordinates of the point on $y = 3x^2 - 4x$ where the tangent is parallel to $y = 8x$.
11. Find the equation of the tangent at (1, 0) to the curve $y = x^3 - 6x^2 + 11x - 6$ and the co-ordinates of the points of contact of the parallel tangent.
12. For the curve $y = 3x - x^2$, find the equation of the tangent which is parallel to the x-axis.

7.4 Speed and acceleration

1. If s is the distance travelled and t the time taken, then $\frac{ds}{dt}$ gives the speed or velocity at which the object is travelling at a given time.
2. If v is the velocity, and t the time, then $\frac{dv}{dt}$ gives the acceleration at a given time.

Note. Velocity is measured in metres per second and either written m/s or ms^{-1}.
Acceleration is measured in metres per second per second and is either written m/s^2 or ms^{-2}.

Example

A point moves on a straight line so that its distance s m. from a point A at a time t seconds is given by

$$s = 9t - 2t^2.$$

Find (a) expressions for the speed and the acceleration,
(b) the speed when $s = 9$ m,
(c) after how many seconds the point is at rest.

(a) $s = 9t - 2t^2$

$\therefore \frac{ds}{dt} = 9 - 4t$ which gives the speed,

and $\frac{dv}{dt} = 9$ which gives the acceleration.

(b) when $s = 9$, $9 = 9t - 2t^2$

and $2t^2 - 9t + 9 = 0$

$(2t - 3)(t - 3) = 0$

$\therefore$ either $2t - 3 = 0$ or $t - 3 = 0$

so $t = 1\frac{1}{2}$ or 3

$\therefore$ the point has travelled 9 metres after $1\frac{1}{2}$ seconds and after 3 seconds.

When $t = 1\frac{1}{2}$, the speed $= 9 - (4 \times 1\frac{1}{2})$
$= 9 - 6 = 3$ m/s

When $t = 3$, the speed $= 9 - (4 \times 3)$
$= 9 - 12 = -3$ m/s.

(c) The point is at rest when the speed is zero,

i.e. when $9 - 4t = 0$

$\therefore 4t = 9$

$t = 2\frac{1}{4}$

$\therefore$ the point is at rest after $2\frac{1}{4}$ seconds.

Exercise 7.4

1. A point moves along a straight line so that its distance s metres at time t seconds from its starting point is given by the following equations. Find its velocity and acceleration at the given times
   (a) $s = 4+t+t^2$ when $t = 2$
   (b) $s = 50t+10t^2$ when $t = 5$
   (c) $s = \dfrac{2}{t^2}$ when $t = 2$
   (d) $s = t(t+2)$ when $t = 15$
   (e) $s = 2(t-1)^2$ when $t = 50$
2. A stone dropped down a well falls s metres in t seconds, where $s = 5t^2$. Find its velocity after two seconds and when it reaches the water, 50 m below.
3. A stone is projected vertically upwards from the top of a tall building 220 m high. Its equation of motion is $s = 100t-5t^2$. Find its speed after 1 second and after 16 seconds. How fast is it moving as it reaches the ground?
4. A ball bearing projected along a tube full of glycerine moves according to the equation $s = 2{\cdot}7t-0{\cdot}1t^3$. How far does it go? Can this equation be true for *any* value of t? Explain briefly why.
5. A body moves according to the equation of motion $s = t^2-2t^3$. Find when it is at rest and when its acceleration is zero.
6. An electric train is moving at uniform speed when the brakes are applied. The distance s metres the train then travelled in t seconds was given by $s = 20t-0{\cdot}1t^2$. What is its speed after 1 minute and how far does it travel before coming to rest?
7. The distance s metres travelled in t seconds by a vehicle after the brakes are applied is given by $s = 15t-0{\cdot}4t^2$. What is its speed just as the brakes are applied and for how long does it run before stopping?
8. The equation of motion of a body which moves s metres in t seconds is given by $s = t^3-4t^2+1$. Find its acceleration when its velocity is zero and its velocity when its acceleration is zero.
9. With the data of question 3 find the greatest height above the ground reached by the stone.
10. A stone thrown vertically upwards from the ground rises s metres in t seconds such that $s = 50t-5t^2$. Find when it is half way up to its greatest height and the total distance it travels before coming to earth.
11. A train starts from rest and runs for two hours before stopping. The distance s kilometres travelled in t hours is given by $s = 10t^2(3-t)$. Did the train ever reach a speed of 60 km/h and if so, when? Did it ever reach 30 km/h and if so, when?
12. If $s = ut+\frac{1}{2}gt^2$ and $v = \dfrac{ds}{dt}$ where u and g are constants, show that $v = u+gt$ and $v^2-u^2 = 2gs$.

7.5 Maxima and minima

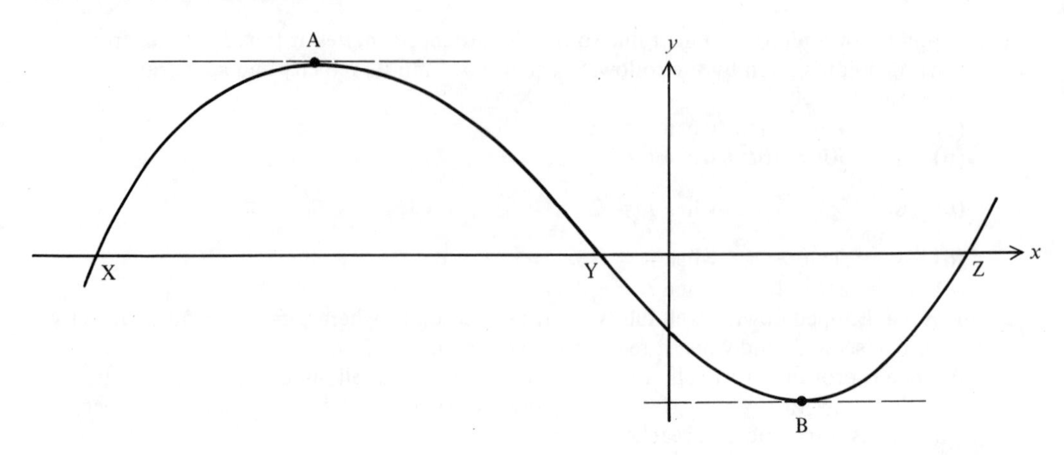

On the curve above, there are two points A and B where the gradient of the curve is zero. These are known as *turning points*. The tangents to the curve at A and B are parallel to the x-axis, i.e. the gradient of the curve at A and B = 0.

Point A is called a *maximum* point.
Point B is called a *minimum* point.

Maximum point

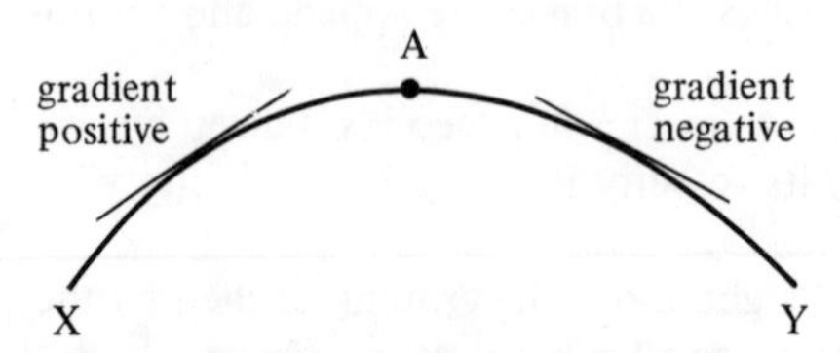

At a maximum point A the gradients are changing from positive to negative.

Minimum point

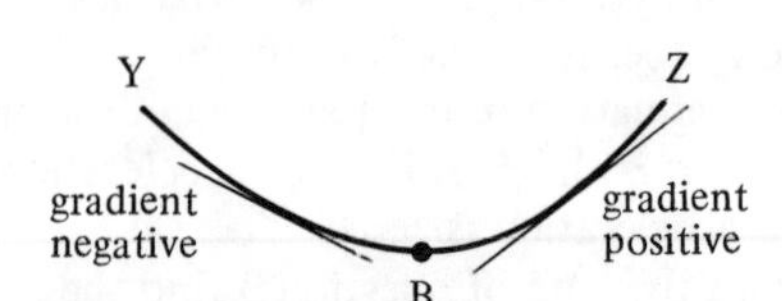

At a minimum point B the gradients are changing from negative to positive.

This change in the gradient can be found from the derived function of the gradient, i.e. $\frac{d^2y}{dx^2}$ or the rate of change of the gradient.

Note. At a maximum point, the value of $\frac{d^2y}{dx^2}$ is *negative.*

At a minimum point, the value of $\frac{d^2y}{dx^2}$ is *positive.*

Example 1

Find the turning point of the curve $y = x^2 - 3x + 2$ and state whether it is a maximum or a minimum point.

$$y = x^2 - 3x + 2$$

$$\frac{dy}{dx} = 2x - 3 \quad \text{which gives the gradient.}$$

Now, at a turning point $\frac{dy}{dx} = 0$,

so $2x - 3 = 0$

and $x = 1\frac{1}{2}$

When $x = 1\frac{1}{2}$,

$$y = (1\tfrac{1}{2})^2 - (3 \times 1\tfrac{1}{2}) + 2 = 2\tfrac{1}{4} - 4\tfrac{1}{2} + 2 = -\tfrac{1}{4}.$$

$\therefore$ the turning point is $(1\frac{1}{2}, -\frac{1}{4})$.

But $\frac{d^2y}{dx^2} = 2$, which gives the rate of change of the gradient, and as it is positive, then the turning point is a *minimum*.

Example 2

Investigate the nature of the turning points of the curve $y = x^3 - 12x + 6$

$$y = x^3 - 12x + 6$$

$$\frac{dy}{dx} = 3x^2 - 12 \quad \text{which gives the gradient.}$$

Now, at a turning point $\frac{dy}{dx} = 0$,

so
$$3x^2 - 12 = 0$$
$$x^2 - 4 = 0$$
$$(x + 2)(x - 2) = 0$$
$$\therefore \quad x = +2 \text{ or } -2.$$

$\therefore$ the graph has two turning points, (a) when $x = 2$ and (b) when $x = -2$.

(a) When $x = 2$,
$$y = (2)^3 - (12 \times 2) + 6 = 8 - 24 + 6 = -10$$

$\therefore$ $(2, -10)$ is a turning point, and at this point, $\frac{d^2y}{dx^2} = 6x$, which is the rate of change of the gradient. Because $x = 2$, $\frac{d^2y}{dx^2} = 6 \times 2 = 12$ which is positive, therefore $(2, -10)$ is a minimum point.

(b) When $x = -2, y = (-2)^3 - (12 \times -2) + 6$
$= -8 + 24 + 6 = +22$

$\therefore$ $(-2, 22)$ is a turning point, and at this point $\frac{d^2y}{dx^2} = 6x$, which is the rate of change of the gradient. Because $x = -2$, $\frac{d^2y}{dx^2} = 6 \times -2 = -12$ which is negative, therefore $(-2, 22)$ is a maximum point.

Exercise 7.5

In questions 1 to 10, find the values of x corresponding to turning points of the following functions. Find whether they are maxima or minima and find their values.

1. $y = x^2 + 2$
2. $y = x^2 + 4x - 3$
3. $y = 4 - x - x^2$
4. $y = 2x^3 - 9x^2 + 12x + 1$
5. $y = 2x^3 + 15x^2 + 36x + 4$
6. $y = x + \frac{1}{x}$
7. $y = x - \frac{1}{x}$
8. $y = x^4 - 8x + 3$
9. $y = 32x - x^4$
10. $y = x^2 + \frac{1}{x^2}$
11. One side of a rectangular field lies along a river bank. The other three sides are fenced with 500 m of fencing. What is the area of the largest possible field?
12. A cylindrical tin can, closed at both ends, has a total surface area of 200 cm^2. Find its greatest volume.
13. A rectangular tank, twice as long as it is wide is to be made out of 2000 cm^2 of steel plate. Find the depth of the tank if it is to hold the maximum possible volume of water.
14. The strength of a beam of rectangular cross section is a constant times the width times the square of the depth. ($S = kwd^2$) Find the dimensions of the strongest beam that can be cut from a tree trunk of diameter 30 cm.
15. The cost per hour of running a ship travelling at V knots is £$\left(\frac{V^2}{20} + 80\right)$. Find the least cost of a voyage of 1000 sea miles.
16. A stone is thrown vertically upwards and travels s metres in t seconds such that $s = 60t - 5t^2$. Find the greatest height it reaches.
17. The sum of the length and girth (distance round) of a parcel, according to Post Office regulations must not exceed 150 cm. Find the volume of the largest parcel of square cross section that may be posted.
18. The total surface area of a solid cylinder is to be as small as possible. Find this area if the volume is 1000 cm^3.
19. An open rectangular box slides into a cover as does a match box. It is twice as wide as it is high, and is made from 50 cm^2 of cardboard. Find its dimensions for maximum volume.
20. Find the volume of the largest cylinder which can be fitted inside a sphere of radius 10 cm.

7.6 Integration

Integration is the inverse of differentiation. It is used to find a function from a derivative, the derivatives being expressed in the form $y = ax^n$.

For example, if $y = x^4$, then $\dfrac{dy}{dx} = 4x^3$ and the integral of $4x^3$, written $\int 4x^3\,dx$ is $x^4 + c$ where c is a constant, known as the constant of integration.

Note. If $y = x^4 + 6$ then $\dfrac{dy}{dx} = 4x^3$.

If $y = x^4 + 10$ then $\dfrac{dy}{dx} = 4x^3$.

$\int 4x^3\,dx$ is called the *indefinite integral* of $4x^3$.

The rule for integration is:

$$\int ax^n\,dx = \frac{ax^{n+1}}{n+1} + c \text{ except when } n = -1.$$

Example 1 Evaluate $\int x^4\,dx$

Let $y = \int x^4\,dx$, then $y = \dfrac{x^{4+1}}{4+1} + c$

$$= \frac{x^5}{5} + c$$

Example 2 Evaluate $\int 3\sqrt{x^5}\,dx$

Let $y = \int 3x^{\frac{5}{2}}\,dx$, then $y = \dfrac{3x^{\frac{5}{2}+1}}{\frac{5}{2}+1} + c$

$$= \frac{3x^{\frac{7}{2}}}{\frac{7}{2}} + c = \frac{6\sqrt{x^7}}{7} + c$$

The constant of integration can be found if further information is given.

Example 3

A curve passes through the point (2, 5) and its gradient at any point is $2x$. Find the equation of the curve.

The gradient is $2x$ which is $\dfrac{dy}{dx}$.

$\therefore\ y = \int 2x\,dx$ and $y = x^2 + c$ is the equation of the curve.

But the point (2, 5) lies on the curve,

so $\qquad 5 = 2^2 + c$

$\therefore\ c = 1$ and the equation is $y = x^2 + 1$.

The *definite integral* of a function $f(x)$ is the value of the integral between defined limits.
Thus, the value of the integral of $f(x)$ between $x = a$ and $x = b$ is written $\int_a^b f(x)\,dx$. On evaluation of a definite integral, no constant of integration is required.

Example 4 Evaluate $\int_1^2 x^2\,dx$

$$\int_1^2 x^2\,dx = \left[\frac{x^3}{3}\right]_1^2$$
$$= \frac{2^3}{3} - \frac{1^3}{3} = \frac{8}{3} - \frac{1}{3} = \frac{7}{3} = 2\tfrac{1}{3}$$

Example 5 Evaluate $\int_{-2}^0 (x+1)^2\,dx$

$$\int_{-2}^0 (x+1)^2\,dx = \int_{-2}^0 (x^2 + 2x + 1)\,dx$$
$$= \left[\frac{x^3}{3} + x^2 + x\right]_{-2}^0$$
$$= \left(\frac{0^3}{3} + 0^2 + 0\right) - \left(\frac{(-2)^3}{3} + (-2)^2 + (-2)\right)$$
$$= 0 - (-2\tfrac{2}{3} + 4 - 2) = --\tfrac{2}{3} = \tfrac{2}{3}.$$

Exercise 7.6

1. If $y = x^3$, find $\frac{dy}{dx}$, and hence find $\int 3x^2\,dx$.
2. Evaluate the following indefinite integrals

(a) $\int x^3\,dx$ (b) $\int 5x^4\,dx$ (c) $\int \frac{1}{3}x^6\,dx$

(d) $\int (x^2 + 2)\,dx$ (e) $\int (x+1)^2\,dx$ (f) $\int \frac{dx}{x^2}$

(g) $\int \sqrt{x}dx$ (h) $\int 3x^{-4}\,dx$ (i) $\int \sqrt{x^3}\,dx$

(j) $\int 7dx$ (k) $\int x^{\frac{2}{3}}\,dx$ (l) $\int \left(x^4 - \frac{1}{x^2}\right)dx$

(m) $\int 0\,dx$

3. Evaluate the following definite integrals

(a) $\int_1^2 x^2\,dx$ (b) $\int_0^3 x^3\,dx$ (c) $\int_3^4 x^{-2}\,dx$

(d) $\int_{-1}^1 (2x-1)^2\,dx$ (e) $\int_{-2}^0 (x+1)(x+2)\,dx$ (f) $\int_{-2}^1 \frac{1}{x^4}\,dx$

(g) $\int_1^2 \frac{x^2-1}{x+1}\,dx$ (h) $\int_2^4 (x+1)^3\,dx$

4. If $\frac{ds}{dt} = 20 + 15t$ and if $s = 100$ when $t = 2$, find an equation for s.
5. If a body travels s metres in t seconds, its velocity is given by $\frac{ds}{dt} = 4 + 5t$. How far has it travelled in (a) 2 seconds? (b) 10 seconds? (c) 1 hour?
6. If $\frac{d^2s}{dt^2} = 6$, find an equation for s.
7. If a body, starting from rest, travels s metres in t seconds, its acceleration is given by $\frac{d^2s}{dt^2} = 2$. Find its velocity after 6 seconds.
8. With the same data as question 7, find how far the body has gone in 10 seconds from the start.
9. A bullet fired from a rifle has a muzzle velocity of 1000 m/s but suffers a retardation of 10 m/s^2, that is $\frac{d^2s}{dt^2} = -10$. How far has it travelled in 2 seconds? At what speed would it have hit a target after travelling for 1 second?
10. With the data of question 9, find the speed with which the bullet strikes a target 300 m away.
11. The gradient of a curve is given by $m = 2x - 3$. If the curve passes through the point (0, 2), find the equation of the curve.
12. The gradient of a curve is given by $m = 2x^2 - x$. If the gradient is zero at the origin, find the equation of the curve.

7.7 Mid-ordinates

The mid-ordinate rule and the trapezoidal rule are methods used to find the approximate area under a curve.

Example

A car starts from rest. After t seconds, its velocity v m/s is given in the following table.

t	0	2	4	6	8	10
v	0	6	16	30	48	70

Find the total distance travelled during the first 10 seconds using (a) the mid-ordinate rule, (b) the trapezoidal rule.

(a) Mid-ordinate rule

1. Plot the graph as shown.
2. Divide the x-axis into a suitable number of equal lengths and read off from the graph the y-ordinates of the mid-points of these lengths.
3. The area under the curve is equal to (sum of ordinates × the chosen length).

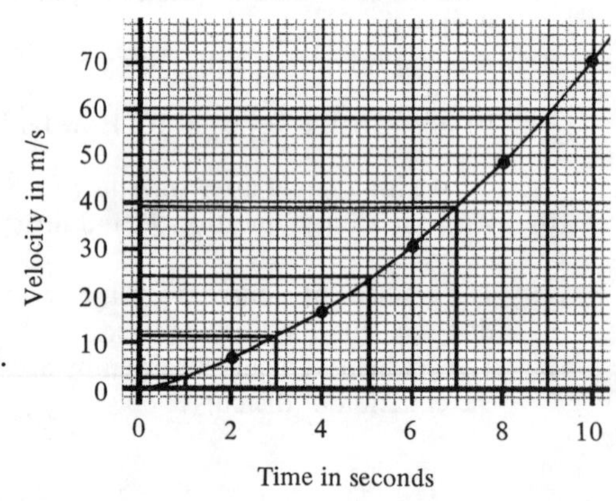

Hence, if we divide the x-axis into five 2 cm lengths, then the mid-ordinates are

mid-point	1	3	5	7	9
mid-ordinate	2·5	11	23	39	59

$$\therefore \text{ the area under the curve } = (2{\cdot}5 + 11 + 23 + 39 + 59) \times 2$$
$$= 134{\cdot}5 \times 2 = 269 \text{ units of area.}$$

But, on a velocity-time graph the area under the curve is equal to the distance travelled.

$\therefore$ distance travelled is 269 metres.

(b) Trapezoidal rule

1. Plot the graph.
2. Divide the x-axis into any number of equal lengths, and draw perpendiculars (ordinates) to the curve from these points.
   If we assume that these perpendiculars are the parallel sides of trapeziums,

then the area under the curve is either

(i) the sum of the areas of these individual trapeziums,

or (ii) calculated from the following rule:

area = half the equal length × (sum of end ordinates + twice the sum of the other ordinates)

Hence, if we divide the x-axis into five 2 cm lengths, the area is found either by method (i) or by method (ii).

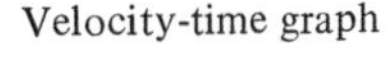
Velocity-time graph

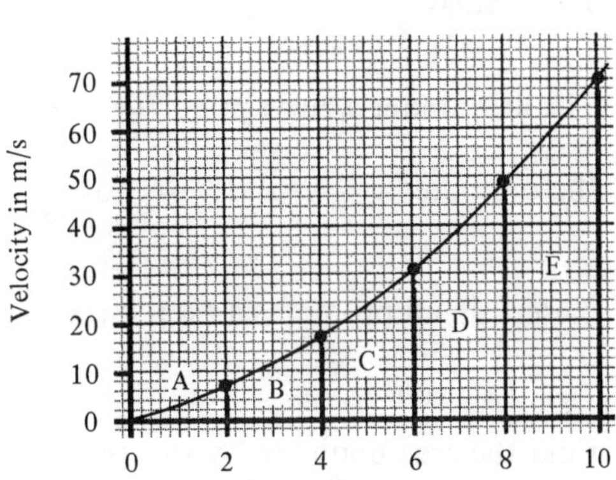

(i) area of trapeziums A + B + C + D + E

$$= \left(\frac{0+6}{2}\right)2 + \left(\frac{6+16}{2}\right)2 + \left(\frac{16+30}{2}\right)2 + \left(\frac{30+48}{2}\right)2 + \left(\frac{48+70}{2}\right)2$$

$= 6 + 22 + 46 + 78 + 118 = 270$ units of area.

(ii) $1 \times [(0+70) + 2(6+16+30+48)]$

$= 1 \times (70 + 200) = 270$ units of area.

$\therefore$ distance travelled = 270 metres.

Exercise 7.7

1. On a piece of graph paper plot the following points

x	0	1	2	3	4
y	1	4	5	4	1

Join the points with a smooth curve and find the area under it and above the x-axis using (a) the mid-ordinate rule and (b) the trapezoidal rule. In each case take 4 strips.

2. Draw a semicircle of radius 6 cm. Estimate its area using (a) the mid-ordinate rule and (b) the trapezoidal rule. In each case use 6 strips and compare your answers with the calculated area.

3. Plot the following curve

x	0	1	2	3	4	5	6
y	1·1	1·6	1·8	1·5	1·1	1·2	1·8

Estimate the area under this curve and above the x-axis using (a) the mid-ordinate rule and (b) the trapezoidal rule. Use 6 strips each time.

4. Soundings taken across the bed of a river show the following depths d m at distances x m from the bank

x m	0	10	20	30	40	50
d m	0	12	18	26	23	0

Using the trapezoidal rule (with 10 strips), find the area of cross section of the river and the number of cubic metres of water which flow down it in one hour if the average rate of flow is 3 m/h.

7.8 Areas

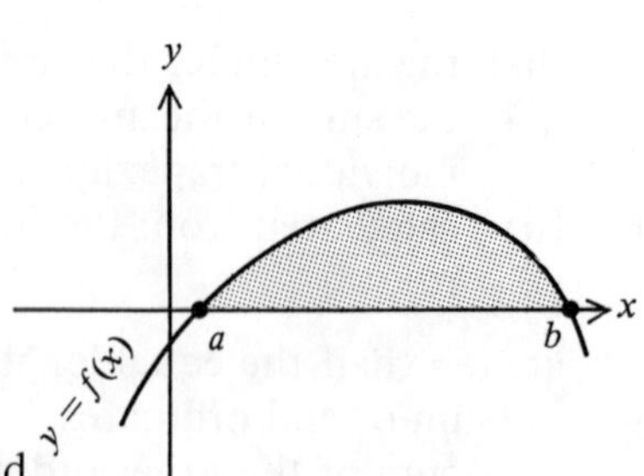

The area under a curve $y = f(x)$ between the ordinates $x = a$ and $x = b$ is $\int_a^b y\,dx$.

Note. In all problems a sketch graph is a useful aid.

Example 1

Find the area bounded by the curve $y = x^3$, the x-axis, and the ordinates $x = 2$ and $x = 3$.

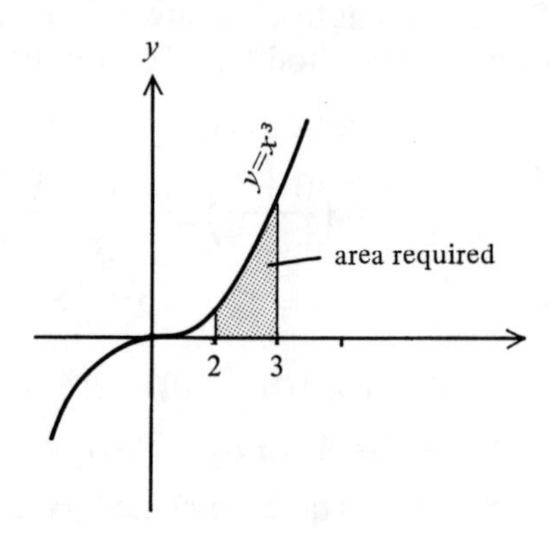

$$\text{area} = \int_2^3 x^3\,dx$$

$$= \left[\frac{x^4}{4}\right]_2^3$$

$$= \frac{3^4}{4} - \frac{2^4}{4}$$

$$= \frac{81}{4} - \frac{16}{4} = \frac{65}{4} = 16\tfrac{1}{4} \text{ units of area.}$$

Example 2

Find the area bounded by the curve $y = x^3 - 4x$ and the x-axis in the diagram opposite.

The graph cuts the x-axis when $y = 0$,

i.e. when $x^3 - 4x = 0$

$$x(x^2 - 4) = 0$$

$$x(x + 2)(x - 2) = 0$$

$$x = 0, 2, \text{ or } -2,$$

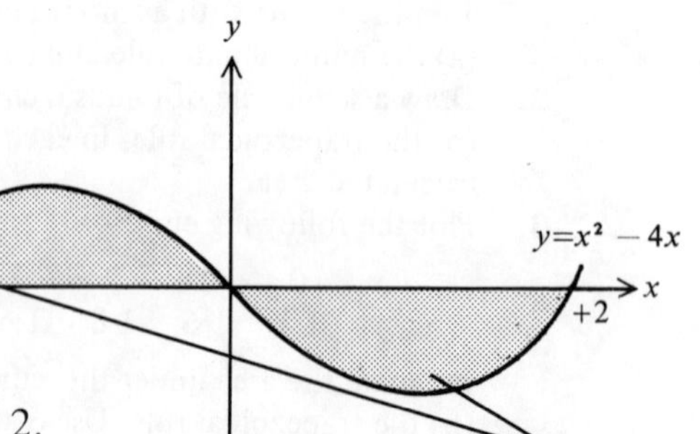

In this case, it is easier to find the area (a) between -2 and 0, and (b) between 0 and 2.

$$\text{area} = \int_{-2}^{0} (x^3 - 4x)\,dx + \int_0^2 (x^3 - 4x)\,dx$$

$$= \left[\frac{x^4}{4} - 2x^2\right]_{-2}^{0} + \left[\frac{x^4}{4} - 2x^2\right]_0^2 = +4 + -4.$$

The negative sign indicates that the area lies under the x-axis.

$\therefore$ area is $4 + 4 = 8$ units.

Example 3

Find the area between the line $y = 4x$ and the curve $y = x^2$.

From the sketch, the area of the shaded portion is found by

(a) finding the area under the curve between O and B,

(b) finding the area of the triangle OAB,

(c) subtracting the area under the curve from the area of the triangle.

The point of intersection of the graphs is when

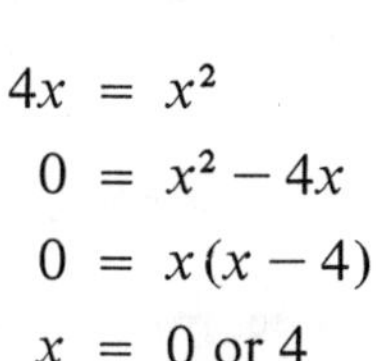

$$4x = x^2$$
$$0 = x^2 - 4x$$
$$0 = x(x-4)$$

i.e. when $x = 0$ or 4

$\therefore$ O is the point (0, 0) and B is the point (4, 16).

$$\therefore \text{ area of triangle OAB} = \frac{\text{OA} \times \text{AB}}{2} = \frac{4 \times 16}{2} = 32 \text{ units.}$$

$$\text{area under curve} = \int_0^4 x^2\,dx = \left[\frac{x^3}{3}\right]_0^4 = 21\tfrac{1}{3} \text{ units.}$$

$$\text{and the required area} = 32 - 21\tfrac{1}{3} = 10\tfrac{2}{3} \text{ units.}$$

Exercise 7.8

1. Find the area bounded by the curve $y = x^2$, the x-axis, and the ordinate $x = 5$.
2. Find the area bounded by the curve $y = x^2$, the ordinates $x = 3$ and $x = 6$, and the x-axis.
3. Find the area between the curve $y = 9 - x^2$ and the x-axis.
4. Find the area between the curve $y = 16 - \dfrac{x^2}{4}$ and the x and y axes.
5. Find the area between the curve $y = x^2 + 3x + 3$ and the line $y = 7$.
6. Find the area between the curve $y = x^2$ and the line $x = y$.
7. Find the area between the curve $y = \sqrt{x}$ and the line $y = \frac{1}{5}x + \frac{6}{5}$.
8. Find the area between the curve $y = \sqrt{x}$, the x-axis, and the line $x + y = 20$.
9. Find the area between the curves $y = x^2$ and $y^2 = x$.
10. Find the area between the curve $y^2 = x^3$ and the line $y = 2x$.
11. Find the area between the curve $y = (x-2)(4-x)$ and the line $y = x - 2$.
12. Find the area between the curve $y = 4x - x^2$, the y-axis, and the line $x + y = 4$.
13. Find the area between the curve $y = x^2 + 1$, the x and y axes, and the tangent to the curve at the point where $x = 2$.

Miscellaneous exercise 7

1. (a) Find the gradient of the curve $y = 2x + x^2 - x^3$ (i) at the origin (ii) at the point $(2, 0)$.
   (b) Show that the gradient of the curve $y = 12x + x^3$ is always positive.
2. Evaluate $\int_{-4}^{0} (-x^2 - 4x)\, dx$.
3. (a) Plot the graph of the function $y = 2x - x^2$ and find the area enclosed between the curve and the x-axis.
   (b) Check your answer to (a) by integration.
4. If $y = \sqrt{x} + \frac{1}{x}$, find $\frac{dy}{dx}$.
5. A railway cutting 10 m wide has to be cut through a small rocky outcrop. The depth of the cutting d m at various distances x m from one end are as follows

x m	0	8	15	21	25	33	40
d m	0	7	10·5	17	20	7	0

   Taking 8 strips and using the trapezoidal rule, estimate the number of cubic metres of rock which must be excavated.
6. A body moves in a straight line and its distance s metres from a point O on the line t seconds after leaving O is given by the expression $s = 36t - t^3$.
   (a) Write down an expression for the velocity v of the body and find the velocity after 2 seconds.
   (b) Write down an expression for the acceleration a of the body and find the acceleration after 2 seconds.
   (c) Find the distance travelled during the 2nd second.
7. A beer barrel is 1 m high. Its top and bottom diameters are each 60 cm and its greatest diameter is 70 cm. Sketch a graph showing its cross-sectional area at its top, bottom, and middle sections. (Let 1 cm represent 100 cm on the x-axis and 1 cm represent 1000 cm^2 on the y-axis). Estimate its volume using this graph.
8. Find the equations of the two tangents to the curve $y = x^3 - 2x^2 + 3x + 7$ which are parallel to the line $y = 2x$. Find also the co-ordinates of the points where these lines cross the y-axis and the distance they are apart.
9. The line $y = 20$ meets the curve $y = 9x - x^2$ at A and at B. Find the gradient of the curve at these points and the angle between the tangents at them.
10. A body starting from rest moves in a straight line so that at the end of t seconds its velocity is $(t^2 + 4t)$ m/s. When it is at point P, its velocity is 5 m/s and it takes 5 more seconds to reach a point Q. Find
    (a) the values of t at P and at Q respectively,
    (b) the distance between P and Q,
    (c) its acceleration when $t = 4$s.
11. ABC is a triangle right-angled at C. AC = 3 cm and BC = 4 cm. P is a point on AB and PNCM is a rectangle with its vertices M and N on BC and AC respectively. Let AP = x cm. P moves from A to B at 2 centimetres per minute. At what rate is the area of PNMC growing when P has been moving away from A (i) for 60 seconds (ii) for 75 seconds?
12. A cylinder is such that the sum of its height and of the circumference of its base is 8 metres. Find its maximum volume.

13. Plot the graph of $y = \dfrac{1}{x+1}$ for values of x between $x = 0$ and $x = 3$. By using either the trapezoidal rule or the mid-ordinate rule, find the area enclosed by the curve, the x-axis, and the ordinates $x = 0$ and $x = 3$. Hence find an approximate value of the integral $\int_0^3 \dfrac{1}{x+1}\,dx$.

14. Find the area between the curve $y = 9 - x^2$, the x-axis and the tangent to the curve at the point where $x = 1$.

15. Find the maximum and minimum values of the function $y = x(12 - x^2)$.

16. If $\dfrac{dy}{dx} = 2x - x^2$ and $x = 1{\cdot}5$ when $y = 0{\cdot}75$, find y in terms of x.

17. If $y^2 = 4ax$, find the equation of the tangent to the curve at the point $(at^2, 2at)$.

18. An open water tank with square ends is made so that it has a volume of $100\,\text{m}^3$. Find the cost of painting the inside of this tank at 50p per square metre so that this cost is kept to a minimum.

19. When a stone is thrown vertically into the air, its height s metres after t seconds is $s = 24t - 3t^2$.
    (a) After how many seconds has it reached its greatest height and what is this height?
    (b) How far does it travel in the 3rd second?
    (c) What is (i) its initial velocity (ii) its final velocity?

20. A curve has an equation of the form $y = ax^2 + bx$ where a and b are constants. If the curve passes through the points $(1, 7)$ and $(3, 117)$, find the values of a and b, and hence find the area between the curve, the x-axis, and the ordinates $x = 1$ and $x = 5$.

Part 8 Further mathematics

8.1 The radian

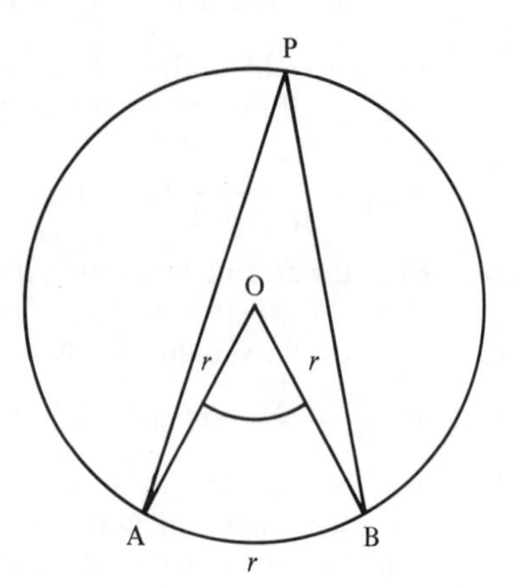

A radian (1 rad) is the angle subtended at the centre of a circle by an arc of a circle equal in length to the radius of the circle.

In the diagram, the arc AB subtends an angle AOB of 1 radian at the centre O and subtends an angle APB of 0·5 radians at the circumference.

The unit of circular measurement is 1 radian, which is approximately 57° 18′ or 57·3°, and π radians = 180°.

Example 1 Express 24° 36′ or 24·6° in radians.

Using tables, 24·6° = 0·4294 rad

By calculation, 24·6° $= \dfrac{24{\cdot}6}{57{\cdot}3}$ = 0·429 rad. (to 3 S.F.)

Example 2 Express 1·26 radians in degrees.

Using tables, 1·26 rad = 72·2° or 72° 12′

By calculation, 1·26 rad = 1·26 × 57·3° = 72·2° (to 3 S.F.)

Length of arc, area of segment and sector

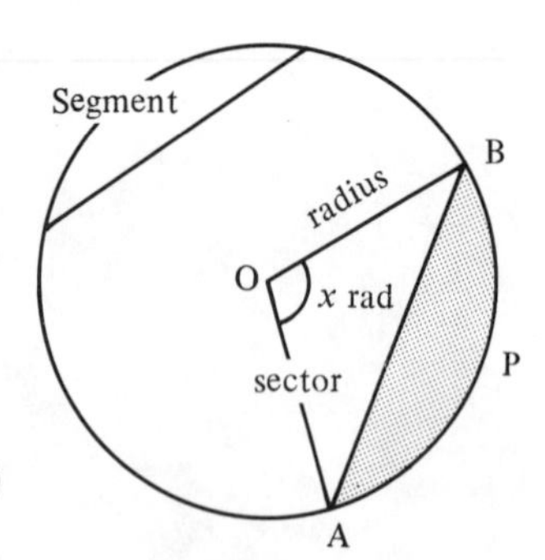

In the diagram, the radius of the circle is r cm. The arc AB subtends an angle of x rad at the centre.

1. Length of arc AB = rx cm
2. Area of sector OAB = $\frac{1}{2}r^2 x$ cm²
3. Area of segment APB
   = (area of sector OAB) − (area of triangle OAB)

Note. A regular polygon has all its sides equal and all its angles equal.
An inscribed figure has all its vertices touching the perimeter of the enclosing shape.

Example

A and B are two adjacent vertices of a regular eight-sided polygon inscribed in a circle. Calculate the difference in length between the chord AB and the arc AB.

In the figure, ABO is an isosceles triangle, and

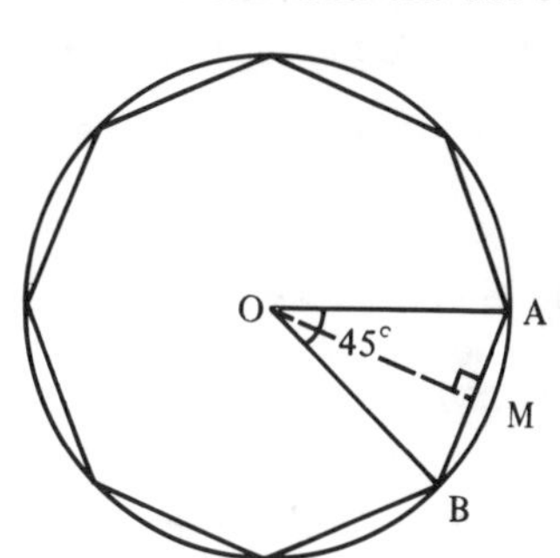

$$A\hat{O}B = \tfrac{360}{8}$$

$$= 45° \text{ or } \frac{\pi}{4} \text{ rad}$$

$$\therefore \quad \text{length of arc AB} = 10 \times \frac{\pi}{4}$$

$$= 10 \times 0{\cdot}7854$$

$$= 7{\cdot}854 \text{ cm}$$

If M is the mid-point of AB, then AMO is a right-angled triangle.

$$\therefore \quad AM = 10 \sin 22{\cdot}5°$$

$$= 10 \times 0{\cdot}3827$$

$$= 3{\cdot}827 \text{ cm}$$

$$\therefore \quad \text{chord AB} = 2 \times 3{\cdot}827 = 7{\cdot}654 \text{ cm}$$

$$\therefore \text{ difference in length} = 7{\cdot}854 - 7{\cdot}654 = 0{\cdot}2 \text{ cm.}$$

Exercise 8.1

1. Convert the following angles into radians
   (a) 38° (b) 42° 6′ (c) 75° 19′ (d) 140° 22′ (e) 184° 33′
2. Convert the following angles into degrees and minutes
   (a) 1·5 rad (b) 2·1 rad (c) 1·44 rad (d) 0·06 rad (e) 3·67 rad
3. A sector of a circle, radius 10 cm subtends an angle of 58° at the centre. Calculate the length of the arc.
4. A piece of wire 15 cm long is bent into an arc of a circle of radius 8 cm. Find the angle subtended at the centre (a) in degrees and (b) in radians.
5. A wheel 2 m in diameter rotates at 2000 revolutions per minute. What is its angular velocity in radians per second and what is the speed in m/s of a point on its rim?
6. How many radians does a chord of length equal to the radius of the circle subtend at the centre?
7. A piece of wire 1 m long is bent into an arc of a circle of radius 2 m. How far apart are the ends of the wire?
8. A wheel is revolving at an angular velocity of 56 radians per second. How many revolutions per minute is this?
9. The angle of lap of a belt passing over a pulley of 10 cm diameter is 84°. What length of belt is in contact with the pulley?
10. A wheel is 5 m in diameter and a point on its circumference has a speed of 2 m/s. Express in radians the angle turned through in 4 seconds and find the speed of rotation in r.p.m.
11. ACB is the arc of a circle of radius 5 cm, centre O, cut off by chord AB. If the length of the arc is 4 cm, calculate
    (a) $A\hat{O}B$ in radians (b) $A\hat{O}B$ in degrees and minutes
    (c) the length of chord AB (d) the area of the sector AOB
    (e) the area of the triangle AOB (f) the area of the segment ACB.

8.2 Logarithms

1. If $a^x = N$, then $\log_a N = x$.
2. $\log a + \log b = \log(ab)$
3. $\log a - \log b = \log(a \div b) = \log\left(\frac{a}{b}\right)$
4. $2\log a = \log a + \log a = \log a^2$
5. $\frac{1}{2}\log a = \log a^{\frac{1}{2}} = \log\sqrt{a}$

Example 1

Express $\log\frac{a^2 b^3}{c}$ in terms of $\log a$, $\log b$, $\log c$.

$$\log\frac{a^2 b^3}{c} = \log a^2 + \log b^3 - \log c$$

$$= 2\log a + 3\log b - \log c$$

Example 2

Express log 144 in terms of log 3 and log 2.

$$\log 144 = \log(9 \times 16) = \log 9 + \log 16$$
$$= \log 3^2 + \log 2^4$$
$$= 2\log 3 + 4\log 2$$

Example 3

If $\log 2 = 0{\cdot}30103$ and $\log 3 = 0{\cdot}47712$, find the value of log 144 without using tables.

From example 2, $\log 144 = 2\log 3 + 4\log 2$
$$= 2 \times 0{\cdot}47712 + 4 \times 0{\cdot}30103$$
$$= 0{\cdot}95424 + 1{\cdot}20412$$
$$= 2{\cdot}15836$$

The following examples illustrate the solution of equations involving logs, in which all logs are in base 10.

Example 4 Find x if $2\log x = 1$

As $\log 10 = 1$, the equation can be written

$$2\log x = \log 10$$
$$\therefore \log x^2 = \log 10$$
and $x^2 = 10$ or $x = \sqrt{10} = \pm 3{\cdot}162$.

Example 5 Find x if $3 \log x = 7{\cdot}5$

$\therefore \log x = 2{\cdot}5$ and x is the number whose log is $2{\cdot}5$.

$\therefore x = 316{\cdot}2.$

Example 6 Find x if $\log (x^3 - 1) - \log (x^2 + x + 1) = 1$

$$\therefore \log (x^3 - 1) - \log (x^2 + x + 1) = \log 10$$

$$\log \left(\frac{x^3 - 1}{x^2 + x + 1}\right) = \log 10$$

$$\therefore \quad \frac{x^3 - 1}{x^2 + x + 1} = 10$$

and

$$\frac{(x-1)(x^2 + x + 1)}{x^2 + x + 1} = 10$$

$$\therefore \quad x - 1 = 10 \text{ and } x = 11.$$

Exercise 8.2

1. Express in terms of $\log a$, $\log b$, and $\log c$

   (a) $\log \frac{ab}{c}$ (b) $\log \frac{a}{bc}$ (c) $\log \frac{a^2b}{c^3}$ (d) $\log \sqrt{abc}$

   (e) $\log a^2b^3c^4$ (f) $\log \frac{\sqrt[3]{a}.\sqrt[4]{b}}{c}$ (g) $\log (ab)^2$ (h) $\log \sqrt[3]{abc}$

2. Express in terms of $\log 2$ and $\log 3$

   (a) $\log 18$ (b) $\log 48$ (c) $\log 81$ (d) $\log 6^3$

3. If $\log 2 = 0{\cdot}30103$ and $\log 3 = 0{\cdot}47712$ evaluate without tables

   (a) $\log 6$ (b) $\log 1{\cdot}5$ (c) $\log 36$ (d) $\log 60$
   (e) $\log 0{\cdot}04$ (f) $\log \sqrt{6}$ (g) $\log 18$ (h) $\log 72$
   (i) $\log \sqrt[3]{162}$ (j) $\log 4{\cdot}5 \times 8^{\frac{1}{2}}$

4. Find x if $\log x = \frac{2}{3} \log 64$

Solve the following logarithmic equations. All logs are to base 10.

5. $2 \log x = 7{\cdot}5$
6. $\log (x + 1) = 2$
7. $\log x + \log x^2 = 1$
8. $\log (x + 1) + \log (x - 1) = 2$
9. $\log (x + 2) - \log (x - 3) = 1$
10. $\log (x + 1) + \log x = 0$
11. $\log 3x + \log (x - 2) = 1$
12. $\log (10x - 1) = 1 + \log (x^2 - 1)$
13. $2 \log (x + 1) - \log (x - 1) = 1$
14. $\log (x - 3) + \log (x + 2) = 0{\cdot}301$
15. $\log (x^2 + 9x + 3) - \log (x + 1) = 1$
16. $\log 3x + \log (x + 2) = \log (2 - x)$
17. $\log (x^2 + 3x + 1) - \log (x + 1) = 1$
18. $\log (x^2 + 3x + 5) - \log (1 + x) = 1$
19. $\log 5x + \log (x - 1) - \log (2x + 1) = 0$
20. $2 \log (2x - 1) - \log (3 - x) = 1$
21. $\log (3x - 2) + \log (x - 2) - \log x = 0$
22. $\log (x^3 + 1) - \log (x^2 - 3x + 2) = \log (x^2 - x + 1)$
23. Use logs to find the least whole number value of x if 3^x exceeds one hundred million.
24. If $a^{3-x} . b^{5x} = a^{x+5} . b^{3x}$ show that $x \log \frac{b}{a} = \log a.$
25. If $x^2 + y^2 = 7xy$ show that $\log (x + y) = \log 3 + \frac{1}{2}\log x + \frac{1}{2}\log y.$

8.3 The remainder theorem

The remainder when an expression is divided by $(x + a)$ is found by substituting $x = -a$ in the expression.
If the remainder is zero, then $(x + a)$ is a factor of the expression.

To factorize an expression
(a) find the value of x which makes the expression zero.
(b) find the remaining factors by inspection or by long division.

Example Factorize $2x^3 - 3x^2 - 72x - 35$

Note. The only values of x which may make this expression zero are

$$\pm 1, \pm 5, \pm 7, \pm 35, \pm\tfrac{1}{2}, \pm\tfrac{5}{2}, \pm\tfrac{7}{2}, \pm\tfrac{35}{2},$$

that is, a factor of 35 divided by a factor of 2.

Let $x = 1$,

then $2x^3 - 3x^2 - 72x - 35 = 2 - 3 - 72 - 35 \neq 0$

$\therefore$ $(x - 1)$ is *not* a factor.

Let $x = -5$,

then $2x^3 - 3x^2 - 72x - 35 = -250 - 75 + 360 - 35 = 0$

$\therefore$ $(x + 5)$ is a factor.

Hence $2x^3 - 3x^2 - 72x - 35$

$= (x + 5)(2x^2 - 13x - 7)$

$= (x + 5)(2x + 1)(x - 7)$.

Exercise 8.3

1. Show that $x - 2$ is a factor of $x^3 + x^2 - 4x - 4$, and find the other factors.
2. Show that $x + 7$ is a factor of $x^3 + 4x^2 - 19x + 14$, and find the other factors.
3. Show that $x + 1$ and $x + 2$ are factors of $x^4 + 10x^3 + 35x^2 + 50x + 24$, and find the other factors.

Factorize the following

4. $x^3 + 2x^2 - x - 2$
5. $x^3 + 9x^2 + 23x + 15$
6. $x^3 - 3x^2 - 10x + 24$
7. $x^3 + 6x^2 - 4x - 24$
8. $x^3 + x^2 - 9x - 9$
9. $x^3 + 7x^2 - x - 7$
10. $x^3 + 2x^2 - 23x - 60$
11. $2x^3 + 7x^2 + 7x + 2$
12. $2x^3 + x^2 - 5x + 2$
13. $2x^3 + 3x^2 - 2x - 3$
14. $2x^3 + x^2 - 8x - 4$
15. $3x^3 + 10x^2 + 9x + 2$
16. $3x^3 - 8x^2 + 3x + 2$
17. $6x^3 + 11x^2 - 3x - 2$
18. $4x^3 + x^2 - 4x - 1$
19. $4x^3 + 8x^2 - x - 2$
20. $2x^3 + 13x^2 - 36$

Find the two factors of the following

21. $x^3 + 2x^2 + 2x + 1$

22. $x^3 - x^2 - 3x + 2$

23. $x^3 + 4x^2 + 4x + 1$

24. $x^3 + 2x^2 - 4x - 3$

25. $4x^3 + 4x^2 + 3x + 1$

Find the repeated factor in each of the following

26. $x^3 + 4x^2 + 5x + 2$

27. $x^3 - 5x^2 + 7x - 3$

28. $x^4 + 4x^3 + 6x^2 + 4x + 1$

29. $8x^3 + 12x^2 + 6x + 1$

30. $x^4 + 6x^3 + 13x^2 + 12x + 4$

31. Find the numerical values of a and b if $x^3 + ax^2 + bx + 6$ is divisible by $x - 1$ and by $x + 2$.

32. Find the numerical values of a and b if $x^3 + ax^2 - 19x + b$ is divisible by $x - 2$ and by $x - 3$.

33. Find the numerical values of a and b if $ax^4 - 2x^3 + bx - 9$ is divisible by both $x + 1$ and $x - 3$. Find the other factor.

34. Find the value of a, b, and c such that $x^3 + ax^2 + bx + c$ is divisible by $x + 1$, $x + 2$, and $x + 3$.

35. Find the numerical values of a and b such that $4x^3 + 9x^2 + ax + b$ is divisible by $x^2 + 2x - 15$. What is the other factor?

36. Given that $x^3 + 4x^2 + 3x + 10$ and $x^3 + 3x^2 - 2x + 4$ have the same remainder when divided by $(x - a)$, find the possible values of a.

37. Show that $a^n + b^n$ always has a factor $(a + b)$ provided that n is an odd integer.

38. Find an expression for the remainder when $a^n + b^n$ is divided by $(a + b)$ where n is an even integer.

39. The expression $2x^3 - ax^2 - bx - 35$ has a factor $(x + 5)$, and leaves a remainder of -108 when divided by $(x - 1)$. Find the values of a and b, and factorize the expression.

40. Factorize $x^2(y - z) + y^2(z - x) + z^2(x - y)$.

8.4 Arithmetic progressions

When a sequence has a constant *difference* between successive terms, it is called an *arithmetic progression* (A.P.)
In the sequence 4, 9, 14, 19, . . . the common difference is 5.
In the sequence $a + 2d, a + d, a, \ldots$ the common difference is $-d$.

1. If the first term of an A.P. is a, and the common difference is d, then the n th term is $a + (n - 1)\,d$.

Example 1

Find the 17th term in the A.P. 4, 9, 14, 19, . . .

Here $a = 4, d = 5$, and $n = 17$.

$\therefore\ 4 + (17 - 1)\,5 = 4 + 80 = 84.$

2. The sum S of an A.P. is

$$S = \frac{n}{2}\{2a + (n - 1)\,d\}$$

or $$S = \frac{n}{2}(a + l)$$ where l is the last term.

Example 2

Find (a) the sum of the first 10 terms of 4, 9, 14, 19, . . .
(b) the sum of the sequence of 16 terms 1, 7, 13, . . . 91

(a) Here $a = 4, d = 5$, and $n = 10$

$$\therefore\ S = \frac{10}{2}\{2 \times 4 + (10 - 1)\,5\}$$

$$= 5\,(8 + 45) = 5 \times 53 = 265$$

(b) Here $a = 1, l = 91, n = 16$

$$\therefore\ S = \frac{16}{2}(1 + 91) = 8 \times 92 = 736$$

3. The arithmetic mean of two quantities a and b is their average $\frac{a + b}{2}$. This quantity when placed between a and b gives three consecutive terms of an A.P. Any number of arithmetic means may be placed between two terms. They and the means are then in A.P.

Example 3

Insert four arithmetic means between 3 and 15. The nth term is given by $a+(n-1)d$, where $a = 3$, $n = 6$ and d is unknown. The nth term is 15.

$$\therefore\ 15 = 3+(6-1)d = 3+5d$$

$$12 = 5d \quad \text{and} \quad d = 2{\cdot}4$$

$\therefore$ the sequence is 3, 5·4, 7·8, 10·2, 12·6, 15.

Exercise 8·4

Find the last term and the sum of the following progressions

1. $2, 4, 6 \ldots$ to 15 terms
2. $3, 6, 9 \ldots$ to 20 terms
3. $18, 14, 10 \ldots$ to 12 terms
4. $1\frac{1}{2}, 3, 4\frac{1}{2} \ldots$ to 15 terms
5. $-5, -7\frac{1}{2}, -10 \ldots$ to 8 terms
6. $17, 14\frac{1}{4}, 11\frac{1}{2} \ldots$ to 19 terms
7. $\frac{1}{4}, \frac{1}{3}, \frac{5}{12} \ldots$ to 60 terms
8. $2\frac{1}{2}, 2\frac{5}{6}, 3\frac{1}{6} \ldots$ to 11 terms
9. $10, 9\frac{2}{5}, 8\frac{4}{5} \ldots$ to 16 terms
10. $2, -1\frac{1}{15}, -4\frac{2}{15} \ldots$ to 8 terms
11. $a, 2a+b, 3a+2b \ldots$ to 10 terms
12. $a, \dfrac{5a+3b}{2}, 4a+3b \ldots$ to 12 terms
13. $\dfrac{5}{\sqrt{7}}, \dfrac{6}{\sqrt{7}}, \sqrt{7} \ldots$ to 6 terms.

14. Find the sum of the first n even numbers.
15. Insert 3 arithmetic means between 2 and 14.
16. Insert 8 arithmetic means between $1\frac{1}{2}$ and $19\frac{1}{2}$.
17. Insert 5 arithmetic means between 4 and -5.
18. Insert 4 arithmetic means between a and $11a$.
19. Write down the first two of the x arithmetic means which lie between x^2 and 1.
20. In a certain A.P., the 4th term is 12 and the 8th term is 24. Find the series.
21. The sum to 9 terms of an A.P. is 54 and the sum to 11 terms is 88. Find the series.
22. The 5th term and also the sum to 5 terms of an A.P. is -5. Find the series.
23. The sum of three numbers in A.P. is 21 and their product is 315. Find the three numbers.
24. The sum of three numbers in A.P. is 24. The sum of their squares is 200. Find the three numbers.
25. The sum to 20 terms of an A.P. is -3600. The common difference is -40. Find the first term.
26. The sum to n terms of the series $1, 1\frac{1}{2}, 2 \ldots$ is 27. Find n.
27. The 7th term of an A.P. is three times the 2nd term and the 4th term is the square of the first term. Find the series.
28. Find the number of terms in the series $7, 10, 13 \ldots 172$.
29. The sum of n terms of the series $15, 12, 9 \ldots$ is 45. Find n.
30. The sum of m terms of an A.P. is n and the sum of n terms is m. Find the sum of $m+n$ terms.

8.5 Geometric progressions

When a sequence has a constant *ratio* between successive terms, it is called a *geometric progression* (G.P.). This constant is called the *common ratio.*
In the sequence 3, 9, 27, 81, 243, . . . the common ratio is 3.
In the sequence $ar, ar^2, ar^3, \ldots$ the common ratio is r.

1. If the first term of a G.P. is a, and the common ratio is r, then the nth term is ar^{n-1}.

Example 1

Find the 11th term in the G.P. 1, 2, 4, 8, 16, . . .
Here $a = 1, r = 2, n = 11$.

$\therefore$ the required term is $1 \times 2^{11-1} = 1 \times 2^{10} = 1 \times 1024 = 1024$.

2. The sum S of a G.P. is

$$S = a\frac{1-r^n}{1-r} \quad \text{when } r < 1$$

or $$S = a\frac{r^n-1}{r-1} \quad \text{when } r > 1$$

Example 2

Find the sum of the first 10 terms of the G.P. 1, 2, 4, 8, 16, . . .
Here $a = 1, r = 2, n = 10$

$$\therefore S = 1 \times \frac{2^{10}-1}{2-1} = 1 \times \frac{1024-1}{1} = 1 \times 1023 = 1023$$

Example 3

Find the sum of the first 10 terms of the G.P. $\frac{1}{2}, \frac{1}{4}, \frac{1}{8}, \frac{1}{16}, \ldots$
Here $a = \frac{1}{2}, r = \frac{1}{2}, n = 10$

$$\therefore S = \tfrac{1}{2} \times \frac{1-(\frac{1}{2})^{10}}{1-\frac{1}{2}}$$

$$= \tfrac{1}{2} \times \frac{\frac{1023}{1024}}{\frac{1}{2}} = \frac{1023}{1024}$$

3. The geometric mean of two quantities a and b is $\sqrt{ab}$.

Example 4

Find the geometric mean of 20 and 45.

Geometric mean $= \sqrt{20 \times 45} = \sqrt{900} = 30.$

Any number of geometric means may be inserted between two terms. They and the means are then in G.P.

Example 5

Insert three geometric means between 3 and 243.

The nth term is ar^{n-1}, in which $a = 3, n = 5$. Because the nth term is 243,

$$3r^{5-1} = 243$$

$$\therefore \quad 3r^4 = 243 \qquad r^4 = 81 \text{ and } r = 3$$

$\therefore$ the sequence is 3, 9, 27, 81, 243, and the means inserted are 9, 27, and 81.

4. If the common ratio r is in the range -1 to $+1$, then the sum to n terms S_n tends to $\dfrac{a}{1-r}$ as n tends to infinity.

   The quantity $\dfrac{a}{1-r}$ is called the *sum to infinity* S_∞ and is the limiting value of the sum of an infinite number of terms.

Example 6

Find the sum to infinity of $1 + \frac{1}{2} + \frac{1}{4} + \ldots$

Here $a = 1, r = \frac{1}{4} \div \frac{1}{2} = \frac{1}{2}$

$$\therefore \; S_\infty = \frac{a}{1-r} = \frac{1}{1-\frac{1}{2}} = \frac{1}{\frac{1}{2}} = 2$$

Exercise 8.5

Find the last term and the sum of the following progressions

1. $2, 4, 8 \ldots$ to 6 terms
2. $1, 3, 9 \ldots$ to 8 terms
3. $1, -2, 4 \ldots$ to 10 terms
4. $3, 4\frac{1}{2}, 6\frac{3}{4} \ldots$ to 7 terms
5. $-\frac{1}{2}, -\frac{1}{4}, -\frac{1}{8} \ldots$ to 6 terms
6. $-1, \sqrt{3}, -3 \ldots$ to 8 terms
7. $3, 2, 1\frac{1}{3} \ldots$ to 7 terms
8. $\frac{1}{2}, -\frac{5}{8}, \frac{25}{32} \ldots$ to 5 terms
9. $4, -1\frac{1}{3}, \frac{4}{9} \ldots$ to 8 terms
10. $3, 0{\cdot}6, 0{\cdot}12 \ldots$ to 9 terms

Find the sum to infinity of the following series

11. $2, 1, \frac{1}{2} \ldots$
12. $5, \frac{5}{3}, \frac{5}{9} \ldots$
13. $3, -1\frac{1}{2}, \frac{3}{4} \ldots$
14. $-4, \frac{8}{3}, -\frac{16}{9} \ldots$
15. $6, 0{\cdot}6, 0{\cdot}06 \ldots$

16. Insert two geometric means between $2\frac{1}{2}$ and $-\frac{5}{16}$.
17. Insert four geometric means between 3 and 729.
18. Insert two geometric means between 4 and $\frac{1}{128}$.

8.6 Variation

1. If y is *directly* proportional to x (or $y \propto x$), then $y = kx$, where k is a constant, and $k = y/x$.

Example 1

If $y \propto x$, and $x = 4$ when $y = 2$, find x when $y = 8$.
When $x = 4$ and $y = 2$, $k = y/x = \frac{2}{4} = \frac{1}{2}$.

$\therefore\ y = \frac{1}{2}x$

So when $y = 8$, $8 = \frac{1}{2}x$ and $x = 16$.

2. If y is *inversely* proportional to x (or $y \propto 1/x$), then $y = k/x$, where k is a constant and $xy = k$.

Example 2

If $y \propto 1/x$, and $x = 1$ when $y = 10$, find x when $y = 20$.
When $x = 1$ and $y = 10$, $k = xy = 10 \times 1 = 10$.

$\therefore\ y = 10/x$

So when $y = 20$, $20 = 10/x$, and $x = \frac{1}{2}$.

3. If V is *jointly* proportional to a^2 and to b, then $V \propto a^2b$ or $V = ka^2b$ where $k = V/a^2b$.

Example 3

a varies directly as b and inversely as c. If $a = 4$ when $b = 1$ and $c = 2$, find a when $b = 4$ and $c = \frac{1}{2}$.

From the question, $a \propto b/c$;

$\therefore\ a = kb/c$ where k is a constant and $k = ca/b$.

But when $b = 1$ and $c = 2$, then $a = 4$.
So $k = (2 \times 4)/1 = 8$; $\therefore\ a = 8b/c$.

$\therefore$ when $b = 4$ and $c = \frac{1}{2}$, $a = (8 \times 4)/\frac{1}{2} = 32/\frac{1}{2} = 64$.

4. If $s = ax + bx^2$, where a and b are constants, then s is said to vary partially with x and partially with x^2.

Example 4

The cost of printing a birthday card is partly constant and partly varies as the number printed. The cost per card is 3·5 pence when 10 cards are printed, and is 3 pence when 20 cards are printed. Find the cost of printing 40 cards.

Let the cost be s pence, and the number of cards printed be x.

$\therefore\ s = a + bx$ where a and b are constants.

When $s = 35$ i.e. $10 \times 3{\cdot}5, x = 10$. $\quad \therefore 35 = a + 10b$ ①
When $s = 60$ i.e. $20 \times 3, \quad x = 20$. $\quad \therefore 60 = a + 20b$ ②

Subtracting ① from ②

$$25 = 10b$$
$$b = 2{\cdot}5$$

In equation ①, when $b = 2{\cdot}5$

$$35 = a + 25$$
$$\therefore a = 10$$

$$\therefore \quad s = 10 + 2{\cdot}5x$$

When $x = 40, s = 10 + 2{\cdot}5 \times 40$
$= 110$

$\therefore$ the cost of printing 40 cards is £1·10.

Exercise 8.6

1. If $x \propto y$ and $x = 4$ when $y = 2$, find x when $y = 5$, and y when $x = 6$.
2. If $y \propto z$ and $y = 15$ when $z = 1\frac{1}{2}$, find y when $z = 6$, and z when $y = 3\frac{1}{2}$.
3. If $p \propto 1/q$ and $p = \frac{1}{2}$ when $q = 4$, find p when $q = 6$, and q when $p = 3$.
4. If $a \propto b^2$ and $a = 27$ when $b = 3$, find a when $b = 7$, and b when $a = 12$.
5. If $x^2 \propto 1/y$ and $x = 2$ when $y = 16$, find x when $y = \frac{1}{16}$, and y when $x = 3$.
6. If $p^2 \propto q^3$ and $p = 16$ when $q = 4$, find p when $q = 4$, and q when $p = 4$.
7. If $y \propto \sqrt{z}$ and $y = 1\frac{1}{2}$ when $z = \frac{1}{4}$, find y when $z = 16$, and z when $y = 9$.
8. If $y \propto 1/(z + 4)$ and $z = 2$ when $y = 2$, find y when $z = 4$, and z when $y = 24$.
9. If $(y + 2) \propto (z - 1)$ and $y = 7$ when $z = 7$, find y when $z = 14$, and z when $y = 2z$.
10. If $(2x + 1) \propto 1/y$ and $y = 2\frac{1}{2}$ when $x = \frac{3}{4}$, find x when $x = y$.
11. x varies jointly as y and z. If $x = 40$ when $y = 2$ and $z = 5$, find y when $x = 9$ and $z = 3$.
12. x varies directly as y and inversely as the square of z. If $x = 3\frac{3}{4}$ when $y = 5$ and $z = 2$, find z when $x = 16$ and $y = 27$.
13. The weight of a cube varies directly as the cube of the length of its edge and directly as its density. If a cube of edge 2 cm and density 3 g/cm^3 weighs 24 g, find the weight of a cube whose edges are twice as long as the first one and whose density is half as great.
14. The resistance of a wire carrying an electric current varies directly as its length and inversely as the square of its diameter. Find the ratio of the resistance of two wires, one twice as long and a quarter as thick as the other.
15. An enclosed quantity of air at atmospheric pressure (1·06 kg/cm^2) and temperature 15°C is compressed in such a way that the volume is halved and the pressure is raised to 2·4 kg/cm^2. The change in temperature, pressure and volume are connected by the relation $pv \propto (t + 273)$. Find, to the nearest degree, the rise in temperature produced.
16. The cost per week of running a private school is partly constant and partly varies directly with the number of pupils. If it costs £350 a week when there are 50 pupils, and £600 a week when there are double that number, find the cost of running the school for 250 pupils.
17. The cost of running a car ferry is the sum of two parts. One part varies directly as the distance run, and the other part varies inversely as the square of the distance. If a 20 km voyage costs £8005, and a 10 km one costs £4020, find the cost of a 15 km voyage.
18. If x varies directly as y and inversely as z^2, find the percentage change in x when y increases by 10% and z decreases by 10%.

8.7 Surds

A root which cannot be expressed as a fraction is called a *surd*. For example, $\sqrt{15}, \sqrt[3]{28}$.

A surd may be simplified in one of two ways:

1. By expressing it in terms of other surds.
   e.g. $\sqrt{72} = \sqrt{(2 \times 36)} = \sqrt{(2 \times 6^2)} = 6\sqrt{2}$.
2. By rationalizing the denominator. This is done by multiplying both the numerator and the denominator by the same expression.

$$\text{e.g.} \quad \frac{1}{\sqrt{2}} = \frac{\sqrt{2}}{\sqrt{2} \times \sqrt{2}} = \frac{\sqrt{2}}{2}$$

Example Simplify the following expression: $\dfrac{1}{2+\sqrt{2}}$

$$\frac{1}{2+\sqrt{2}} = \frac{2-\sqrt{2}}{(2+\sqrt{2})(2-\sqrt{2})};$$

$$(2+\sqrt{2})(2-\sqrt{2}) = 2^2 - (\sqrt{2})^2 = 4 - 2 = 2$$

$$\therefore \quad \frac{1}{2+\sqrt{2}} = \frac{2-\sqrt{2}}{2} = 1 - \frac{\sqrt{2}}{2}.$$

In general, when the denominator is in the form $(a \pm \sqrt{b})$, rationalize the expression by multiplying both the numerator and the denominator by $(a \mp \sqrt{b})$.

Exercise 8.7

Simplify the following expressions.

1. $\dfrac{1}{\sqrt{2}}$
2. $\dfrac{1}{\sqrt{3}}$
3. $\dfrac{2}{\sqrt{5}}$
4. $\dfrac{5}{\sqrt{7}}$
5. $\dfrac{2}{3\sqrt{11}}$
6. $\dfrac{1}{1+\sqrt{2}}$
7. $\dfrac{1}{1-2\sqrt{3}}$
8. $\dfrac{2}{\sqrt{2}+\sqrt{5}}$
9. $\dfrac{1+\sqrt{3}}{1-\sqrt{3}}$
10. $\dfrac{3-2\sqrt{2}}{3+2\sqrt{2}}$
11. $\dfrac{\sqrt{2}(\sqrt{3}-\sqrt{2})}{\sqrt{3}+\sqrt{2}}$
12. $\dfrac{\sqrt{5}(1-2\sqrt{3})}{1+\sqrt{3}}$
13. $\dfrac{(1-\sqrt{2})(1-\sqrt{8})}{1+\sqrt{2}}$
14. $\dfrac{(2+\sqrt{2})(1+\sqrt{3})}{2+\sqrt{3}}$
15. $\dfrac{(\sqrt{5}-1)(\sqrt{5}+2)}{2\sqrt{5}-1}$
16. $\dfrac{2-\sqrt{3}}{2+\sqrt{3}} + \dfrac{2+\sqrt{3}}{2-\sqrt{3}}$
17. $\dfrac{\sqrt{5}-2}{\sqrt{5}+2} + \dfrac{\sqrt{5}+2}{\sqrt{5}-2}$
18. $\left(\dfrac{\sqrt{3}-\sqrt{2}}{\sqrt{3}+\sqrt{2}}\right)^2$
19. $\dfrac{2\sqrt{2}-3}{2\sqrt{2}+3} - \dfrac{2\sqrt{2}+3}{2\sqrt{2}-3}$
20. $\left(\dfrac{\sqrt{2}-1}{\sqrt{2}+1}\right)^3$
21. $(1+\sqrt{2})^4$
22. $(1+\sqrt{2}+\sqrt{3})^2$

8.8 Special angles

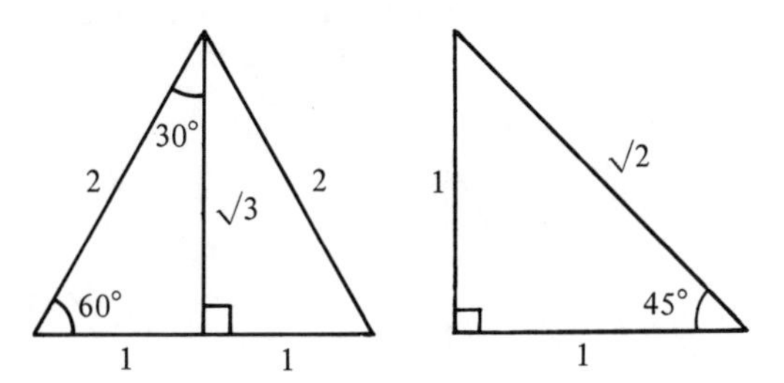

From the two figures above, the special trigonometric ratios shown in the table can be deduced.
When using these ratios, the answer can be left in surd form.

	sin	cos	tan
0°	0	1	0
30°	$\frac{1}{2}$	$\frac{\sqrt{3}}{2}$	$\frac{1}{\sqrt{3}} = \frac{\sqrt{3}}{3}$
45°	$\frac{1}{\sqrt{2}} = \frac{\sqrt{2}}{2}$	$\frac{1}{\sqrt{2}} = \frac{\sqrt{2}}{2}$	1
60°	$\frac{\sqrt{3}}{2}$	$\frac{1}{2}$	$\sqrt{3}$
90°	1	0	∞

Example 1

In the figure, find DC without using trigonometric tables.

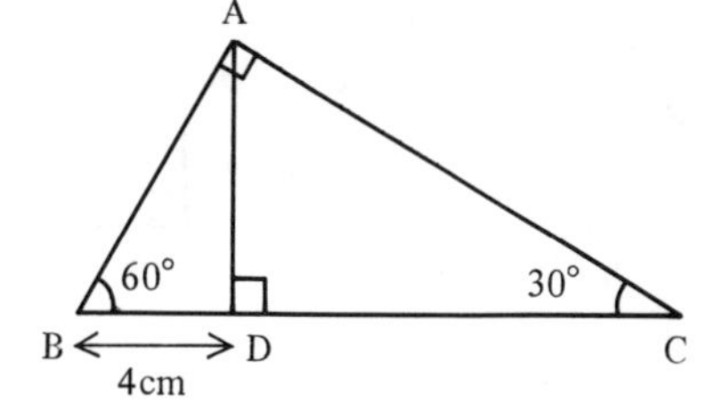

In triangle ABD, $\tan 60° = \frac{AD}{4}$.

$\therefore\ AD = 4 \tan 60° = 4\sqrt{3}$ cm.

In triangle ACD, $\frac{AD}{DC} = \tan 30°$

or $\frac{4\sqrt{3}}{DC} = \frac{1}{\sqrt{3}}$

$\therefore$ $DC = 4\sqrt{3} \,.\, \sqrt{3} = 12$ cm.

Example 2 Find the value of $\frac{1 - \sin 2A}{1 + \sin 2A}$ when $A = 15°$.

$\sin 2A = \sin (2 \times 15°) = \sin 30° = \frac{1}{2}$

$\therefore\ \frac{1 - \sin 2A}{1 + \sin 2A} = \frac{1 - \frac{1}{2}}{1 + \frac{1}{2}} = \frac{\frac{1}{2}}{\frac{3}{2}} = \frac{1}{3}$.

Exercise 8.8a

Calculate the unknown lengths marked on the diagrams below, following the alphabetical order. All lengths may be taken as cm. Leave your answers in surd form.

1.

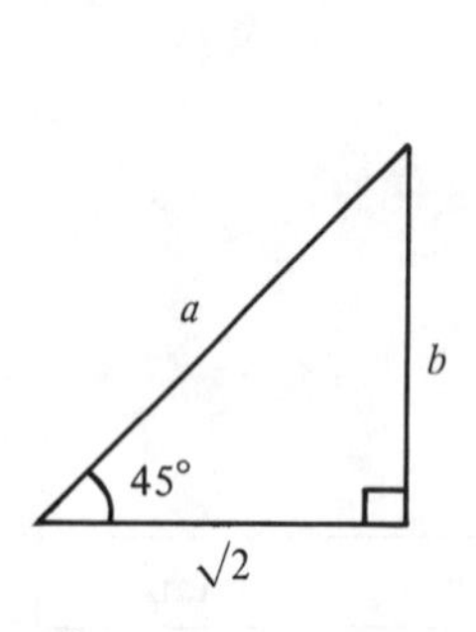

2.

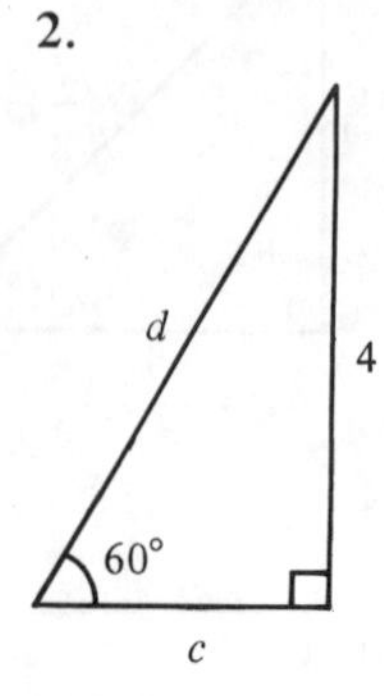

3.

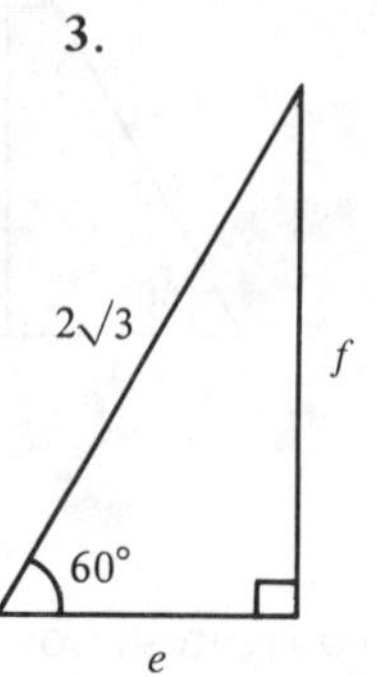

4.

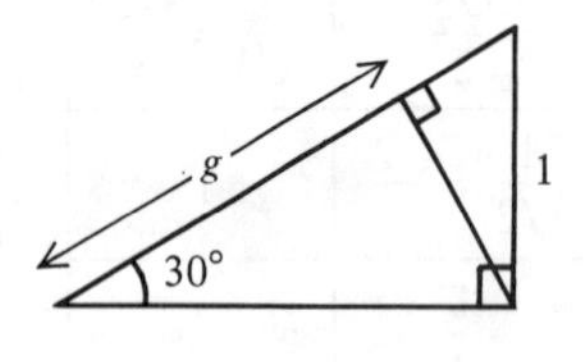

5.

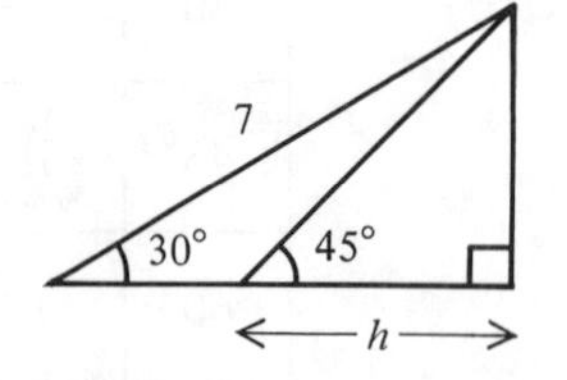

6.

30°
6
i

7.

j
45°
2
60°

8.

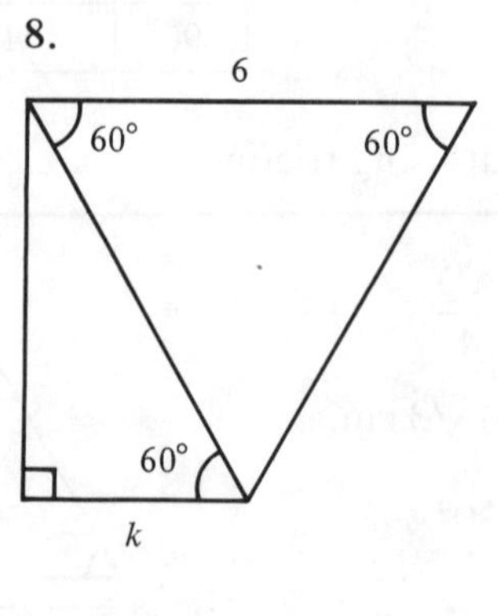

9.

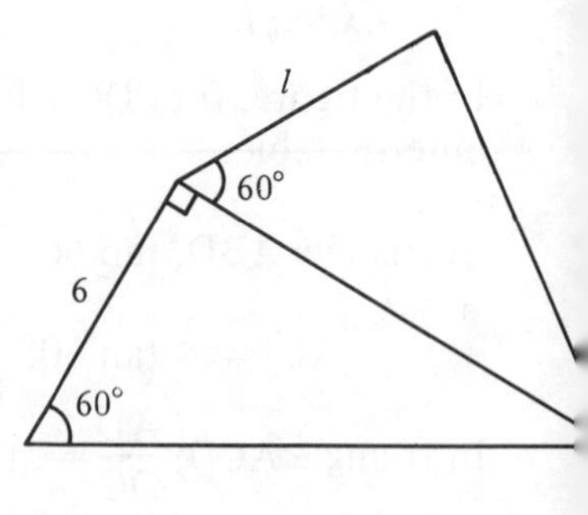

10. Evaluate the following.

(a) $\dfrac{\sin A}{\cos A}$ when $A = 60°$

(b) $\dfrac{1 - \sin A}{1 + \sin A}$ when $A = 30°$

(c) $\dfrac{1 - \tan A}{\cos 2A}$ when $A = 30°$

(d) $\sin^2 A + \cos^2 A$ when $A = 60°$

(e) $\dfrac{\sin^2 A - 1}{\cos^2 A - 1}$ when $A = 60°$

(f) $\dfrac{2 + \cos 2A}{1 - \sin 2A}$ when $A = 15°$

The following two identities should be remembered.

$$\sin^2 \hat{A} + \cos^2 \hat{A} = 1$$

$$\frac{\sin \hat{A}}{\cos \hat{A}} = \tan \hat{A}$$

Example 3

If $\hat{A}$ is acute and $\sin \hat{A} = \frac{5}{13}$, without using tables find the value of (a) $\tan \hat{A}$, (b) $\cos (180° - \hat{A})$.

(a) $\sin^2 \hat{A} + \cos^2 \hat{A} = 1 = (\frac{5}{13})^2 + \cos^2 \hat{A}$

$\therefore \quad \cos^2 \hat{A} = 1 - (\frac{5}{13})^2$

$= 1 - \frac{25}{169} = \frac{144}{169}$

and $\cos \hat{A} = \frac{12}{13}$

$$\tan \hat{A} = \frac{\sin \hat{A}}{\cos \hat{A}} = \frac{\frac{12}{13}}{\frac{5}{13}} = \frac{12}{5}$$

(b) $\cos (180° - \hat{A}) = -\cos \hat{A} = -\frac{12}{13}$

Example 4

Find θ if $8 \sin^2 \theta + 6 \cos \theta - 9 = 0$ and θ is less than $90°$.

$\sin^2 \theta + \cos^2 \theta = 1; \quad \therefore \sin^2 \theta = 1 - \cos^2 \theta$

$\therefore \quad 8 (1 - \cos^2 \theta) + 6 \cos \theta - 9 = 0$

$8 - 8 \cos^2 \theta + 6 \cos \theta - 9 = 0$

$8 \cos^2 \theta - 6 \cos \theta + 1 = 0$

$(4 \cos \theta - 1)(2 \cos \theta - 1) = 0$

$\therefore \quad \cos \theta = \frac{1}{4}$ or $\frac{1}{2}$

$\theta = 75°31'$ or $60°$

Exercise 8.8b

1. Without using any tables, calculate the value of sin A when cos A $= 0{\cdot}6$ and the value of cos A when sin A $= 0{\cdot}8$.
2. Using only square and square root tables and/or logs, find the value of cos A when sin A is (a) $0{\cdot}5$ (b) $0{\cdot}7071$ (c) $0{\cdot}8192$ (d) $0{\cdot}4147$ (e) $0{\cdot}5990$

Solve the following equations for angles less than $90°$

3. $2 \cos^2 \theta + 7 \sin^2 \theta = 3{\cdot}25$
4. $2 \sin^2 \theta + 4 \cos^2 \theta = 3$
5. $3 \sin^2 \theta + 4 \cos^2 \theta = 3{\cdot}25$
6. $5 \sin^2 \theta + 6 \cos^2 \theta = 5{\cdot}5$
7. $4 \sin^2 \theta - \cos^2 \theta = 2$
8. $4 \sin^2 \theta + 12 \cos \theta - 9 = 0$

8.9 Extensions of Pythagoras' theorem

1. In triangle ABC, if BC is opposite the obtuse angle A, then

$$BC^2 = AB^2 + AC^2 + 2\,AB\,.\,AD$$

2. In triangle ABC, if BC is opposite the acute angle A, then

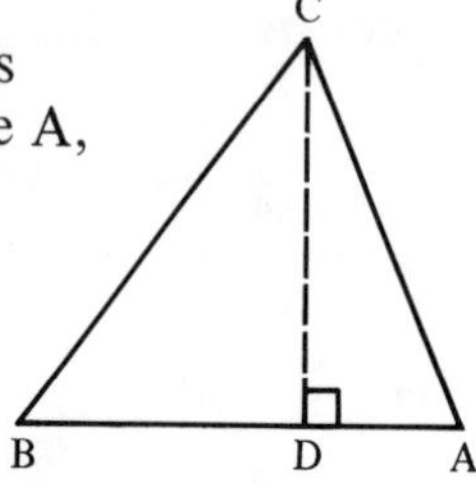

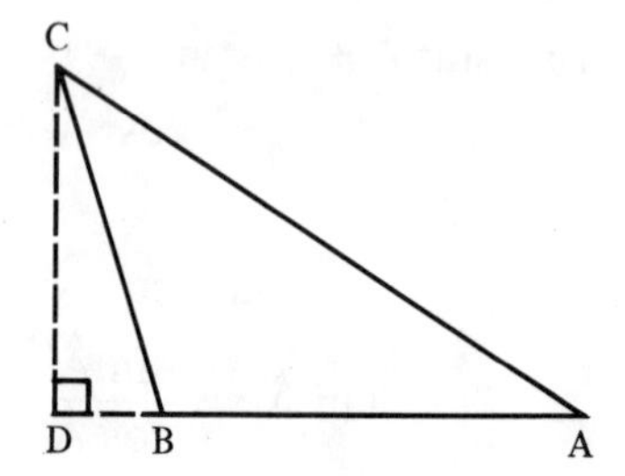

$$BC^2 = AB^2 + AC^2 - 2\,AB\,.\,AD.$$

3. In the triangle ABC, if AD is a median, then

$$AB^2 + AC^2 = 2\,BD^2 + 2\,AD^2$$

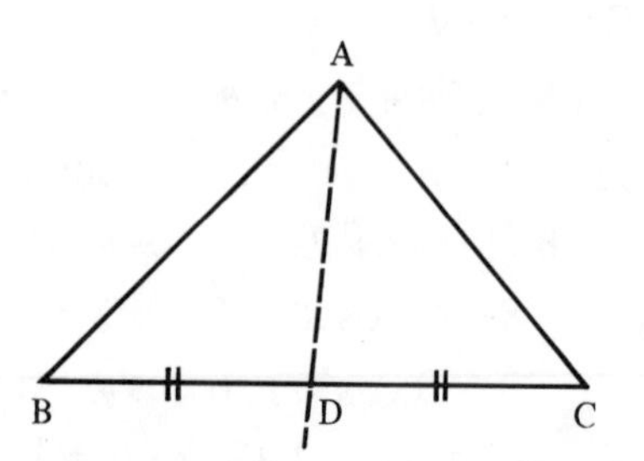

This is known as the Theorem of Apollonius.

Example 1

In the diagram on the right, find AD.

Because angle A is obtuse, then

$$\begin{aligned} BC^2 &= AB^2 + AC^2 + 2AB\,.\,AD \\ 15^2 &= 10^2 + 11^2 + 2 \times 10 \times AD \\ 225 &= 100 + 121 + 20AD \\ 225 - 221 &= 20\,AD \\ 4 &= 20AD \\ AD &= \frac{4}{20} = 0{\cdot}2 \text{ cm.} \end{aligned}$$

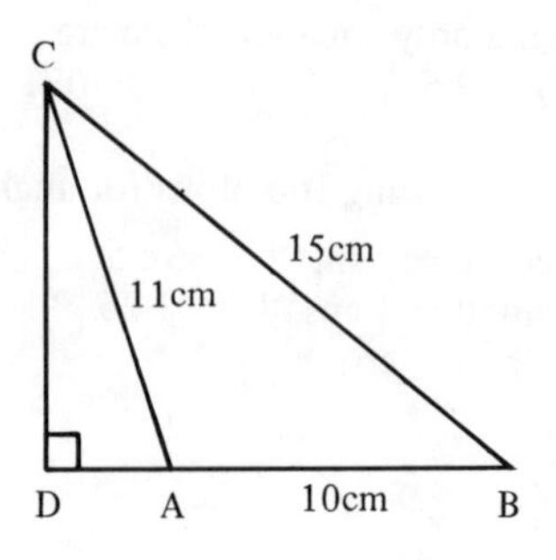

Example 2

Find the shortest median in a triangle in which the sides are 7 cm, 11 cm, and 14 cm long.

Let the triangle be ABC, then the median AD bisects BC.
Because AD is a median, then

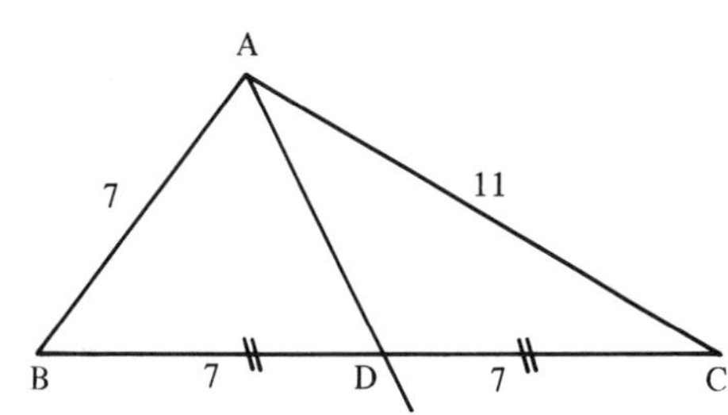

$$AB^2 + AC^2 = 2BD^2 + 2AD^2$$
$$7^2 + 11^2 = 2 \times 7^2 + 2 \times AD^2$$
$$\therefore \quad 49 + 121 = 98 + 2AD^2$$
$$170 - 98 = 2AD^2$$
$$72 = 2AD^2$$
$$36 = AD^2$$
$$\therefore \quad AD = \sqrt{36} = 6 \text{ cm}$$

Example 3

Find by calculation if a triangle with sides 7 cm, 11 cm, and 14 cm long is acute-angled, obtuse-angled, or right-angled.

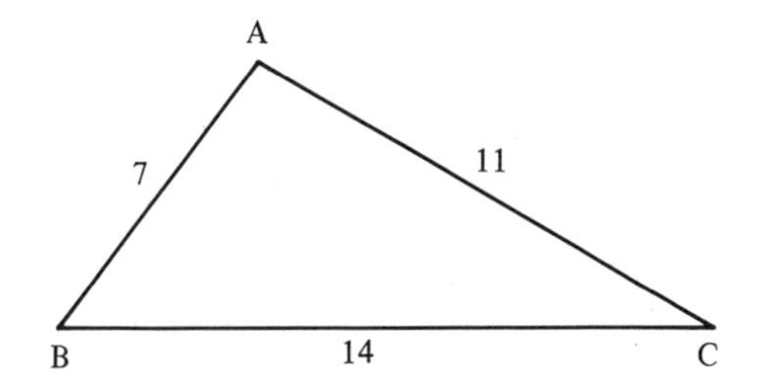

Let the triangle be ABC.
Then $a^2 = 14^2 = 196$

$b^2 = 11^2 = 121$

$c^2 = 7^2 = 49$

$\therefore a^2 > b^2 + c^2$

so triangle ABC is obtuse-angled at A.

Exercise 8.9a

Calculate the unknown lengths marked on the diagrams below (following the alphabetical order). All lengths may be taken as cm.

1.

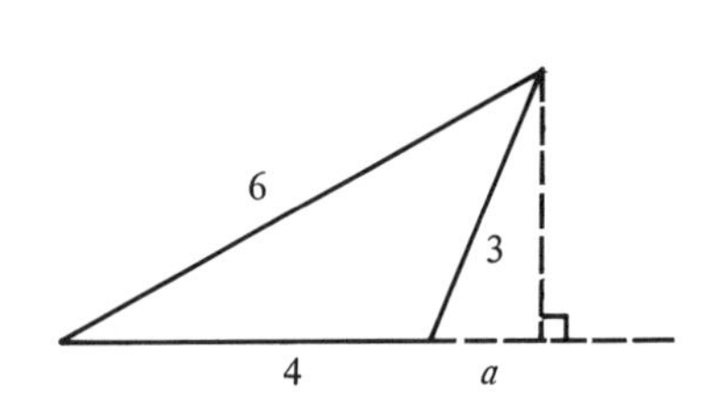

2.

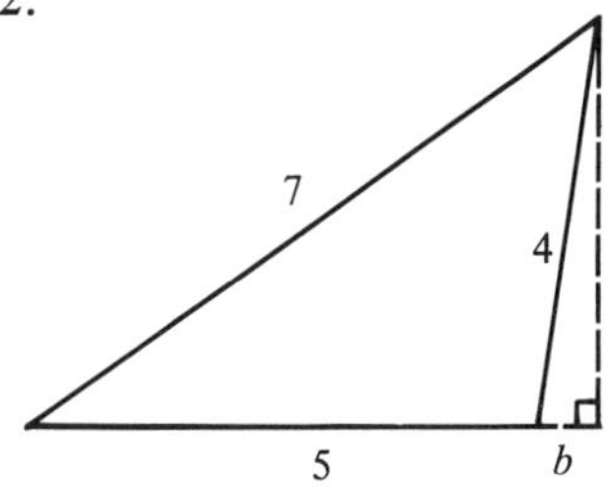

3.

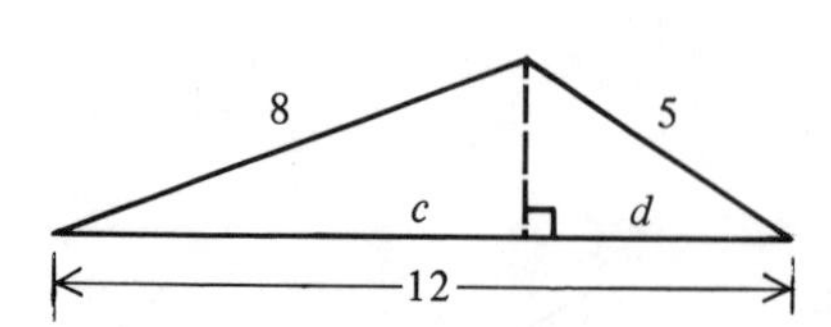

4.

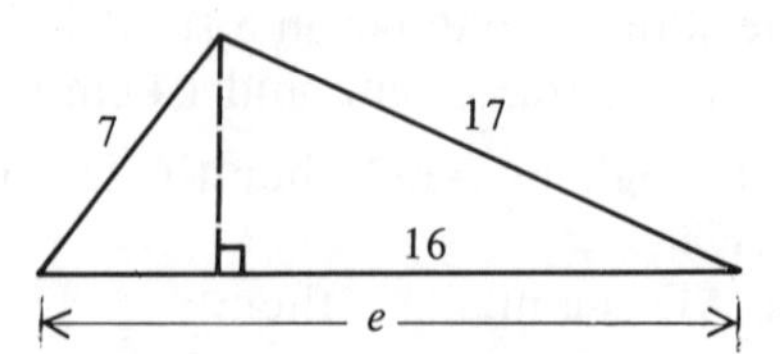

5.

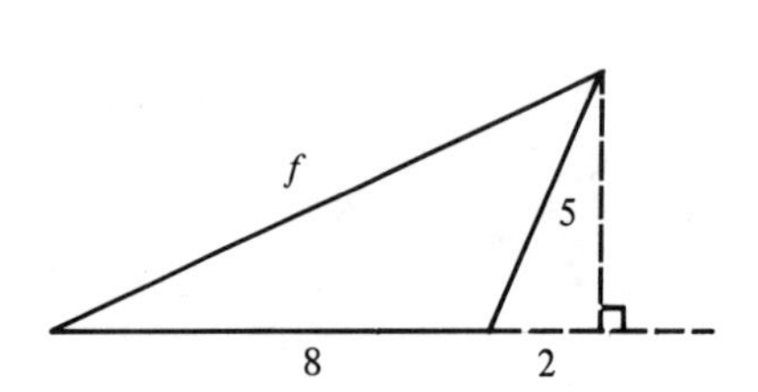

6.

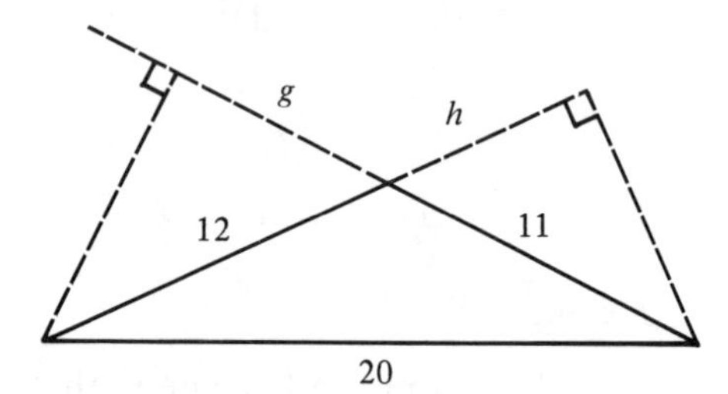

7.

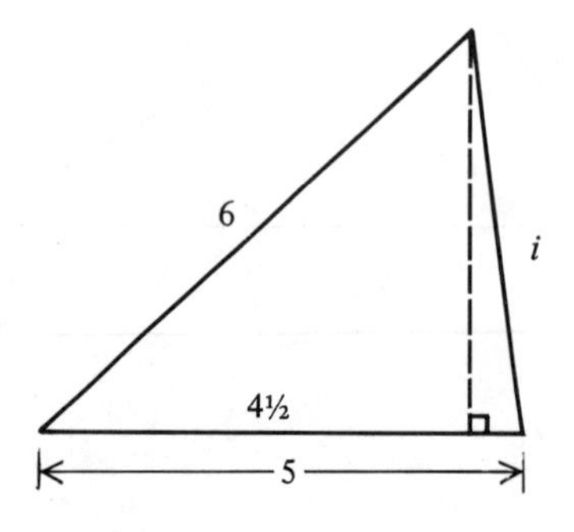

8.

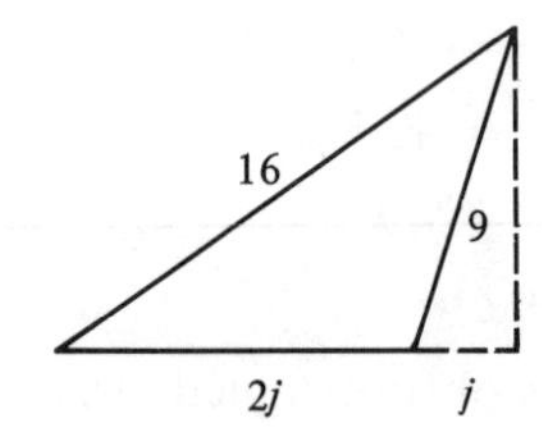

9.

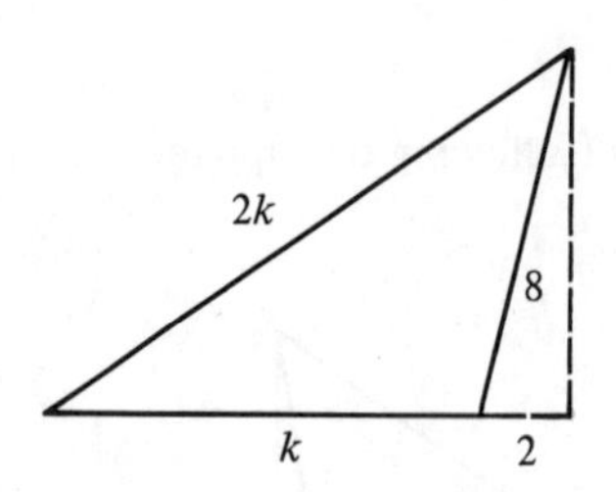

10.

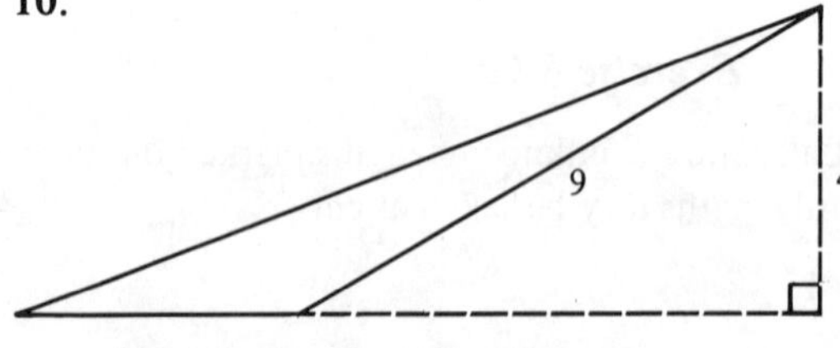

Find the length of the longest side of the above triangle whose area is 20 cm^2.

Exercise 8.9b

Calculate the length of the shortest median of the following triangles, the lengths of whose sides are given. These may be taken as centimetres.

1. 3, 4, 5 **2.** 7, 24, 25 **3.** 8, 9, 10 **4.** 12, 15, 21

Questions 5 to 9 refer to the diagram.

5. If $a = 8, c = 5$ and $d = 4$, find b.
6. If $a = 10, b = 7$ and $d = 5$, find c.
7. If $b = 8, c = 5$ and $d = 6$, find a.
8. If $a = b, c = 5$ and $d = 6$, find b.
9. If $a = c, b = 14$ and $d = 7$, find a.

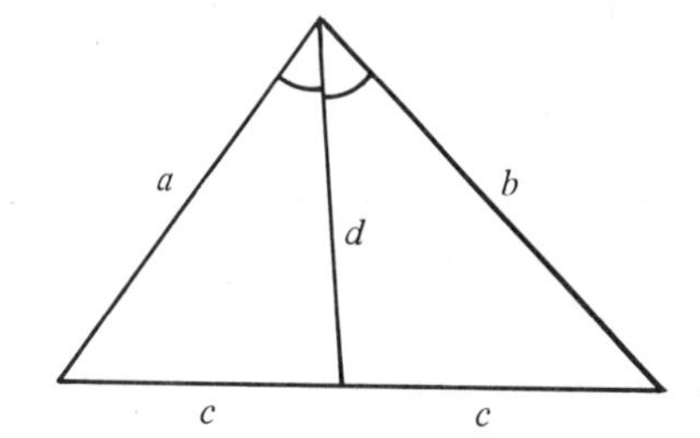

10. The diagonals of a parallelogram are 6 cm and 15 cm long. If one side is 9 cm long, find the other.
11. D and E are the points of trisection of the base BC of triangle ABC. If AB = 6 cm, AE = 5 cm, and BC = 12 cm, find the lengths of AD and AC.
12. Using the same data as question **11**, if AD = 4 cm, AE = 5 cm, and AC = 6 cm, find AB and BD. What is unusual about this triangle?
13. AD is the median of triangle ABC. If AC = 2 AB = 4 AD, and BD = 5 cm, find the length of AD.
14. The medians of a triangle are 4, 5, and 6 cm long. Find the length of its sides.

Exercise 8.9c

State whether the following triangles, whose sides are given, are right-angled, acute-angled, or obtuse-angled. The lengths may be taken as cm.

1. 9, 11, 14 **2.** 2, 4, 5 **3.** 9, 12, 17 **4.** 6, 7, 9
5. 4, 8, 11 **6.** 10, 24, 26 **7.** 10, 14, 17 **8.** 7, 12, 18
9. 10, 15, 18 **10.** 19, 15, 18.

11. A right-angled triangle ABC has sides AB = 7 cm, AC = 24 cm, and BC = 25 cm. A line is drawn from the vertex A to the hypotenuse BC to cut it at D. Find the maximum length of DC for triangle ADC to be obtuse-angled. How many such triangles can be drawn if DC is a whole number of centimetres long?
12. An isosceles triangle ABC has AB = AC = 14 cm and its altitude is 12 cm long. If a line MN is drawn from the mid-point of the base, M to a point N on AC 1 cm from C, is the triangle NCM obtuse-angled or not?

8.10 Harder plane problems

These problems should be attempted in the same way as outlined in section 6.5. Be prepared to use the sine and cosine rules in addition to basic trigonometric ratios.

Note. Use the sine rule where possible in preference to the cosine rule.

Example

A house B is 400 m due East of A. From A, the bearing of a tower T is 046°. From B, the bearing of the tower is 308°. Find the distance of the tower from the road joining A and B.

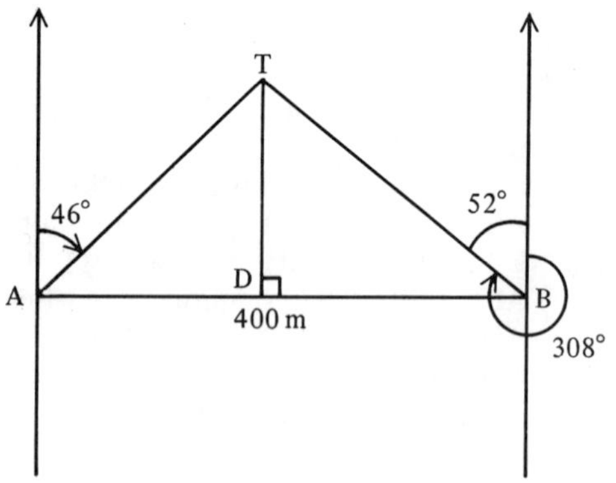

In the diagram, TD is the required distance.

In triangle TAD:

$$\text{TAD} = 44° \ (90° - 46°)$$

$$\text{ATD} = 46° \ \text{(alternate angles)}$$

$$\text{BTD} = 52° \ \text{(alternate angles)}$$

$$\therefore \ \text{ATB} = 98° \ (52° + 46°)$$

and $$\text{ABT} = 38° \ (90° - 52°)$$

T
46°
52°
D
A
B
400 m
308°

Using the sine rule to find the length of AT in triangle ATB

$$\frac{\text{AT}}{\sin \text{B}} = \frac{\text{AB}}{\sin 98°}$$

$$\frac{\text{AT}}{\sin 38°} = \frac{400}{\sin 82°} \quad (\sin 98° = \sin(180° - 98°) = \sin 82°)$$

$$\therefore \quad \text{AT} = \frac{400 \times \sin 38°}{\sin 82°} = 248{\cdot}7 \text{ m.}$$

In the right-angled triangle ATD:

$$\text{TD} = \text{AT} \sin 44° = 248{\cdot}7 \times 0{\cdot}6947 = 172{\cdot}8 \text{ m.}$$

Exercise 8.10

1. A ship steams 5 km on a bearing of 080° and then 6 km on a bearing of 010°. Find its distance and bearing from its starting point.
2. P and Q are two points on opposite sides of a small hill. To get from P to Q it is necessary to walk 200 m up a path inclined at 10° to the horizontal and then down 150 m at 12° to the horizontal. Find the length and inclination of a straight path from P to Q.

3. The diagram represents a roof truss in which AB = 9 m, BC = 7 m and AC = 10 m. The ridge of the roof, through B, is supported by struts DA, DB and DC such that $D\hat{A}C = 25°$ and $D\hat{C}A = 35°$. Find the length of the three struts.

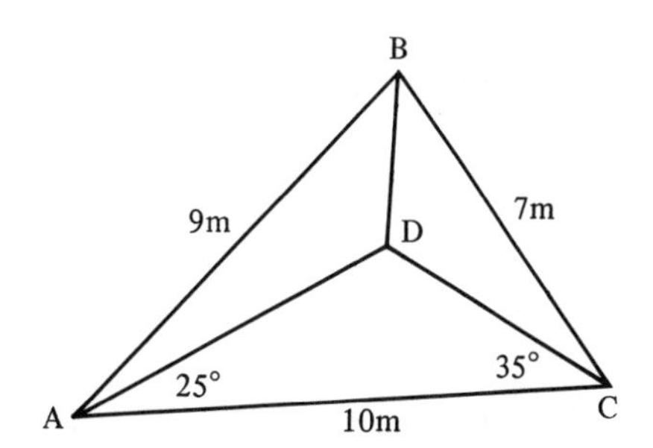

4. The angles of elevation of the top of a tree from two points P and Q in line with its foot are 12° and 15°. If PQ is 10 m long, find the height of the tree.
5. Two points P and Q on opposite sides of a tower are 100 m apart. The angles of elevation of the top of the tower are 40° and 48° respectively. How high is the tower?
6. Of two masts of a ship, one is 5 m taller than the other. The angles of elevation of the top of each when viewed from the foot of the other are 42° and 46°. Find the length of a straight rope stretched between the tops of the two masts.
7. The angle of elevation of the summit of a hill is 10° 15′ and on walking 300 m up a slope of 7° 30′ it is found to be 15° 40′. How high is the hill?
8. ABCD is a cyclic quadrilateral inscribed in a circle of radius 5 cm. AB = BC = CD = 8 cm. O is the centre of the circle. Find
   (a) $A\hat{O}D$ (b) the length of AD (c) the area of ABCD.
9. The diagram represents a jib crane. The jib JB is 10 m long and is held by a tie rod BT to a frame TKJ. $B\hat{T}J = 100°$, TK = TJ = 6 m, and KJ = 4 m. Find the distance JL between the foot of the frame and the point where the crane can deposit its load.

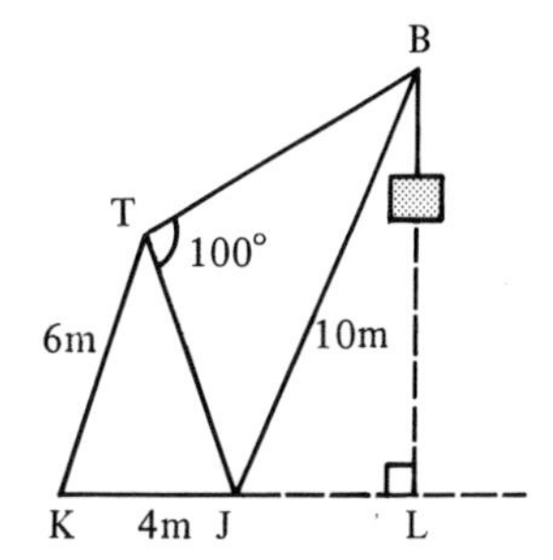

10. ABCD is a quadrilateral. AB = 6 cm, BC = 9 cm, and CD = 10 cm. If $A\hat{B}C = 140°$ and $B\hat{C}D = 120°$, find the length of AD.
11. In the quadrilateral ABCD, AB = 9 cm, BC = 6 cm, $A\hat{B}C = 145°$, and $A\hat{D}C = 50°$ when $D\hat{A}C = 70°$. Find the length of DC.
12. In the crane shown find the length of CD.

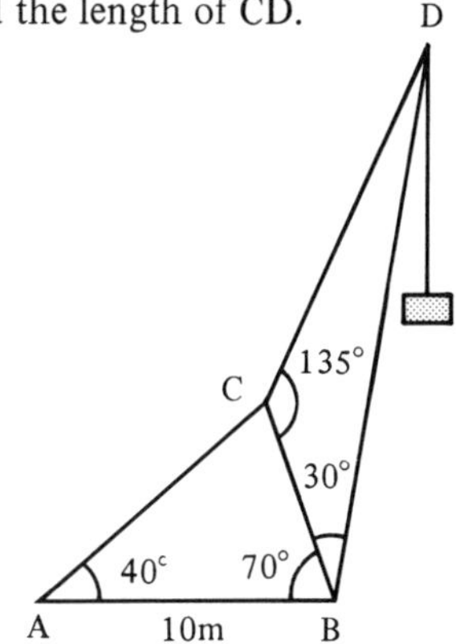

8.11 Volumes of revolution

When the area under a curve between $x = a$ and $x = b$ is rotated about the x-axis, the resultant solid is called a *solid of revolution.*

For example, the volume under a line parallel to the x-axis between $x = 2$ and $x = 5$ is a cylinder whose length is 3 units.

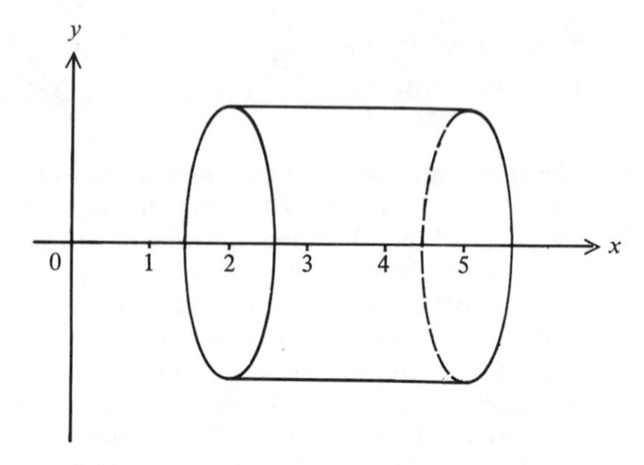

The volume of a solid of revolution about the x-axis is $\int_a^b \pi (y^2)\, dx$ or $\pi \int_a^b y^2\, dx$ and is usually left in terms of π.

The volume of a solid of revolution about the y-axis is $\pi \int_a^b x^2\, dy$.

Example 1

Find the volume generated by revolving about the x-axis that part of the curve $y = x^2$ which lies between $x = 2$ and $x = 3$.

$$\begin{aligned}
\text{Volume} &= \pi \int_2^3 (x^2)^2\, dx \\
&= \pi \int_2^3 x^4\, dx \\
&= \pi \left[\frac{x^5}{5}\right]_2^3 \\
&= \pi \left(\frac{243}{5} - \frac{32}{5}\right) \\
&= \pi \left(\frac{211}{5}\right) \\
&= 42\tfrac{1}{5}\pi \text{ units of volume.}
\end{aligned}$$

Example 2

The equation of a circle with radius r is $x^2 + y^2 = r^2$. Use this equation to deduce the formula for the volume of a sphere.

Diagram (a) shows the quadrant of a circle of radius r.

Diagram (b) shows the solid of revolution of this quadrant about the x-axis to give a hemisphere.

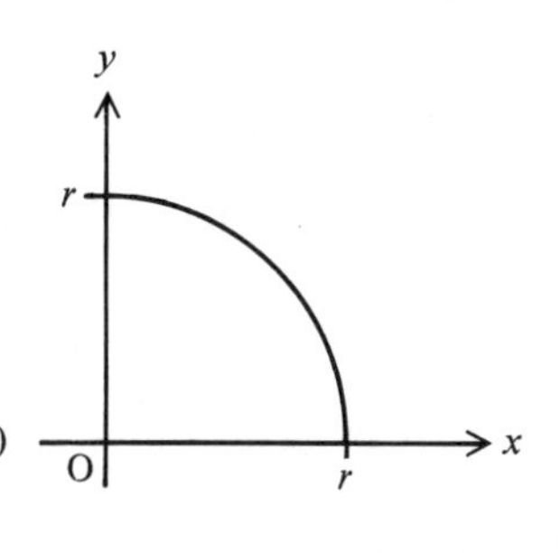

$$\text{Volume of hemisphere} = \pi \int_0^r y^2\,dx$$

but $$y^2 = r^2 - x^2$$

$$\therefore \quad \text{volume} = \pi \int_0^r (r^2 - x^2)\,dx$$

$$= \pi \left[r^2 x - \frac{x^3}{3} \right]_0^r$$

$$= \pi \left(r^3 - \frac{r^3}{3} \right) - 0$$

$$= \pi \frac{2r^3}{3} = \tfrac{2}{3}\pi r^3$$

$$\therefore \quad \text{volume of sphere} = 2 \times \tfrac{2}{3}\pi r^3 = \tfrac{4}{3}\pi r^3.$$

Exercise 8.11

1. The area bounded by the curve $y = x^2$, the x-axis and the ordinate $x = 4$ rotates through 360° about the x-axis. Find the volume swept out.
2. The area between the curve $y = 3\sqrt{x}$, $y = 3$, and the y-axis rotates through 360° about the y-axis. Find the volume swept out.
3. The area between the curve $y = \sqrt{3x + 1}$ and the two axes, rotates through 360° about the x-axis. Find the volume swept out.
4. The area in question **3** now rotates through 360° about the y-axis. Find the volume swept out this time.
5. The area between the line $y = 2x$, the x-axis, and the ordinate $x = 4$ rotates through 360° about the x-axis. Find the volume swept out.
6. The area between the line $y = \left(\frac{r}{h}\right)x$, the x-axis, and the ordinate $x = h$, rotates through 360° about the x-axis; r and h are constants. Find the volume swept out. Write down the formula for the volume of a cone of height h and base radius r.
7. The area between the line $y = x + 3$, the two axes, and the ordinate $x = 5$, rotates through 360° about the x-axis. Find the volume swept out.
8. The area between the curve $x^2 + y^2 = r^2$ (r is a constant), the x-axis, and the ordinate $x = \frac{1}{2}r$, rotates through 360° about the x-axis. Find the volume swept out. (Note that this example will enable you to find the volume of a cap of a sphere.)
9. The area between the curve $y = 4x - x^2$, and the line $y = 3$, rotates through 360° about the x-axis. Find the volume of the resulting ring.
10. The area between the curve $y = 4x - x^2$ and the line $y = x + 2$ rotates through 360° about the x-axis. Find the volume swept out.

8.12 Rates of change

If a relationship between x and y is established, then the derivative of y with respect to x, $\frac{dy}{dx}$, compares the rate of change of y with that of x.

For example, if $\frac{dy}{dx}$ equals 4, then y is increasing at a rate 4 times faster than x.
i.e. if x is increasing at 3 m/s, then y is increasing at 12 m/s.

Example 1

The radius of a circle increases at a rate of 0·4 cm/s. Find the rate of increase of the area when the radius is 2 cm.

Let the area be A cm² and the radius r cm.

$$A = \pi r^2$$

$$\therefore \quad \frac{dA}{dr} = 2\pi r$$

i.e. the area is increasing $2\pi r$ times as fast as the radius.

When $r = 2$ cm, $\frac{dA}{dr} = 2\pi \times 2 = 4\pi$ cm.

So the area is increasing 4π times as fast as the radius.
But the radius is increasing at 0·4 cm/s.

$\therefore$ The area is increasing at $0{\cdot}4 \times 4\pi = 1{\cdot}6\pi$ cm²/s.

Example 2

Water is flowing out of a conical funnel having a semi-vertical angle of 45°. When the depth of water is 4 cm, the water level is falling by 0·2 cm/s. Calculate the volume rate of flow of the water.

Let the volume of water be V cm³ when the depth of water is h cm and the radius r cm.

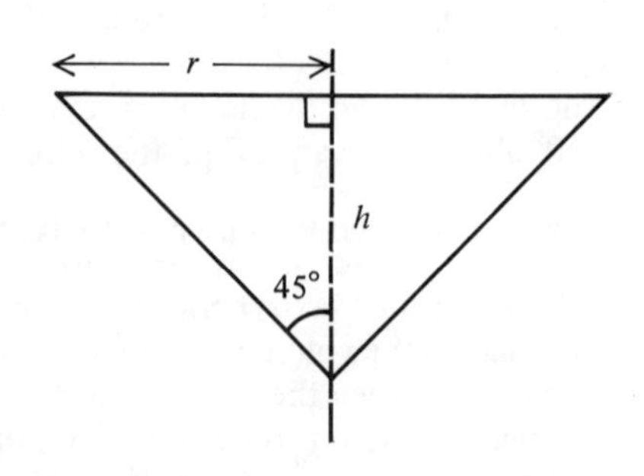

$$V = \tfrac{1}{3}\pi r^3 \quad \text{(because } h = r\text{)}$$

$$\therefore \quad \frac{dV}{dr} = \pi r^2 = \frac{dV}{dh}$$ (h always equals r because the semi-vertical angle is 45°).

Thus the volume of water is decreasing πr^2 faster than the radius.

When $h = 4$ cm,

$$\frac{dV}{dr} = \frac{dV}{dh} = \pi \times 4^2 = 16\pi \text{ cm}^3/\text{cm}.$$

Thus V is decreasing 16π times faster than the height when $h = 4$ cm. But the height is decreasing by 0·2 cm/s.

$$\therefore \text{ The flow rate of water } = 0{\cdot}2 \times 16\pi \text{ cm}^3/\text{s}$$
$$= 3{\cdot}2\pi \text{ cm}^3/\text{s}.$$

Exercise 8.12

1. A stone dropped into a pond causes ripples to spread out from the point of impact. How fast is the disturbed area growing if the ripple is moving at 2 m/s and the radius of the outermost ripple is 4 m?
2. A spherical balloon is expanding at the rate of 10 cm^3/s. At what rate is its radius increasing when it is 6 cm?
3. If the radius of the balloon in question 2 now decreases at the rate of 0·2 cm/s, at what rate will the surface area be decreasing when the radius is 15 cm?
4. A cube expands so that its edge increases at the rate of 0·1 cm/h. At what rate is the volume increasing when it reaches 8 cm^3?
5. A man 2 metres tall walks at 5 km/h towards a street lamp which is 8 metres high. Find the rate in km/h at which his shadow decreases in length.
6. The volume of a circular cylinder is constant at 300 cm^3. Its height is increasing at the rate of 2 cm/s. At what rate is its radius altering when it has reached 5 cm?
7. The cross section of a 5 metre long water trough is a right-angled isosceles triangle. Water is poured into the trough at the rate of 5 m^3/s.
   (a) How fast is the water level rising when the depth is 1 metre?
   (b) How fast is it rising after it has been flowing in for 2 seconds?
8. The height of a cone is increasing at the rate of 4 cm/s but the length of the slant side remains constant at 20 cm. How fast is the volume changing
   (a) when the height is 8 cm? (b) when the height is 15 cm?
9. A cylindrical water tank of radius 1·5 metres has a small hole in its base through which water runs out at the rate of $0{\cdot}1\sqrt{x}$ m^3/s, where x is the depth of water in the tank. At what rate will the water level be dropping when the depth is 0·4 metres?
10. A bowl is formed by the rotation of the parabola $y = x^2$ about its axis. Using integration, write down an expression for the volume of water it would contain when the depth is y units. How fast is the depth increasing when the volume of water contained is $625\,\pi$ cm^3 and increasing at the rate of 100 cm^3/s?
11. A and B are points on two perpendicular lines OX and OY. Triangle OAB is of constant area 50 m^2. If A is moving at 2 m/s when OA = 16 m, find the speed at which B is moving.
12. Sand falls onto the ground at a steady rate of 500 cm^3/s and forms a cone whose base radius and height remain equal. At what rate is the height increasing
    (a) when it reaches 20 cm? (b) 10 seconds after the sand started falling?

8.13 $y = mx + c$

Any straight line can be expressed in the form $y = mx + c$ where m is the gradient, and c is the intercept on the y-axis.
The highest power of x in a linear equation is 1. Every point on this line must satisfy this equation.
For example, the line represented by the equation $y = 6x + 2$ has a gradient of 6 and cuts the y-axis at (0, 2).

Example 1

Give the gradient and the intercept on the y-axis of the line $4y = 3 - 7x$.

$$4y = 3 - 7x$$
$$\therefore \quad y = \tfrac{3}{4} - \tfrac{7}{4}x$$

The gradient of the line is therefore $-\tfrac{7}{4}$.
The line cuts the y-axis at $(0, \tfrac{3}{4})$.

Example 2

Find the coordinates of the points where the line $3x + 4y = 7$ cuts the x-axis and the y-axis.
At the point of intersection on the x-axis, $y = 0$

$$\therefore \quad 3x + 0 = 7$$
$$x = \tfrac{7}{3}$$ and the coordinates are $(\tfrac{7}{3}, 0)$

At the point of intersection on the y-axis, $x = 0$

$$\therefore \quad 0 + 4y = 7$$
$$y = \tfrac{7}{4}$$ and the coordinates on $(0, \tfrac{7}{4})$

Example 3

Show that the lines $3x + 2y = 7$ and $12y = 17 - 18x$ are parallel.

$3x + 2y = 7$; $\quad \therefore y = \tfrac{7}{2} - \tfrac{3}{2}x$ and gradient is $-\tfrac{3}{2}$
$12y = 17 - 18x$; $\quad \therefore y = \tfrac{17}{12} - \tfrac{18}{12}x$ and gradient is $-\tfrac{18}{12} = -\tfrac{3}{2}$.

Thus the lines are parallel because the gradient of each line is the same.

Example 4

Find the equation of the straight line passing through the points (2, 5) and (3, 10).

The point (2, 5) lies on the line $\quad y = mx + c$
$$\therefore \quad 5 = 2m + c \quad ①$$

The point (3, 10) lies on the line $\quad y = mx + c$
$$\therefore \quad 10 = 3m + c \quad ②$$

Subtracting ① from ②, $m = 5$

Substituting $m = 5$ in ①, $5 = 2 \times 5 + c$

$c = -5$

$\therefore$ the equation of the line is $y = 5x - 5$.

Exercise 8.13

1. Express the following in the form $y = mx + c$ and give the gradient of each line.
(a) $2y - 6 = 8x$ (b) $5x - 3y = 12$ (c) $4x = 9y - 13\frac{1}{2}$
(d) $5y + 21 - 2x = 0$ (e) $3x = \frac{1}{2}y$ (f) $1{\cdot}3x + 1{\cdot}6y - 7{\cdot}2 = 0$

2. Find whether the point $(3, -2)$ lies on the curve
(a) $y = x^2 - 4x + 1$ (b) $y = x^3 - 4x^2 + 7$ (c) $y = -\dfrac{6}{x}$
(d) $y = x^4 - 5x^2 - 30$

3. Give the coordinates of the point at which the following lines intersect (i) the x-axis (ii) the y-axis.
(a) $2x - 3y + 5 = 0$ (b) $4y = 6 - 2x$ (c) $1{\cdot}5y - 6x + 4{\cdot}2 = 0$
(d) $3y = 7x$ (e) $x = 0{\cdot}35y + 0{\cdot}21$ (f) $2{\cdot}4 - 80y = 1{\cdot}372x$

4. Which of the following straight lines pass through the point at which $P = 3, L = 4$?
(a) $P = \frac{1}{2}L + 1$ (b) $2P - 1\frac{1}{2}L = 0$ (c) $6P = 5L - 3$
(d) $5P - 4L + 1 = 0$ (e) $1{\cdot}3P = L + 2{\cdot}7$ (f) $3{\cdot}5P = 2L + 2{\cdot}5$

5. Which of the following straight lines are parallel to the line $v = 32t + 47$?
(a) $\frac{1}{4}v = 9t - 4$ (b) $\frac{1}{20}v - 2 = 1\frac{3}{5}t$ (c) $\frac{1}{6}v = \frac{7}{8} + 5\frac{1}{3}t$
(d) $\frac{3}{16}v = 6t + 15\frac{1}{2}$ (e) $4\frac{3}{7}t + 2 = \frac{1}{7}v$ (f) $9{\cdot}6t = 0{\cdot}3v - 8$

6. Which of the following functions are linear?
(a) $x + 3$ (b) $5x^2$ (c) $3/x$ (d) $\frac{1}{2}x - 13$ (e) $2x^2 + 3x$
(f) $4x$ (g) $5 - 3t$ (h) $3(8 + 2t)$ (i) $(x + 4)(2x - 1)$
(j) $\dfrac{3x^2}{x} + 2$ (k) $0{\cdot}01x - 4$ (l) $\dfrac{2w - 5}{3}$ (m) $\dfrac{4}{3x - 1}$
(n) $-0{\cdot}2R + 6$ (o) x

7. What angle does each of the following make with the x-axis?
(a) $y = 1{\cdot}8x - 3$ (b) $y = 0{\cdot}7x + 1$ (c) $y = -\frac{1}{5}x + 2$
(d) $y = x + 15$ (e) $y = 2 - 3x$ (f) $y = 1 - \frac{1}{4}x$

8. Find the equation of the straight line which passes through the given pairs of points.
(a) $(1, 3)$ and $(2, 7)$ (b) $(-2, 3)$ and $(1, -2)$ (c) $(-2, -5)$ and $(2, 4)$
(d) $(0, 2)$ and $(3, 5)$ (e) $(0, 5)$ and $(3, 2)$ (f) $(-2, 6)$ and $(3, -4)$

9. Find the equations of the following lines.
(a) A line passing through the origin and inclined at 30° to the x-axis.
(b) A line passing through a point on the y-axis 3 units above the origin and inclined at 60° to the x-axis.
(c) A line parallel to the line $x + 2y = 6$ and passing through the point $(1, 4)$.

10. At what point do the two lines joining the pairs of points $(1\frac{1}{2}, 2)$, $(4\frac{1}{2}, 4)$ and $(1\frac{1}{2}, 2\frac{3}{4})$, $(6, 3\frac{1}{2})$ cross?

8.14 Harder 3-D problems

These problems should be attempted in the same way as outlined in section 6.6, but more care has to be taken in picking out suitable triangles, especially when dealing with the tetrahedron (the solid formed by joining four points in space).

Example

ABCD is a tetrahedron. AB = BC = CA = 10 cm, and DA = DB = DC = 12 cm.
Calculate
(a) the vertical height of the tetrahedron from the base ABC.
(b) the angle that the edge BD makes with the plane ABC.
(c) the angle between the planes ABC and DBC.

Let DM be the vertical height of the tetrahedron.
Then M is the incentre of triangle ABC, and X is the mid-point of BC.

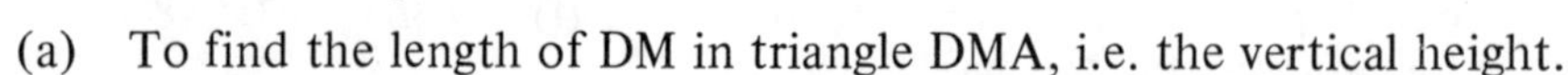

(a) To find the length of DM in triangle DMA, i.e. the vertical height.

First find the length of AM by considering triangle AYM in which Y is the mid-point of edge AB.
In triangle AYM:

$$Y\hat{A}M = 30° \quad \text{(X is the mid-point of BC)}$$

then $$\frac{AY}{AM} = \cos 30°$$

$$\frac{5}{AM} = \cos 30°$$

$$\therefore \quad AM = \frac{5}{\cos 30°} = \frac{5}{\frac{\sqrt{3}}{2}} = \frac{10}{\sqrt{3}}$$

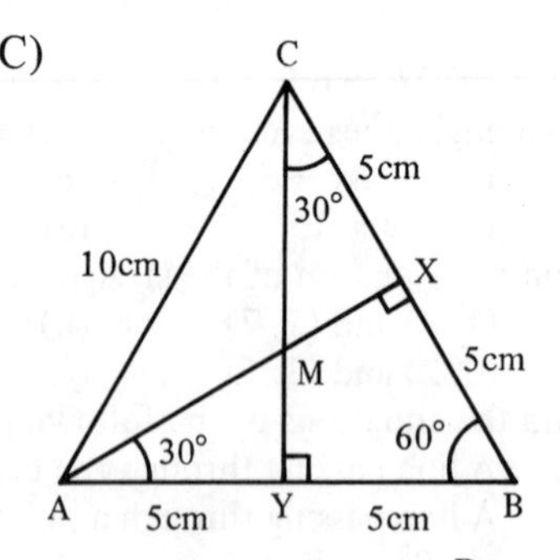

In triangle DMA:

$$AD^2 = AM^2 + DM^2$$

$$12^2 = \left(\frac{10}{\sqrt{3}}\right)^2 + DM^2$$

$$144 = \frac{100}{3} + DM^2$$

$$\therefore \quad DM = \sqrt{110{\cdot}7} = 10{\cdot}52 \text{ cm.}$$

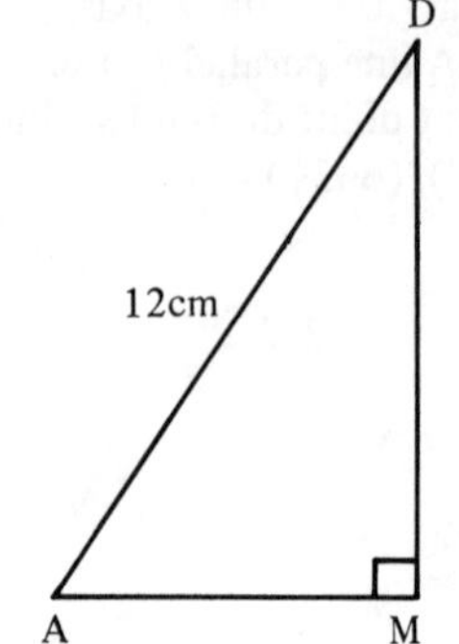

Note. In triangle MXC, $\frac{MX}{5} = \tan 30°$

$$\therefore \quad MX = 5 \times \frac{1}{\sqrt{3}} = \frac{5}{\sqrt{3}}$$

and $MX : AM = \frac{5}{\sqrt{3}} : \frac{10}{\sqrt{3}} = 1 : 2.$

i.e. in an equilateral triangle, the incentre lies on a median so that the median is divided in the ratio 1 : 2.

(b) To find $M\hat{B}D$, the angle that the edge BD makes with the plane ABC.

In triangle DMB:

$$\sin M\hat{B}D = \frac{10{\cdot}52}{12} = 0{\cdot}8767$$

$$\therefore \quad M\hat{B}D = 61°\,15'.$$

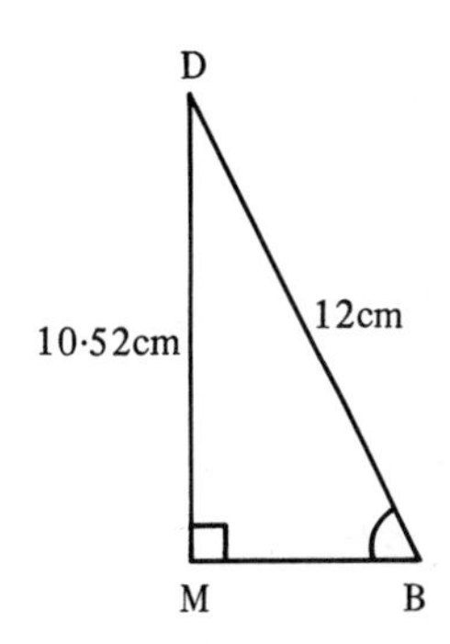

(c) To find $D\hat{X}M$, the angle between the planes ABC and DBC.

In triangle DMX:

$$\tan D\hat{X}M = \frac{10{\cdot}52}{\frac{5}{\sqrt{3}}}$$

$$= \frac{10{\cdot}52 \times \sqrt{3}}{5}$$

$$= \frac{10{\cdot}52 \times 1{\cdot}7321}{5} = 3{\cdot}644$$

$$\therefore \quad D\hat{X}M = 74°\,40'.$$

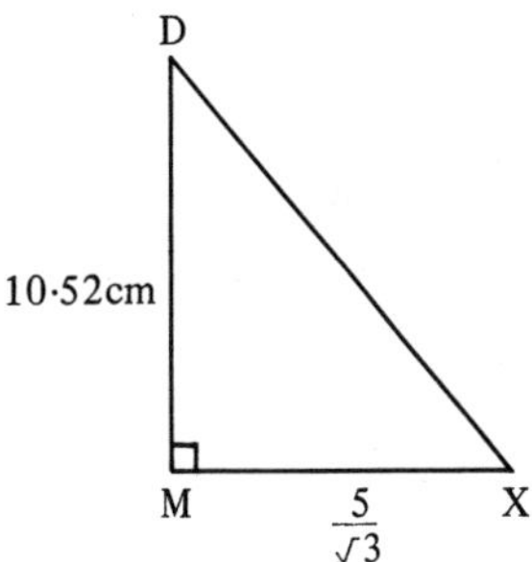

Thus (a) the height of the tetrahedron is 10·5 cm (3 S.F.)
(b) the angle that the edge BD makes with the plane ABC is 61° 15′
(c) the angle between the planes ABC and DBC is 74° 40′.

Note. In this type of calculation, only the answers should be corrected to the required accuracy. Always use 4-figure accuracy within the calculations.

Exercise 8.14

1. The diagram shows a triangular prism, $A\hat{B}C = 44°$, $A\hat{C}B = 55°$, BC = 5 cm and CF = 10 cm. Find the length of AB and angle BEA.

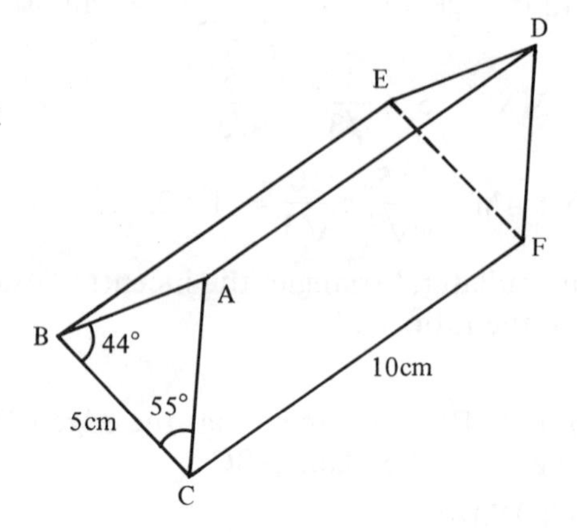

2. The four diagonals of a cube cross at X. Find the angle subtended at X by (a) the diagonal of a face and (b) an edge.
3. Three poles of height 3, 4 and 5 m stand at the corners of an equilateral triangle of side 6 m. Find the angle subtended at the top of the longer pole by the tops of the other two.
4. VABCD is a pyramid, vertex V, on a square base of side 8 cm and perpendicular height 6 cm. M is the mid-point of edge VB. Find $M\hat{C}B$ and $M\hat{D}B$.
5. A cone has base diameter 16 cm and perpendicular height 14 cm. Its vertex V and two points A and B on the rim of its base are such that $A\hat{V}B = 10°$. Find the length of the chord AB and the angle this chord subtends at any point on the circumference of the base.
6. A pole VA is 3 m long and is inclined at 70° to the ground. AB is its projection on the ground. C is another point on the ground such that $B\hat{A}C = 45°$ and AC = 2 m. Find the angle of elevation of V from C and also $C\hat{V}A$.

Examples 7 to **10** refer to a tetrahedron of vertex V and base ABC. M is the mid-point of AB and G is the point of intersection of the medians of triangle ABC. Triangle ABC is equilateral.

7. If AB = 10 cm, calculate
   (a) CM (b) MG (c) BG.
8. If VG = 15 cm and AB = 10 cm, calculate
   (a) VB (b) angle VBC.
9. If VG = 15 cm and AB = 10 cm, calculate
   (a) VM (b) angle VMG.
10. If all edges are 20 cm long calculate
    (a) VG (b) angle VBG.

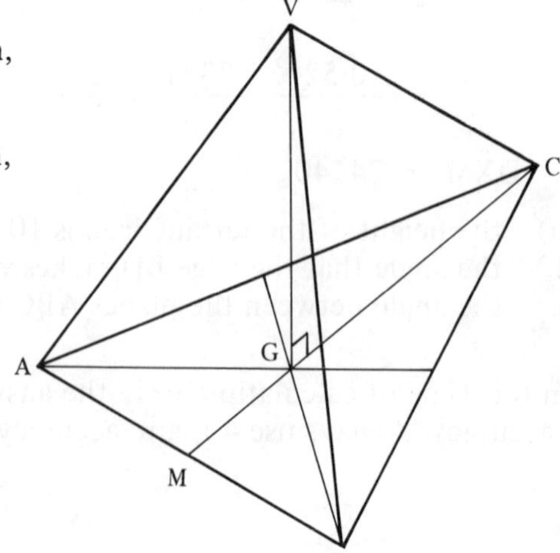

Miscellaneous exercise 8

1. One diagonal of a rhombus of side 7 cm is 6 cm long. Find the length of the other.
2. AM is the median of triangle ABC. If AB = 8 cm long and AM = AC = BC, find the length of AC.
3. A triangle has two of its sides 5 cm and 15 cm long. The third side is a whole number of centimetres long. How many possible obtuse-angled triangles are there and what are the lengths of their third sides?
4. With the data of question **3**, find how many possible acute-angled triangles there are. What are the lengths of their third sides?

Questions **5** to **8** refer to the cuboid. OA, OB and OC are perpendicular to each other. OA = 3 cm, OB = 5 cm and OC = 4 cm.

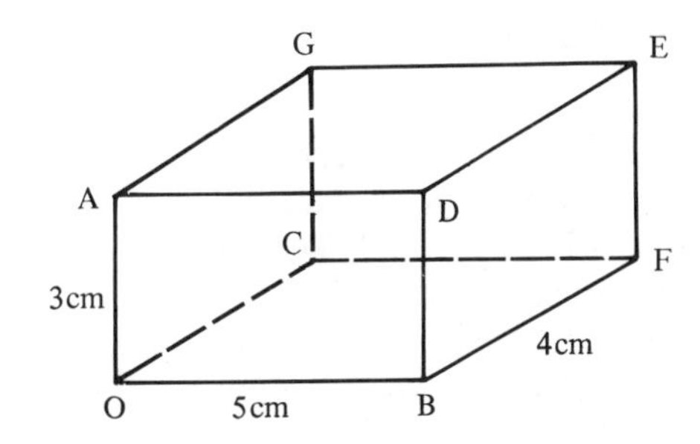

5. Find the lengths of
   (a) AB (b) AC (c) OE.
6. Find the angles
   (a) DAG (b) DAC (c) ADC.
7. Find the volume of the tetrahedron OABC.
8. Find the perpendicular distance of O from the triangle ABC.
   (Hint. Think of tetrahedron OABC turned round so that ABC becomes the base. What is the volume?)
9. ACB is the arc of a circle centre O radius 5 cm cut off by chord AB; $A\hat{O}B = 50°$.
   Calculate
   (a) the length of the chord AB (b) the length of the arc AB
   (c) the area of the sector AOB (d) the area of the triangle AOB
   (e) the area of the segment ACB.
10. A regular 18-sided figure is inscribed in a circle of radius 10 cm. Calculate
    (a) the length of a side of the figure (b) its area
    (c) the area between the sides of the figure and the circumference of the circle.
11. ACB is the arc of a circle, centre O and radius 30 cm. The area of triangle AOB is 300 cm^2.
    Calculate
    (a) $A\hat{O}B$ in degrees (b) the length of chord AB
    (c) the length of the arc ACB (d) the area of the sector AOB.

Solve the following equations for all angles between 0° and 360°

12. $6 \sin^2\theta + 7 \cos\theta - 8 = 0$
13. $2 \sin^2\theta - 4 \cos^2\theta + 5 \sin\theta + 5 = 0$
14. $\cos^4\theta - \sin^4\theta = 0$
15. $\sin^3\theta - \sin\theta = 0$
16. $\dfrac{1}{\sin^2\theta} + \dfrac{1}{\cos^2\theta} = 4$
17. Find the area swept out by the rotation through 360° about the y-axis of the area between the curve $y = \sqrt[3]{x^2}$ and the line $2y = x$.

Simplify the following:

18. $\dfrac{1+2\sqrt{2}-\sqrt{3}}{\sqrt{2}-1}$
19. $(2+\sqrt{2}-2\sqrt{3})(3-2\sqrt{2})$
20. $(1+\sqrt{2})(1+\sqrt{3})(1+2\sqrt{3})$
21. $\dfrac{(1+\sqrt{2})^2}{(1-\sqrt{2})(1-\sqrt{3})}$

Part 9 Modern mathematics

9.1 Sets

A *set* is any collection of things or numbers and may be defined by

(a) a title describing the set
e.g. the set of prime numbers less than 10.

or (b) listing all the members of the set inside curly brackets
e.g. $\{2, 3, 5, 7\}$.

A set is often denoted by a capital letter, e.g. $A = \{2, 3, 5, 7\}$.

If $\mathcal{E} = \{1, 2, 3, 4, 5, 6\}$, $A = \{2, 3, 5\}$, and $B = \{2, 4, 6\}$, then the *universal set* $\mathcal{E}$ is the set of the first six numbers and both A and B are *subsets* ($\subset$) of $\mathcal{E}$:

i.e. $A \subset \mathcal{E}$, $\quad B \subset \mathcal{E}$

2, 3, and 5 are called elements of set A:

e.g. $5 \in A$, but $4 \notin A$.

$A \cap B = \{2\}$, i.e. the *intersection* of sets A and B (or the elements that are in both set A and set B).

$A \cup B = \{2, 3, 4, 5, 6\}$, i.e. the *union* of sets A and B (or the elements that are in set A or set B or both).

$A' = \{1, 4, 6\}$, i.e. the *complement* of set A (or the elements of the universal set which are *not* members of set A).

$n(B) = 3$, i.e. the number of elements in set B.

A set which contains no elements is called an empty set ($\emptyset$ or $\{\quad\}$).

Example If
$$\mathcal{E} = \{2, 3, 5, 7, 9, 11, 13, 15, 17\}$$
$$A = \{2, 3, 5, 7, 11, 13, 17\}$$
$$B = \{3, 9, 15\}$$
$$C = \{5, 11, 17\}$$

(a) describe set A,
(b) list the elements in (i) $A \cap C$; (ii) $B \cap C$; (iii) $(A \cup C)'$,
(c) show that $A \cap (B \cup C) = (A \cap B) \cup (A \cap C)$.

(a) A is the set of the first seven prime numbers.

(b) (i) $A \cap C = \{5, 11, 17\}$
(ii) $B \cap C = \{\emptyset\}$
(iii) $(A \cup C) = \{2, 3, 5, 7, 11, 13, 17\}$
$\therefore (A \cup C)' = \{9, 15\}$

(c) $B \cup C = \{3, 5, 9, 11, 15, 17\}$; $\quad A \cap B = \{3\}$
$\therefore A \cap (B \cup C) = \{3, 5, 11, 17\}$; $\quad A \cap C = \{5, 11, 17\}$
$\therefore (A \cap B) \cup (A \cap C) = \{3, 5, 11, 17\}$

Hence $A \cap (B \cup C) = (A \cap B) \cup (A \cap C)$.

Exercise 9.1

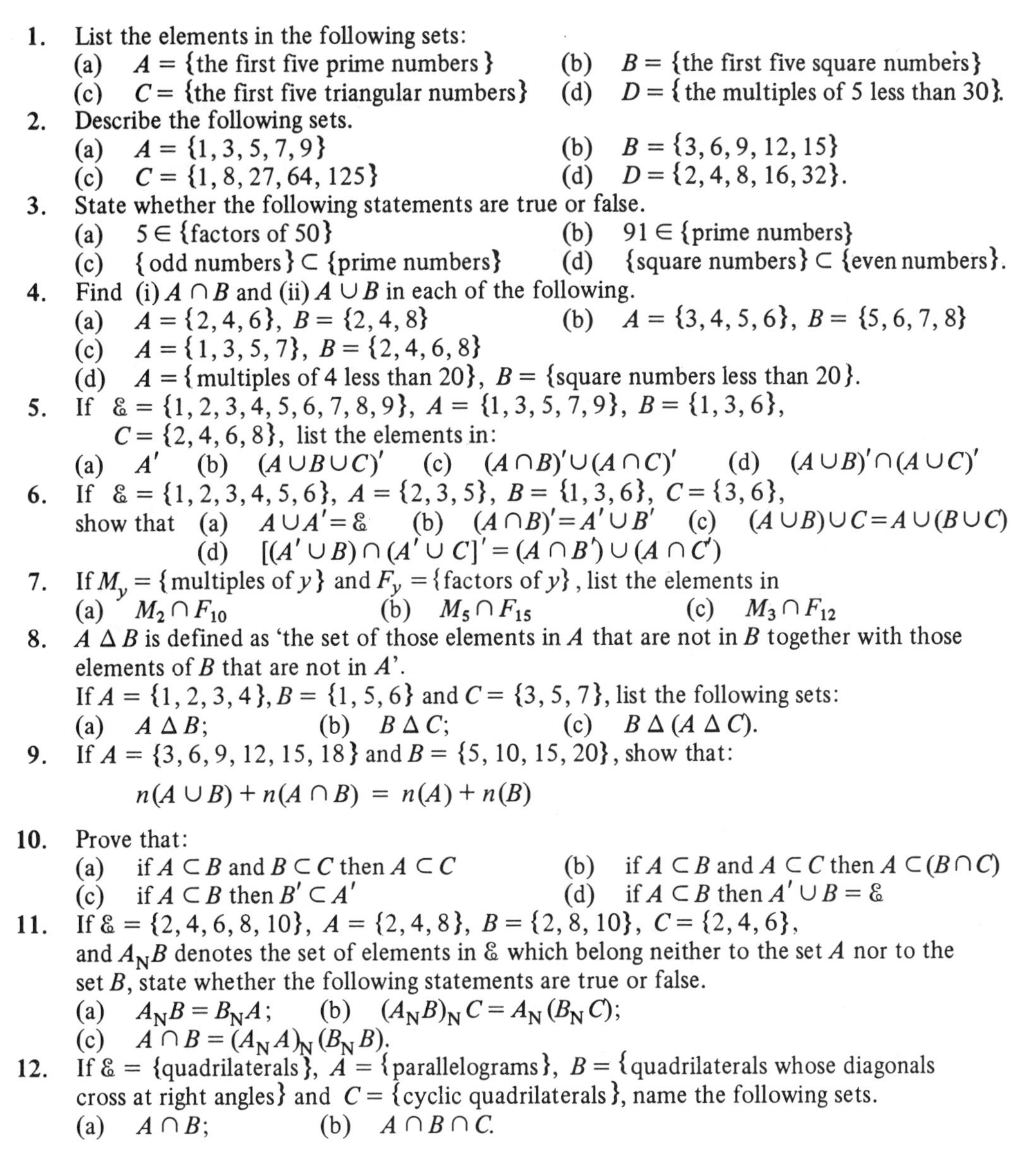

1. List the elements in the following sets:
   (a) $A = \{$the first five prime numbers$\}$ (b) $B = \{$the first five square numbers$\}$
   (c) $C = \{$the first five triangular numbers$\}$ (d) $D = \{$the multiples of 5 less than 30$\}$.
2. Describe the following sets.
   (a) $A = \{1, 3, 5, 7, 9\}$ (b) $B = \{3, 6, 9, 12, 15\}$
   (c) $C = \{1, 8, 27, 64, 125\}$ (d) $D = \{2, 4, 8, 16, 32\}$.
3. State whether the following statements are true or false.
   (a) $5 \in \{$factors of 50$\}$ (b) $91 \in \{$prime numbers$\}$
   (c) $\{$odd numbers$\} \subset \{$prime numbers$\}$ (d) $\{$square numbers$\} \subset \{$even numbers$\}$.
4. Find (i) $A \cap B$ and (ii) $A \cup B$ in each of the following.
   (a) $A = \{2, 4, 6\}$, $B = \{2, 4, 8\}$ (b) $A = \{3, 4, 5, 6\}$, $B = \{5, 6, 7, 8\}$
   (c) $A = \{1, 3, 5, 7\}$, $B = \{2, 4, 6, 8\}$
   (d) $A = \{$multiples of 4 less than 20$\}$, $B = \{$square numbers less than 20$\}$.
5. If $\mathcal{E} = \{1, 2, 3, 4, 5, 6, 7, 8, 9\}$, $A = \{1, 3, 5, 7, 9\}$, $B = \{1, 3, 6\}$,
   $C = \{2, 4, 6, 8\}$, list the elements in:
   (a) A' (b) $(A \cup B \cup C)'$ (c) $(A \cap B)' \cup (A \cap C)'$ (d) $(A \cup B)' \cap (A \cup C)'$
6. If $\mathcal{E} = \{1, 2, 3, 4, 5, 6\}$, $A = \{2, 3, 5\}$, $B = \{1, 3, 6\}$, $C = \{3, 6\}$,
   show that (a) $A \cup A' = \mathcal{E}$ (b) $(A \cap B)' = A' \cup B'$ (c) $(A \cup B) \cup C = A \cup (B \cup C)$
   (d) $[(A' \cup B) \cap (A' \cup C]' = (A \cap B') \cup (A \cap C')$
7. If $M_y = \{$multiples of $y\}$ and $F_y = \{$factors of $y\}$, list the elements in
   (a) $M_2 \cap F_{10}$ (b) $M_5 \cap F_{15}$ (c) $M_3 \cap F_{12}$
8. $A \,\Delta\, B$ is defined as 'the set of those elements in A that are not in B together with those elements of B that are not in A'.
   If $A = \{1, 2, 3, 4\}$, $B = \{1, 5, 6\}$ and $C = \{3, 5, 7\}$, list the following sets:
   (a) $A \,\Delta\, B$; (b) $B \,\Delta\, C$; (c) $B \,\Delta\, (A \,\Delta\, C)$.
9. If $A = \{3, 6, 9, 12, 15, 18\}$ and $B = \{5, 10, 15, 20\}$, show that:

$$n(A \cup B) + n(A \cap B) = n(A) + n(B)$$

10. Prove that:
    (a) if $A \subset B$ and $B \subset C$ then $A \subset C$ (b) if $A \subset B$ and $A \subset C$ then $A \subset (B \cap C)$
    (c) if $A \subset B$ then $B' \subset A'$ (d) if $A \subset B$ then $A' \cup B = \mathcal{E}$
11. If $\mathcal{E} = \{2, 4, 6, 8, 10\}$, $A = \{2, 4, 8\}$, $B = \{2, 8, 10\}$, $C = \{2, 4, 6\}$, and $A_N B$ denotes the set of elements in $\mathcal{E}$ which belong neither to the set A nor to the set B, state whether the following statements are true or false.
    (a) $A_N B = B_N A$; (b) $(A_N B)_N C = A_N (B_N C)$;
    (c) $A \cap B = (A_N A)_N (B_N B)$.
12. If $\mathcal{E} = \{$quadrilaterals$\}$, $A = \{$parallelograms$\}$, $B = \{$quadrilaterals whose diagonals cross at right angles$\}$ and $C = \{$cyclic quadrilaterals$\}$, name the following sets.
    (a) $A \cap B$; (b) $A \cap B \cap C$.

9.2 Venn diagrams

Sets can be represented pictorially by Venn diagrams.
A rectangle is usually drawn to represent the universal set and circles to represent the subsets.
Care must be taken when representing subsets to make the number of intersections fit the given data.

Illustrate the following on Venn diagrams

Example 1

If $\mathcal{E} = \{1, 3, 5, 6, 7, 9, 10, 15\}$
$A = \{1, 3, 5, 7\}$,
and $B = \{1, 3, 6, 10, 15\}$

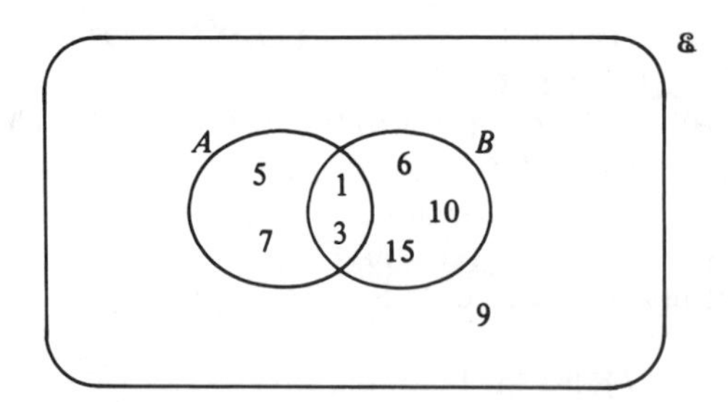

Example 2

If $\mathcal{E} = \{1, 2, 3, 4, 5, 6\}, A = \{1, 3, 5\}$,
$B = \{2, 4, 6\}$, and $C = \{2, 4\}$,

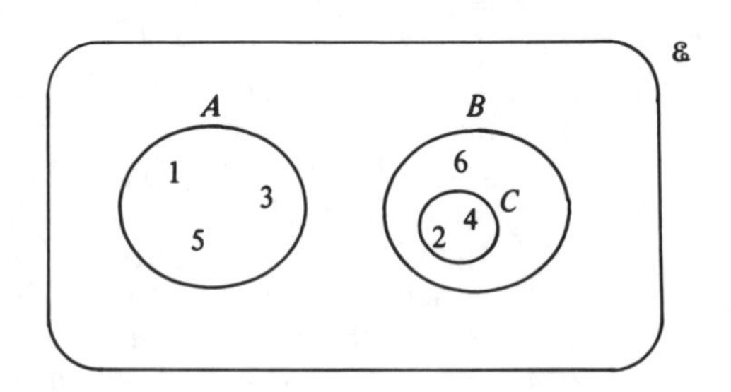

Note. In example 2 sets A and B are *disjoint* sets, and set C is a subset of set B.

Example 3

In a class of 30, all the pupils study Mathematics or Physics. If 19 study Mathematics, 18 study Physics, how many study both?

Let M = {pupils who study Mathematics}

and P = {pupils who study Physics}

then $n(M \cup P) = 30;\ n(M) = 19;\ n(P) = 18$

and $n(M \cap P) = n(M) + n(P) - n(M \cup P)$ see Ex. 9.1, Question 9.

$= 19 + 18 - 30 = 7$

Note. Some numerical problems involving sets are often more easily solved if a Venn diagram is drawn.

Example 4

A group of 70 science pupils studied Physics, Biology, and Chemistry; each pupil studied at least one of these three subjects. 15 took Physics only, 18 took Biology only, and 21 took Chemistry only. 6 pupils took both Physics and Chemistry, 9 took Physics and Biology, and 5 took Biology and Chemistry.
Using a suitable Venn diagram, find:
(a) how many took all three subjects; (b) how many took Chemistry.

Let P = {pupils who studied Physics} C = {pupils who studied Chemistry}
B = {pupils who studied Biology} x = {pupils who studied all three}

Then the following Venn diagram can be drawn.

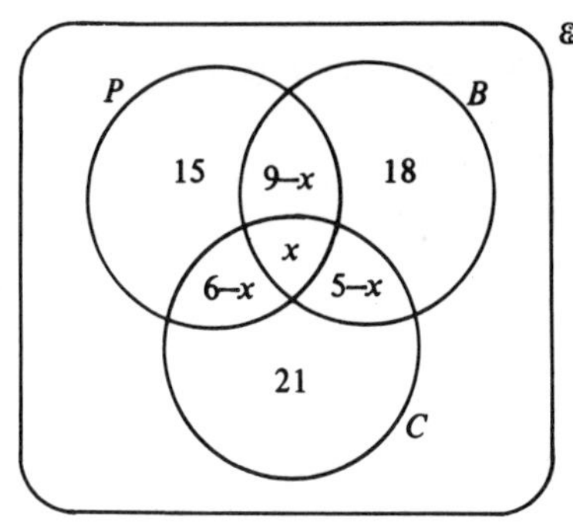

$$\therefore\ 15 + (6-x) + x + (9-x) + 18 + (5-x) + 21 = 70$$
$$74 - 2x = 70$$
$$4 = 2x$$
$$2 = x$$

(a) Hence 2 pupils studied all three subjects.
(b) The number who took chemistry is

$$21 + (6-2) + 2 + (5-2) = 30$$

Exercise 9.2

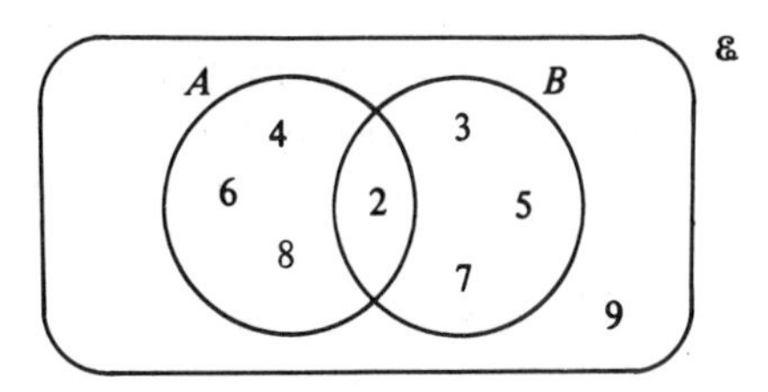

1. From the Venn diagram, list the following sets:
   (a) $A \cup B$ (b) $A \cap B$
   (c) A' (d) B'
   (e) $(A \cup B)' \cap (A \cap B)'$
2. If & = {Positive integers less than 17}, A = {Square numbers}, B = {Even numbers}, C = {Multiples of 8}, draw a Venn diagram to illustrate this information, putting each element in its correct region.
3. Draw Venn diagrams to illustrate:
   (a) $A \subset B$ (b) $X \cap Y = \phi$ (c) $A \cup B = A$ (d) $A \subset B \subset C$
4. If $n(A) = 39, n(B) = 63, n(A \cap B) = 15$, find $n(A \cup B)$.
5. If $n(X) = 21, n(Y) = 33, n(X \cup Y) = 46$, find $n(X \cap Y)$.
6. If $n(X) = 60, n(Y) = 48, n(Z) = 63, n(X \cap Y) = 21, n(X \cap Z) = 24, n(Y \cap Z) = 15$, $n(X \cup Y \cup Z) = 120$, find $n(X \cap Y \cap Z)$.
7. In a group of 50 students, 12 study History, 28 study Geography, and 6 study both. How many study neither History nor Geography?
8. 64 students were questioned about their favourite subject from Geography, Mathematics and Chemistry. 40 liked Geography, 36 liked Mathematics, 30 liked Chemistry, and 10 liked all three. If 4 liked both Geography and Mathematics and assuming that each student liked at least one subject, how many liked Chemistry only?
9. Out of a group of 272 people, 134 liked 'pop' music, 112 liked 'classical' music and 80 liked 'folk' music. 22 liked both pop and classical, 24 both classical and folk and 27 both pop and folk. How many liked all three?
10. In a group of 205 students, each one speaks French or German or both. 50 speak German but not French and 25 speak French but not German. How many speak both?
11. Show by means of Venn diagrams that:
    (a) $(A \cup B)' = A' \cap B'$
    (b) $(A \cap B') \cup (A' \cap B) \cup (A \cap B) = A \cup B$

9.3 Inequalities

The symbol $<$ means 'is less than'.
The symbol $>$ means 'is greater than'.
The equation $x = 6$ has only one solution; but in an inequality such as $x < 6$, x can have any numerical value less than 6.
Inequalities are solved in similar ways to equations (see page 60).

Example 1 Find the solution of the following.

(a) $x + 8 < 12$
$x < 12 - 8$
$\therefore \ x < 4$

(b) $8 - x > 6$
$\therefore 8 - 6 > x$ or $-x > 6 - 8$
$2 > x$ $\quad -x > -2$ (A)
$x < 2$

Note. When multiplying both sides of an inequality by -1 at (A), remember to change the sign of the inequality.
If the domain of x is given, then the inequality has a *solution set* (or truth set). Thus in the above examples, if x is a positive integer, then the solution sets are as follows:

(a) $x = \{1, 2, 3\}$ (b) $x = \{1\}$

The solution of inequalities can be shown pictorially by means of a number line.

Example 2 Solve the following, showing the solution on a number line.

$x + 8 < 12$: hence $x < 4$

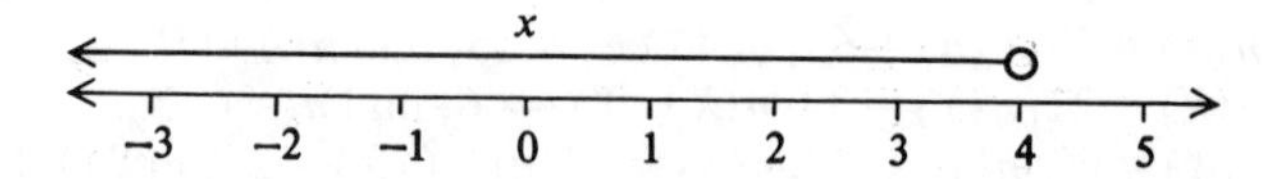

The symbols $\not>$ and $\leqslant$ both mean 'is not greater than' or 'is less than or equal to'.
Thus, if x is a positive integer, the solution set for

$x + 8 \leqslant 12$ is $x = \{1, 2, 3, 4\}$

i.e. 4 is included. This is shown on the number line opposite.

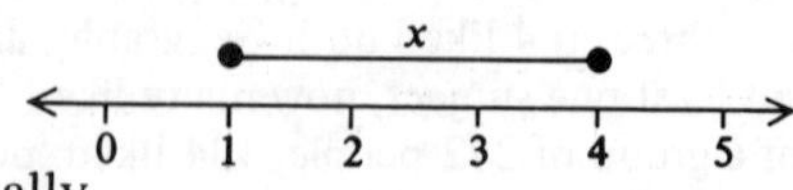

Inequalities can also be illustrated graphically.

Example 3

Sketch the graph $x \not< 4$.

The shaded region together with the set of points on the line $x = 4$ is the required solution.

Note. On a graph, the boundary for $x < 4$ is shown by a broken line, and the boundary for $x \geqslant 4$, ($x \not< 4$) is shown by a continuous line.

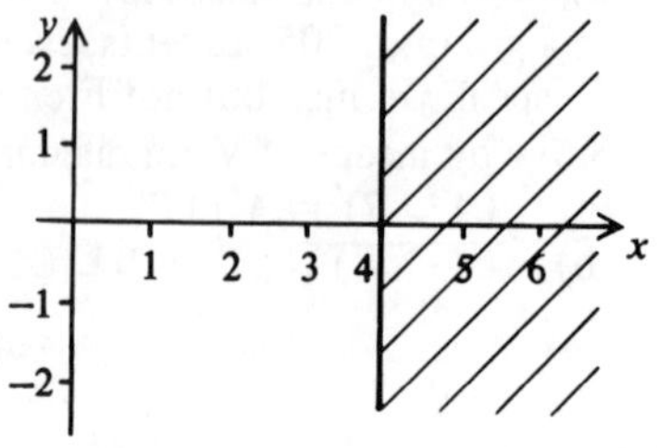

Example 4

The graph of $x + y = 6$ is shown. The set of points on the line is given by

$$\{(x, y) : x + y = 6\}$$

and the set of points in the shaded region is given by

$$\{(x, y) : x + y \leqslant 6\}.$$

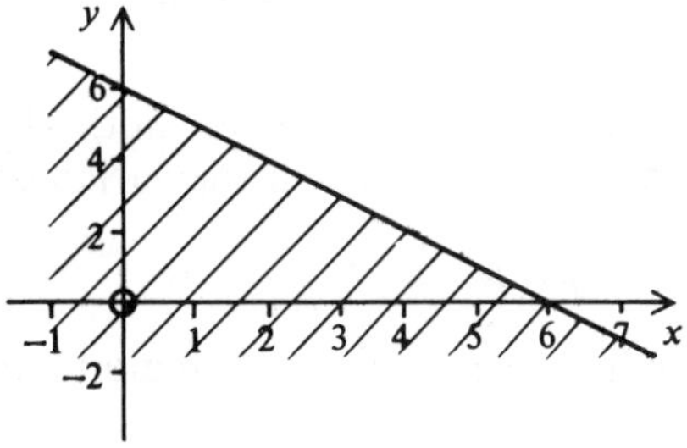

Example 5

If $A = \{x : 2x + 8 \geqslant 0\}$, $B = \{x : 4x \leqslant 12\}$ and $x \in \mathcal{E}$ where $\mathcal{E}$ is the set of integers, list the set of elements in $A \cap B$.

$2x + 8 \geqslant 0$ $4x \leqslant 12$

$x \geqslant -4$ $x \leqslant 3$

$\therefore\ A = \{-4, -3, -2, \ldots\}$ $\therefore\ B = \{3, 2, 1, \ldots\}$

$\therefore\ A \cap B = \{-4, -3, -2, -1, 0, 1, 2, 3\}$

Exercise 9.3

1. Which of the following statements are true?
   (a) $x - 3 < 5, \therefore x < 8$ (b) $x + 6 \geqslant 9, \therefore x \geqslant 3$ (c) $x - 1 > 3, \therefore x > 2$
   (d) $\dfrac{1}{x} < \dfrac{1}{2}, \therefore x < 2$ (e) $\dfrac{1}{x} < \dfrac{1}{5}, \therefore x > 5$ (f) $4x + 8 < 0, \therefore x < -2$
   (g) $x^2 < 25, \therefore x < 5$ (h) $x^2 < 16, \therefore -4 < x < 4$
   (i) $x > 6, \therefore -36 > x^2 > 36$ (j) $\dfrac{1}{2x + 1} < 3, \therefore x > -\dfrac{1}{3}$
2. Solve the following inequalities, showing the solution on a number line.
   (a) $x + 5 > 9$ (b) $2x + 6 \geqslant 18$ (c) $x - 2 < 2x + 3$
   (d) $x + 2 \geqslant 3x - 4$ (e) $2x - 1 \leqslant 3(x + 3)$ (f) $x \ngtr 4$
   (g) $-2 < 4x < 12$ (h) $-7 < x + 1 \leqslant 9$ (i) $16 < x^2 < 25$
   (j) $2 \leqslant \sqrt{x} \leqslant 4$
3. Give the solution set of the inequalities.
   (a) $6 < 16 - 2z$ (b) $6y + 5 \geqslant 12 - y$ (c) $5(x + 2) - 3(x - 5) < 29$
   (d) $\dfrac{3}{z - 1} > \dfrac{2}{z - 5}$ (e) $\sqrt{x} \leqslant 5$
4. Sketch the graphs of the following.
   (a) $2x > 4$ (b) $x + 6 \geqslant 4$ (c) $\frac{1}{2}(x - 2) \nless 4$
   (d) $4 < x \leqslant 9$ (e) $6 \leqslant 2x - 4 \leqslant 18$
5. If $A = \{x : 5 - 2x < 9\}$, $B = \{x : x \leqslant 3\}$, and x is an integer, find $A \cap B$.
6. If $X = \{x : 5(2x - 1) \leqslant 3(x + 3) + 14\}$, and $Y = \{x : 4x \geqslant 8\}$
   (a) find $X \cap Y$; (b) illustrate your answer on a number line, assuming x is an integer.
7. If $\mathcal{E}$ represents the set of all real numbers, $A = \{x : -2 \leqslant x \leqslant 5\}$, and $B = \{x : -2 \leqslant 2x \leqslant 16\}$, find $A' \cap B$.
8. 3 is added to a certain whole number and the answer is then doubled. If the result exceeds 51, form an inequation and find its solution set.

9.4 Linear programming

Linear programming is a method of finding the largest or the smallest value of a linear function when the variables are made up of linear inequalities.

Example 1

Indicate on a graph the region defined by the three inequalities:

$y \leqslant 3x, y \geqslant \frac{1}{2}x, x + y \leqslant 4$

If x and y are integers, state a number pair (x, y) which satisfies all three inequalities.

1. Draw the line $y = 3x$ and shade in the region $y > 3x$.
2. Draw the line $y = \frac{1}{2}x$ and shade in the region $y < \frac{1}{2}x$.
3. Draw the line $x + y = 4$ and shade in the region $x + y > 4$.

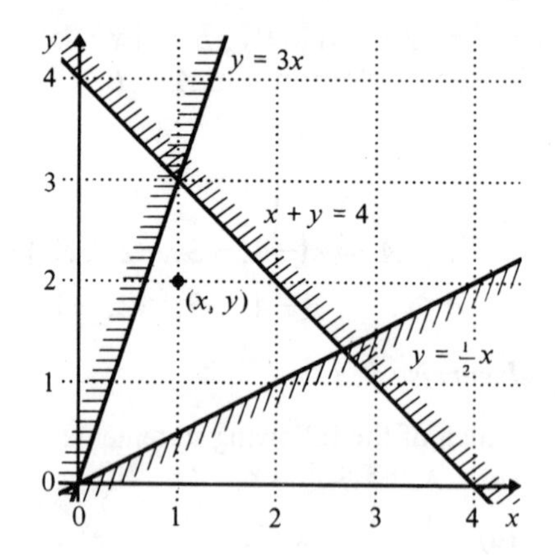

The required region is then the unshaded area.
Any point which lies in this region satisfies all three inequalities.
So a number pair is $(1, 2)$.

Example 2

A garage owner intends to buy a number of radial and cross-ply tyres. Radials cost £25 each and cross-ply tyres cost £20 each. The man has only space for 40 tyres. He has orders for 15 radials and 10 cross-ply tyres, and the maximum he can spend is £900.
Find the number of each type of tyre he should buy to make the largest profit if his expected profit is £6 on each radial tyre and £8 on each cross-ply tyre.

Suppose he buys x radial tyres and y cross-ply tyres. Then the following inequalities apply.

(a) $x + y \leqslant 40$
(b) $x \geqslant 15$
(c) $y \geqslant 10$
(d) $25x + 20y \leqslant 900$
or $\quad 5x + 4y \leqslant 180$

The graph shows this information and all possible values will be found in the shaded region ABCD.
The profit will be $(6x + 8y)$ and is represented by any line $6x + 8y = c$, (of which the broken line shown is one example) and that part of it passing through the region ABCD.
Maximum profit is obtained at the point (x, y) that satisfies all these conditions and that is furthest from the origin. From the graph, this is the point (16, 24).

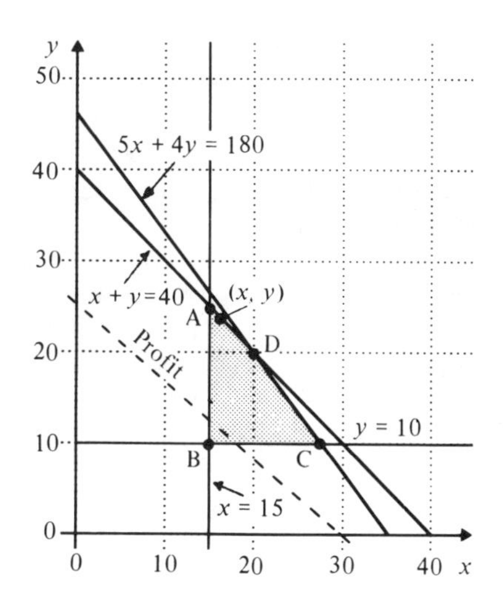

So maximum profit = (16 × £6) + (24 × £8) = £96 + £192 = £288.

Exercise 9.4

1. Indicate on a graph the region defined by:
   (a) $x > 3, y < 2$, and $x + y > 4$
   (b) $x > -1, y > x + 1$, and $y > 1$
   (c) $x \leqslant 2, y \geqslant x + 2$, and $y \geqslant 3x$
   In each case if a and b are integers, give a number pair (a, b) which satisfies all three inequalities.
2. If $A = \{(x, y) : x + y \leqslant 4\}$, $B = \{(x, y) : x < y \leqslant 2\}$,
   draw a suitable graph and shade in the region represented by $A \cap B$.
3. If $A = \{(x,y) : y \leqslant 6\}$
   $B = \{(x,y) : x + y \geqslant 7\}$
   $C = \{(x,y) : y \geqslant x\}$
   draw a suitable graph and shade in the region represented by $A \cap B \cap C$.
4. A rectangle has a length of a cm and a width of b cm with a maximum area of 30 cm^2. If its perimeter is 22 cm, find from a graph suitable integral values for a and b.
5. A girl wishes to make a photographic record of her sister's wedding. She has £7.50 to spend and she has to pay 15p each for colour prints and 10p each for black-and-white prints. If her album can only hold 60 prints and she wishes to fill all the spaces, find the smallest number of black-and-white prints she will have to include in the album.
6. A rectangle is to fulfil the following conditions:
   (i) the perimeter must be more than 20 cm and less than 30 cm,
   (ii) the length must be greater than twice the width.
   If each dimension is to be an exact number of cm, find
   (a) the rectangle with the largest possible area,
   (b) the rectangle with the smallest possible area.
7. A woman is buying sweets for a party. Chewwie bars cost 8p each and Chocco bars cost 24p each. She decides that she needs twice as many Chewwies as Choccos, but she must have at least 4 Chocco bars. If she does not want to spend more than £2, find
   (a) the greatest total number of bars she can buy,
   (b) the greatest number of Chocco bars she can buy.

8. The secretary of a football supporters club has to arrange transport for 9000 supporters to an away match. Two types of transport are available: special trains which can carry a maximum of 600 passengers each, and coaches each with a maximum capacity of 50 passengers. The train fare is £1.50 per head and the coach fare £1 per head, but the police advise that at least half the supporters must travel by train and both trains and buses must be filled.
   If the maximum number of trains available is 10 and the maximum number of coaches is 100, find the most economical way of transporting the supporters.
9. The manager of a holiday park has permission to extend his estate. He has 960 m^2 of land available and planning permission for a maximum of 28 sites for caravans or tents. A tent needs 32 m^2 of land and a caravan needs 48 m^2 of land. If the manager expects to charge an average price of £5 per night per site for caravans and £4 per night per site for tents, find the best use of his land to secure maximum income.

9.5 Number bases

In any number base N the column headings are $\ldots N^5; N^4; N^3; N^2; N; 1; \ldots$
e.g. in base 10 the column headings are 10^5 (hundred thousands), 10^4 (ten thousands), 10^3 (thousands), 10^2 (hundreds), 10 (tens), 1 (units).

Example 1

324_6 means $(3 \times 6^2) + (2 \times 6) + (4 \times 1) = (3 \times 36) + 12 + 4 = 108 + 16 = 124_{10}$.
In any base, the largest digit which can be placed in any column is always one less than the base.
e.g. in base 10, nine is the greatest number which appears in any column.

Example 2 Change 124_{10} into base 6.

This is best done by repeated division by 6.

6)124		
6)20	+ 4 units (1)	↑ Read the remainders this way.
6)3	+ 2 sixes (6)	
0	+ 3 thirty-sixes (6^2)	

$\therefore \quad 124_{10} = 324_6$.

1. In bases greater than 10, symbols have to be found to represent some numbers used in the columns.
   e.g. in base 12, T would represent 10 and E would represent 11.
2. To change from one base to another, first change into base 10 and then into the new base.
   e.g. change $TE6_{12}$ to base 8. i.e. $TE6_{12} = 1578_{10} = 3052_8$.

It is possible to add, subtract, multiply, and divide numbers in *all* bases.

Example 3 Add 2364_8 to 7456_8

```
  2364
  7456
 ------
 12 042
```

$\therefore 2364_8 + 7456_8 = 12\,042_8$.

Example 4 Subtract 2054_6 from 4032_6

```
  4032
- 2054
 ------
  1534
```

$\therefore 4032_6 - 2054_6 = 1534_6$

Example 5 Multiply 213_5 by 42_5.

Method 1

```
    213
  X  42
 ------
    431
 14 120
 ------
 20 101
```

Method 2

```
    213
  X  42
 ------
 14 120
    431
 ------
 20 101
```

$\therefore 213_5 \times 42_5 = 20\,101_5$

Example 6 Divide 862_9 by 24_9.

```
      35
 24)862
     73
    ---
    132
    132
    ---
    ...
```

$\therefore 862_9 \div 24_9 = 35_9$

Note. To check calculations such as those shown above, carry out the same calculation in base 10.

Exercise 9.5a

Add the following pairs of binary numbers (base 2).

1. 1011 + 101 **2.** 1100 + 101 **3.** 10110 + 101 **4.** 10101 + 110
5. 11001 + 1011 **6.** 10001 + 1111

Find the difference between the following pairs of binary numbers.

7. 11011 − 1101 **8.** 10110 − 111 **9.** 101000 − 11011
10. 111001110 − 101010 **11.** 11010010 − 1011011 **12.** 1110111 − 11100

Multiply together the following pairs of binary numbers.

13. 1011 X 101 **14.** 1111 X 111 **15.** 11010 X 1011 **16.** 100011 X 1110
17. 101010 X 1011 **18.** 1011 X 1101

Express the following denary numbers (base 10) in binary form.

19. 18 **20.** 35 **21.** 49 **22.** 57 **23.** 85 **24.** 567

Express the following binary numbers in denary form.

25. 101 **26.** 1100 **27.** 11101 **28.** 1011101
29. 1001110 **30.** 1010101

Add the following pairs of numbers which are all in base 5.

31. 14 + 21 **32.** 33 + 42 **33.** 123 + 441 **34.** 304 + 433
35. 3214 + 4113 **36.** 3404 + 1243

Find the difference between the following pairs of base five numbers.

37. 43 − 21 **38.** 32 − 24 **39.** 312 − 203 **40.** 411 − 224
41. 2312 − 1404 **42.** 3221 − 2334

Multiply together the following pairs of base five numbers.

43. 14 × 4 **44.** 22 × 3 **45.** 123 × 11 **46.** 402 × 23
47. 242 × 24 **48.** 413 × 43

Divide the following pairs of base five numbers.

49. 210 ÷ 21 **50.** 440 ÷ 11 **51.** 1241 ÷ 12 **52.** 3231 ÷ 41

Exercise 9.5b

Add the following pairs of numbers which are all in base 12.

1. 4T + E6 **2.** E9 + T4 **3.** 12T + 3E5 **4.** T91 + EE6
5. TT2 + 43E **6.** 369E + 84T6

Find the difference between the following pairs of base twelve numbers.

7. E7 − T4 **8.** T5 − 1E **9.** 3T6 − 24E **10.** 4TT − 1EE
11. E456 − T567 **12.** 2E3T − TEE

Multiply together the following pairs of base twelve numbers.

13. 21 × 16 **14.** 5T × 4E **15.** T4 × E6 **16.** TT × 41
17. 29 × EE **18.** TT × EE

Express the following denary numbers in base twelve form.

19. 14 **20.** 46 **21.** 92 **22.** 104 **23.** 237 **24.** 1814

Express the following base twelve numbers in denary form.

25. 15 **26.** 2E **27.** 2T4 **28.** E59 **29.** T6E **30.** EET

Write the base (or bases) in which the following statements are true.

31. 42 − 23 = 15 **32.** 476 + 757 = 1344 **33.** 214 − 33 = 131
34. 42 + 11 = 53 **35.** 62 × 15 = 1353

9.6 Transformations

Reflection

In a reflection, each point on the image A_1 is the same perpendicular distance from the axis of reflection r as the corresponding point on the object A.

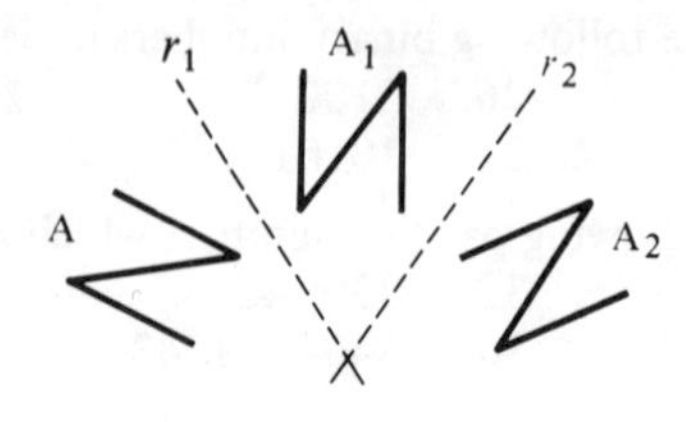

Rotation

In a rotation, the object is displaced by rotating through an angle about a given centre O. The direction of the rotation may be either clockwise (negative) or anti-clockwise (positive).

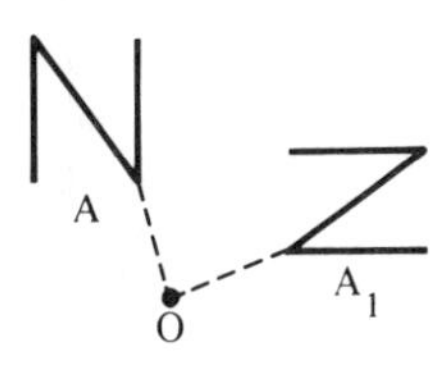

90° clockwise rotation (– ve) 120° anticlockwise rotation (+ ve)

Translation

In a translation, the object is displaced by moving it along a straight line for a given distance.

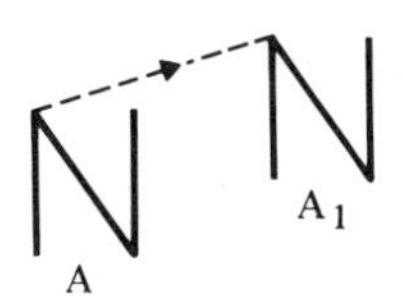

A translation is often written as a column vector, e.g. $\begin{pmatrix} 3 \\ -2 \end{pmatrix}$ when the x-value of every point is changed by +3 and the y-value by –2. See also section 9.9, page 250.

Enlargement

An enlargement will increase or decrease the size of an object in a given ratio about a given point O which is the *centre* of enlargement. The ratio is called the *scale factor*. In the figures below, A_1 is an enlargement of scale factor 2; A_2 is an enlargement of scale factor $-\frac{1}{2}$.

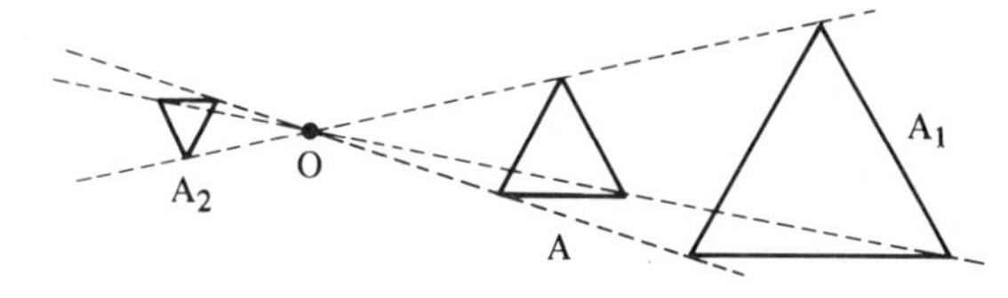

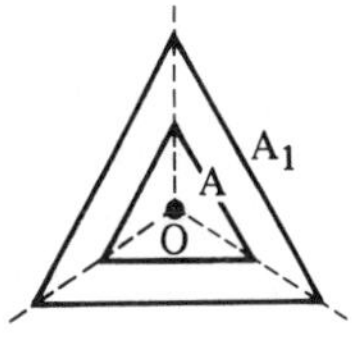

Shear

A shear is a transformation in which every point on the object is moved parallel to an axis for a distance which is proportional to its distance from that axis.

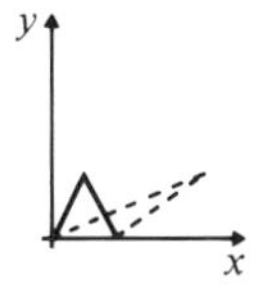

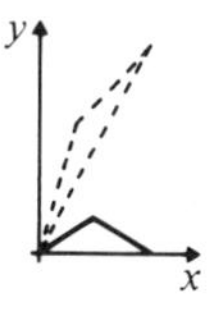

shear of 2 units parallel to the x-axis shear of 2 units parallel to the y-axis.

If a transformation leaves all distances the same, it is called an isometry.

Any point, line, or area remaining the same after a transformation is said to be invariant; e.g. in any shear, the area is invariant.

Exercise 9.6

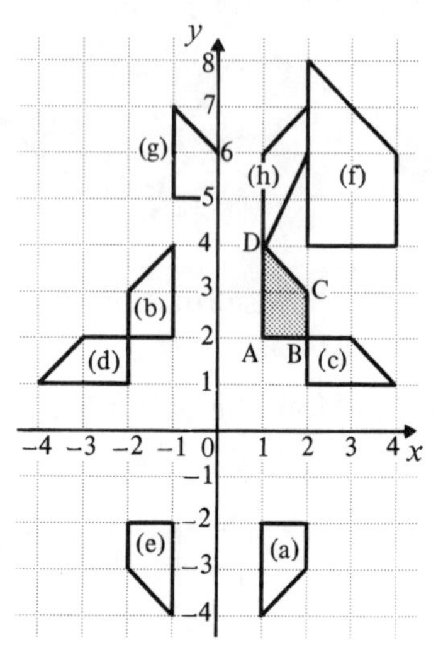

1. Describe in full each single transformation which which maps the trapezium ABCD in the figure onto each of the shapes (a) to (h).

2. Plot the arrowhead A(−4, 2), B(−2, 4), C(0, 2), and D(−2, 3). Draw the image of the arrowhead for each of the following transformations.
   (a) reflection in the line $y = 0$ (b) reflection in the line $x = 0$
   (c) rotation $+90°$ about (0, 0) (d) rotation $180°$ about (0, 0)
   (e) reflection in the line $y = x$, followed by reflection in the line $y = -x$
   (f) a translation given by $\begin{pmatrix} -3 \\ 2 \end{pmatrix}$
   (g) an enlargement, scale factor 2, centre A
   (h) an enlargement, scale factor $-\frac{1}{2}$, centre B
   (i) a shear of 2 units parallel to the x-axis
   (j) a shear of 2 units parallel to the y-axis

3. In each of the following describe the resulting figure when the triangle is rotated 180° about the point P which is the mid-point of side AC.
   (a) ABC is an equilateral triangle (b) ABC is an isosceles triangle with AB = BC
   (c) ABC is an isosceles right-angled triangle with AB = BC
   (d) ABC is a scalene triangle (e) ABC is a scalene triangle with $\hat{B} = 90°$

4. A is the point (−2, 4). Write down the coordinates of the image of A under the following transformations.
   (a) reflection in the x-axis (b) reflection in the y-axis
   (c) reflection in the line $x + y = 4$ (d) rotation $+90°$ about (0, 0)
   (e) rotation $180°$ about (0, 0) (f) enlargement, scale factor $\frac{1}{2}$, centre (0, 0)
   (g) translation by the vector $\begin{pmatrix} 3 \\ -2 \end{pmatrix}$
   (h) rotation $-90°$ about (0, 0), followed by a transformation given by the vector $\begin{pmatrix} -2 \\ -2 \end{pmatrix}$

5. A point (3, 2) is mapped onto the following points. In each case, describe the transformation other than a translation.
   (a) (−3, 2) (b) (2, 3) (c) (3, −2) (d) (−3, −2) (e) (6, 4)
   (f) (2, −3) (g) (−2, −3) (h) (−6, −4) (i) (2, 1) (j) (1, −2)

9.7 Combined transformations

The transformations described in section 9.6 can be combined, but in some cases the resultant image may be the same as that produced by some other single transformation.

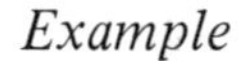

Example

Triangle ABC has vertices A(2,1), B (3, 2), C (2, 3). On a sheet of graph paper with $-4 \leqslant x \leqslant 4$ and $-4 \leqslant y \leqslant 4$, plot the triangle ABC.
On the same diagram
(a) plot the image $A_1B_1C_1$ of ABC under a rotation of 90° anticlockwise about the point (0, 0).
(b) plot the image $A_2B_2C_2$ of $A_1B_1C_1$ under a reflection in the line $y = 0$.
(c) plot the image $A_3B_3C_3$ of $A_2B_2C_2$ under a rotation of 270° clockwise about the point (0, 0).
(d) describe the single transformation which would map $A_3B_3C_3$ onto ABC.

Solution

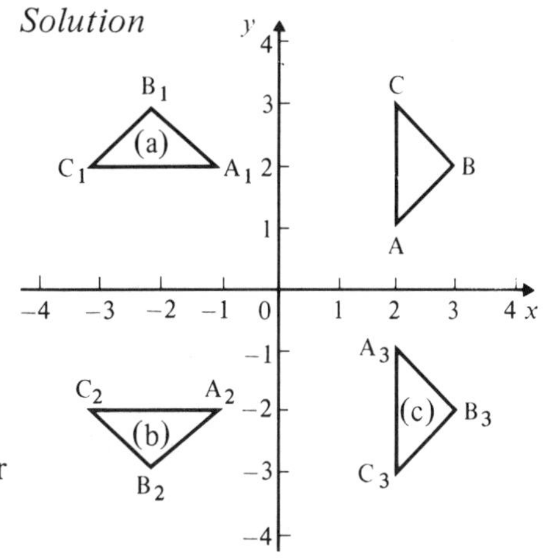

The single transformation required to map $A_3B_3C_3$ onto ABC is a reflection in the line $y = 0$ (the x-axis).

Exercise 9.7

1. Trapezium ABCD has vertices A (2, 1), B (3, 1), C (3, 2) and D (2, 3).
   (a) Draw the image of this trapezium under each of the following transformations.
      (i) a reflection in the y-axis, label $A_1B_1C_1D_1$.
      (ii) an enlargement with centre of enlargement $(2, \frac{1}{2})$ and scale factor 2, label $A_2B_2C_2D_2$.
      (iii) a rotation of 270° anticlockwise about the point (0, 1), label $A_3B_3C_3D_3$.
   (b) Describe the single transformation that will map $A_3B_3C_3D_3$ onto ABCD.
2. Plot a trapezium ABCD with coordinates A (0, 0), B (2, 0), C (1, 2), D (0, 2).
   (a) Plot the image $A_1B_1C_1D_1$ of ABCD when reflected in the line $y = -x$.
   (b) Plot the image $A_2B_2C_2D_2$ of $A_1B_1C_1D_1$ under the translation $\begin{pmatrix}4\\4\end{pmatrix}$.
   (c) Describe a single transformation that will map $A_2B_2C_2D_2$ on to ABCD.
3. Triangle ABC has coordinates A (2, 1), B (7, 2), C (4, 3).
   (a) Plot the image $A_1B_1C_1$ of ABC when rotated 180° about the point (0, 0).
   (b) Plot the image $A_2B_2C_2$ of $A_1B_1C_1$ when rotated 180° about the point (0, −3).
   (c) Describe a single transformation which will map $A_2B_2C_2$ on to ABC.
4. Triangle ABC has coordinates A (1, 1), B (3, 1), C (3, 2).
   (a) Plot the image $A_1B_1C_1$ of ABC when reflected in the line $y = x$.
   (b) Plot the image $A_2B_2C_2$ of $A_1B_1C_1$ when reflected in the y-axis.
   (c) Plot the image $A_3B_3C_3$ of $A_2B_2C_2$ when rotated 180° about the point (0, 0).
   (d) Give a single transformation which maps
      (i) ABC on to $A_2B_2C_2$; (ii) $A_3B_3C_3$ on to ABC.

5. Triangle ABC has coordinates A (2, −7), B (−4, 3), C (4, 9).
   (a) Plot the image $A_1B_1C_1$ of ABC when rotated 180° about (0, 0). Then plot the image $A_2B_2C_2$ of $A_1B_1C_1$ when reflected in the x-axis.
   (b) On another sheet of paper plot the image $A_1B_1C_1$ of ABC when reflected in the x-axis. Then plot the image $A_2B_2C_2$ of $A_1B_1C_1$ when rotated 180° about (0, 0).
   (c) Are the images $A_2B_2C_2$ in (a) and (b) the same?
6. Ox and Oy are perpendicular coordinate axes.

   R denotes a translation $\begin{pmatrix}0\\4\end{pmatrix}$;
   S denotes a rotation of 180° about (0, 0);
   T denotes a reflection in the x-axis.
   Find the image of a point (x, y) under each of the transformations below where (for example) **RS** means **S** followed by **R**.
   (a) **RS** (b) **SR** (c) **ST** (d) **TS** (e) **RT** (f) **TR**
   If any two transformations give the same result in the reverse order, they are said to be commutative. Which of the above are commutative?
7. Trapezium ABCD has coordinates A (0, 0), B (2, −2), C (2, −4), D (0, −4).
   (a) With centre (2, 0) and scale factor 3, plot the image $A_1B_1C_1D_1$ of ABCD.
   (b) What is the scale factor which maps $A_1B_1C_1D_1$ back on to ABCD?
   (c) With centre (2, 0) and scale factor −2, plot the image $A_2B_2C_2D_2$ of ABCD.
   (d) What single transformation will map $A_2B_2C_2D_2$ on to $A_1B_1C_1D_1$?

9.8 Symmetry

A shape which can be divided by a straight line so that each part is the mirror image of the other has *reflective symmetry*. This line is the *axis of symmetry*.

Example 1

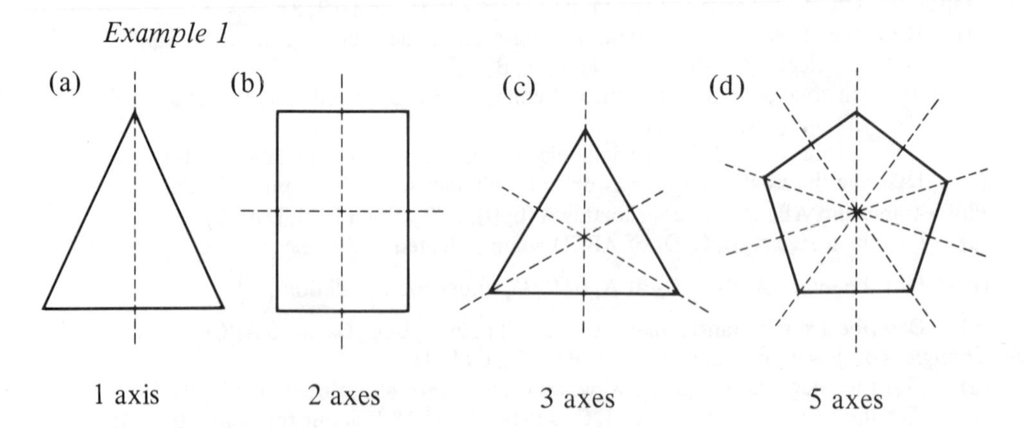

Example 2

PQ is the cushion of a billiards table and R, B, W represent three balls.
Find the point on PQ that W should strike so that it hits R on the rebound.

To find the point on PQ, reflect R in PQ to give R′. Join WR′. The point where this line cuts PQ is the required point.

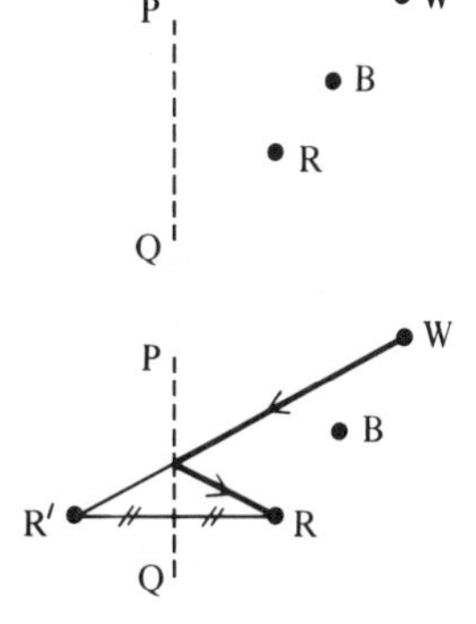

A figure which is invariant after an angular displacement about a point O has *rotational symmetry*. The point O is called the *centre* of rotational symmetry. The number of times this is possible in a complete turn is known as the *order* of rotational symmetry.

Example 3

(a)

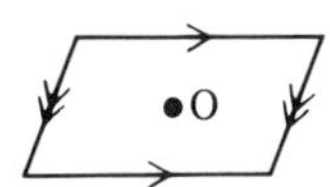

rotational symmetry order 2

(b)

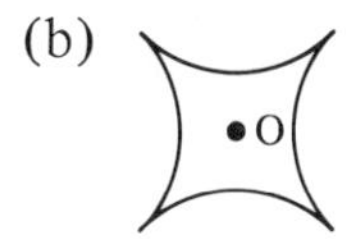

rotational symmetry order 4

Exercise 9.8

1. Describe the symmetry, reflective and rotational of each of the following.
(a) an isosceles triangle (b) an equilateral triangle (c) a trapezium
(d) an isosceles trapezium (e) a regular octagon (f) a circle
(g) an ellipse (h) two equal intersecting circles
(i) two unequal intersecting circles (j) a kite
(k) a rhombus (l) a parallelogram (m) any right-angled triangle
(n) the Club on a playing card (o) the Spade on a playing card
(p) the Six of Diamonds

2. Draw plane geometrical figures with the following symmetrical properties.
(a) two axes of reflective symmetry (b) six axes of reflective symmetry
(c) rotational symmetry order 5
(d) no axes of reflective symmetry, rotational symmetry order 2
(e) no rotational symmetry, one axis of reflective symmetry

3. Construct the following plane figures and describe their symmetry.
(a) a quadrilateral ABCD in which $\hat{A} = \hat{C} = 90°$, $\hat{B} = 120°$, and AB = BC = 10 cm
(b) a hexagon ABCDEF with all its sides 10 cm long and internal angles as follows: $\hat{A} = \hat{C} = \hat{E} = 30°$; $\hat{B} = \hat{D} = \hat{F} = 210°$.

4. Draw a nine-square grid and shade in:
   (a) three squares so that the resultant figure has two lines of symmetry and rotational symmetry order 2.
   (b) five squares so that the resultant figure has four lines of symmetry and rotational symmetry order 4.
   (c) four squares so that the resultant figure has four lines of symmetry and rotational symmetry order 4.

   In each case, state how many different results are possible.

5. The position of two electrical points A and B is shown in the plan. At what point on the wall should a switch be placed so that the wire used in connecting the points is a minimum?

6. A and B are two schools. Where should a footbridge be built so that the distance from A to B is a minimum?

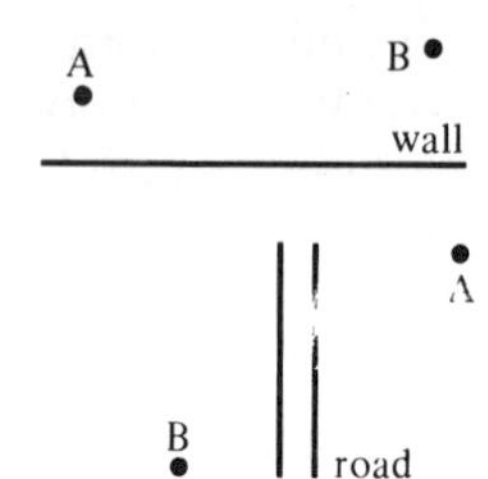

7. Copy the diagram and on it draw the image of the T shape when rotated:
   (a) 90° clockwise about 0
   (b) 90° anticlockwise about 0
   (c) 180° about 0

   What kind of symmetry has the final figure?

8. The vertices of a square ABCD are A (0, 0), B (2, 0), C (2, 2) and D (0, 2). The square is reflected in the following lines. Give the new coordinates of each of the resulting squares.
   (a) $y = 0$ (b) $x = 0$ (c) $y = x$ (d) $y = -x$

9.9 Displacements and vectors

The displacement PQ, written $\overrightarrow{PQ}$, is expressed by the column vector $\begin{pmatrix}1\\3\end{pmatrix}$.

The distance PQ is $\sqrt{1^2 + 3^2} = \sqrt{10}$.

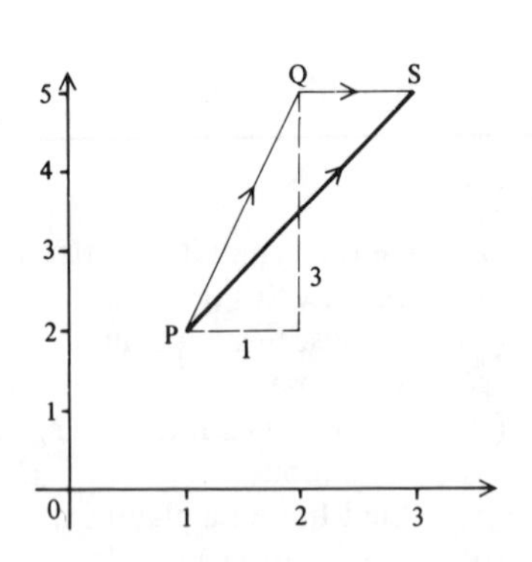

Notes

1. The column vector PQ is the difference between the Cartesian coordinates of Q and P, i.e. $\begin{pmatrix}2\\5\end{pmatrix} - \begin{pmatrix}1\\2\end{pmatrix} = \begin{pmatrix}1\\3\end{pmatrix}$.
2. The vector $\overrightarrow{PS}$ is equivalent to $\overrightarrow{PQ} + \overrightarrow{QS}$, i.e. $\begin{pmatrix}1\\3\end{pmatrix} + \begin{pmatrix}1\\0\end{pmatrix} = \begin{pmatrix}2\\3\end{pmatrix}$.
3. $\overrightarrow{QP} = -\overrightarrow{PQ} = \begin{pmatrix}-1\\-3\end{pmatrix}$.
4. $3\,\overrightarrow{PQ} = 3\begin{pmatrix}1\\3\end{pmatrix} = \begin{pmatrix}3\\9\end{pmatrix}$.
5. Vectors are often represented by a small letter in heavy type or in writing by a curly underline, e.g. $\overrightarrow{PQ} = \mathbf{a} = \underset{\sim}{a}$.

Example 1

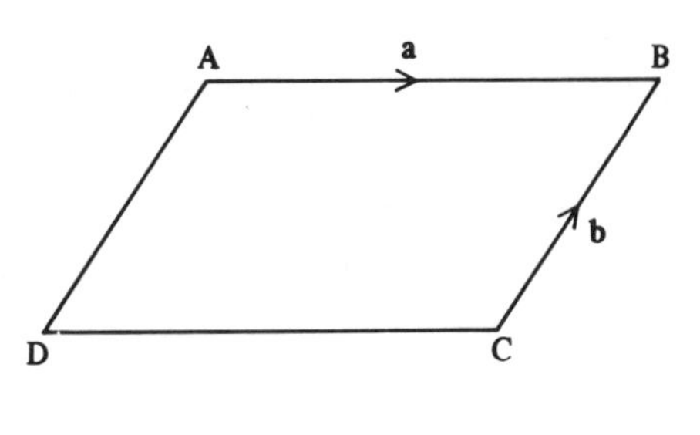

ABCD is a parallelogram in which $\overrightarrow{AB} = \mathbf{a}$, and $\overrightarrow{CB} = \mathbf{b}$.
Give the following displacements in terms of **a** and **b**.

(a) $\overrightarrow{DC} = \mathbf{a}$

(b) $\overrightarrow{AD} = -\mathbf{b}$

(c) $\overrightarrow{DB} = \overrightarrow{DA} + \overrightarrow{AB} = \mathbf{b} + \mathbf{a} = \mathbf{a} + \mathbf{b}$

(d) $\overrightarrow{AC} = \overrightarrow{AB} + \overrightarrow{BC} = \mathbf{a} - \mathbf{b}$

Example 2

In triangle ABC, M and N are the mid-points of the sides AB and AC respectively.
Show that
(a) MN is parallel to BC
(b) $MN = \frac{1}{2}BC$

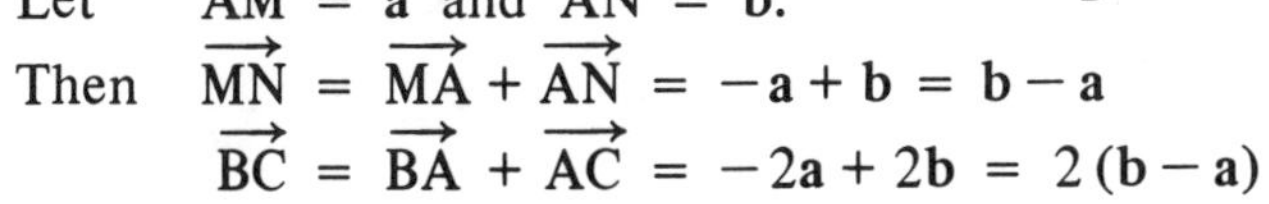

Let $\overrightarrow{AM} = \mathbf{a}$ and $\overrightarrow{AN} = \mathbf{b}$.

Then $\overrightarrow{MN} = \overrightarrow{MA} + \overrightarrow{AN} = -\mathbf{a} + \mathbf{b} = \mathbf{b} - \mathbf{a}$

$\overrightarrow{BC} = \overrightarrow{BA} + \overrightarrow{AC} = -2\mathbf{a} + 2\mathbf{b} = 2(\mathbf{b} - \mathbf{a})$

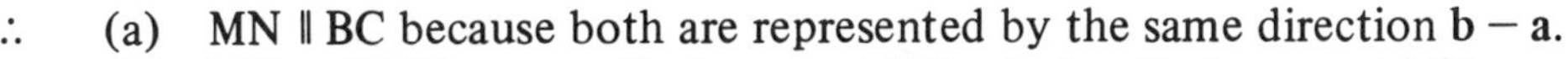

$\therefore$ (a) MN ∥ BC because both are represented by the same direction $\mathbf{b} - \mathbf{a}$.
(b) $MN = \frac{1}{2}BC$ because displacement BC = twice displacement MN.

Example 3

ABCD is a parallelogram where A is (2, 1), B is (3, 4) and C is (−1, 2).

Find (a) the column vector of $\overrightarrow{BA}$ and the coordinates of D,
(b) the length of AC.

(a) Let the coordinates of D be (x, y).

$$\overrightarrow{BA} = \begin{pmatrix}2\\1\end{pmatrix} - \begin{pmatrix}3\\4\end{pmatrix} = \begin{pmatrix}-1\\-3\end{pmatrix} \qquad \text{see note 1.}$$

But $\overrightarrow{CD} = \overrightarrow{BA}$ because ABCD is a parallelogram.

$$\therefore \begin{pmatrix}x\\y\end{pmatrix} - \begin{pmatrix}-1\\2\end{pmatrix} = \begin{pmatrix}-1\\-3\end{pmatrix}$$

$$\begin{pmatrix}x\\y\end{pmatrix} = \begin{pmatrix}-1\\-3\end{pmatrix} + \begin{pmatrix}-1\\2\end{pmatrix} = \begin{pmatrix}-2\\-1\end{pmatrix} \qquad \therefore x = -2, y = -1$$

(b)
$$\overrightarrow{AC} = \begin{pmatrix}-1\\2\end{pmatrix} - \begin{pmatrix}2\\1\end{pmatrix} = \begin{pmatrix}-3\\1\end{pmatrix}$$

$$\therefore AC = \sqrt{(-3)^2 + (1)^2} = \sqrt{9 + 1} = \sqrt{10} \text{ units.}$$

Exercise 9.9

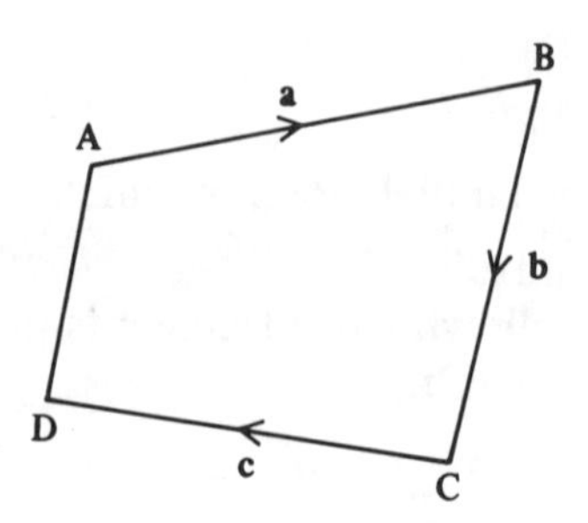

1. If $\overrightarrow{AB} = \mathbf{a}$, $\overrightarrow{BC} = \mathbf{b}$, and $\overrightarrow{CD} = \mathbf{c}$, express the following in terms of **a**, **b**, **c**.
   (a) $\overrightarrow{AC}$ (b) $\overrightarrow{CA}$
   (c) $\overrightarrow{BD}$ (d) $\overrightarrow{AD}$

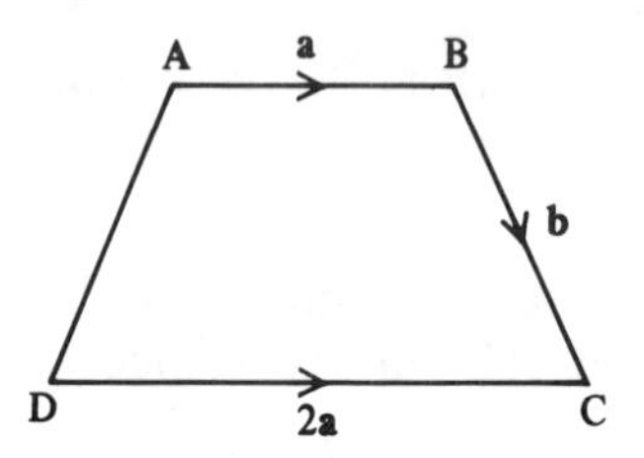

2. If $\overrightarrow{AB} = \mathbf{a}$, $\overrightarrow{DC} = 2\mathbf{a}$, and $\overrightarrow{BC} = \mathbf{b}$, express the following in terms of **a** and **b**.
   (a) $\overrightarrow{AC}$ (b) $\overrightarrow{BD}$ (c) $\overrightarrow{DA}$

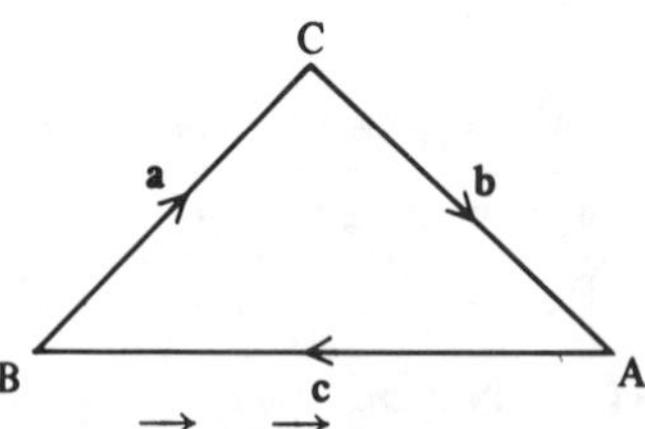

3. Write each of the following as single vectors.
   (a) $\mathbf{a} + \mathbf{b}$ (b) $\mathbf{b} + \mathbf{c}$
   (c) $-\mathbf{a} - \mathbf{c}$ (d) $\mathbf{a} + \mathbf{b} + \mathbf{c}$

4. ABCD is a quadrilateral. Given that $\overrightarrow{AB} = \mathbf{a}$, $\overrightarrow{AD} = \mathbf{b}$, and $\overrightarrow{AD} = \overrightarrow{BC}$, write down in terms of **a** and **b** (a) $\overrightarrow{BD}$; (b) $\overrightarrow{AC}$; (c) $\overrightarrow{DC}$.
   Hence state the relationship between AB and DC and name the figure.
5. OABC is a parallelogram in which OC is produced to D so that OC = CD and M is the mid-point of side BC. If $\overrightarrow{OA} = 2\mathbf{a}$ and $\overrightarrow{OC} = 2\mathbf{b}$, express in terms of **a** and **b**
   (a) $\overrightarrow{CD}$; (b) $\overrightarrow{CM}$; (c) $\overrightarrow{MD}$; (d) $\overrightarrow{AM}$.
   Hence state the relationships between (i) CM and OA and (ii) AM and MD.
6. PQR is a triangle in which A, B, and C are the mid-points of the sides PQ, QR, and RP respectively. If $\overrightarrow{AQ} = \mathbf{a}$ and $\overrightarrow{QB} = \mathbf{b}$, express in terms of **a** and **b**
   (a) $\overrightarrow{PA}$; (b) $\overrightarrow{QR}$; (c) $\overrightarrow{AB}$; (d) $\overrightarrow{PR}$; (e) $\overrightarrow{CR}$.
   What special type of quadrilateral is ABRC?
7. ABCD is a rhombus. If $\overrightarrow{DA} = \mathbf{a}$ and $\overrightarrow{AB} = \mathbf{b}$, express in terms of **a** and **b**.
   (a) $\overrightarrow{DB}$; (b) $\overrightarrow{CA}$.
   Hence show that the diagonals of a rhombus are perpendicular to each other.
8. OAB is a triangle and M is the mid-point of AB. If $\overrightarrow{OA} = \mathbf{a}$ and $\overrightarrow{OB} = \mathbf{b}$, find $\overrightarrow{OM}$ in terms of **a** and **b**.
   If M is also the mid-point of OC, show that OACB is a parallelogram.
9. OABC is a parallelogram with coordinates O $(0, 0)$, A $(2, -1)$ and B $(-\frac{1}{2}, -2\frac{1}{2})$.
   Find the coordinates of
   (a) the point C.
   (b) the point X at which the diagonals OB and AC intersect.

9.10 Matrices

The order of a matrix is defined by the number of rows multiplied by the number of columns.

Thus the matrix $\begin{pmatrix} 2 & 6 \\ 1 & 4 \\ 3 & 2 \end{pmatrix}$ has the order 3×2.

Addition and subtraction

Only matrices of the same order can be added or subtracted.

Example 1

If $\mathbf{A} = \begin{pmatrix} 2 & 1 \\ 3 & 4 \end{pmatrix}$, $\mathbf{B} = \begin{pmatrix} -1 & 0 \\ 3 & -2 \end{pmatrix}$, $\mathbf{C} = \begin{pmatrix} 2 & 0 & 1 \\ 0 & 1 & 2 \end{pmatrix}$, find (if possible) the value of

(a) $\mathbf{A} + \mathbf{B}$; (b) $\mathbf{A} - \mathbf{B}$; (c) $\mathbf{B} + \mathbf{C}$; (d) $\mathbf{C} + \mathbf{C} + \mathbf{C}$

(a) $\mathbf{A} + \mathbf{B} = \begin{pmatrix} 2 & 1 \\ 3 & 4 \end{pmatrix} + \begin{pmatrix} -1 & 0 \\ 3 & -2 \end{pmatrix} = \begin{pmatrix} 1 & 1 \\ 6 & 2 \end{pmatrix}$

(b) $\mathbf{A} - \mathbf{B} = \begin{pmatrix} 2 & 1 \\ 3 & 4 \end{pmatrix} - \begin{pmatrix} -1 & 0 \\ 3 & -2 \end{pmatrix} = \begin{pmatrix} 3 & 1 \\ 0 & 6 \end{pmatrix}$

(c) $\mathbf{B} + \mathbf{C}$ cannot be evaluated because $\mathbf{B}$ is a 2×2 matrix, $\mathbf{C}$ is a 2×3 matrix.

(d) $\mathbf{C} + \mathbf{C} + \mathbf{C} = 3\mathbf{C} = 3\begin{pmatrix} 2 & 0 & 1 \\ 0 & 1 & 2 \end{pmatrix} = \begin{pmatrix} 6 & 0 & 3 \\ 0 & 3 & 6 \end{pmatrix}$

Matrix multiplication

Matrices can only be multiplied together if the number of columns in the first matrix is the same as the number of rows in the second matrix. The resultant matrix then has the same number of rows as the first and the same number of columns as the second.
Thus the product of a 3×2 matrix and a 2×4 matrix will be a 3×4 matrix.

Example 2

If $\mathbf{A} = \begin{pmatrix} 2 \\ 3 \end{pmatrix}$, $\mathbf{B} = \begin{pmatrix} 1 & 3 \\ -2 & 1 \end{pmatrix}$, $\mathbf{C} = \begin{pmatrix} 1 & 0 & 2 \\ 2 & 1 & 3 \end{pmatrix}$, evaluate (if possible)

(a) $\mathbf{AB}$; (b) $\mathbf{B}^2$; (c) $\mathbf{BC}$

(a) $\mathbf{AB} = \begin{pmatrix} 2 \\ 3 \end{pmatrix} \begin{pmatrix} 1 & 3 \\ -2 & 1 \end{pmatrix}$ which is not possible (1 column in $\mathbf{A}$ and 2 rows in $\mathbf{B}$).

(b) $\mathbf{B}^2 = \mathbf{B} \times \mathbf{B} = \begin{pmatrix} 1 & 3 \\ -2 & 1 \end{pmatrix} \begin{pmatrix} 1 & 3 \\ -2 & 1 \end{pmatrix} = \begin{pmatrix} -5 & 6 \\ -4 & -5 \end{pmatrix}$

(c) $\mathbf{BC} = \begin{pmatrix} 1 & 3 \\ -2 & 1 \end{pmatrix} \begin{pmatrix} 1 & 0 & 2 \\ 2 & 1 & 3 \end{pmatrix} = \begin{pmatrix} 7 & 3 & 11 \\ 0 & 1 & -1 \end{pmatrix}$

Two matrices are equal only if the corresponding elements in each matrix are the same.

Example 3

Find a and b if $\begin{pmatrix} a \\ b \end{pmatrix} + \begin{pmatrix} 2 \\ 3 \end{pmatrix} = \begin{pmatrix} 4 \\ 6 \end{pmatrix}$.

Because the matrices are equal, the corresponding elements are the same.

$$a + 2 = 4 \qquad b + 3 = 6$$
$$\therefore \quad a = 2 \qquad \therefore \quad b = 3$$

Exercise 9.10

1. If $\mathbf{A} = \begin{pmatrix} 1 & 2 \\ 3 & 4 \end{pmatrix}$, $\mathbf{B} = \begin{pmatrix} -2 & -1 \\ 3 & -4 \end{pmatrix}$, $\mathbf{C} = \begin{pmatrix} 0 & -3 \\ -2 & 1 \end{pmatrix}$, find the value of:

   (a) $\mathbf{A} + \mathbf{B}$; (b) $\mathbf{B} + \mathbf{C}$; (c) $\mathbf{A} - \mathbf{B}$; (d) $\mathbf{B} - \mathbf{C}$; (e) $\mathbf{A} - \mathbf{B} - \mathbf{C}$

2. If $\mathbf{X} = \begin{pmatrix} a & 2a \\ 3a & 4a \end{pmatrix}$, $\mathbf{Y} = \begin{pmatrix} 2a & -3a \\ -4a & 5a \end{pmatrix}$, find the value of:

   (a) $\mathbf{X} + \mathbf{Y}$; (b) $\mathbf{X} - \mathbf{Y}$; (c) $2\mathbf{X}$; (d) $4\mathbf{Y}$; (e) $3\mathbf{X} - 2\mathbf{Y}$

3. If $\mathbf{A} = \begin{pmatrix} 1 & 0 \\ 0 & -1 \end{pmatrix}$, $\mathbf{B} = \begin{pmatrix} 4 & -2 \\ -2 & 4 \end{pmatrix}$, $\mathbf{C} = \begin{pmatrix} -1 & 0 \\ 0 & -1 \end{pmatrix}$, find the value of:

   (a) $\mathbf{AB}$; (b) $\mathbf{BA}$; (c) $\mathbf{BC}$; (d) $\mathbf{CB}$; (e) $\mathbf{ABC}$; (f) $\mathbf{A}^2$

4. If $\mathbf{X} = \begin{pmatrix} a & 2a \\ 3a & 4a \end{pmatrix}$ and $\mathbf{Y} = \begin{pmatrix} 2a & a \\ -a & -2a \end{pmatrix}$, find the value of:

   (a) $\mathbf{XY}$; (b) $\mathbf{X}^2$; (c) $\mathbf{Y}^2$; (d) $\mathbf{YX}$ (e) $(\mathbf{X} + \mathbf{Y})^2$

5. Find x and y in the following:

   (a) $\begin{pmatrix} x \\ 3 \end{pmatrix} + \begin{pmatrix} 2 \\ y \end{pmatrix} = \begin{pmatrix} 6 \\ 4 \end{pmatrix}$ (b) $\begin{pmatrix} x \\ 3 \end{pmatrix} - \begin{pmatrix} 2 \\ y \end{pmatrix} = \begin{pmatrix} 6 \\ 4 \end{pmatrix}$

   (c) $\begin{pmatrix} 0 & x \\ y & 3 \end{pmatrix} + \begin{pmatrix} 5 & 2x \\ 3y & 6 \end{pmatrix} = \begin{pmatrix} 5 & 9 \\ 8 & 9 \end{pmatrix}$ (d) $\begin{pmatrix} 0 & -2 \\ 1 & 2 \end{pmatrix} + \begin{pmatrix} 1 & 2 \\ x & y \end{pmatrix} = \begin{pmatrix} 1 & 0 \\ 2 & 0 \end{pmatrix}$

6. If $\mathbf{X} = \begin{pmatrix} 1 & 1 \\ 2 & 2 \end{pmatrix}$ and $\mathbf{Y} = \begin{pmatrix} 2 & 2 \\ 1 & 1 \end{pmatrix}$, find the value of

   (a) $\mathbf{X}^2$; (b) $\mathbf{Y}^2$; (c) $\mathbf{X}^2 - \mathbf{Y}^2$;
   (d) $(\mathbf{X} - \mathbf{Y})(\mathbf{X} + \mathbf{Y})$; (e) $(\mathbf{X} + \mathbf{Y})(\mathbf{X} - \mathbf{Y})$
   Does $\mathbf{X}^2 - \mathbf{Y}^2 = (\mathbf{X} - \mathbf{Y})(\mathbf{X} + \mathbf{Y})$? Does $\mathbf{X}^2 - \mathbf{Y}^2 = (\mathbf{X} + \mathbf{Y})(\mathbf{X} - \mathbf{Y})$?

7. Find x in each of the following:

   (a) $\begin{pmatrix} x & 2 \\ 0 & 0 \end{pmatrix}\begin{pmatrix} 3 \\ 1 \end{pmatrix} = \begin{pmatrix} 26 \\ 0 \end{pmatrix}$; (b) $\begin{pmatrix} 2 & 3 \\ 1 & 4 \end{pmatrix}\begin{pmatrix} 2 \\ x \end{pmatrix} = \begin{pmatrix} 1 \\ -2 \end{pmatrix}$; (c) $\begin{pmatrix} 2 & 3 \\ x & 1 \end{pmatrix}\begin{pmatrix} 1 \\ x \end{pmatrix} = \begin{pmatrix} x \\ -2 \end{pmatrix}$

8. If $\mathbf{P} = \begin{pmatrix} a & b \\ c & d \end{pmatrix}$, find a matrix $\mathbf{Q}$ such that $\mathbf{PQ} = \begin{pmatrix} a + 2b & a + b \\ c + 2d & c + d \end{pmatrix}$.

   What is the value of $\mathbf{QP}$?

9. $\mathbf{I}=\begin{pmatrix}1 & 0\\0 & 1\end{pmatrix}$; $\mathbf{A}=\begin{pmatrix}0 & -1\\1 & 0\end{pmatrix}$;
$\mathbf{B}=\begin{pmatrix}0 & 1\\-1 & 0\end{pmatrix}$; $\mathbf{C}=\begin{pmatrix}-1 & 0\\0 & -1\end{pmatrix}$

Copy and complete the product table shown.

×	**I**	**A**	**B**	**C**
I				
A				
B				
C				

10. If $\mathbf{A}=\begin{pmatrix}a & b\\c & d\end{pmatrix}$, its transpose $\mathbf{A}'=\begin{pmatrix}a & c\\b & d\end{pmatrix}$.
Does $\mathbf{AA}' = \mathbf{A}'\mathbf{A}$?

9.11 Inverse matrices

If **A** and **B** are two 2 × 2 matrices and their product **AB** is the identity matrix $\begin{pmatrix}1 & 0\\0 & 1\end{pmatrix}$, then matrix **B** is the multiplicative *inverse* of matrix **A**.

Example 1

If $\mathbf{A}=\begin{pmatrix}2 & 5\\1 & 3\end{pmatrix}$, find its inverse $\mathbf{A}^{-1}$.

Let $\mathbf{A}^{-1}=\begin{pmatrix}a & b\\c & d\end{pmatrix}$, then $\begin{pmatrix}2 & 5\\1 & 3\end{pmatrix}\begin{pmatrix}a & b\\c & d\end{pmatrix} = \begin{pmatrix}1 & 0\\0 & 1\end{pmatrix}$.

This gives $\begin{aligned}2a+5c&=1\\a+3c&=0\end{aligned}$ and $\begin{aligned}2b+5d&=0\\b+3d&=1\end{aligned}$

Solving these pairs of simultaneous equations (see page 72) gives $a = 3$, $b = -5$, $c = -1$, $d = 2$.

$$\therefore \mathbf{A}^{-1} = \begin{pmatrix}3 & -5\\-1 & 2\end{pmatrix}$$

In general, the inverse of the matrix $\begin{pmatrix}a & b\\c & d\end{pmatrix}$ is $\dfrac{1}{ad-bc}\begin{pmatrix}d & -b\\-c & a\end{pmatrix}$.

The term $ad - bc$ is called the *determinant* of the matrix.

Example 2

Use matrices to solve the simultaneous equations $\begin{aligned}x+2y&=8\\3x-y&=3\end{aligned}$

1. Write the equations in the form $\begin{pmatrix} 1 & 2 \\ 3 & -1 \end{pmatrix}\begin{pmatrix} x \\ y \end{pmatrix} = \begin{pmatrix} 8 \\ 3 \end{pmatrix}$.

2. The determinant of the matrix $\begin{pmatrix} 1 & 2 \\ 3 & -1 \end{pmatrix}$ is $(1 \times -1) - (2 \times 3) = -7$, so the inverse of the matrix is $-\frac{1}{7}\begin{pmatrix} -1 & -2 \\ -3 & 1 \end{pmatrix}$.

3. Premultiply both sides of the matrix equation by the inverse and then solve.

$$-\tfrac{1}{7}\begin{pmatrix} -1 & -2 \\ -3 & 1 \end{pmatrix}\begin{pmatrix} 1 & 2 \\ 3 & -1 \end{pmatrix}\begin{pmatrix} x \\ y \end{pmatrix} = -\tfrac{1}{7}\begin{pmatrix} -1 & -2 \\ -3 & 1 \end{pmatrix}\begin{pmatrix} 8 \\ 3 \end{pmatrix}$$

$$\Rightarrow \quad -\tfrac{1}{7}\begin{pmatrix} -7 & 0 \\ 0 & -7 \end{pmatrix}\begin{pmatrix} x \\ y \end{pmatrix} = -\tfrac{1}{7}\begin{pmatrix} -14 \\ -21 \end{pmatrix}$$

$$\Rightarrow \quad \begin{pmatrix} 1 & 0 \\ 0 & 1 \end{pmatrix}\begin{pmatrix} x \\ y \end{pmatrix} = \begin{pmatrix} 2 \\ 3 \end{pmatrix}$$

$$\Rightarrow \quad \begin{pmatrix} x \\ y \end{pmatrix} = \begin{pmatrix} 2 \\ 3 \end{pmatrix} \qquad \therefore x = 2, y = 3$$

Note. If the determinant is zero, the matrix is called a *singular* matrix. If this situation arises when solving simultaneous equations, then the two equations represent either the same straight line or a pair of parallel lines.

Example 3

State which of the following simultaneous equations has
(i) a unique solution, (ii) an infinite number of solutions, (iii) no solution.

(a) $3x + 4y = 8$, $6x + 8y = 16$ (b) $2x + 6y = 10$, $x + 3y = 12$ (c) $4x - 3y = 0$, $2x + y = 10$

(a) $(3 \times 8) - (4 \times 6) = 0$. The determinant is zero. By inspection both equations represent the same straight line; therefore there are an infinite number of solutions.

(b) $(2 \times 3) - (6 \times 1) = 0$. The determinant is zero. By inspection both lines have the same gradient ($\frac{1}{3}$); so the equations represent a pair of parallel lines. Therefore there is no solution.

(c) The determinant is *not* zero; the two equations have the unique solution $x = 3, y = 4$.

Exercise 9.11

1. Calculate the inverse of each matrix.

(a) $\begin{pmatrix} 3 & 2 \\ 1 & 1 \end{pmatrix}$ (b) $\begin{pmatrix} 3 & -2 \\ -4 & 3 \end{pmatrix}$ (c) $\begin{pmatrix} 3 & 7 \\ 2 & 5 \end{pmatrix}$

(d) $\begin{pmatrix} -5 & -4 \\ -16 & -13 \end{pmatrix}$ (e) $\begin{pmatrix} -5 & 13 \\ -7 & 18 \end{pmatrix}$

2. Calculate the inverse of each matrix.

(a) $\begin{pmatrix} 0 & -1 \\ 1 & 0 \end{pmatrix}$ (b) $\begin{pmatrix} 4 & 6 \\ 3 & 4 \end{pmatrix}$ (c) $\begin{pmatrix} 2 & 3 \\ -1 & 2 \end{pmatrix}$

(d) $\begin{pmatrix} -5 & -4 \\ -2 & -3 \end{pmatrix}$ (e) $\begin{pmatrix} a & -b \\ a & b \end{pmatrix}$

3. Use matrices to solve each pair of simultaneous equations.

(a) $3x + 5y = 8$, $x + 2y = 3$ (b) $3x + 11y = 17$, $x + 4y = 6$ (c) $7x + 4y = 3$, $5x + 3y = 2$

(d) $4x + 9y = 6$, $3x + 7y = 5$ (e) $2x - 3y = 7$, $5x - 7y = 12$ (f) $5x - 2y = 4$, $3x - y = 2$

4. Solve the following simultaneous equations, giving reasons where not possible.

(a) $3x + 4y = 6$, $6x + 8y = 12$ (b) $3x + 4y = 1$, $6x - 8y = 34$ (c) $3x + 4y = 9$, $6x + 8y = 24$

(d) $3a + b = 7$, $4a - 2b = 6$ (e) $5c - 3d = 54$, $6c + 2d = 20$ (f) $4x - 6y = 0$, $x - y = 0$

(g) $3x + 4y = 2$, $5x - 7y = 17$ (h) $3x - 2y = 10$, $6x - 4y = 12$ (i) $3s - 2t = -6$, $5s - 3t = 30$

5. Given that $\begin{pmatrix} 4 & -1 \\ 3 & 2 \end{pmatrix}\begin{pmatrix} a \\ b \end{pmatrix} = \begin{pmatrix} 6 \\ 2 \end{pmatrix}$, find the value of

(a) $7a + b$ (b) ab

6. Perform the following matrix multiplication.

$$\begin{pmatrix} -3 & 2 & 1 \\ 9 & -5 & -2 \\ -5 & 3 & 1 \end{pmatrix}\begin{pmatrix} 1 & 1 & 1 \\ 1 & 2 & 3 \\ 2 & -1 & -3 \end{pmatrix}$$

Hence solve the simultaneous equations

$$\begin{aligned} x + y + z &= 0 \\ x + 2y + 3z &= -7 \\ 2x - y - 3z &= 17 \end{aligned}$$

9.12 Matrix operators

The point P (x, y) may be written as a column vector $\begin{pmatrix} x \\ y \end{pmatrix}$. If this column vector is multiplied by a 2×2 matrix (known as the operator), then a geometrical transformation takes places.

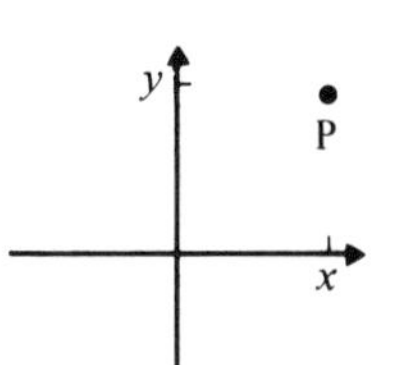

Some of the more common matrix operators are listed below.

1. $\begin{pmatrix}1 & 0\\0 & 1\end{pmatrix}$ leaves the point unchanged.
2. $\begin{pmatrix}0 & 1\\1 & 0\end{pmatrix}$ maps $\begin{pmatrix}x\\y\end{pmatrix}$ onto $\begin{pmatrix}y\\x\end{pmatrix}$; a reflection in the line $y = x$.
3. $\begin{pmatrix}1 & 0\\0 & -1\end{pmatrix}$ maps $\begin{pmatrix}x\\y\end{pmatrix}$ onto $\begin{pmatrix}x\\-y\end{pmatrix}$; a reflection in the line $y = 0$.
4. $\begin{pmatrix}-1 & 0\\0 & 1\end{pmatrix}$ maps $\begin{pmatrix}x\\y\end{pmatrix}$ onto $\begin{pmatrix}-x\\y\end{pmatrix}$; a reflection in the line $x = 0$.
5. $\begin{pmatrix}-1 & 0\\0 & -1\end{pmatrix}$ maps $\begin{pmatrix}x\\y\end{pmatrix}$ onto $\begin{pmatrix}-x\\-y\end{pmatrix}$; a rotation of 180° about (0, 0).
6. $\begin{pmatrix}k & 0\\0 & k\end{pmatrix}$ maps $\begin{pmatrix}x\\y\end{pmatrix}$ onto $\begin{pmatrix}kx\\ky\end{pmatrix}$; an enlargement, scale factor k, centre (0, 0).
7. $\begin{pmatrix}1 & k\\0 & 1\end{pmatrix}$ maps $\begin{pmatrix}x\\y\end{pmatrix}$ onto $\begin{pmatrix}x + ky\\y\end{pmatrix}$; a shear parallel to the x-axis.
8. $\begin{pmatrix}k & 0\\0 & 1\end{pmatrix}$ maps $\begin{pmatrix}x\\y\end{pmatrix}$ onto $\begin{pmatrix}kx\\y\end{pmatrix}$; a stretch.

Example

Plot the rectangle A (0, 0), B (4, 0), C (4, 2), D (0, 2). Illustrate on a graph the result of applying each of the following transformations.

(a) $\mathbf{R} = \begin{pmatrix}0 & -1\\1 & 0\end{pmatrix}$ (b) $\mathbf{E} = \begin{pmatrix}0 & 2\\-2 & 0\end{pmatrix}$ (c) $\mathbf{H} = \begin{pmatrix}1 & 2\\0 & 1\end{pmatrix}$ (d) **HR**

(a) A rotation of +90° about (0, 0)

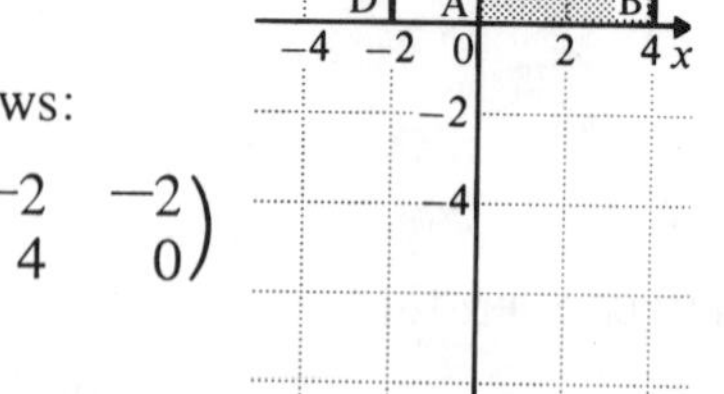

New coordinates are calculated as follows:

$$\begin{pmatrix}0 & -1\\1 & 0\end{pmatrix}\begin{pmatrix}0 & 4 & 4 & 0\\0 & 0 & 2 & 2\end{pmatrix} = \begin{pmatrix}0 & 0 & -2 & -2\\0 & 4 & 4 & 0\end{pmatrix}$$

(b) A rotation of −90° followed by an enlargement, scale factor 2 about (0, 0).

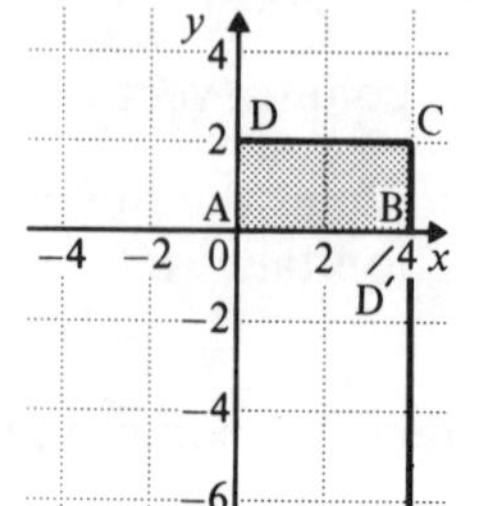

New coordinates are calculated as follows:

$$\begin{pmatrix}0 & 2\\-2 & 0\end{pmatrix}\begin{pmatrix}0 & 4 & 4 & 0\\0 & 0 & 2 & 2\end{pmatrix} = \begin{pmatrix}0 & 0 & 4 & 4\\0 & -8 & -8 & 0\end{pmatrix}$$

(c)

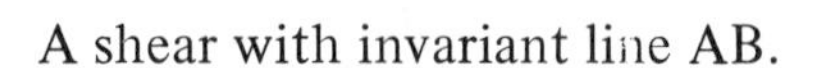

A shear with invariant line AB.

$$\begin{pmatrix}1 & 2\\0 & 1\end{pmatrix}\begin{pmatrix}0 & 4 & 4 & 0\\0 & 0 & 2 & 2\end{pmatrix} = \begin{pmatrix}0 & 4 & 8 & 4\\0 & 0 & 2 & 2\end{pmatrix}$$

(d)

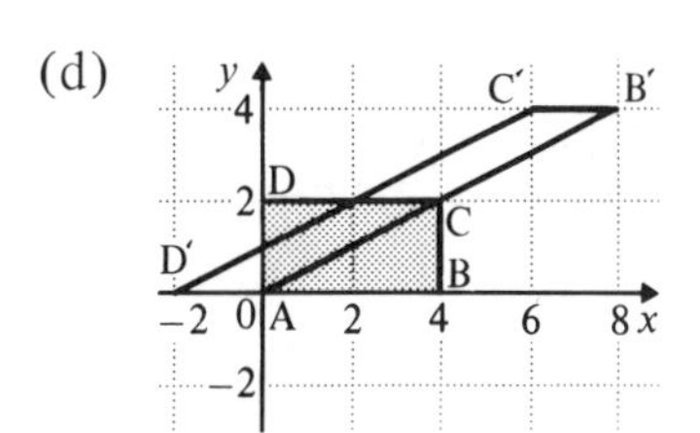

HR represents the combination of the rotation **R** followed by the shear **H**.

$$\begin{pmatrix}1 & 2\\0 & 1\end{pmatrix}\begin{pmatrix}0 & 0 & -2 & -2\\0 & 4 & 4 & 0\end{pmatrix} = \begin{pmatrix}0 & 8 & 6 & -2\\0 & 4 & 4 & 0\end{pmatrix}$$

Exercise 9.12

1. Plot the rectangle A (0, 0), B (4, 0), C (4, 2), D (0, 2). Illustrate and describe the result of applying each of the following transformations to ABCD.

   (a) $\begin{pmatrix}1 & 0\\0 & 1\end{pmatrix}$ (b) $\begin{pmatrix}0 & 1\\1 & 0\end{pmatrix}$ (c) $\begin{pmatrix}0 & 1\\-1 & 0\end{pmatrix}$ (d) $\begin{pmatrix}2 & 0\\0 & 2\end{pmatrix}$ (e) $\begin{pmatrix}2 & 0\\0 & 1\end{pmatrix}$

   (f) $\begin{pmatrix}1 & 3\\0 & 1\end{pmatrix}$ (g) $\begin{pmatrix}1 & 0\\2 & 1\end{pmatrix}$ (h) $\begin{pmatrix}2 & 0\\0 & \frac{1}{2}\end{pmatrix}$ (i) $\begin{pmatrix}0 & 1\\0 & 1\end{pmatrix}$ (j) $\begin{pmatrix}4 & 1\\1 & 0\end{pmatrix}$

2. Write down the matrix operator for each of the following transformations.
   (a) reflection in the line $y = 0$ (b) rotation of 180° about (0, 0)
   (c) enlargement, scale factor 2 (d) rotation of −270° about (0, 0)
   (e) a shear parallel to the x-axis, magnitude 2
   (f) a stretch parallel to the x-axis
   (g) rotation of −90° followed by an enlargement, scale factor 2 about (0, 0)
   (h) rotation +45° about (0, 0).

3. Plot the square A (0, 0), B (2, 0), C (2, 2), D (0, 2). Illustrate and describe the result of applying each of the following transformations to ABCD.

   (a) $\mathbf{P} = \begin{pmatrix}1 & 0\\2 & 1\end{pmatrix}$ (b) $\mathbf{Q} = \begin{pmatrix}0 & 1\\1 & 0\end{pmatrix}$ (c) **PQ** (d) **QP**

4. Plot the triangle A (0, 0), B (2, 2), C (4, 0). Illustrate and describe the result of applying each of the following transformations to ABC.

   (a) $\mathbf{M} = \begin{pmatrix}1 & 0\\1 & 1\end{pmatrix}$ (b) $\mathbf{N} = \begin{pmatrix}0 & -1\\-1 & 0\end{pmatrix}$ (c) **MN** (d) **NM**

5. Plot the quadrilateral A (0, 0), B (2, 1), C (2, 4), D (0, 4). Illustrate the result of applying each of the following transformations to ABCD.

   (a) $\begin{pmatrix}0 & 1\\-1 & 0\end{pmatrix}$ (b) $\begin{pmatrix}0 & -1\\1 & 0\end{pmatrix}$ (c) $\begin{pmatrix}0 & -3\\3 & 0\end{pmatrix}$ (d) $\begin{pmatrix}0 & 3\\-3 & 0\end{pmatrix}$

   (e) $\begin{pmatrix}0 & \frac{1}{2}\\-\frac{1}{2} & 0\end{pmatrix}$ (f) $\begin{pmatrix}0 & -\frac{1}{2}\\\frac{1}{2} & 0\end{pmatrix}$

   What sort of transformation does each of the above operators represent?

6. Plot the set of points A (2, 0), B (3, 2), C (2, 3), D (1, 2) and join them to produce the kite ABCD.

(a) Illustrate the results of applying each of the following transformations.

(i) $\mathbf{P} = \begin{pmatrix} -1 & 0 \\ 0 & -1 \end{pmatrix}$ (ii) $\mathbf{Q} = \begin{pmatrix} 0 & -1 \\ 1 & 0 \end{pmatrix}$ (iii) $\mathbf{R} = \begin{pmatrix} -1 & 0 \\ 0 & 1 \end{pmatrix}$

(iv) **PQ** (v) **QR** (vi) **PQR**

(b) Give the transformation matrix that would produce the same result as
(i) **PQ** (ii) **QP**

(c) Give in each case the matrix that would transform the images in (a) back onto the kite ABCD.

7. The matrix $\mathbf{R} = \begin{pmatrix} \cos\theta & -\sin\theta \\ \sin\theta & \cos\theta \end{pmatrix}$ represents a rotation of $\theta°$ about the origin.

(a) Find the matrix which gives a positive rotation of
(i) 90° (ii) 180° (iii) 270° (iv) 30°
(v) 60° (vi) 120° (vii) 45° (viii) 315°

(b) Find the angle of rotation (to the nearest degree) resulting from the transformation of a point by the following operators.

(i) $\begin{pmatrix} 0{\cdot}7 & -0{\cdot}7 \\ 0{\cdot}7 & 0{\cdot}7 \end{pmatrix}$ (ii) $\begin{pmatrix} -0{\cdot}6 & 0{\cdot}8 \\ -0{\cdot}8 & -0{\cdot}6 \end{pmatrix}$

8. If $\mathbf{A} = \begin{pmatrix} 0 & -1 \\ 1 & 0 \end{pmatrix}$; $\mathbf{B} = \begin{pmatrix} -1 & 0 \\ 0 & -1 \end{pmatrix}$; $\mathbf{C} = \begin{pmatrix} 0 & 1 \\ -1 & 0 \end{pmatrix}$; $\mathbf{D} = \begin{pmatrix} 1 & 0 \\ 0 & 1 \end{pmatrix}$;

Copy and complete the product table shown and comment on your results.

X	A	B	C	D
A				
B				
C				
D				

9.13 Relations and functions

If $A = \{a, b, c\}$ and $B = \{m, n\}$,
then the set of ordered pairs (x, y) where $x \in A$ and $y \in B$ is called the *product set* of A and B.

$$\text{product set} = \{(a, m), (a, n), (b, m), (b, n), (c, m), (c, n)\}$$

The *domain* is the set of first elements in the ordered pairs.

$$\text{domain} = \{a, b, c\}$$

The *range* (or image set) is the set of second elements in the ordered pairs.

$$\text{range} = \{m, n\}$$

A *relation* is a subset of the product set.

A *one-to-one* relation is one in which, for any value of x there is one and only one value of y, and for any value of y there is one and only one value of x; e.g. $y = 2x - 1$.

A *many-to-one* relation is one in which there are several values of x for any one value of y; e.g. $y = x^2$.

A *one-to-many* relation is one in which there are several values of y for any one value of x; e.g. $y^2 = x$.

A *many-to-many* relation is one in which there are several values of y for any value of x and several values of x for any value of y; e.g. $y^2 = x^4$.

A *function* is either a many-to-one or a one-to-one relation and can be expressed in one of the following ways:
(a) $f: x \to x^2 - 1$ (b) $f(x) = x^2 - 1$ (c) $y = x^2 - 1$

Example 1

If $y = 2x - 1$, list the range for the domain $0 < x \leqslant 3$ where x is an integer.
When $x = 1, y = 1$; when $x = 2, y = 3$; when $x = 3, y = 5$.

$\therefore$ range is $\{1, 3, 5\}$

Example 2

If $f: x \to x^2 - 1$, find the domain whose range is $\{0, 3\}$.

When $y = 0$, then
$$\begin{aligned} x^2 - 1 &= 0 \\ x^2 &= 1 \\ x &= +1 \text{ or } -1 \end{aligned}$$

When $y = 3$, then
$$\begin{aligned} x^2 - 1 &= 3 \\ x^2 &= 4 \\ x &= +2 \text{ or } -2 \end{aligned}$$

$\therefore$ domain is $\{-2, -1, 1, 2\}$.

Example 3

If $f(x) = x^2 - 1$, find $f(x-2)$.

$$\begin{aligned} f(x-2) &= (x-2)^2 - 1 \\ &= x^2 - 4x + 4 - 1 \\ &= x^2 - 4x + 3 \end{aligned}$$

If $f(x)$ maps A onto B and if there exists a function which maps B back onto A, this function is called the *inverse* of $f(x)$. It is written $f^{-1}(x)$.

Example 4

Find the inverse of $f(x) = 5x - 2$

Let $y = 5x - 2$. $\therefore\ y + 2 = 5x$, and $x = \dfrac{y+2}{5}$

$$\text{Hence} \quad f(y) = \frac{y+2}{5}$$

$$\therefore \quad f^{-1}(x) = \frac{x+2}{5}$$

If $f(x)$ and $g(x)$ are both functions, then the *composite* function fg is $f[g(x)]$.

Example 5

If $f(x) = 2x - 1$ and $g(x) = 3x + 2$, find:
(a) fg (b) gf (c) ff^{-1}

(a) $fg = f(3x+2) = 2(3x+2) - 1 = 6x - 3$

(b) $gf = g(2x-1) = 3(2x-1) + 2 = 6x - 1$

(c) $ff^{-1} = f\left(\dfrac{x+1}{2}\right) = 2\left(\dfrac{x+1}{2}\right) - 1 = x.$

Exercise 9.13

1. Give the type of relation which is produced by the following equations.
   (a) $y = 5x$ (b) $y = x^2 - 1$ (c) $y = x^3$ (d) $y^2 = 4ax$
   (e) $y^2 = x^6$ (f) $x + y = 1$ (g) $y = x^2 - 3x + 2$
   (h) $y^2 = 8x^2$ (i) $y^2 - 6x = y$ (j) $y = 2^x$
2. List the range for the domain $-2 \leqslant x \leqslant 2$ where x is an integer for each of the following.
   (a) $y = 4x - 1$ (b) $y = x^2$ (c) $y = 4x^2 - 1$ (d) $y^3 = 4x$
   (e) $y = x^3 - 4x$ (f) $y = 2^x$
3. In each of the following, find the domain for the given range.
   (a) $f: x \rightarrow 2x - 1$, range $\{0, 1, 2\}$ (b) $f: x \rightarrow x^3$, range $\{-8, -1, 0, 1, 8\}$
   (c) $f: x \rightarrow 2x + 3$, range $\{0, 3, 7\}$ (d) $f: x \rightarrow x^2 - 4$, range $\{5, 4, 3\}$
4. If $f(x) = x^2 - 3x + 2$, find the values of the following.

   (a) $f(0)$ (b) $f(3)$ (c) $f(x)$ (d) $f\left(\dfrac{1}{x}\right)$ (e) $f(x+1)$

5. Find the inverse of each of the following functions.
   (a) $f(x) = 3x + 1$ (b) $f(x) = \frac{x+1}{2}$ (c) $f(x) = \frac{2}{x}$
   (d) $f(x) = x^2 + 1$ (e) $f(x) = \sqrt{x+1}$ where x is a positive integer.
6. If $f(x) = x^2 - 1$ and $g(x) = x + 1$, find
   (a) fg (b) gf (c) $f^{-1}g^{-1}$ (d) $g^{-1}f^{-1}$ (e) $(gf)^{-1}$
   (f) f^2
   Does $(gf)^{-1}$ equal $g^{-1}f^{-1}$ or $f^{-1}g^{-1}$?
7. Find $f(x)$ for each of the following.
   (a) $f(1) = 3, f(2) = 5, f(3) = 7$ (b) $f(1) = 2, f(2) = 5, f(3) = 8$
   (c) $f(1) = 9, f(2) = 5, f(3) = 1$ (d) $f(1) = 1, f(2) = 4, f(3) = 9$
   (e) $f(1) = 2, f(2) = 4, f(3) = 8$
8. If $f(x) = \frac{x^2+1}{x}$, show that $f(m) = f\left(\frac{1}{m}\right)$.

9.14 Operations

A *binary* operation combines any pair of elements of a set into a single element; e.g. the addition of positive integers.

Example 1

If $a * b$ denotes $a^2 + b^2$, find $1{\cdot}5 * 3$.

$$\begin{aligned} 1{\cdot}5 * 3 &= 1{\cdot}5^2 + 3^2 \\ &= 2{\cdot}25 + 9 = 11{\cdot}25 \end{aligned}$$

Example 2

If $x \circ y$ denotes $x + y + xy$, find y if $6 \circ y = 20$.

$$\begin{aligned} 6 \circ y &= 6 + y + 6y \\ \therefore 20 &= 6 + y + 6y \\ 14 &= 7y \\ y &= 2 \end{aligned}$$

If a binary operation produces an element of the same set, then the set is called a *closed* set; e.g. {even numbers} under multiplication.

The operation is *associative* if for the set $\{a, b, c, \ldots\}$, $(a * b) * c = a * (b * c)$
e.g. $(3 \times 4) \times 5 = 3 \times (4 \times 5)$

There is an *identity* element I in the set if $a * I = I * a = a$
e.g. $3 + 0 = 0 + 3 = 3$

There is an *inverse* element a^{-1} in the set if $a * a^{-1} = a^{-1} * a = I$
e.g. $3 - 3 = -3 + 3 = 0$

The operation is *commutative* if $a * b = b * a$ for all a and b.
e.g. $3 \times 4 = 4 \times 3$

The table of a commutative operation is symmetrical about its leading diagonal (see below).

Example 3

A binary operation $*$ is defined by the following table.
(a) Is the operation commutative?
(b) Is the operation associative?
(c) Is the set closed?
(d) What is the identity element?
(e) What is the inverse of (i) 4 (ii) 8?

*	2	4	6	8
2	4	8	2	6
4	8	6	4	2
6	2	4	6	8
8	6	2	8	4

(a) The operation is commutative because
(i) $2 * 4 = 4 * 2 = 8$
(ii) $8 * 6 = 6 * 8 = 8$
(iii) $4 * 6 = 6 * 4 = 4$ etc.
The table is symmetrical about the diagonal 4, 6, 6, 4.

(b) The operation is associative because
(i) $(2 * 4) * 8 = 8 * 8 = 4$ and
(ii) $2 * (4 * 8) = 2 * 2 = 4$ so that $(2 * 4) * 8 = 2 * (4 * 8)$

(c) The set is closed under the operation $*$ because only the elements 2, 4, 6 and 8 appear on the table.

(d) The identity element is 6 because
(i) $4 * 6 = 4$ and (ii) $6 * 4 = 4$

(e) (i) The inverse of 4 is 4 because $4 * 4 = 6$ which is the identity element.
(ii) The inverse of 8 is 2 because $8 * 2 = 6$.

Exercise 9.14

1. If $S = \{\text{positive integers}\}$, state which of the following are closed operations, giving reasons in each case.
(a) multiplication (b) division (c) squaring a number
(d) finding the L.C.M.
2. If $a * b$ denotes $3a - 2b$, find:
(a) $2 * 3$ (b) $3 * 4$ (c) $2\frac{1}{3} * 4\frac{1}{2}$ (d) $(2 * 3) * 4$
(e) $(2\frac{1}{2} * 1\frac{1}{2}) * 4\frac{1}{2}$
3. If $x * y$ denotes $x^2 - 2xy + y^2$, find:
(a) $3 * 4$ (b) $1{\cdot}2 * 2{\cdot}5$ (c) $0{\cdot}6 * 0{\cdot}8$
Show that this operation is not associative.
4. If $m \circ n$ denotes $\dfrac{m^2 - n^2}{n}$, find:
(a) m when $m \circ 6 = 18$ (b) m when $m \circ \frac{1}{2} = \frac{5}{8}$
(c) n when $1{\cdot}2 \circ n = 0{\cdot}44$ (d) m when $m \circ n = n$.

5. If $x \triangle y$ denotes twice x divided by three times y, find a in terms of b when $a \triangle b = 3b \triangle a$.

6. A binary operation $\oplus$ is defined by the table shown.

(a) Is the operation (i) commutative?
(ii) associative?
(iii) closed?

(b) What is the identity element?

(c) State the inverse of (i) 2; (ii) 1.

$\oplus$	0	1	2	3
0	0	1	2	3
1	1	2	3	0
2	2	3	0	1
3	3	0	1	2

7. The combination table for a set of four elements $\{w, x, y, z\}$ under the operation $*$ is shown.

(a) State the identity element.

(b) What is the inverse of (i) w? (ii) z?

(c) Is the operation (i) closed?
(ii) commutative?
(iii) associative?

$*$	w	x	y	z
w	x	y	w	w
x	y	z	x	w
y	w	x	y	z
z	w	w	z	x

8. The binary operation $a * b$ denotes that for the product of a and b the units digit only is written down. Construct the operation table for the set $\{1, 3, 5, 7, 9\}$ under this operation.

(a) Is the operation (i) commutative?
(ii) associative?
(iii) closed?

(b) Is there an identity element?

9. Copy and complete the composition table shown for matrix multiplication using $\{\mathbf{P}, \mathbf{Q}, \mathbf{R}, \mathbf{S}\}$

where $\mathbf{P} = \begin{pmatrix} 1 & 0 \\ 0 & 1 \end{pmatrix}$; $\mathbf{Q} = \begin{pmatrix} -1 & 0 \\ 0 & -1 \end{pmatrix}$;

$\mathbf{R} = \begin{pmatrix} 0 & -1 \\ 1 & 0 \end{pmatrix}$; $\mathbf{S} = \begin{pmatrix} 0 & 1 \\ -1 & 0 \end{pmatrix}$

×	**P**	**Q**	**R**	**S**
P				
Q				
R				
S				

Write down (a) the identity element
(b) the inverse of each element.

10. A set of elements form a group if all the following conditions are fulfilled.

(a) closure (b) associativity (c) identity element
(d) inverse element

Do the following sets form a group? If so, give the identity element.

(i) {positive integers under addition}
(ii) {all rational numbers under multiplication}
(iii) {all 2×2 matrices under addition}
(iv) {all non-singular 2×2 matrices under multiplication}
(v) {all subsets of the universal set $\mathscr{E}$}

9.15 Statistics charts

The following table shows the number of non-fiction books in a school library.

Subject	Commerce	Geography	History	Languages	Mathematics	Science
Number	20	50	25	15	30	40

The representation of such data is far more effective when displayed pictorially.

Bar charts

In this type of display 'bars' are drawn of equal width; the area of each bar is proportional to the data. The bars can be drawn either horizontally or vertically.
Bar charts are used to show the comparative size of quantities.

Example 1

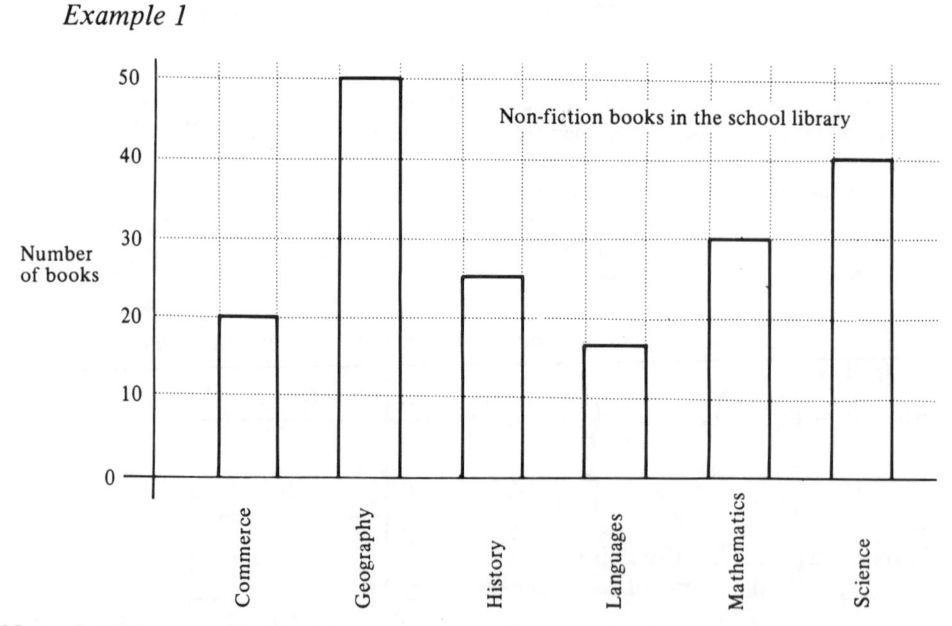

Note. In this example the bars are separated because the variables are discrete.

Pie charts

In such charts, the area of sectors of a circle represent the data.
Note. The sum of all the sector angles should be 360°.
Pie charts are used for comparing quantities relative to the whole.

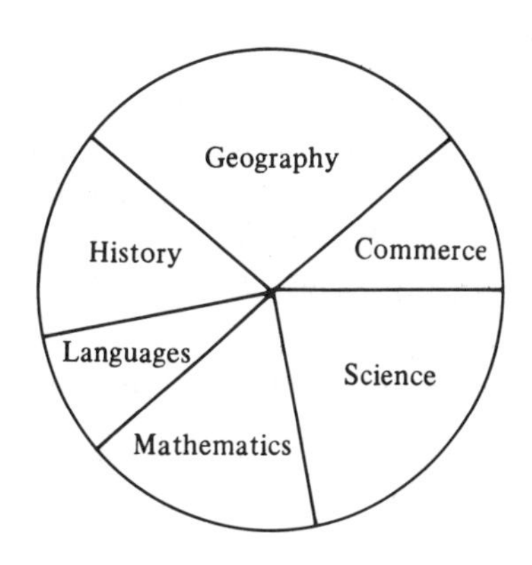

Calculation of angle of sector

Total number of books = 180

Commerce: $\frac{20}{180}$ of $360° = 40°$

Geography: $\frac{50}{180}$ of $360° = 100°$

and similarly for the other subjects.

Frequency distribution and histograms

The following are the test marks of a sample of 35 pupils:

1, 10, 5, 1, 4, 6, 4, 7, 9, 4, 2, 5, 5, 5, 4, 6, 3, 4, 5, 7, 8, 3, 6, 7, 9, 8, 5, 6, 3, 6, 8, 6, 6, 6, 7.

This data can be put in a frequency table by means of a tally chart, as shown.

Mark x	Tally	Frequency f	$f \times x$
1	11	2	2
2	1	1	2
3	1111	4	12
4	~~1111~~	5	20
5	~~1111~~ 1	6	30
6	~~1111~~ 11	7	42
7	1111	4	28
8	111	3	24
9	11	2	18
10	1	1	10
		35	188

This *frequency distribution* can then be represented by a *histogram*, as shown below. A histogram is similar to a bar chart except that adjacent bars are connected and different sized class intervals can be represented by the width of the rectangles.

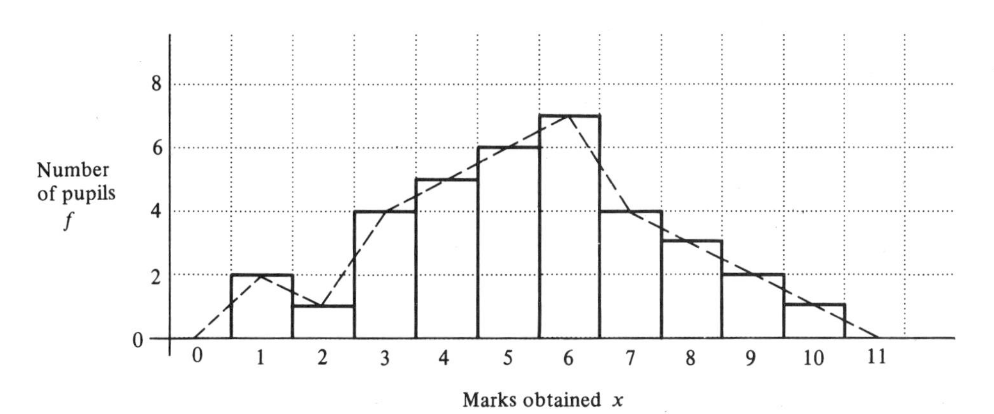

The dotted line shows the outline of the *frequency polygon*. A frequency polygon is formed by joining the mid-points of the tops of the rectangles and a space is left at each end to allow the polygon to be drawn down to the base line.
Note. Where the information covers a wide range the data may be grouped in suitable class intervals, e.g. 0–4, 5–9, etc.

The mean, median, and mode (see Section 1.9) are found as follows.

$$\text{Mean} = \frac{\text{sum of } (f \times x)}{\text{total frequency}} = \frac{188}{35} = 5{\cdot}4 \text{ (correct to 1 D.P.)}$$

$\text{Median} = \dfrac{n+1}{2}$ th item, i.e. the 18th mark in the sample of pupils and the 18th mark is 5.

Mode is the most frequently occurring mark, i.e. 6.

Exercise 9.15

1. Six hundred pupils were asked which of four subjects they preferred. The pie chart shows how they voted.
   (a) How many preferred Mathematics?
   (b) If 280 voted for 'Art and crafts', what is the sector angle?
   (c) If 15% preferred History, what is the sector angle?
   (d) Draw a bar chart to illustrate the data.

2. The table shows the number of books in a school library.

Subject	Mathematics	History	Geography	Science	Art	Languages	Fiction
Number	240	400	640	320	960	800	1440

   Illustrate this data (a) on a bar chart; (b) on a pie chart.

3. The cost of producing a radio programme is made up as follows.

Actors' fees	£10 000·00
Script writers' fees	£ 5 000·00
Production costs	£30 000·00
Musicians' fees	£12 500·00
Authors' royalties	£ 2 500·00

   Draw a pie chart to illustrate this information.

4. The production of edible oils in Nigeria is shown in the table.

Year	1949	1950	1951	1952	1953
Weight (tonne)	843	1283	2122	5684	7628

   Display these facts on a bar chart as accurately as you can.

5. The table shows the average distance from the Sun and the length of the year of the six nearer planets.

Planet	Mercury	Venus	Earth	Mars	Jupiter	Saturn
Average distance from Sun (km $\times 10^6$)	58	107	149	227	773	1417
Length of year	88 days	225 days	$365\frac{1}{4}$ days	687 days	11·86 years	29·5 years

Draw two bar charts to display each set of data. What do you notice about them?

6. The table shows the frequency of marks obtained in a class test.

Mark	1	2	3	4	5	6	7	8	9	10
Frequency	1	1	2	5	6	10	12	7	4	1

Display this information on a histogram and draw the frequency polygon.

7. The table shows monthly rainfall over a five-year period.

Rainfall (cm)	0–3	3–6	6–9	9–12	12–15	15–18	18–21	21–24
Frequency (months)	7	13	13	15	8	2	1	1

Display this information on a histogram and draw the frequency polygon.

8. The number of pupils in the various classes of five schools are as follows:

30 31 37 29 42 35 32 29 33 35 29 37 43 45 28 32
42 44 41 46 48 42 43 39 25 27 26 31 29 28 33 22
38 29 37 32 28 33 35 41

(a) Make a frequency table and display the information on a histogram.
(b) Find the mean, median, and mode of this data.

9. Make a frequency table of the following scores in a golf match and display the results on a histogram.

71 68 69 71 76 84 77 72 66 65 71 73 75 69 68 83
79 66 78 82 80 66 72 74 77

What is the mean score?

10. The following marks were obtained in an examination.
15 5 21 12 17 41 43 12 20 18 39 16 30 43 16
21 30 42 32 37 26 16 9 7 32 21 27 24 11 35

Make a frequency table for these marks, grouping them in class intervals of 5 (i.e. 0–4, 5–9, etc.) and display them on a histogram. Comment on your result.

11. The following marks (expressed as a percentage) were obtained in an examination.

31 10 41 21 35 79 85 26 43 39 52 48 64 73 41
57 67 42 37 55 76 8 57 71 99 53 33 100 63 72
22 15 61 45 53 48 42 24 56 47 83 54 78 17 75
32 66 82 23 34 64 47 63 88 58 54 59 62 31 68

(a) Make a frequency table of these marks, grouping them in class intervals of 10.
(b) Display the result on a histogram.
(c) If the pass mark was 40%, how many students failed? What percentage of students passed?

9.16 Scatter and cumulative frequency

The *range* is the difference between the largest and the smallest term.

The median divides the distribution into two equal portions. The median of the upper half is called the *upper quartile* and the median of the lower half is called the *lower quartile.*

The *interquartile range* is the difference between the upper and the lower quartiles. Often this measure of dispersion is halved to give the *semi-interquartile range* (S.I.R.).

The *mean deviation* is the average of the sum of all the differences (disregarding the sign) between each separate item and the median (or the mean).

Example 1

Find (a) the range, (b) the median, (c) the S.I.R., (d) the mean deviation from the median of the following set: {10, 15, 18, 17, 22, 15, 19, 11, 16, 13, 15}.

Arranged in ascending order, the numbers are 10, 11, 13, 15, 15, 15, 16, 17, 18, 19, 22.

(a) The range is $22 - 10 = 12$.

(b) The median of a set of n numbers is the $\left(\frac{n+1}{2}\right)$th term, i.e. $\frac{11+1}{2} = 6$.

The sixth term is 15, and this is the median.

(c) The upper quartile is the term $\frac{3(n+1)}{4}$.

Here $\frac{3(n+1)}{4} = \frac{3(11+1)}{4} = 9$ and the ninth term is 18.

The lower quartile is the term $\frac{n+1}{4}$.

Here $\frac{(n+1)}{4} = \frac{11+1}{4} = 3$ and the third term is 13.

$\therefore$ S.I.R. $= \frac{18-13}{2} = 2{\cdot}5.$

(d) Deviations from the median, ignoring signs, are 5, 4, 2, 0, 0, 0, 1, 2, 3, 4, 7. The sum of these deviations = 28

$\therefore$ mean deviation $= \frac{28}{11} = 2{\cdot}55$ (3 S.F.)

Example 2

Find (a) the median, (b) the S.I.R. of the following:

Mark	1	2	3	4	5	6	7	8	9	10
Frequency	2	1	3	5	6	8	4	3	2	1

Total frequency = 35.

So the median is given by the term $\dfrac{35+1}{2} = 18$, and this term is 6.

The upper quartile is given by the term $\dfrac{3(35+1)}{4} = 27$, and this term is 7.

The lower quartile is given by the term $\dfrac{(35+1)}{4} = 9$, and this term is 4.

$$\therefore \quad \text{S.I.R.} = \frac{7-4}{2} = 1{\cdot}5.$$

The above method can be tedious when a grouped frequency distribution is being considered, so the median and quartiles are often estimated from a *cumulative frequency* graph.

Example 3

The marks of 100 candidates in an examination were as follows.

Marks (%)	0–9	10–19	20–29	30–39	40–49	50–59	60–69	70–79	80–89	90–99
Frequency	2	3	5	7	13	15	20	17	13	5

Construct a cumulative frequency diagram, and from it estimate
(a) the median, (b) the S.I.R., (c) the pass mark if 32 candidates failed,
(d) the number of candidates who scored 33% or more.

Cumulative frequency table

less than 10 marks	2
less than 20 marks	5.
less than 30 marks	10
less than 40 marks	17
less than 50 marks	30
less than 60 marks	45
less than 70 marks	65
less than 80 marks	82
less than 90 marks	95
less than 100 marks	100

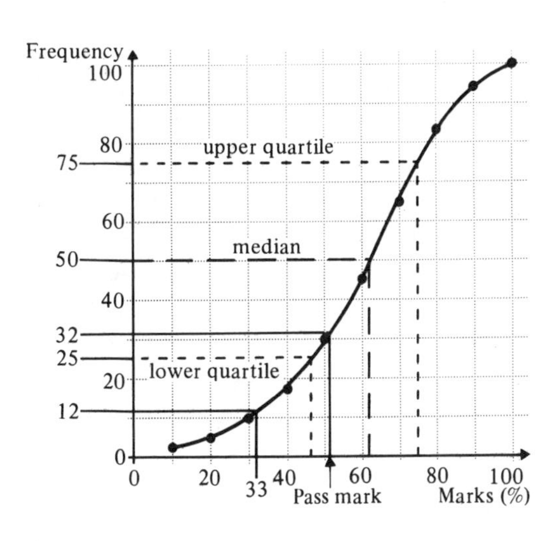

From the graph of cumulative frequency:
(a) median mark is 63.

(b) S.I.R. is $\frac{74-47}{2} = \frac{27}{2} = 13{\cdot}5.$

(c) If 32 candidates failed, the pass mark was 53%.
(d) The number of candidates who scored less than 33% was 12. So the number who scored 33% or more was 88.

Exercise 9.16

1. Find (i) the median, (ii) the S.I.R., of the following:

(a)

Mark	1	2	3	4	5	6	7	8	9	10
Frequency	1	2	2	5	6	10	12	7	4	1

(b)

Weight (g)	2·8	2·9	3·0	3·1	3·2	3·3	3·4	3·5	3·6
Frequency	1	1	6	6	7	5	2	1	1

(c)

Goals scored	0	1	2	3	4	5	6	7	8
No. of teams	19	36	23	10	8	0	1	0	2

(d)

Height (cm)	140	141	142	143	144	145	146	147	148
Frequency	4	2	7	9	14	9	5	4	6

(e)

Shoe size	1	2	3	4	5	6	7	8	9	10	11	12
Frequency	2	4	12	16	20	26	30	27	16	12	4	1

2. Find (i) the range, (ii) the median, (iii) the S.I.R., (iv) the mean, (v) the mean deviation from the mean, (vi) the mean deviation from the median.
(a) 11, 11, 11, 12, 12, 12, 12, 12, 12, 13, 14
(b) 21, 21, 22, 22, 22, 22, 23, 23, 30, 34
(c) 1, 2, 3, 7, 9, 2, 7, 11, 13
(d) 3, 5, 4, 5, 8, 5, 6, 5, 4, 5
(e) 102, 103, 104, 107, 105, 107, 103, 103, 110, 104, 109
(f) 46, 42, 38, 53, 46, 44, 50, 45, 39, 46, 45, 48, 41, 47

3. The following marks were obtained by 50 pupils in an examination.

Mark	0–4	5–9	10–14	15–19	20–24	25–29	30–34	35–39
Frequency	2	3	4	6	7	10	11	7

Construct a cumulative frequency diagram and from it estimate
(a) the median, (b) the S.I.R.
(c) the number of candidates who scored less than 23.

4. A sample of 150 people were asked to give the number of hours they watched BBC 1 during a given week. The results were as follows.

No. of hours	0–5	6–10	11–15	16–20	21–25	26–30	31–35	36–40
Frequency	2	8	17	52	38	26	5	2

Construct a cumulative frequency diagram and from it estimate
(a) the median,
(b) the percentage of people who watched 17 hours or more each week.

5. The following are the marks of 100 pupils in a French examination. Using class intervals 0–9, 10–19, etc., construct a frequency table and from it draw the cumulative frequency diagram. Then estimate:
(a) the median, (b) the S.I.R.,
(c) the number of candidates who passed the examination if the pass mark was 44.

2	14	32	16	44	50	62	86	12	18	24	20	8	20	22	14	32	32	20	60
36	82	84	46	30	64	70	94	10	68	18	35	62	27	82	20	86	60	54	14
34	3	38	85	12	35	29	20	24	32	55	13	16	24	5	18	39	38	20	11
47	7	15	20	4	12	12	49	5	53	46	44	12	10	38	39	24	93	57	87
85	50	45	69	43	49	66	76	66	12	99	83	1	65	44	45	75	68	39	81

9.17 Probability

The probability p of any one of m events occurring out of n equally probable events is $\frac{m}{n}$.
The probability of this event *not* occurring is $1 - \frac{m}{n}$.

Example 1

If a letter is chosen at random from the word MATHEMATICS, what is the probability that it is (a) a vowel, (b) not the letter T?
(a) number of vowels $m = 4$, i.e. A, A, E, I.

number of letters $n = 11$

$$\therefore p = \frac{4}{11}$$

(b) number of T's $m = 2$

$$\therefore p = 1 - \frac{2}{11} = \frac{9}{11}$$

Combined probabilities

1. *The addition rule*
If two events P and Q are mutually exclusive, i.e. they cannot happen at the same time, then

$$p\,(\text{P or Q}) = p\,(\text{P}) + p\,(\text{Q}).$$

Example 2

In a partly used box of paper tissues there are 12 purple, 15 green, 17 white, 10 yellow and 6 blue tissues. What is the probability that the last one is
(a) either blue or yellow? (b) not white?

(a) total number of tissues $= 60$

$$\therefore p\text{ (last one blue)} = \frac{6}{60}$$

and

$$p\text{ (last one yellow)} = \frac{10}{60}$$

$$\therefore p\text{ (last one blue or yellow)} = \frac{6}{60} + \frac{10}{60} = \frac{16}{60} = \frac{4}{15}$$

(b)

$$p\text{ (last one white)} = \frac{17}{60}$$

$$p\text{ (last one not white)} = 1 - \frac{17}{60} = \frac{43}{60}$$

2. *The multiplication rule*

If two events P and Q are independent of each other, i.e. one does not affect the other, then

$$p\text{ (P and Q)} = p\text{ (P)} \times p\text{ (Q)}$$

Example 3

The probability of a darts champion scoring 'treble 20' is $\frac{1}{4}$. If he throws three darts in succession, what is the probability that he scores
(a) at least one 'treble 20'? (b) exactly one 'treble 20'?

(a) p (first throw not 'treble 20') $= \frac{3}{4}$
p (second throw not 'treble 20') $= \frac{3}{4}$
p (third throw not 'treble 20') $= \frac{3}{4}$

$\therefore$ p (no 'treble 20') $= \frac{3}{4} \times \frac{3}{4} \times \frac{3}{4} = \frac{27}{64}$

$\therefore$ p ('treble 20') $= 1 - \frac{27}{64} = \frac{37}{64}$

(b) p (first throw 'treble 20') $= \frac{1}{4}$
p (second throw not 'treble 20') $= \frac{3}{4}$
p (third throw not 'treble 20') $= \frac{3}{4}$

$\therefore$ p (first one in, others not in) $= \frac{1}{4} \times \frac{3}{4} \times \frac{3}{4} = \frac{9}{64}$
Similarly p (second one in, others not in) $= \frac{3}{4} \times \frac{1}{4} \times \frac{3}{4} = \frac{9}{64}$
p (third one in, others not in) $= \frac{3}{4} \times \frac{3}{4} \times \frac{1}{4} = \frac{9}{64}$

$\therefore$ p (exactly one 'treble 20') $= \frac{9}{64} \times 3 = \frac{27}{64}$

Exercise 9.17

1. A number is selected at random from the set of numbers $\{1, 2, 3, 4, 5, 6, 7, 8, 9\}$. What is the probability that the number selected is
(a) even; (b) prime; (c) a square number; (d) divisible by 3;
(e) not divisible by 5; (f) 6 or more?

2. A box contains white balls and black balls. If the probability of choosing a white ball is $\frac{3}{7}$, what is the probability of choosing a black ball? If there are 28 black balls in the bag, how many balls are there altogether in the bag?
3. If two dice are thrown together, what is the probability of scoring
   (a) a total of exactly 5; (b) a total of less than 4; (c) a double;
   (d) a 3 on one die and a 5 on the other die?
4. Each of the letters of the word PROBABILITY are printed on a separate card and placed face downwards on a table.
   (a) If one card is chosen, what is the probability that
   (i) a vowel is printed on it? (ii) it is either a P or a B?
   (b) If two cards are picked together, what is the probability that they are both B's?
5. If two cards are drawn in succession from a pack of 52 cards, what is the probability of a Heart and a Spade being drawn?
6. A woman is selected for interview for two separate jobs. At the first interview there are 7 candidates and at the second there are 8. What is the probability that she is offered one or other of the jobs provided the chances of each candidate are equally likely?
7. A box contains 36 balls, 3 of which are painted blue. If 2 balls are taken from the box, what is the probability that at least one of them is blue?
8. The probability that a pupil in a school will have a red felt tip pen is $\frac{1}{6}$. If three pupils are selected at random, what is the probability of getting
   (a) no red pens? (b) at least one red pen? (c) three red pens?
9. What is the probability
   (a) that three successive tosses of a coin show Tails?
   (b) of scoring 5 from throwing three dice?
   (c) of throwing only one 6 if a dice is thrown four times in succession?
   (d) of being dealt four aces in succession from a pack of 52 cards (answer correct to 3 significant figures)?
10. A man writes six letters and addresses six envelopes. If the letters are picked up at random and placed in the envelopes, what is the probability that all the letters are placed in the correct envelopes?
11. In a survey of 220 pupils in a school it was found that 82 studied English, 82 studied French, 108 studied German, 20 studied both English and French, 30 studied both French and German, 34 studied both English and German, and 12 studied all three subjects.
    What is the probability that a pupil chosen at random
    (a) studied French only?
    (b) studied none of these three subjects?
12. A die is suspected of being unfair. It is thrown a sufficient number of times to establish that the numbers 1 and 6 occur with the same frequency, 2 and 5 with the same frequency but three times more often, and 3 and 4 with the same frequency but only half as often as 1 and 6.
    (a) Calculate the probability of each number being thrown.
    (b) If this die is thrown twice, calculate the probability of
    (i) 6 followed by 6
    (ii) 2 followed by an odd number
    (iii) 2 followed by an even number
    (iv) two odd numbers
    (v) a total of 4
    (vi) the total *not* being a triangular number

Miscellaneous exercise 9

1. In Octavia where the Octal system is always used, the ages of a family were 6_8, 10_8, 14_8, 21_8, 54_8, 56_8, 110_8 and 113_8 years respectively. Calculate their average age.
2. Copy each Venn diagram and shade the appropriate region.

(a) $A \cap B$

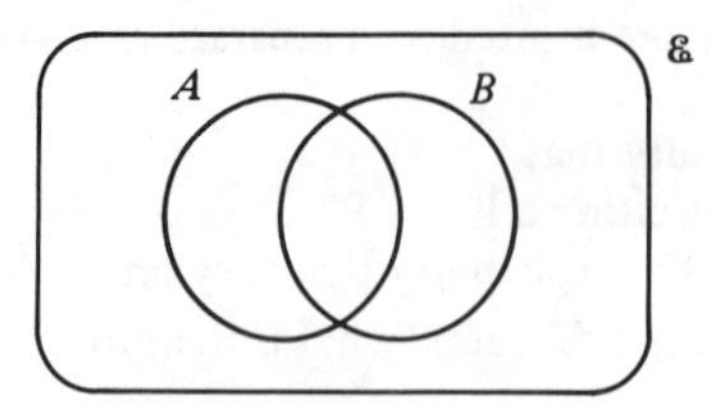

(b) $(A \cap B)'$

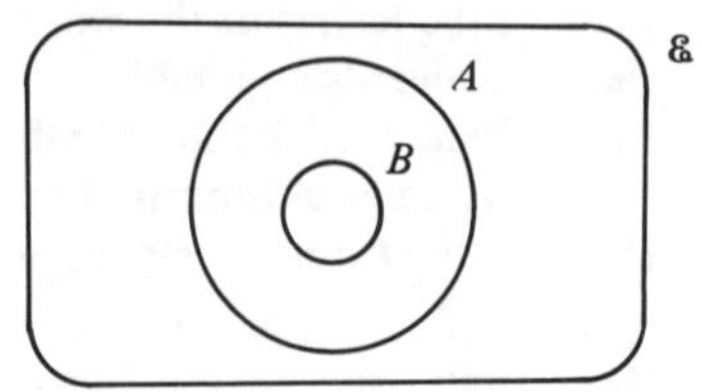

(c) $(A \cap B) \cup C$

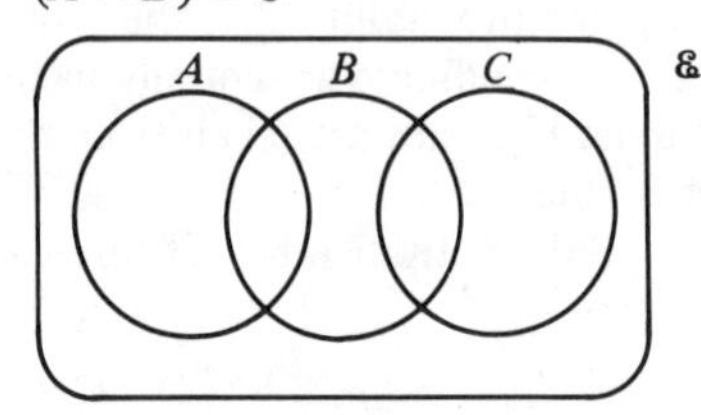

(d) $A' \cap B$

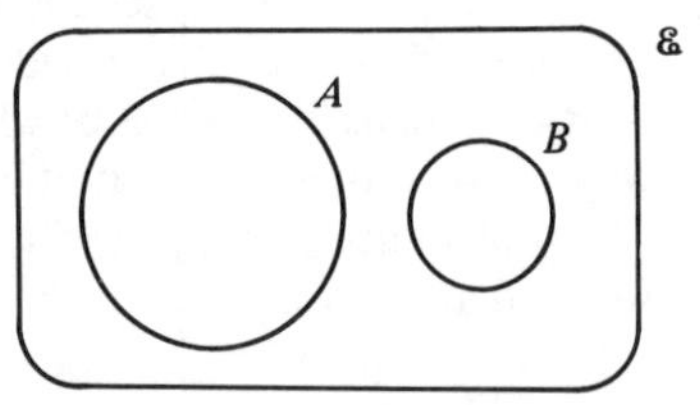

3. (a) If a man stopped at random was not born in a leap-year, what is the probability that
   (i) he was born on 1st January?
   (ii) he was born on the 31st of a month?
   (iii) his birthday was on a Monday or a Tuesday in 1978?

   (b) Two men are applying for a job. The first has a $\frac{3}{5}$ chance of being accepted and the second has a $\frac{1}{3}$ chance of being accepted. What is the probability that neither is accepted?
4. (a) Sketch the net of a regular octahedron.
   (b) Sketch the net of a pentagonal prism.
   (c) Sketch the solid formed by the net shown and name the solid. How many such solids are required to make a cube?

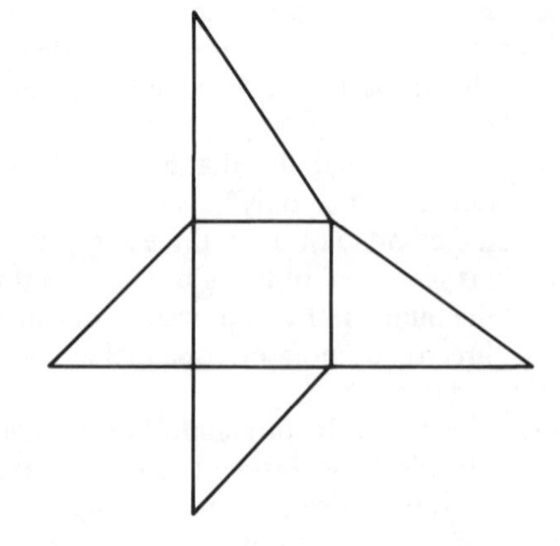

5. $\mathscr{E}$ = {positive real numbers}
$A = \{(x,y) : x - y \leqslant 10\}$
$B = \{(x,y) : x + y \leqslant 10\}$
$C = \{(x,y) : x^2 + y^2 \leqslant 100\}$
Draw graphs to illustrate the above inequalities and shade in the region which contains the set of points for which $(x,y) \in A \cap B \cap C$.

6. (a) In what number base is the calculation correct?
(i) $236 + 415 = 653$; (ii) $423 - 325 = 87$

(b) The equations below are written in base 2. Solve the equations, leaving your answer in base 2.
(i) $11x - 10y = 101$
$10x + y = 1000$
(ii) $x^{10} - 100x - 101 = 0$

7. (a) Plot the points A(2, 0), B(2, 2), C(3, 2), D(3, 1), E(4, 1) and F(4, 0).
(b) On the same graph plot the image $A_1B_1C_1D_1E_1F_1$ of ABCDEF after reflection in the line $x = 0$.
(c) On the same graph plot the image $A_2B_2C_2D_2E_2F_2$ of ABCDEF after reflection in the line $y = x$.
(d) What single transformation will map $A_1B_1C_1D_1E_1F_1$ on to $A_2B_2C_2D_2E_2F_2$?
(e) $A_3(0, -2)$, $B_3(-2, -2)$, $C_3(-2, -3)$, $D_3(-1, -3)$, $E_3(-1, -4)$, $F_3(0, -4)$ is another image of ABCDEF. What transformation will produce this image?

8. If $\mathscr{E}$ = {positive integers less than 10};
$A = \{1, 3, 5, 7, 9\}$;
$B = \{2, 3, 5, 7\}$;
$C = \{3, 6, 9\}$;
show that

$$n(A \cup B \cup C) = n(A) + n(B) + n(C) - n(A \cap B) - n(B \cap C) - n(C \cap A) + n(A \cap B \cap C)$$

9. OABC is a parallelogram, and X and Y are on the diagonal AC so that AX = YC. Prove by a vector method that OXBY is a parallelogram.

10. In each of the following Venn diagrams, describe the shaded area.

(a)
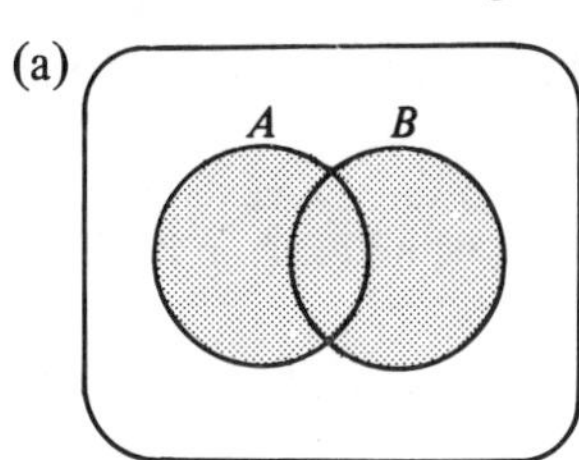

(b)
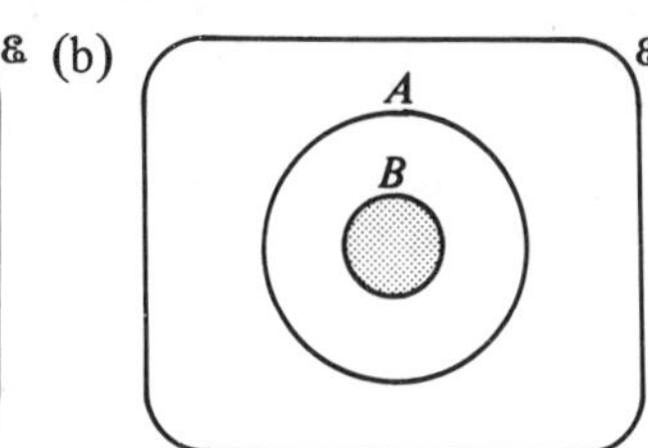

(c)
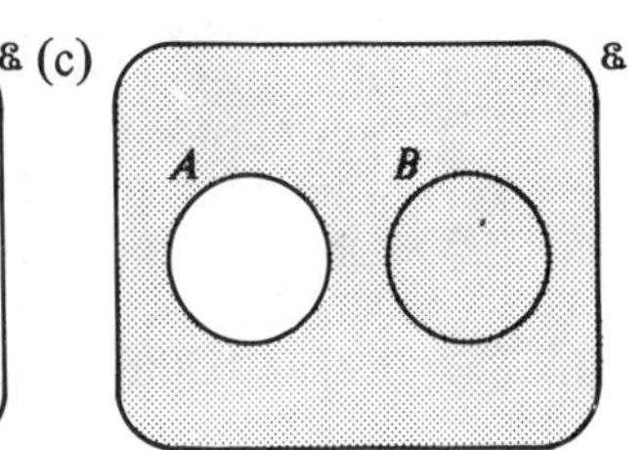

(d)
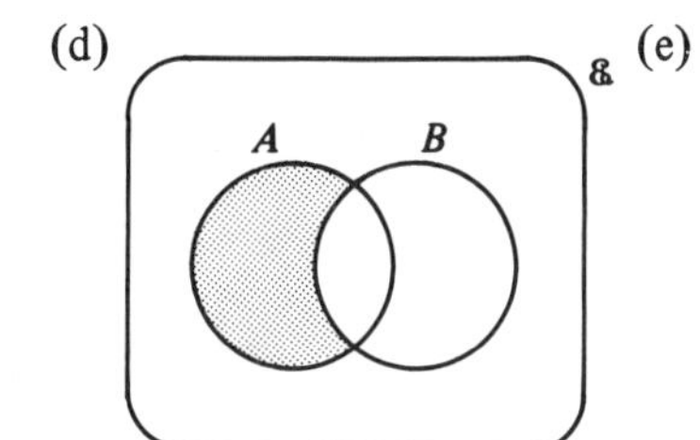

(e)
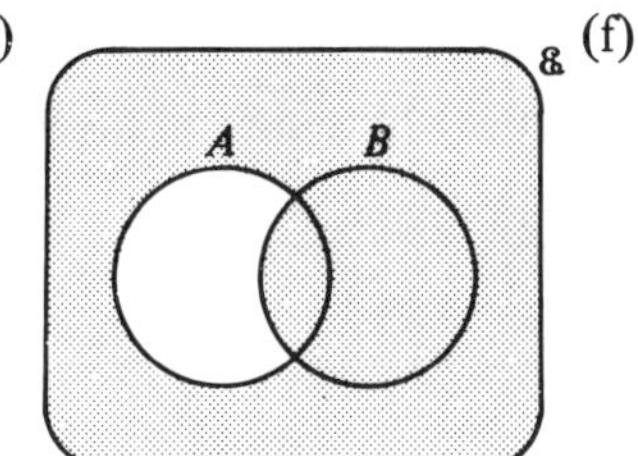

(f)
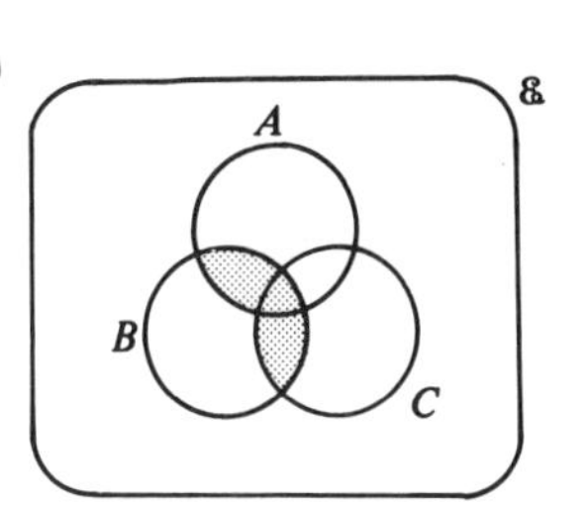

11.

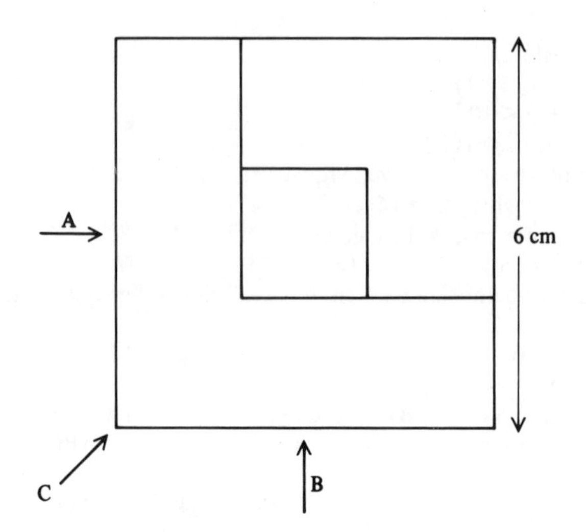

The figure is a plan of three cubes placed on top of each other.

(a) Draw full size
 (i) an elevation looking from the direction A;
 (ii) an elevation looking from the direction B.

(b) Sketch the solid from the direction C.

12. An insurance assessor is researching the incidence of traffic accidents in Bangaland. Before visiting one of four different places, he obtains the following information on the average numbers of days in August on which there is a car crash.

In Crushu there was a crash on 10 days of the month,
in Jami there was a crash on 13 days of the month,
in Safur there was a crash on 5 days of the month,
and in Walopu there was a crash on 12 days of the month.

(a) If he decides to go to Crushu, what is the probability that
 (i) there will be a crash on the day he arrives?
 (ii) there will be *no* crash on the day he arrives?

(b) If he goes to Jami, what is the probability there will be *no* crash on his birthday, 8th August?

(c) What is the probability that there will be a crash on two successive days in Safur?

(d) On 10th August what is the probability that there will be no crash in both Safur and Walopu?

13. (a) Calculate the coordinates of the images of the triangle A (2, 1), B (1, 2), C(2, 2) when transformed by the matrix $\begin{pmatrix} 0{\cdot}6 & -0{\cdot}8 \\ 0{\cdot}8 & 0{\cdot}6 \end{pmatrix}$.

(b) Describe the rotation.

(c) Give the matrix that would transform the image back onto ABC.

14. The functions f and g are as follows:

$f : x \rightarrow \frac{1}{x}$ $\qquad g : x \rightarrow 2x - 1$

(a) Find (i) fg (ii) gf (iii) $f^{-1}g$ (iv) fg^{-1}

(b) Sketch the graphs of these composite functions.

15. A tester estimates that 3% of all light bulbs are faulty. If this is true, what is the probability that in the first 100 bulbs he tests none are faulty? (Answer to 3 significant figures.)

16. V is the vertex of a rectangular based pyramid VABCD. If AB = DC = 8 cm and AD = BC = 6 cm, and each slant edge is 13 cm, draw (i) the plan and (ii) three elevations on vertical planes parallel to AB, BC and AC. From your drawings find
(a) the height of the pyramid
(b) the angle each face makes with the base.

17. The operation Δ is defined by $x \Delta y$ = the tens digit in the value of $(x + y)^2$.
(a) Construct the combination table to show the value of $x \Delta y$ where x and y are elements of $\{1, 3, 5, 7, 9\}$.
(b) Is the set closed under operation Δ?
(c) Is the operation commutative? Give a reason for your answer.
(d) Give examples to show whether the operation is associative or not.

18. (a) Fifteen articles are bought, some at 5p and some at 8p. If the total cost is more than 90p, what can you say about the number of articles bought at 8p?
(b) If x is added to the numerator and the denominator of the fraction $\frac{4}{7}$, the new fraction is greater than $\frac{7}{10}$. What can you say about the value of x?
(c) Two sides of a triangle of perimeter 100 cm differ by 12 cm. The other side is more than twice as long as the shortest side. What can you say about the length of the shortest side?

19. In an aptitude test it was found that the time taken for 200 candidates to answer one question ranged from 15 seconds to 3 minutes. The median time was 70 seconds and the S.I.R. was 25 seconds. Using this information plot a cumulative frequency curve and from it estimate the percentage of candidates who completed the test in less than 90 seconds.

20. In making a drive a man uses hard core and concrete. The lorry bringing these can carry a maximum load of 3 tonnes. The man decides that the mass of hard core will not be less than the mass of concrete used and not more than 2·5 times the mass of concrete used. Estimate
(a) the maximum mass of concrete he could use,
(b) the maximum mass of hard core he could use.

Answers

Part 1

Exercise 1.1 page 2

1. 36	**2.** 77	**3.** 161	**4.** 241	**5.** 418
6. 661	**7.** 1235	**8.** 2047	**9.** 1550	**10.** 2327
11. 25 468	**12.** 20 763	**13.** 169 841	**14.** 85 957	**15.** 96 016
16. 128 827	**17.** 167 629	**18.** 227 991	**19.** 182 795	**20.** 130 753
21. 14	**22.** 12	**23.** 2	**24.** 19	**25.** 112
26. 689	**27.** 61	**28.** 86	**29.** 263	**30.** 207
31. 89	**32.** 9	**33.** 89	**34.** 28	**35.** 368
36. 5	**37.** 1824	**38.** 2877	**39.** 2385	**40.** 588
41. 76	**42.** 168	**43.** 324	**44.** 656	**45.** 312
46. 630	**47.** 1932	**48.** 4140	**49.** 6552	**50.** 20 160
51. 62 212	**52.** 138 116	**53.** 142 911	**54.** 212 256	**55.** 87 885
56. 104 272	**57.** 1 019 392	**58.** 325 416	**59.** 450 042	**60.** 172 200
61. 84	**62.** 49	**63.** 81	**64.** 152	**65.** 154
66. 51	**67.** 92	**68.** 21	**69.** 34	**70.** 88
71. 184	**72.** 202	**73.** 21	**74.** 52	**75.** 48
76. 71	**77.** 2021	**78.** 2005	**79.** 3007	**80.** 1009
81. 20	**82.** 96	**83.** 0	**84.** 15	**85.** 14
86. 4	**87.** 28	**88.** 49	**89.** 128	**90.** 99
91. 69	**92.** 105	**93.** 12	**94.** 49	**95.** 7
96. 1	**97.** 10	**98.** 4	**99.** 1272	**100.** 72

Exercise 1.2a page 4

1. 4·14	**2.** 7·21	**3.** 101·3	**4.** 140·8	**5.** 69·16
6. 79·07	**7.** 225·42	**8.** 154·51	**9.** 977·22	**10.** 221·25
11. 2528·3	**12.** 2138·7	**13.** 1822·16	**14.** 1019·487	**15.** 2150·046
16. 1960·227	**17.** 0·263 986	**18.** 25·1765	**19.** 0·489 11	**20.** 0·4
21. 0·019	**22.** 0·869	**23.** 34·633	**24.** 80·99	**25.** 109·1
26. 0·181	**27.** 8·198	**28.** 14·1814	**29.** 212·07	**30.** 174·34
31. 0·113	**32.** 7600·8368	**33.** 65·016	**34.** 65·016	**35.** 1·479
36. 387·293	**37.** 0·004 826			

Exercise 1.2b page 5

1. (i) 63; 630 (ii) 80·4; 804 (iii) 6·1; 61 (iv) 0·37; 3·7 (v) 0·65; 6·5

2. 136	**3.** 10	**4.** 10	**5.** 1·26	**6.** 5·04
7. 0·0432	**8.** 5·12	**9.** 0·0504	**10.** 0·001 250 4	**11.** 10·571
12. 0·07488	**13.** 0·1413	**14.** 0·027 526 4	**15.** 0·956 15	**16.** 6·651 12
17. 10·517 62	**18.** 13·666 32	**19.** 0·993 708	**20.** 8·762 92	**21.** 0·000 085 739 1
22. 0·219 608 84		**23.** 9·067 622	**24.** 0·264 196 2	

Exercise 1.2c page 7

1. (i) 0·63; 0·063 (ii) 6·6; 0·66 (iii) 0·061; 0·0061 (iv) 0·0301; 0·003 01
(v) 176·429; 17·6429

2. 0·17 **3.** 0·0152 **4.** 0·104 **5.** 3·333 **6.** 3·3
7. 2·6 **8.** 15 **9.** 23·58 **10.** 68·42 **11.** 49·5
12. 57·03 **13.** 0·160 **14.** 0·70 **15.** 0·000 92 **16.** 2420
17. 12·9 **18.** 2·042 **19.** 10·4 **20.** 20 010 **21.** 0·09
22. 16 600 **23.** 19·8 **24.** 0·000 000 185

25. (a) $1{\cdot}86 \times 10^5$ (b) $6{\cdot}336 \times 10^4$ (c) $3{\cdot}1536 \times 10^7$ (d) $6{\cdot}2 \times 10^{-5}$
(e) 2×10^{-4} (f) $2{\cdot}13 \times 10^{-9}$

26. (a) 180 (b) 4520 (c) 869 000 (d) 0·018 (e) 0·004 52
(f) 0·000 0869

27. (a) $3{\cdot}69 \times 10^4$ (b) $1{\cdot}64 \times 10^{-3}$ (c) $2{\cdot}25 \times 10^8$

28. 431 **29.** £36·44 **30.** 39·6p

Exercise 1.3 page 10

1. $\frac{5}{6}$ **2.** $\frac{11}{12}$ **3.** $1\frac{11}{20}$ **4.** $1\frac{5}{24}$ **5.** $1\frac{2}{21}$
6. $\frac{32}{45}$ **7.** $\frac{71}{88}$ **8.** $\frac{19}{26}$ **9.** $4\frac{7}{36}$ **10.** $5\frac{7}{16}$
11. $6\frac{2}{3}$ **12.** $3\frac{11}{24}$ **13.** $12\frac{1}{3}$ **14.** $6\frac{11}{24}$ **15.** $6\frac{71}{150}$
16. $8\frac{19}{42}$ **17.** $7\frac{13}{36}$ **18.** $6\frac{29}{48}$ **19.** $6\frac{45}{56}$ **20.** $8\frac{19}{72}$
21. $\frac{7}{12}$ **22.** $\frac{1}{30}$ **23.** $1\frac{1}{16}$ **24.** $\frac{17}{18}$ **25.** $1\frac{19}{24}$
26. $3\frac{29}{42}$ **27.** $\frac{11}{12}$ **28.** $\frac{131}{150}$ **29.** $2\frac{25}{48}$ **30.** $5\frac{3}{56}$
31. $\frac{3}{4}$ **32.** 1 **33.** $\frac{5}{7}$ **34.** $\frac{1}{3}$ **35.** $3\frac{1}{2}$
36. $6\frac{1}{2}$ **37.** 16 **38.** 9 **39.** $8\frac{5}{9}$ **40.** $6\frac{3}{7}$
41. $1\frac{1}{2}$ **42.** $\frac{2}{3}$ **43.** $\frac{1}{6}$ **44.** $\frac{8}{15}$ **45.** $1\frac{3}{5}$
46. $2\frac{2}{3}$ **47.** $\frac{4}{9}$ **48.** $\frac{3}{4}$ **49.** $8\frac{5}{9}$ **50.** $\frac{1}{12}$
51. $\frac{3}{4}$ **52.** $\frac{7}{8}$ **53.** $\frac{9}{16}$ **54.** 1 **55.** $1\frac{13}{35}$
56. $1\frac{4}{5}$ **57.** $1\frac{27}{59}$ **58.** $3\frac{19}{24}$ **59.** $3\frac{1}{9}$ **60.** $\frac{2}{9}$
61. 0·625 **62.** 0·6 **63.** 0·05 **64.** 0·313 **65.** 0·094
66. 0·719 **67.** 0·12 **68.** 0·76 **69.** 0·34 **70.** 0·525
71. 0·636 **72.** 0·667 **73.** 0·833 **74.** 0·294 **75.** 0·308
76. $\frac{1}{8}$ **77.** $\frac{7}{8}$ **78.** $\frac{3}{20}$ **79.** $\frac{17}{20}$ **80.** $\frac{1}{20}$
81. $\frac{1}{500}$ **82.** $\frac{9}{16}$ **83.** $\frac{147}{200}$ **84.** $\frac{421}{500}$ **85.** $\frac{213}{2000}$
86. $\frac{20}{29}$ **87.** 33 **88.** 32p **89.** £26·10 **90.** 11 250 litres

91. (a) 3·142 857; greater by 0·001 264 **92.** 0·000 0028 π
(b) 3·141 667; greater by 0·000 074
(c) 3·141 593; the same

93. (a) $\frac{185}{300}$ (b) 0·617 (c) $6{\cdot}17 \times 10^{-1}$ **94.** 126 **95.** 585

Exercise 1.4 page 13

1. $\frac{3}{4}$; 3 : 4 **2.** $\frac{2}{3}$; 2 : 3 **3.** $\frac{6}{5}$; 6 : 5 **4.** $\frac{9}{4}$; 9 : 4
5. $\frac{2}{15}$; 2 : 15 **6.** $\frac{5}{2}$; 5 : 2 **7.** $\frac{3}{1}$; 3 : 1 **8.** $\frac{9}{2}$; 9 : 2
9. $\frac{9}{7}$; 9 : 7 **10.** $\frac{3}{40}$; 3 : 40

11. 1·33 : 1; 1·5 : 1; 2nd **12.** 1·25 : 1; 1·19 : 1; 1st
13. 4·5 : 1; 4 : 1; 1st **14.** 2·5 : 1; 3 : 1; 2nd
15. 4·67 : 1; 3·2 : 1; 1st **16.** 5·1 : 1; 5·67 : 1; 2nd
17. 24:1; 28 : 1; 2nd **18.** 24 **19.** 12

20. 27
21. 12
22. £13·50
23. 4 : 3
24. 5 : 3
25. 1 : 6
26. 17 : 18
27. 13 : 9 13 : 22
28. 7 : 20
29. 6 : 5
30. 7 : 15
31. 533·3 g
32. 15·6 km
33. 11 hours 40 minutes
34. 68p
35. £27·50
36. £6·18
37. £18
38. 2850; 3000
39. £8·80
40. £2000; £3000; £5000

Exercise 1.5 page 15

1. 50%; 25%; 75%
2. $33\frac{1}{3}$%; $66\frac{2}{3}$%
3. 20%; 40%; 60%; 80%
4. $16\frac{2}{3}$%; $83\frac{1}{3}$%
5. $14\frac{2}{7}$%; $42\frac{6}{7}$%; $71\frac{3}{7}$%
6. $12\frac{1}{2}$%; $37\frac{1}{2}$%; $62\frac{1}{2}$%; $87\frac{1}{2}$%
7. $11\frac{1}{9}$%; $55\frac{5}{9}$%; $77\frac{7}{9}$%
8. $9\frac{1}{11}$%; $27\frac{3}{11}$%; $63\frac{7}{11}$%
9. $23\frac{1}{13}$%; $46\frac{2}{3}$%
10. $13\frac{1}{23}$%; $58\frac{18}{29}$%
11. 65%; 25%
12. 2%; 9%
13. 12·5%; 45·5%
14. 0·25%; 0·75%
15. 132·5%; 467·5%
16. $\frac{1}{20}$; $\frac{1}{10}$; $\frac{4}{5}$
17. $\frac{3}{25}$; $\frac{9}{50}$; $\frac{12}{25}$
18. $\frac{1}{3}$; $\frac{61}{75}$
19. $1\frac{1}{4}$; $1\frac{2}{7}$
20. $\frac{1}{15}$; $\frac{23}{160}$
21. 0·75; 0·83
22. 0·06; 0·01
23. 0·125; 0·875
24. 0·0625; 0·0375
25. 1·36, 6·185
26. 15p
27. 3·45 g
28. 15·04 m
29. 25·9 min
30. 28·7 km/h
31. 54p
32. £1·40
33. 1·76 m
34. 81·25 m
35. £36·24
36. 20%
37. $37\frac{1}{2}$%
38. $85\frac{5}{12}$%
39. $215\frac{5}{13}$%
40. $158\frac{8}{9}$%
41. $13\frac{1}{3}$%
42. $117\frac{11}{17}$%
43. $31\frac{3}{7}$%
44. $\frac{4}{35}$%
45. $\frac{23}{100}$%
46. £975
47. 138
48. $46\frac{2}{3}$% yes
49. £840
50. 20 000

Exercise 1.6 page 17

1. $3\frac{1}{3}$%
2. $4\frac{6}{11}$%
3. 12%
4. $2\frac{1}{2}$%
5. $\frac{5}{6}$%
6. 30%
7. 50%
8. 8%
9. $14\frac{2}{7}$%
10. $16\frac{2}{3}$%
11. £21·80
12. 35p
13. £81
14. £69
15. £106·25
16. £2812·50
17. £23·72$\frac{1}{2}$
18. £22·77
19. £12·50
20. £20
21. £200
22. £52·50
23. £90
24. £400
25. £64
26. £25
27. £25
28. £66·67
29. £2·88
30. £80
31. 25%
32. £625
33. 32%
34. 35·85%
35. £99·75

Exercise 1.7 page 18

1. £6; £106
2. £12; £212
3. £48; £448
4. £60; £560
5. £105; £805
6. £18; £168
7. £20; £220
8. £26·25; £276·25
9. £11·25; £136·25
10. £19·50; £149·50
11. £2·30
12. £13·86
13. £11·34
14. £8·91
15. £24·96
16. £7·65
17. £651·95
18. £419·06
19. £1332·77
20. £979·21
21. £109; 3%
22. £100; £112
23. £200; $13\frac{1}{3}$ years
24. £140; $8\frac{1}{3}$ years
25. £1081; 1·8%
26. £17; 6 months
27. £765; £867
28. £105; $3\frac{1}{2}$%
29. £726; $3\frac{1}{2}$ years
30. £200·80; 20 months
31. £48
32. £538·20
33. $33\frac{1}{3}$%
34. £12·50
35. £10
36. £3600
37. $2\frac{1}{2}$ years
38. £19 000
39. £551·25
40. £20 108

Exercise 1.8 page 21

1.	£18·45	**2.**	£26·22	**3.**	£8·22	**4.**	£11·34
5.	£178·06	**6.**	£304·92	**7.**	£116·60	**8.**	£80·24
9.	£16·11	**10.**	£12·64	**11.**	£127·90	**12.**	£162·90
13.	£124·70	**14.**	£274·60	**15.**	£251·70	**16.**	£3097
17.	£401	**18.**	£1352	**19.**	£1787	**20.**	£2475
21.	£847·80	**22.**	£10 830	**23.**	14 years	**24.**	10 years
25.	4·6%	**26.**	£4	**27.**	£1126	**28.**	18 years
29.	(a) 10% (b) £720			**30.**	(a) £1228·25		(b) £2000

Exercise 1.9 page 23

1. (a) 6 (b) 20·4 (c) 7·14 g (d) 33 h 36 min (e) 18°40′24″

2.	£6·25	**3.**	6·25 seconds	**4.**	24 runs	**5.**	£4·87
6.	22·2p	**7.**	13	**8.**	61 kg	**9.**	13·5 km/h
10.	1·92 km/h	**11.**	68 km/h	**12.**	90 km/h	**13.**	40 km/h, 46 km/h
14.	2, 2, 2	**15.**	4, 2, 2	**16.**	6·1, 2 *or* 7, 7	**17.**	5, 5, 5
18.	22, 12, 13·5	**19.**	5·2, 3, 4	**20.**	23, 21, 22·5	**21.**	3, 3, 3
22.	85, 86, 85·5						

Exercise 1.10 page 24

1.	(a)	400	(b)	3600	(c)	250 000	(d)	0·04	(e)	0·0144
	(f)	900	(g)	8100	(h)	490 000	(i)	0·36	(j)	1·21
	(k)	1600	(l)	14 400	(m)	640 000	(n)	0·0049	(o)	6·25
2.	(a)	4	(b)	0·5	(c)	20	(d)	0·8	(e)	0·06
	(f)	7	(g)	0·3	(h)	30	(i)	1·2	(j)	0·03
	(k)	9	(l)	0·1	(m)	60	(n)	1·3	(o)	0·01
3.	(a)	0·2	(b)	0·25	(c)	0·125	(d)	2	(e)	$0{\cdot}\dot{4}\dot{5}$ or $\frac{5}{11}$
	(f)	0·1	(g)	0·01	(h)	2	(i)	4	(j)	100
	(k)	0·05	(l)	0·001	(m)	10	(n)	8	(o)	1 000 000
4.	(a)	361	(b)	5776	(c)	7056	(d)	14 880	(e)	147 500
	(f)	674 000	(g)	11·9	(h)	34·46	(i)	1584	(j)	145 500
	(k)	683 800	(l)	0·2109	(m)	1925	(n)	1·869	(o)	0·000 031 36
	(p)	0·011 28	(q)	9 624 000 000			(r)	0·003 695		
5.	(a)	1·095	(b)	2·516	(c)	2·89	(d)	1·614	(e)	2·332
	(f)	2·892	(g)	3·873	(h)	8·485	(i)	6·066	(j)	9·262
	(k)	4·739	(l)	7·937	(m)	112·6	(n)	69·44	(o)	28·65
	(p)	0·9452	(q)	0·2608	(r)	0·028 75				
6.	(a)	0·2941	(b)	0·012 99	(c)	0·001 449	(d)	0·001 214	(e)	0·000 144
	(f)	0·007 576	(g)	0·012 28	(h)	12·62	(i)	0·1451	(j)	259
	(k)	0·000 116	(l)	0·000 027 08			(m)	218·5	(n)	0·000 012 56
	(o)	0·6272	(p)	0·003 763	(q)	5·577	(r)	1·218		
7.	(a)	0·6421	(b)	0·015 64	(c)	32·492	(d)	·009 94	(e)	0·033 08

8. 0·1682 **9.** 0·1101 **10.** 20·46

Exercise 1.11 page 27

1.	1944	**2.**	3675	**3.**	391 600	**4.**	22 400
5.	82·15	**6.**	5328	**7.**	236·3	**8.**	415·2
9.	2792	**10.**	1·394	**11.**	1·423	**12.**	1·729
13.	1·914	**14.**	1·080	**15.**	1·014	**16.**	1·032
17.	1·171	**18.**	1·662	**19.**	111·3	**20.**	41 340 000
21.	99·31	**22.**	3·198	**23.**	34·33	**24.**	4·979
25.	2·871	**26.**	8·277	**27.**	9·995	**28.**	19·75
29.	27·34	**30.**	1·391	**31.**	80·56	**32.**	4·434
33.	131·1	**34.**	0·2474	**35.**	6·059	**36.**	1·589
37.	7·138	**38.**	1·554	**39.**	5·542	**40.**	0·5306
41.	19·82	**42.**	0·6394	**43.**	0·8664	**44.**	16·56
45.	15·88	**46.**	68·14	**47.**	0·049 26	**48.**	0·016 15
49.	0·010 66	**50.**	14·78	**51.**	0·012 58	**52.**	0·2085
53.	0·000 026 38	**54.**	0·2055	**55.**	0·2595	**56.**	0·3075
57.	0·2095	**58.**	0·9351	**59.**	0·6624	**60.**	0·8907
61.	0·9164	**62.**	0·4585	**63.**	0·2865	**64.**	0·6236
65.	0·004 981	**66.**	0·7208	**67.**	16·1	**68.**	0·005 463
69.	4·643	**70.**	0·4403				

Exercise 1.12a page 28

1. £171 **2.** £1·12 **3.** £88·40 **4.** £225·60; £40·80
5. £12 less **6.** 20p; £14 **7.** 2p; £3·50 **8.** £58 462
9. £1 349 600; £45·92 **10.** £48 280; £2 188 235

Exercise 1.12b page 29

1. £508·20 **2.** £1061·67 **3.** £375 **4.** £30
5. £3534·30 **6.** (a) £1523·20 (b) 26·34% (c) £6330
7. (a) £38·10 (b) 29·46%

Exercise 1.13 page 31

1. (a) Fr 164·92 (b) M $ 74·85 (c) ₦ 28·14 (d) C $ 4169·44
(e) Y 791 552 (f) HK $ 170·72 (g) US $ 61·78 (h) DM 99·05

2. (a) £26 (b) £783·41 (c) £1369·05 (d) £5833·33
(e) £66·67 (f) £937·50 (g) £21·82 (h) £613·64
(i) £434·26 (j) £113·12

3. (a) $11\frac{1}{2}$p (b) $55\frac{1}{2}$p (c) 0·2p (d) 23p
(e) $11\frac{1}{2}$p (f) 22p (g) $22\frac{1}{2}$p (h) $47\frac{1}{2}$p
(i) $59\frac{1}{2}$p (j) $1\frac{1}{2}$p (k) 57p (l) 2p

4. 19p **5.** ₦ 4·32 **6.** £180·70 **7.** £10·75
8. US $ 603·41 **9.** (a) 500·6 (b) 55·18
10. England by $65\frac{1}{2}$p per kg. **11.** 12 900 rupees
12. £350 **13.** 50 francs

Miscellaneous exercise 1 page 32

1. (a) 1·165 (b) $\frac{3}{8}$ (c) 385 000 mm (d) 0·39
2. 8%
3. $2\frac{2}{11}$
4. £2·75
5. (a) 40 (b) 0·0525
6. 52·8 km
7. 3·5p
8. £865
9. 24p less
10. (a) 454 (b) £1·13
11. (a) £443·22 (b) £299·60 (c) 3 years (d) £1109
12. $33\frac{1}{3}$%
13. 24%
14. 60·2
15. 15·2%
16. (a) £12 600, £7800 (b) £16 170
17. 53p
18. $3·97 \times 10^7$ km
19. (a) £33 (b) £11 (c) £8·10
20. 2·665 seconds past noon

Part 2

Exercise 2.1 page 35

1. (a) 4 cm^2; 8 cm (b) 36 cm^2; 24 cm (c) 72·25 cm^2; 34 cm (d) 392 cm^2; 79·2 cm
2. (a) 24 cm^2; 20 cm (b) 96 cm^2; 40 cm (c) 76 cm^2; 35 cm (d) 16·25 cm^2; 18 cm
3. (a) 80 cm^2 (b) 115 cm^2 (c) 143 cm^2 (d) 104 cm^2 (e) $132\frac{1}{2}$ cm^2 (f) 77 cm^2
4. 34 m^2
5. 44 800
6. 400; 2400 cm^2
7. (a) 135 cm^2 (b) 78·75 cm^2 (c) 26·53 cm^2 (d) 19·53 cm^2
8. (a) 48 cm^2 (b) 108 cm^2 (c) 24 cm^2 (d) 26·64 cm^2
9. (a) 15 cm^2 (b) 52·5 cm^2 (c) 30 cm^2 (d) 208·6 cm^2

Exercise 2.2 page 36

1. (a) 27 cm^3 (b) 512 cm^3 (c) 6859 cm^3 (d) 592 700 cm^3
2. (a) 24 cm^3 (b) 360 cm^3 (c) 6783 cm^3 (d) 170·75 cm^3
3. (a) 36 cm^3 (b) 360 cm^3 (c) 492·8 cm^3 (d) 20·09 cm^3
4. 230·5 cm^3
5. 92·2 g
6. 1169 cm^3; 584·5 g
7. 0·16 m^3
8. 175·5 g
9. 0·192 cm
10. 30 minutes; 1 hour
11. 3·8 m^3
12. 320 m
13. 1335 g
14. (a) 1 : 4 (b) 1 : 8 (c) 1 : 4
15. 316 cm^3
16. 23·8%; no
17. 450 m^3
18. 39 m^2
19. 1266 cm^2
20. £22·80

Exercise 2.3a page 39

1. 44 cm; 154 cm^2
2. 176 cm; 2464 cm^2
3. 62·86 cm; 314·2 cm^2
4. 123·2 cm; 1208 cm^2
5. 6·675 cm; 3·545 cm^2
6. 1·75 cm
7. 15·75 cm
8. 16·55 cm
9. 1·315 cm
10. 0·1295 cm
11. 1386 cm^3; 396 cm^2
12. 1232 cm^3; 176 cm^2
13. 1273 cm^3; 282·8 cm^2
14. 27·79 cm^3; 33·48 cm^2
15. 17 510 cm^3; 1892 cm^2

Exercise 2.3b page 40

1. $47{\cdot}13\text{ cm}^2$ 2. $82{\cdot}5\text{ cm}^2$ 3. $125{\cdot}7\text{ cm}^2$ 4. $117{\cdot}9\text{ cm}^2$
5. $357{\cdot}5\text{ cm}^2$ 6. $70\,700\text{ cm}^3$ 7. 6183 cm^3 8. 6267 cm^3
9. $69{\cdot}14\text{ cm}^3$ 10. 1709 cm^3
11. 803·9 kg; 70·3 kg; 71·27 kg; 786·1 g; 19·43 kg

Exercise 2.3c page 41

1. 11·58 revs per second 2. 440 m/s 3. 414 cm; 9864 cm^2
4. 704 cm^2 5. 176 cm 6. 45·25 cm 7. $2\frac{2}{3}\%$
8. $67\,490\text{ m}^2$; 4 382 000 9. 2·309 cm 10. 1 minute
11. 365 kg 12. 3·464 cm 13. 188·5 litres 14. 28·3 s
15. 2·828 litres 16. 14 140 l/h 17. 29·47 m/s 18. 1·33 m/s
19. 1·415 m/s 20. 28·29 km/h

Exercise 2.4 page 43

1. (a) 2·75 cm; $4{\cdot}813\text{ cm}^2$ (b) 7·333 cm; $25{\cdot}67\text{ cm}^2$ (c) 2·689 cm; $1{\cdot}882\text{ cm}^2$
(d) 2·64 cm; $8{\cdot}316\text{ cm}^2$ (e) 82·5 cm; $866{\cdot}3\text{ cm}^2$
2. (a) 3·5 cm (b) 5·576 cm (c) 4·5 cm (d) 1·8 cm (e) 67·5 cm
3. (a) $1{\cdot}417\text{ cm}^2$ (b) $8{\cdot}748\text{ cm}^2$ (c) $2{\cdot}59\text{ cm}^2$ (d) $1{\cdot}708\text{ cm}^2$ (e) $17{\cdot}54\text{ cm}^2$
4. (a) 1·571 cm (b) 5·5 cm (c) 11·79 cm (d) 28·29 cm (e) 226·3 cm
5. (a) $77°20'$ (b) $324°38'$

Exercise 2.5 page 45

1. 128 cm^3 2. 50 cm^3 3. 70 cm^3 4. 8 cm^3
5. 36 cm^3 6. 3 cm 7. 120 cm^2 8. 96 cm^2

Exercise 2.6 page 47

1. 21 cm^3 2. $754{\cdot}1\text{ cm}^3$ 3. $25\frac{2}{3}\text{ m}^3$ 4. 35 cm^3
5. 3490 cm^3 6. $150{\cdot}8\text{ cm}^2$ 7. 704 cm^2 8. $47{\cdot}13\text{ cm}^2$
9. $188{\cdot}5\text{ cm}^2$ 10.. $204{\cdot}2\text{ cm}^2$ 11. 800 12. 90 000
13. $23\,570\text{ cm}^3$ 14. 10·61 cm 15. 10 cm

Exercise 2.7 page 48

1. (a) $523{\cdot}7\text{ cm}^3$; $314{\cdot}2\text{ cm}^2$ (b) $998{\cdot}4\text{ cm}^3$; $483{\cdot}1\text{ cm}^2$
(c) $25{\cdot}68\text{ m}^3$; $42{\cdot}09\text{ m}^2$ (d) $0{\cdot}3029\text{ m}^3$; $2{\cdot}181\text{ m}^2$
2. 9·12 cm 3. 4·593 cm 4. $142{\cdot}5\text{ cm}^3$ 5. 1·723 cm
6. $\frac{1}{3}$ mm 7. 2121 cm^2 8. $0{\cdot}7855\text{ m}^3$; $4{\cdot}81\text{ m}^2$
9. 37·04 cm 10. 4·102 : 1; 16·83 : 1 11. 22·63 : 1
12. (a) 28·13% (b) 3 : 8 13. (a) 7595 m^3 (b) $7{\cdot}595\text{ m}^3$
14. 20 370 15. (a) $25\,166\text{ cm}^3$ (b) 52·38%; 809 boxes

Exercise 2.8 page 51

1. (a) $\frac{1}{10\,000}$ (b) $\frac{1}{50\,000}$ (c) $\frac{1}{63\,360}$ (d) $\frac{1}{150\,000}$ (e) $\frac{1}{9}$
2. (a) 1 km (b) 0·7 km (c) 4·65 km (d) 3·07 km (e) 3·635 km
3. (a) 5 cm (b) 3·125 cm (c) 4·2 cm (d) 0·485 cm
4. (a) 0·25 km^2 (b) 0·4 km^2 (c) 6·25 km^2 (d) 25 km^2 (e) 350 km^2
5. (a) 25 cm^2 (b) 42·2 cm^2 (c) 288·9 cm^2 (d) 58·4 cm^2 (e) 76·4 cm^2
6. (a) 5°44′ (b) 14°29′ (c) 8°13′ (d) 3°49′ (e) 16°36′
7. (a) 1 : 10·05; 5°43′ (b) 1 : 20·02; 2°52′
   (c) 1 : 4·123; 14°2′ (d) 1 : 7·566; 7°36′
   (e) 1 : 34·01; 1°41′
8. £750 000 9. 15·87 m 10. 0·6789 km^2

Exercise 2.9 page 54

1. (a) 1787 km (b) 3575 km (c) 7358 km (d) 6380 km
2. (a) 4114 km (b) 4902 km (c) 3762 km (d) 668·8 km (e) 5672 km
3. (a) 5501 km (b) 9272 km (c) 4429 km (d) 350·9 km
4. 14°32′48″ W 5. 41°45′ N 6. 2°13′51″ 7. 1°20′35″
8. 4 hours 38·2 minutes later 9. 15·71 cm; 15 cm
10. (a) 3513 km (b) 3474 km 11. (a) 4016 km (b) 4000 km
12. (a) 32°E (b) 2541 km

Miscellaneous exercise 2 page 56

1. 636·5 2. 2·652 m/s; 10 800 kg 3. 100 cm^2; 3 km/h
4. 13 890 litres per second; 88·42 h 5. (a) 26·71 cm^2 (b) 110·6 cm^2
6. (a) 77 cm (b) 117·9 cm^2 7. 16·5 kg
8. (a) 50·29 cm^2; 41·57 cm^2; 1·454 cm^2 (b) 43·03 cm^2; 38·72 cm^2; 0·5388 cm^2
9. 450 000 litres; 1·326 m/s
10. (a) 15 cm^2 (b) 199·5 cm^2 (c) 32·25 cm^2 (d) 12·19 cm^2
11. 8°3′ 12. $\frac{61}{125}$; 127 13. 112 cm^3 14. 12·5 cm
15. 20 cm^3; 57·66 cm^2 16. 1468 cm^2; 407·3 cm^3
17. 14·91 cm^3; 50·43 cm^2 18. 0·365 m^3; 916·2 kg
19. 28 440 km; 44°S; 46°S 20. 23·4 m^2, 1·989 kg; 14 700 mm^3

Part 3

Exercise 3.1a page 58

1. $a+2$ 2. $b-4$ 3. $3a$ 4. $\frac{1}{4}b$ or $\frac{b}{4}$ 5. $b+a$
6. $d-c$ 7. ab 8. $11-a$ 9. $36/x$ 10. $1000\,y$
11. $3x$ pence 12. $100\,y$ 13. $x/100$ 14. $1000\,x$
15. $50/y$ 16. $x+1$ 17. $x+3$ 18. £$(y-x)$
19. £$(A-B)$ 20. $(100-6x)$ pence

Exercise 3.1b page 59

1. £$(y+2)$ **2.** $x+y$

3. (a) £$(m-n)$ (b) £$(m-n-62)$ (c) £$(\frac{1}{2}m-\frac{1}{2}n-31)$

4. (a) mn pence (b) £$mn/100$ **5.** m/g litres **6.** $(y-x)$ years; $(y+z)$ years

7. £$\left(\frac{k}{m}\right)$ **8.** £$\left(\frac{xy}{z}\right)$ **9.** $\frac{pq+rs}{p+r}$ **10.** £$\left(Y-\frac{pY}{100}\right)$

11. £$\left(\frac{yz}{x}\right)$ **12.** $\frac{bc+de+fg}{b+d+f}$ **13.** $\left(\frac{pq}{r}-\frac{st}{u}\right)$ pence

14. (a) $2x$ (b) $x+2$ **15.** $50-x$ **16.** $x-50$

17. $y-x$ **18.** £$\left[I-\frac{(I-F)\,p}{100}\right]$ **19.** (a) 120% (b) 144%

20. $x^2(\frac{3}{2}\sqrt{3}-1)$

Exercise 3.2 page 61

1. -4 **2.** 1 **3.** -8 **4.** $5\frac{1}{2}$ **5.** $-\frac{1}{2}$ **6.** 9 **7.** $-13\frac{2}{3}$

8. 2 **9.** -16 **10.** 3 **11.** 8 **12.** $-2\frac{1}{2}$ **13.** $3\frac{1}{3}$ **14.** 0

15. $-1\frac{5}{8}$ **16.** $\frac{1}{2}$ **17.** $-\frac{2}{3}$ **18.** $2\frac{3}{8}$ **19.** 3 **20.** $-\frac{1}{8}$ **21.** -9

22. 1 **23.** 14 **24.** 9 **25.** 0 **26.** -9 **27.** 11 **28.** 7

29. -9 **30.** 7 **31.** -5 **32.** -6 **33.** $1\frac{1}{4}$ **34.** 1 **35.** 9

36. 1 **37.** $7\frac{7}{12}$ **38.** $-\frac{1}{8}$ **39.** 2·19

40. $-0{\cdot}759$ **41.** -8 **42.** -8 **43.** 8

44. 8 **45.** 48 **46.** 48 **47.** -48

48. -48 **49.** $-\frac{1}{8}$ **50.** $\frac{1}{8}$ **51.** -40

52. 30 **53.** -2 **54.** -2 **55.** 2

56. $-2\frac{1}{2}$ **57.** -2 **58.** 5 **59.** $-\frac{2}{3}$

60. $\frac{1}{3}$ **61.** 4 **62.** -64 **63.** -8

64. $\frac{1}{16}$ **65.** -10p **66.** $-$£100; £100

67. (a) 5 km (b) -6 km (c) -3 km (d) 3 km/h (e) -5 km/h (f) -6 km/h

68. (a) -16°C (b) -3°C (c) 3°C (d) 51°C (e) 24°C

69. 0 **70.** A: 70; B: 75; C: 100; D: 10; E: -53

Exercise 3.3a page 62

1. 4 **2.** 9 **3.** 7 **4.** 6 **5.** 0 **6.** 2 **7.** 22 **8.** 12

9. $1\frac{1}{2}$ **10.** 4 **11.** 27 **12.** 81 **13.** 0 **14.** 48 **15.** 32 **16.** 10

17. ± 2 **18.** ± 6 **19.** 2 **20.** ± 4 **21.** 0 **22.** 40 **23.** 5 **24.** $\pm\frac{3}{4}$

25. ± 8 **26.** 4 **27.** 0 **28.** 133 **29.** $\frac{1}{16}$ **30.** $\frac{1}{4}$ **31.** $\frac{1}{12}$ **32.** 1

33. 0 **34.** $\frac{1}{36}$ **35.** ∞ **36.** 0 **37.** $\frac{5}{36}$ **38.** $\frac{97}{36}$ **39.** 1 **40.** $5\frac{2}{3}$

Exercise 3.3b page 63

1. -8 **2.** 16 **3.** -64 **4,** -8 **5.** -12 **6.** -32 **7.** 30

8. -1 **9.** 0 **10.** ± 16 **11.** 3 **12.** -5 **13.** 12 **14.** 5

15. 1 **16.** -2 **17.** -3 **18.** 3 **19.** 18 **20.** -3 **21.** $2\frac{1}{2}$

22. $-1\frac{1}{3}$ **23.** -1 **24.** 45 **25.** $1\frac{1}{3}$ **26.** ± 13 **27.** 3·553

28. 960 **29.** 0·5067 **30.** 0·777

Exercise 3.4 page 65

1. $5x$
2. $12y$
3. $5a$
4. $9ab$
5. $3a + b$
6. $2p - 3q$
7. $13x - 8y$
8. $3x + 3xy$
9. $5pq$
10. abc
11. $3a + 4b$
12. $x - 2y$
13. $x + 2y$
14. $2x - y$
15. $2x + y$
16. $3p + q$
17. $12x + 3y$
18. $-2f - 3g$
19. $2ab + ac$
20. $xy + 2xz$
21. $5x + 4y$
22. $2ab + ac + bc$
23. $10 - 2mn$
24. $-xy - yz$
25. $6m + 3mn - 6n + 3n^2$
26. $6xy + 11xyz + 48yz$
27. $3rp + 2qr - 2pq$
28. $x^2 + 2y^2$
29. $4x^2 - 6xy + 4y^2$
30. $3pr - 2qr - 2p^2$
31. $2a - 2b + 4c$
32. $3x^2 + 3xy + 3xz - 15x$
33. $-5ap + 5aq$
34. $8p - 10pq$
35. $1 + \frac{x}{y}$
36. $4b - 2a$
37. $2mn + \frac{m^2n}{2} + \frac{mn^2}{2}$
38. $x^2 + 5x + 6$
39. $x^2 + x - 6$
40. $x^2 - 5x + 6$
41. $x^2 - 9$
42. $x^2 - 6x + 9$
43. $x^2 + 6x + 9$
44. $x^2 + 3xy + 2y^2$
45. $x^2 - 3xy + 2y^2$
46. $x^2 - y^2$
47. $2a^2 - 5ab + 3b^2$
48. $4x^2 + 4xy - 3y^2$
49. $6p^2 - 5pq - 4q^2$
50. $6a^2 - 22ab + 20b^2$
51. $5m^2 - 24mn - 5n^2$
52. $9a^2 + 12ab - 12b^2$
53. $12x^2 - 14xy - 6y^2$
54. $a^2 + 2ab + ac + b^2 + bc$
55. $9a^2 + 12ab + 4b^2$
56. $6x^2 - xy + 8x - y^2 - 4y$
57. $\frac{x}{y} + 2 + \frac{y}{x}$
58. $6x^2 + 3x - 2$
59. $8x^2 + 11x - 12$
60. $-x^2 + 9x + 36$
61. $9x^2 - 12xy + 4y^2$
62. $25a^2 - 10ab + b^2$
63. $16x^2 + 48x + 36$
64. $3x^3 + 6x^2y + 3xy^2 - 6xy$
65. $-a^2 + 6ab - b^2$

Exercise 3.5 page 67

1. 8
2. 15
3. 6
4. 10
5. 7
6. 7
7. 6
8. 16
9. 12
10. 8
11. 10
12. 5
13. $13\frac{1}{2}$
14. 32
15. 5
16. 3
17. 9
18. 3
19. 8
20. 3
21. 6
22. 6
23. 6
24. 18
25. 36
26. 14
27. 96
28. 15
29. $5\frac{1}{4}$
30. $1\frac{7}{8}$
31. $\frac{1}{2}$
32. 3
33. 3
34. 1
35. $7\frac{1}{2}$
36. 3
37. 2
38. 2
39. $\frac{5}{28}$
40. $\frac{1}{5}$
41. 1
42. $-\frac{5}{13}$
43. $-1\frac{3}{4}$
44. $2\frac{3}{10}$
45. $2\frac{2}{7}$
46. $3\frac{7}{10}$
47. $-\frac{13}{30}$
48. $\frac{25}{24}$

Exercise 3.6 page 69

1. 3
2. 12
3. 7; 8; 9
4. 29; 31; 33; 35
5. 4, 7, 10 yrs
6. £59; £131
7. $3\frac{3}{4}$yrs
8. £8000
9. 8 miles
10. 9 m
11. £15
12. 1
13. 88
14. 84
15. 60 km/h
16. 60 km/h
17. 16 yrs
18. 40 litres
19. 34
20. 11

Exercise 3.7 page 71

1. $B = \frac{A}{L}$
2. $b = \frac{2A}{h}$
3. $r = \frac{C}{2\pi}$
4. $h = \frac{3V}{\pi r^2}$

5. $L = \dfrac{S}{\pi r}$
6. $v = \dfrac{c}{p}$
7. $h = \dfrac{V}{r^2}$
8. $c = \dfrac{V}{ab}$
9. $B = \frac{1}{2}P - L$
10. $f = \dfrac{v-u}{t}$
11. $s = \dfrac{v^2 - u^2}{2f}$
12. $f = \dfrac{2(s-ut)}{t^2}$
13. $L = \dfrac{2S}{n} - a$
14. $F = 32 + \dfrac{9C}{5}$
15. $v = \dfrac{2s}{t} - u$
16. $R = \dfrac{V}{\pi h t} - r$
17. $y = \dfrac{p-a}{x}$
18. $y = \dfrac{p}{x} - a$
19. $r = \sqrt{\left(\dfrac{V}{\pi h}\right)}$
20. $r = \sqrt{\left(\dfrac{A}{4\pi}\right)}$
21. $t = \left(\dfrac{Hb}{a}\right)^2$
22. $N = \sqrt{\left(\dfrac{5M}{P}\right)}$
23. $r = \sqrt{\left(\dfrac{3V}{\pi h}\right)}$
24. $r = \sqrt{\left(R^2 - \dfrac{A}{\pi}\right)}$
25. $v = u + ft$
26. $z = \dfrac{p(20-p)}{10-p}$
27. $V = \frac{1}{2}Ar$
28. $V = \frac{1}{6}(A^3/\pi)^{\frac{1}{2}}$; $A = (36\pi V^2)^{\frac{1}{3}}$
29. $K = \dfrac{5M - 2A}{A - 3}$
30. $b = \dfrac{x^4 - a^2y^2}{2x^2y}$

Exercise 3.8 page 73

	x	y		x	y		x	y		x	y
1.	9	3	9.	$2\frac{1}{3}$	3	17.	4	3	25.	5	$-\frac{1}{2}$
2.	4	2	10.	3	2	18.	12	−6	26.	4	−2
3.	1	6	11.	0	−1	19.	3	−2	27.	$\frac{1}{2}$	6
4.	$2\frac{1}{2}$	2	12.	−1	−1	20.	2	0	28.	$\frac{2}{3}$	$\frac{1}{4}$
5.	3	4	13.	$\frac{1}{2}$	1	21.	12	9	29.	$-\frac{1}{3}$	$-1\frac{1}{3}$
6.	3	2	14.	$1\frac{1}{2}$	$\frac{1}{2}$	22.	10	6	30.	$\frac{1}{2}$	−3
7.	6	−1	15.	1	2	23.	$1\frac{1}{2}$	$\frac{1}{4}$	31.	12	2
8.	−2	−3	16.	0	−1	24.	−1	3	32.	9	−1

33. $a = \frac{1}{2}$; $b = 2$
34. $m = 2$; $c = 3$
35. 28
36. 15

Exercise 3.9 page 74

1. 10p; 15p
2. £2400; £1600
3. 10
4. £8; £5
5. £2
6. 7 and 11
7. £500; £300
8. 120; 80
9. £1·20
10. 25, 40 yrs
11. 14, 21 yrs
12. £62; £72
13. 72 or 27
14. 45
15. 15 knots
16. 8 km/h
17. 240·625 cm^2
18. 121 dogs
19. $x = 12\%$; $y = 14\%$
20. 11 km

Exercise 3.10a page 77

1. $2(a + 2b)$
2. $3(2a + 3b)$
3. $a(x + y)$
4. $ab(y + z)$
5. $x(x + y)$
6. $2x(x + 4y)$
7. $3xy(x + y)$
8. $x^2(x + y + 2z)$
9. $ab(2a + bc + c^2)$
10. $3p^2q(pq + 2rs)$
11. $2(x - 2y + z)$
12. $3x(a + b^2 - 2c)$
13. $5p(2p^2 - 3pq - r)$
14. $17mn(m^2 - 3n^2 + p)$
15. $13x(3x^2y^2 - 1)$
16. $9a^2(ab - bc + 4c^2)$
17. $4xz(x^2 - xyz + 2z^2)$
18. $3rs(2s^2 - 3t^2 + st)$
19. $11xy(x^2 - 2y^2 - z^2)$
20. $8p(3q^2 + r^2 - s^2)$
21. $(a + b)(c + d)$
22. $(x - y)(2 - z)$
23. $(p + 2q)(r + s)$
24. $(a + 2b)(c - d)$
25. $(3a + 2b)(c + d)$
26. $(2a - 3b)(c - d)$
27. $(2x - y)(w + 2z)$

28. $(m-n)(2x+3y)$
29. $(a+2b)(c-3d)$
30. $(3x-2y)(2c+d)$
31. $(x+y)(x+z)$
32. $(x+2y)(y+2z)$
33. $(x-y)(x+2z)$
34. $(a-b)(b-c)$
35. $(p-m)(2p-n)$
36. $(ab+2)(p+q)$
37. $(ab-1)(a-b)$
38. $(2xy+3)(x-y)$
39. $(a+b+2c)(p-2q)$
40. $(x-3y+z)(c-d)$

Exercise 3.10b page 78

1. $(x+1)(x+2)$
2. $(x+2)(x+3)$
3. $(x+3)(x+4)$
4. $(x+1)(x+4)$
5. $(x+2)(x+2)$
6. $(x+3)(x+1)$
7. $(x+3)(x+5)$
8. $(x+2)(x+6)$
9. $(x+3)(x+7)$
10. $(x+2)(x+9)$
11. $(x-1)(x+2)$
12. $(x-3)(x+4)$
13. $(x-2)(x+6)$
14. $(x-1)(x-3)$
15. $(x+6)(x-1)$
16. $(x-4)(x-2)$
17. $(x-6)(x+3)$
18. $(x-6)(x-3)$
19. $(x-4)(x-8)$
20. $(x+9)(x-1)$
21. $(2x+1)(x+1)$
22. $(2x+3)(x+1)$
23. $(3x+2)(2x+1)$
24. $(3x+1)(2x+3)$
25. $(3x+1)(x+2)$
26. $(4x+3)(x+1)$
27. $(4x+1)(x+3)$
28. $(7x+2)(x+1)$
29. $(9x+1)(x+2)$
30. $(8x+3)(x+2)$
31. $(2x-1)(x+1)$
32. $(x-3)(2x+1)$
33. $(3x+2)(x-1)$
34. $(3x-2)(x-1)$
35. $(4x-3)(x+1)$
36. $(2x-3)(x-2)$
37. $(4x-3)(x-1)$
38. $(7x-1)(x-2)$
39. $(9x-1)(x+2)$
40. $(8x-3)(x-2)$
41. $4(x-1)(x-2)$
42. $3(x+2)(x-6)$
43. $5(x+1)(x+3)$
44. $2(4x-3)(x-1)$
45. $2(9x-1)(x-2)$
46. $2(3x-4y)(4x-5y)$
47. $(x+y)(x+y+3)$
48. $(x+2)(8x-2)$ or $2(x+2)(4x-1)$

Exercise 3.10c page 79

1. $(x-y)(x+y)$
2. $(a-2b)(a+2b)$
3. $(2p-3q)(2p+3q)$
4. $(4m-9n)(4m+9n)$
5. $2(x-2y)(x+2y)$
6. $3(2x-3y)(2x+3y)$
7. $2(x-5y)(x+5y)$
8. $x(y-z)(y+z)$
9. $2(x-5)(x+5)$
10. $4(2x-1)(2x+1)$
11. $3(2x-5y^2)(2x+5y^2)$
12. $(ab-cd)(ab+cd)$
13. $5(ab-2)(ab+2)$
14. $4(2a-3bc)(2a+3bc)$
15. $2a(2a-3b)(2a+3b)$
16. $ab(a-2b)(a+2b)$
17. $2x(3x-y)(3x+y)$
18. $(x-y)(x+y)(x^2+y^2)$
19. $(x-2y)(x+2y)(x^2+4y^2)$
20. $(3y-2z)(3y+2z)(9y^2+4z^2)$
21. 200
22. 400
23. 4000
24. 5800
25. 974 000
26. 682 000
27. 2000
28. 1000
29. 20
30. $50\frac{3}{4}$
31. $(a+b+2)(a+b-2)$
32. $4(x+y)(3x+2y)$
33. $4(3x-2y)(x-y)$
34. $(x+3+2y)(x+3-2y)$
35. $(x-y+a)(x-y-a)$

Exercise 3.11 page 81

1. a
2. $\frac{ac}{b}$
3. $\frac{xy}{8}$
4. $\frac{q}{5pr}$
5. $8ac$
6. $\frac{3p}{2qr}$
7. $2b$
8. $\frac{2c^3}{d^4}$
9. $\frac{2}{3}yz^2$
10. $\frac{2pr}{21}$
11. bcd
12. $\frac{4p^2}{q^2}$
13. xz
14. 1
15. $\frac{a^2}{b^2}$
16. $\frac{5}{2c}$
17. 6
18. $\frac{a}{b}$
19. $\frac{y(x+y)}{x(x-y)}$
20. 1

21. $\dfrac{a+b}{ab}$ 22. $\dfrac{2d-c}{cd}$ 23. $\dfrac{y+4x}{2xy}$ 24. $\dfrac{2a}{a^2-b^2}$

25. $\dfrac{x+5y}{x^2-y^2}$ 26. $\dfrac{2(x^2+y^2)}{x^2-y^2}$ 27. $a+b$ 28. $\dfrac{4}{x^2-4}$

29. $\dfrac{-1}{a(a+b)}$ 30. $\dfrac{2x}{(x^2-9)(x-3)}$ 31. $\dfrac{1+c}{1-a}$ 32. $\dfrac{-5}{x^2-x-6}$

33. $\dfrac{1+a}{a(a+b)}$ 34. $\dfrac{3}{x^2+5x+4}$ 35. 1

Exercise 3.12 page 83

1. (a) x^{10} (b) x^{13} (c) x^{12} (d) $\frac{3}{32}x^{10}$
2. (a) x^3 (b) x^{12} (c) x^5 (d) x^{-4} or $1/x^4$
3. (a) x^6 (b) x^3 (c) $x^8/20$ (d) x^{11}
4. (a) x^{14} (b) x^{12} (c) $8x^6$ (d) $\frac{1}{4}x^6$ (e) $8/x^6$
5. (a) x^2 (b) x^4 (c) x^3 (d) $4x^6$ (e) $\frac{1}{2}x^5$
6. (a) $x^{\frac{1}{4}}$ (b) $x^{\frac{2}{5}}$ (c) $x^{\frac{7}{3}}$ (d) $x^{\frac{5}{2}}$
7. (a) $\sqrt{x}$ (b) $\sqrt[4]{x^3}$ (c) $\sqrt[8]{x^7}$ (d) $\sqrt[8]{x^3}$ (e) $\sqrt[b]{x^a}$
8. (a) $1/x^4$ (b) $1/x^5$ (c) x^3y^2 (d) $1/x^5$ (e) $1/x^{\frac{1}{2}}$
   (f) $8x^4$ (g) $4x^{\frac{3}{2}}$ (h) $1/x^{\frac{1}{5}}$ (i) $\frac{1}{4}x^{\frac{1}{2}}$ (j) $1/x^{\frac{13}{3}}$
9. (a) $\frac{1}{2}$ (b) 4 (c) $\frac{1}{125}$ (d) 32 (e) $\frac{1}{8}$ (f) 8
   (g) 1 (h) 27 (i) 16 (j) 5 (k) 32
10. (a) 8 (b) 25 (c) 1 (d) 5
11. (a) 108 (b) $\frac{40}{3}$ (c) 9
12. (a) 1000 (b) 26
13. (a) 27 (b) 2 (c) 4
14. (a) $\frac{64}{125}$ (b) $\frac{9}{4}$ (c) $\frac{216}{343}$ (d) $\frac{4}{9}$ (e) 3

Exercise 3.13a page 86

1. 0, 3 2. 0, 3 3. 2, 3 4. $-\frac{1}{2}$, 4
5. 3, −3 6. 0, 9 7. 0, 3 8. 0, 2
9. 0, $-8\frac{1}{2}$ 10. 0, $-2\frac{2}{3}$ 11. 0, $-1\frac{1}{3}$ 12. ± 3
13. ± 11 14. ± 4 15. 1, 2 16. −2, 3
17. 3, 4 18. 5, 1 19. −2, −3 20. 5, −6
21. 2, −8 22. −3, −4 23. 1, 6 24. $\frac{2}{3}$, 2
25. $-\frac{1}{2}$, 1 26. $\frac{2}{3}$, $\frac{1}{4}$ 27. $\frac{3}{4}$, 3 28. $-\frac{1}{2}$, $\frac{2}{3}$
29. $-\frac{3}{4}$, 1 30. $-\frac{1}{3}$, $1\frac{1}{2}$ 31. $\frac{1}{5}$, −4 32. $-\frac{1}{12}$, −8
33. $\frac{1}{6}$, $4\frac{1}{2}$ 34. −0·439, −4·56 35. 0·268, 3·73 36. 0·303, −3·30
37. −0·354, −5·65 38. 1·70, 5·30 39. −0·792, 3·79 40. 0·209, 4·79
41. 0·281, −1·78 42. 1·27, −2·77 43. −0·279, −2·39 44. −0·134, −1·87
45. $-1 \pm \sqrt{-5}$
46. $x=2,\ y=4$, or $x=3,\ y=5$
47. $x=4,\ y=3$, or $x=-1,\ y=-2$
48. $x=\frac{1}{2},\ y=1\frac{1}{2}$ or $x=-\frac{2}{3},\ y=\frac{1}{3}$
49. $x=-1,\ y=0$ or $x=\frac{1}{3},\ y=1\frac{1}{3}$
50. $x=3,\ y=-6$ or $x=-9,\ y=6$
51. $x=1,\ y=1$ or $x=2,\ y=-1$
52. $x=\frac{1}{4},\ y=\frac{1}{8}$ or $x=-3,\ y=5$
53. $x=-\frac{1}{2},\ y=-2$ or $x=-\frac{1}{3},\ y=-2\frac{1}{3}$
54. $x=\frac{2}{5},\ y=\frac{32}{25}$ or $x=-\frac{1}{4},\ y=\frac{9}{5}$
55. $x=\frac{1}{2},\ y=\frac{1}{3}$ or $x=\frac{1}{3},\ y=\frac{1}{2}$

Exercise 3.13b page 88

1. 8 cm 2. 9, 27 3. 3 4. 5 cm, 7 cm 5. 8 cm, 16 cm
6. 9·66 cm 7. 11 m 8. 5 km/h 9. £2 10. 11 cm
11. 100 kg, 20 p/kg 12. 2, 3 minutes

Miscellaneous exercise 3 page 88

1. (a) $\frac{1}{4}$ (b) $-\frac{1}{8}$ (c) 1 (d) $-\frac{2}{3}$ (e) $\frac{1}{12}$ (f) 16
(g) 2 (h) 8 (i) $\frac{1}{512}$ (j) $-\frac{3}{2}$
2. (a) $-6x - 18$ (b) $-x^2 - 6xy - 8y^2$ (c) $4ab$
(d) $-x^2$ (e) $15ab - 15b^2$
3. (a) 1 (b) -2 (c) $3\frac{7}{10}$ (d) $-1\frac{3}{4}$ (e) $-3\frac{4}{9}$
4. (a) 278, 280, 282, 284 (b) 299, 301, 303, 305 (c) 290, 291, 292, 293
5. (a) $h = \dfrac{A}{2\pi r}$ (b) $r = \sqrt[3]{\left(\dfrac{3V}{4\pi}\right)}$ (c) $u = \dfrac{(B-2b)^2 - b^2}{6b}$
(d) $k = \dfrac{-An \pm \sqrt{A^2n^2 + 2Anbd}}{bd}$
7. (a) $-4·56, -0·44$ (b) 1, 5 (c) $0·30, -3·30$
(d) $\frac{2}{3}, \frac{1}{4}$ (e) $\frac{2}{3}, -\frac{1}{2}$ (f) $-8, -\frac{1}{12}$
(g) $-1·87, -0·13$ (h) no real roots
8. 150 cm^2 9. 246 10. $4\frac{3}{4}$ minutes late
12. $13\frac{1}{11}$ 13. 1·85 14. $y^2 - x^2$ 15. $-5·87, -1·33$

Part 4

Exercise 4.1 page 91

1. (a) Thursday (b) Saturday (c) Thursday (d) can't say
2. (a) April, June (b) can't say

Exercise 4.2a page 93

1. (a) 12 cm, 18 cm, 33 cm (b) 7·5 cm, 3·25 cm, 8·125 cm
2. (a) £73·50, £54·60, £79·80 (b) 25 h, 30 h, 32·5 h
3. (a) 18·75 miles, 48·75 miles, 90 miles (b) 16 km, 115·2 km, 150·4 km
4. (a) 16·5 cm, 23·25 cm, 30 cm (b) 2 kg, 5·5 kg, 12·5 kg (c) 12 cm

Exercise 4.2b page 94

1. After 2 h $46\frac{2}{3}$ min, $55\frac{5}{9}$ km from A
2. 20 km away, 3 h $51\frac{1}{2}$ min
3. After 8 s, 20 m from the start
4. After $19\frac{1}{2}$ s, 42 m from the start
5. 2·8 km upstream
6. 1 h 20 min, 24 km from the start
7. After $2\frac{1}{4}$ h and after $4\frac{1}{4}$ h
8. (a) 10 s (b) 50 m (c) $6\frac{2}{3}$ m/s

Miscellaneous exercise 4a page 95

1. (a) Jan. to Jul. and Sept. to Dec. (b) Jul. to Sept. (c) can't say
2. (a) 11a.m. to 12 noon and 1p.m. to 2p.m. (b) 7p.m. to 8p.m.
3. 1951–3
4. 75 km/h; at 11.22a.m. 118·2 km from A; 1 h 40 min sooner
5. 72 km

Exercise 4.3 page 98

1. (a) $(-2, 0)$; $(0, 2)$ (b) $(\frac{1}{2}, 0)$; $(0, -1)$ (c) $(-\frac{1}{2}, 0)$; $(0, 1)$
   (d) $(-\frac{1}{3}, 0)$; $(0, \frac{1}{2})$ (e) $(4, 0)$; $(0, 4)$ (f) $(6, 0)$; $(0, -6)$
   (g) $(\frac{5}{2}, 0)$; $(0, 5)$ (h) $(-2, 0)$; $(0, -1)$
2. (a) $x = 3$; $y = 2$ (b) $x = 1$; $y = 4$ (c) $x = 2\frac{1}{2}$; $y = \frac{1}{2}$
   (d) $x = -2$; $y = -3$

Exercise 4.4 page 99

1. $a = -2{\cdot}5$; $b = 15$
2. $a = 5$; $b = 0{\cdot}1$
3. $a = -1$; $b = 0{\cdot}8$
4. $a = -15$; $b = 11$

Exercise 4.5 page 101

1. 1 or 2; 3·6 or −0·6
2. (a) 3·7 or 0·3 (b) 1 or 3 (c) 4·3 or 0·7 (d) 3·3 or −0·3
3. (a) 3·8 or −1·8 (b) 3·45 or −1·45 (c) 3 or −2 (d) 1·9 or −2·9
4. $(5, 3)$; $(-2, -4)$; $x^2 - 3x - 10 = 0$
5. $y = 0{\cdot}83$ when $x = 0{\cdot}2$; $x = -0{\cdot}23$ when $y = 1{\cdot}3$; $-0{\cdot}7 < x < 2{\cdot}7$

Miscellaneous exercise 4b page 102

1. $(0, 3)$; $(4, 0)$; $(1, -4)$; $(-3, -1)$; 5 units
2. $(1, 1)$
3. (a), (b), and (d) are parallel
4. One of each pair is perpendicular to the other.
5. (b) 37°, 53°, 90° (c) 7·5 square units
6. $a = 0$; $b = 6{\cdot}28$
7. $x = 0{\cdot}7$ or $1{\cdot}25$
8. (a) 160 m (b) after 4 s (c) after 0·5 s and 7·5 s
9. 8·4 units
10. −3·4, −1, and 4·4
11. $E = 0{\cdot}15\,W + 2$
12. (a) $y = 4$ (b) $x = 3$ or -1; $x = -2$ or 1
13. $x^3 + x^2 - 2 = 0$; $x = 1$
14. (a) 14·4 m (b) 9·6 s (c) 1·1 m/s and 2·15 m/s
15. (a) $(1\frac{1}{2}, -22)$, $(-1\frac{1}{2}, 32)$ (b) $-\infty$ to −2·7 and 0·2 to 2·5
    (c) (i) (−2·7, 0·2, and 2·5) (ii) (−2·18, 0, and 2·18)

Part 5

Exercise 5.1a page 107

9. 86° **10.** 8·7 cm **11.** 7·2 cm

Exercise 5.1b page 107

1. 5 cm **2.** 4·7 cm **3.** 5·1 cm and 3·9 cm
4. 14 cm **5.** 41·6 cm^2 **6.** 9·8 cm, 6 cm **7.** 10 cm
8. 6 cm **10.** 2·7 cm

Exercise 5.2a page 108

2. (a) 52° (b) 66° (c) 54° (d) 72° (e) 89°
3. (a) 104° (b) 157° (c) 126° (d) 178° (e) 179°
4. (a) 212° (b) 89° (c) 269° (d) 316° (e) 179°
5. (a) 21° (b) 15° (c) 50° (d) $27\frac{2}{3}°$ (e) 28°
6. (a) 30° (b) 160° (c) 80° (d) 72°

Exercise 5.2b page 110

1. (a) 60° (b) 108° (c) 90° (d) 45°
2. (a) 60° (b) 72° (c) 44°
3. (a) $x = y = 50°$ (b) $y = 56°$ (c) $a = 110°$ (d) $y = 120°$
4. (a) 135° (b) 84° (c) 18° (d) $67\frac{1}{2}°$ (e) $118\frac{3}{4}°$
5. (a) 45° (b) 18° (c) 9° (d) $67\frac{1}{2}°$ (e) $58\frac{3}{4}°$
6. 30° **7.** 18°
8. (a) yes (b) no (c) yes (d) yes (e) no
(f) $A\hat{O}C = D\hat{O}B = 180°$ (g) $A\hat{O}C = 180°$ (h) nothing
(i) nothing (j) $D\hat{O}B = 180°$
9. (a) yes (b) POR, QOS (c) nothing (d) no (e) yes; no

Exercise 5.3 page 113

1. 62°; 118° **2.** 109° **3.** 110°; 110° **4.** 100°; 135°
5. 75°; 30°; 75° **6.** 60°; 70° **7.** 62° **8.** 130°
9. 65° **10.** 54° **11.** 75°; 105° **12.** 20°; 80°; 120°
13. 110° **14.** 60° **15.** 50° **16.** 80°; 120°; 160°
17. 60° **18.** AP and BZ; AQ and BY

Exercise 5.5a page 119

1. 30°; 80°; 110°
2. 35°; 104°
3. 90°
4. 90°
5. 60°
6. 90°; 60°
7. 108°
8. 75°
9. 115°
10. 72°; 36°
11. 35°
12. 90°
13. 45°
14. 88°; 58°
15. 55°; 35°
16. 30°

Exercise 5.5b page 121

1. 50°; 50°
2. 108°
3. 36°
4. 36°
5. 80°
6. 72°; 36°
7. 20°
8. 51°
9. 128°
10. $40\frac{1}{2}$°; $37\frac{1}{2}$°

Exercise 5.6 page 123

1. (a) 108° (b) 120° (c) 135° (d) 156°
2. (a) $51\frac{3}{7}$° (b) 40°
3. (a) 36 sides (b) 9 sides (c) no
4. (a) 18 sides (b) no (c) 12 sides
5. $121\frac{1}{4}$°
6. $166\frac{2}{13}$°
7. 36°
8. $77\frac{9}{13}$°
9. ADE: 36°, 36°, and 108°; ADC: 36°, 72°, 72°
10. 36°, 72°, 72°
11. 18°, 54°, 108°
12. 720°
13. 1260°
14. 1440°
15. 60°, 75°, 45°

Exercise 5.8a page 127

1. 9 cm, 12 cm
2. $9\frac{1}{3}$ cm, $6\frac{2}{3}$ cm
3. $2\frac{2}{5}$ cm, 12 cm
4. $1\frac{1}{2}$ cm, $3\frac{3}{4}$ cm
5. $6\frac{2}{3}$ cm, $8\frac{1}{2}$ cm
6. 5 cm
7. $4\frac{2}{3}$ cm
8. 2 cm
9. 42 cm
10. $27\frac{1}{7}$ cm
11. $33\frac{1}{3}$ m
12. 3 m
13. 55·2 cm
14. 12 m
15. $8\frac{1}{3}$ cm

Exercise 5.8b page 129

1. $4\frac{2}{3}$ cm, $6\frac{2}{3}$ cm; 9 : 25
2. $6\frac{3}{4}$ cm, $5\frac{1}{7}$ cm; 9 : 40
3. 12 cm, 6 cm, 16 cm; 2 : 1
4. $5\frac{5}{9}$ cm, $2\frac{2}{9}$ cm; 3 : 8
5. $6\frac{2}{3}$ cm, $1\frac{1}{3}$ cm; 4 : 1; 2 : 1
6. 3 : 1; 4 : 1; 1 : 9
7. $1\frac{5}{7}$ cm, $2\frac{2}{7}$ cm; 3 : 4
8. 25 : 12

Miscellaneous exercise 5a page 131

2. 9·9 cm
3. 7·1 cm
4. 10 cm
5. 6 cm
6. 8·5 cm
7. 2·6 cm
8. 5·5 cm, 6·5 cm; 3·5 cm
11. $n = 57{\cdot}5°$
12. $p = 72°, q = 36°$

Exercise 5.9 page 133

1. 60°, 120° **2.** 30° **3.** 20°, 40° **4.** 29°
5. 140° **6.** 108° **7.** 110°, 100° **8.** 45°, 135°
9. 170°, 5° **10.** 55°, 45°, 80°; 125° **11.** 55°, 105°
12. 140° **13.** 112·5°, 67·5°, 22·5°

Exercise 5.10 page 135

1. (a) 13 cm (b) 25 cm (c) 13·45 cm (d) 68·63 cm (e) 4·471 cm
2. (a) 6 cm (b) 5·657 cm (c) 5·723 cm (d) 43·62 cm (e) 2·121 cm
3. 4·583 m **4.** 11·18 m **5.** 5·196 cm **6.** 8·485 cm
7. 22·36 cm **8.** 14·42 cm **9.** 6 cm, 24 cm^2 **10.** 36·66 cm
11. 25·3 cm **12.** 0·5 cm

Exercise 5.11 page 137

1. (a) 12 cm (b) 5 cm (c) 5 cm (d) 13·42 cm (e) 18·87 cm
2. (a) 12·81 cm (b) 6·561 cm **3.** 3·606 cm **4.** 8·66 cm
5. 261·8 cm^2 **6.** 31·18 cm **7.** 10·73 cm **8.** 19·04 cm
9. 5·568 cm **10.** 21·82 cm

Exercise 5.12 page 139

1. (a) 70°, 110° (b) 120°, 120° (c) 80° (d) 10° (e) 110°
2. (a) 40°, 50° (b) 5° (c) 30°, 40°, 50°
(d) 15°, 70° (e) 136°

3. 50°, 50° **4.** 50° **5.** 20° **6.** 30°, 60° **7.** 140°
8. 120° **9.** 30° **10.** 80°, 100°, 110°, 120°, 130°

Exercise 5.13 page 140

1. 54° **2.** 47° **3.** 60°, 120° **4.** 72°, 11° **5.** 75°
6. 72°, 108° **7.** 112° **8.** 12°, 42°

Exercise 5.14 page 143

1. (a) 5 cm (b) 55° (c) 5·6 cm (d) 10° (e) 7·42 cm
(f) 40°, 10° (g) 30° (h) 7 cm (i) 13·44 cm (j) 3 cm

2. $x = 120°$; 70°, 90°, 90°, 110° **3.** 5 cm, 6 cm, 7 cm **4.** 65° **5.** 20°
6. 8·66 cm

Exercise 5.15 page 145

1. (a) 65°, 85° (b) 63°, 40° (c) 68°, 81°, 31° (d) 68° (e) 54°
2. 48° *or* 132° **3.** 55°, 60°, 65° **4.** 48°, 48° **5.** 50°, 100°
6. 40°, 124°, 16° **7.** 56°, 62°, 62° **8.** 61°
9. (a) 65°; 20°, 45°, 115° (b) 110°, 35° (c) 14 cm **10.** 50°, 90°, 90°, 130°

Exercise 5.16 page 147

1. (a) $4\frac{2}{3}$ cm (b) 2 cm (c) 17 cm (d) 8 cm (e) 15 cm (f) 5 cm, 20 cm
2. (a) 2 cm (b) 1 cm (c) 4 cm (d) 4 cm (e) $10\frac{1}{2}$ cm
3. $4\frac{2}{5}$ cm, 20 cm

Exercise 5.17 page 149

1. $1\frac{1}{4}$ cm **2.** 4·8 cm **3.** $6\frac{2}{3}$ cm **4.** 4 cm **5.** 5·4 cm
6. 9·6 cm **7.** $2\frac{8}{13}$ cm, $9\frac{2}{13}$ cm **8.** 12 cm **9.** 4 cm; 1 : 3
10. 3·2 cm, 31·9 cm **11.** 20 cm **12.** $\frac{14}{45}$ cm **13.** 51 : 28
14. $3\frac{3}{4}$ cm **15.** 8 : 3 **16.** 0 cm

Miscellaneous exercise 5b page 152

1. 3 cm **2.** 7·1 cm, 8·8 cm, 9·7 cm **3.** 8·6 cm **6.** 60°
7. 20° **8.** 25 : 81 : 40 : 16 : 24 : 1 **9.** 22·5°, 67·5°
10. 30° **11.** 15° **12.** 3·536 cm **13.** 0·209 cm
14. (a) 4·69 cm (b) 10·58 cm (c) 5·745 cm
15. 15·69 cm **16.** 3·724a cm **17.** $\sqrt{(5a^2 + 6ab + 2b^2)}$ cm
18. $b\sqrt{(a^2 - b^2/4)}$ **19.** 154·9 cm **20.** 16 000 m², 536·6 m
21. (c) 17·58 m (d) 160 km **22.** 6 cm, 2 cm
23. 48°, 24° **24.** 112°, 124° **25.** 9·849 cm, 3·849 cm
26. 34 cm **27.** 277·2 km **28.** (a) 19·6 cm (b) 14·28 cm
29. 5·215 cm **30.** 63 km

Part 6

Exercise 6.1 page 156

1. (a) 0·3907 (b) 0·9272 (c) 0·4258 (d) 0·9774 (e) 0·5821
(f) 0·9885 (g) 0·3270 (h) 0·4607 (i) 0·9679 (j) 0·5733
(k) 0·8646 (l) 0·9896

2. (a) 0·6820 (b) 0·2924 (c) 0·5090 (d) 0·4099 (e) 0·7837
(f) 0·7672 (g) 0·7981 (h) 0·1435 (i) 0·9536 (j) 0·2602
(k) 0·5686 (l) 0·8697

3. (a) 0·2867 (b) 4·3315 (c) 14·30 (d) 0·3269 (e) 1·0105
(f) 1·4605 (g) 3·0595 (h) 0·8205 (i) 31·82 (j) 0·3902
(k) 0·7513 (l) 3·4085

4. (a) 23° (b) 62° (c) 71° 12′ (d) 24° 24′ (e) 16° 48′
(f) 61° 8′ (g) 13° 40′ (h) 49° 16′ (i) 51° 5′ (j) 6° 27′
(k) 69° 55′ (l) 59° 33′

5. (a) 14° (b) 57° (c) 72° 30′ (d) 27° 36′ (e) 16° 48′
(f) 73° 7′ (g) 67° 19′ (h) 10° 35′ (i) 23° 56′ (j) 55° 25′
(k) 14° 22′ (l) 31° 37′

6. (a) 15° (b) 47° (c) $20^\circ 24'$ (d) $67^\circ 24'$ (e) $59^\circ 24'$
(f) $64^\circ 19'$ (g) $10^\circ 55'$ (h) $53^\circ 9'$ (i) $13^\circ 39'$ (j) $66^\circ 37'$
(k) $75^\circ 49'$ (l) $84^\circ 30'$

7. (a) $\bar{1}{\cdot}9313$ (b) $\bar{1}{\cdot}6685$ (c) $\bar{1}{\cdot}9932$ (d) $\bar{1}{\cdot}8677$
8. (a) $\bar{1}{\cdot}9762$ (b) $\bar{1}{\cdot}9058$ (c) $\bar{1}{\cdot}8113$ (d) $\bar{1}{\cdot}1525$
9. (a) $\bar{1}{\cdot}8716$ (b) 0·4327 (c) 1·056 (d) 0·7826
10. (a) $6^\circ 6'$ (b) $3^\circ 30'$ (c) $4^\circ 49'$ (d) $14^\circ 7'$
11. (a) $89^\circ 12'$ (b) $53^\circ 3'$ (c) $25^\circ 45'$ (d) $67^\circ 23'$
12. (a) 87° (b) $52^\circ 26'$ (c) $38^\circ 45'$ (d) $5^\circ 1'$

Exercise 6.2 page 159

1. 1·71 cm **2.** 6·6577 cm **3.** 2·2075 cm **4.** 27·88 cm
5. 10·7 cm **6.** 8·424 cm **7.** 23·76 cm **8.** 33·2 cm
9. 67·36 cm **10.** 9·99 cm **11.** 12·29 cm **12.** 26 cm
13. 505·3 cm **14.** 18·45 cm **15.** 41·55 cm **16.** 11·8 cm
17. 2013 cm **18.** 136·3 cm **19.** 19·3 cm **20.** 168·3 cm
21. $53^\circ 8'$ **22.** $27^\circ 49'$ **23.** $66^\circ 27'$ **24.** 59°
25. $19^\circ 28'$ **26.** 30° **27.** $39^\circ 18'$ **28.** $60^\circ 41'$

Exercise 6.3 page 161

1. 4·045 cm **2.** 8·917 cm **3.** 49·59 cm **4.** 25·53 cm
5. 69·05 cm **6.** 119·5 cm **7.** 9·951 cm **8.** 40·47 cm
9. 6·581 cm **10.** 752·7 cm **11.** 10·02 cm **12.** 54·1 cm
13. 39·04 cm **14.** 94·21 cm **15.** 35·06 cm **16.** 7307 cm
17. 1·287 cm **18.** 18·95 cm **19.** 289·8 cm **20.** 1954 cm
21. $43^\circ 46'$ **22.** $59^\circ 16'$ **23.** $49^\circ 29'$ **24.** $34^\circ 36'$
25. $40^\circ 42'$ **26.** $44^\circ 9'$ **27.** $38^\circ 37'$ **28.** $28^\circ 10'$
29. $33^\circ 6'$ **30.** $57^\circ 11'$

Exercise 6.4 page 163

1. 48·26 cm **2.** 34·65 cm **3.** 17·81 cm **4.** 69·36 cm
5. 17·75 cm **6.** 53·21 cm **7.** 18·87 cm **8.** 4·525 cm
9. 0·010 44 cm **10.** 65·33 cm **11.** 20·98 cm **12.** 10·18 cm
13. 36·97 cm **14.** 12 820 cm **15.** 2·452 cm **16.** 0·021 74 cm
17. 47·21 cm **18.** 0·0906 cm **19.** 12 170 cm **20.** 0·1403 cm
21. $51^\circ 33'$ **22.** $44^\circ 10'$ **23.** $27^\circ 21'$ **24.** $73^\circ 23'$
25. $69^\circ 16'$

Exercise 6.5 page 166

1. 14·14 cm **2.** $9^\circ 36'$ **3.** 2·145 m **4.** 97·43 cm^2
5. $35^\circ 7'$ **6.** $37^\circ 36'$ **7.** $66^\circ 35'$ **8.** 44·02 km; $061^\circ 21'$
9. 9·282 km; $097^\circ 58'$ **10.** 73·93 m **11.** 87·39 m
12. 3·584 m **13.** 9·953 cm; 21·84 cm **14.** 16·63 km
15. 4·243 m; 0·9117 m **16.** 10·44 m **17.** 28·74 m
18. (a) 15·54 cm (b) 119·8 cm^2 **19.** 488 m
20. (a) 9·784 cm (b) 7·495 cm (c) 6·289 cm

Exercise 6.6 page 169

1. 54°44′; 35°16′ **2.** 5°43′; 4°3′; 8°3′ **3.** 97·2 m
4. 29·74 m **5.** 240·4 m **6.** 4°58′
7. 46°41′ **8.** 1624 m

Exercise 6.7 page 171

1. 4·454 cm **2.** 5·222 cm **3.** 9·577 cm **4.** 27·36 cm
5. 5·007 cm **6.** 0·8379 cm **7.** 51·74 cm **8.** 69·03 cm
9. 38·71 cm **10.** 10·15 cm **11.** 51·3 cm **12.** 19°13′
13. 3·345 km **14.** 9·362 km **15.** 52·39 m **16.** 97·31 m
17. 74·11 m **18.** 39·49 cm **19.** A by 11·39 m
20. 1. 3·464 cm, 13·16 cm^2 2. 5·222 cm, 20·57 cm^2 3. 7·449 cm, 63 cm^2
4. 13·89 cm, 128 cm^2 5. 4·240 cm, 19·17 cm^2 6. 1·589 cm, 1·307 cm^2
7. 42·68 cm, 1977 cm^2 8. 46·93 cm, 2536 cm^2 9. 21·17 cm, 378·6 cm^2
10. 7·685 cm, 68·11 cm^2

Exercise 6.8 page 173

1. 2·8 cm **2.** 4·727 cm **3.** 7·408 cm **4.** 21·85 cm
5. 15·26 cm **6.** 8·817 cm **7.** 8·267 cm **8.** 7·668 cm
9. 8·636 cm **10.** 2·915 cm **11.** 26°23′ **12.** 24°9′
13. 18°12′ **14.** 43°24′ **15.** 39°24′ **16.** 48°41′
17. 49°49′ **18.** 25°35′ **19.** 48°46′ **20.** 49°40′
21. 4·583 km; 10°54′ **22.** 3·196 km **23.** 66·39 m **24.** 24°8′
25. 31·97 light years
26. (a) 5·333 cm^2 (b) 8·183 cm^2 (c) 10·93 cm^2 (d) 65·95 cm^2 (e) 31·43 cm^2

Exercise 6.9 page 174

1. 0·866 **2.** −0·5 **3.** −1·732 **4.** 0·7071
5. −0·7071 **6.** −1 **7.** −0·866 **8.** −5·671
9. 0·9962 **10.** 0·5 **11.** −0·1736 **12.** −0·5774
13. 0·0872 **14.** 0·766 **15.** −11·43 **16.** −0·3420
17. −0·4452 **18.** 0·5736 **19.** −0·4663 **20.** −0·7193
21. −0·9659 **22.** −0·9744 **23.** −0·9397 **24.** −0·2924
25. −0·6947 **26.** −0·6249 **27.** 1·7321 **28.** 0·4067
29. −0·4067 **30.** 0·6018
31. 210°, 330° **32.** 120°, 240° **33.** 153°26′, 333°26′
34. 45°, 225° **35.** 60°, 120° **36.** 30°, 330° **37.** 135°, 315°
38. 141°, 219° **39.** 240°, 300° **40.** 90°, 270° **41.** 221°49′, 318°11′
42. 51°19′, 308°41′ **43.** 123°, 303°
44. 30°, 90°, 150°, 210°, 270°, 330° **45.** 135°, 315°
46. 18°, 42°, 138°, 162°, 258°, 282° **47.** 32°, 148° **48.** 145°5′, 214°55′
49. 37°14′, 217°14′
50. 39°30′, 84°30′, 129°30′, 174°30′, 219°30′, 264°30′, 309°30′, 354°30′
51. −sin 10° **52.** cos 10° **53.** sin 70° **54.** −cos 70°
55. −sin 35° **56.** −cos 35° **57.** tan 40° **58.** −tan 55°
59. −tan 45° **60.** −sin 30° **61.** tan 10° **62.** cos 60°
63. $\frac{4}{5}, -\frac{4}{3}$ **64.** $\frac{11}{61}, -\frac{60}{61}$ **65.** 3·08, −0·73
66. $-\frac{11}{15}$ **67.** 396°52′, 576°52′
68. (a) 1 (b) $\frac{5}{12}$ **69.** 210°, 330°, 570°, 690° **70.** $\frac{375}{136}, -\frac{375}{136}$

Exercise 6.10 page 177

1.	43° 52′	**2.**	41° 37′	**3.**	46° 25′	**4.**	45° 4′	**5.**	40° 9′
6.	47° 24′	**7.**	22° 21′	**8.**	31° 31′	**9.**	44° 21′	**10.**	25° 12′
11.	127° 10′	**12.**	117° 17′	**13.**	125° 6′	**14.**	132° 10′	**15.**	133° 26′
16.	92° 52′	**17.**	104° 8′	**18.**	113° 48′	**19.**	137° 38′	**20.**	143° 36′
21.	7·16 cm	**22.**	9·644 cm	**23.**	11·49 cm	**24.**	24 cm	**25.**	28·56 cm
26.	33·2 cm	**27.**	13·21 cm	**28.**	13·59 cm				

Exercise 6.11 page 180

1.	5 km/h, 53° 8′	**2.**	8·602 km/h, 54° 28′	**3.**	8·944 km/h, 41° 49′
4.	10·72 km/h, 50°	**5.**	7·431 km/h, 6·691 km/h	**6.**	4·583 km/h, 49° 6′
7.	5·269 km/h, 41° 38′	**8.**	96·59 km/h, 70·71 km/h	**9.**	91·38 km/h, 58·74 km/h
10.	43·68 km/h, 73° 14′	**11.**	005° 25′, 405·6 km/h	**12.**	9·165 knots, 349° 6′
13.	4·349 knots, 198° 37′	**14.**	39·28 minutes	**15.**	390·4 km/h

Miscellaneous exercise 6 page 180

1. (a) 27·55 cm (b) 34·15 cm
2. (a) 342° 52′; 24 knots (b) 283° 38′; 2 h 46 min
3. 11° 43′; 8·833 m **4.** (a) 9·06 cm (b) 66° 44′ (c) 51° 16′
5. 42·43 cm²; 58° 59′ **6.** 55·53 m; 54° 14′
7. 33° 6′ **8.** 57° 11′ **9.** 61·24 m **10.** 58° 27′
11. 36·32 m; 50 m **12.** 98·18 m **13.** 13° 11′
14. 99·03 km/h; 018° 46′
15. (a) 17 cm (b) 28° 4′ (c) 9·13 cm
16. (a) 14·14 cm (b) 13·23 cm (c) 61° 53′ (d) 69° 18′
17. (a) 313° (b) 57·86 km (c) 551·6 km²
18. 51° 39′ **19.** 28·88 cm²

Part 7

Exercise 7.1 page 182

1. (a) 2 cm (b) 14 cm (c) 12 cm/s (d) 10 cm/s (e) 16 cm/s
2. (a) 6 (b) 5 (c) 4, 6, 8
3. (a) 80 m (b) 10 m/s (c) 45 m/s (d) 60 m/s (e) 80 m/s
4. $-\frac{1}{4}$ **5.** 4, 4 **6.** −6, 6 **7.** 128 m/s, 48 m/s, −32 m/s
8. 0 m/s, $\frac{3}{4}$ m/s, $\frac{8}{9}$ m/s **9.** −15 m/s, −3 m/s **10.** 3, 3, $\frac{3}{16}$
11. (b) (1, 0) (c) 1, −1
12. (a) −1 (b) −3 (c) 3 (d) 0

Exercise 7.2 page 185

1.	$4x^3$	**2.**	$7x^6$	**3.**	$20x$	**4.**	$-2/x^3$
5.	$1 - 1/x^2$	**6.**	$8x - 6$	**7.**	0	**8.**	x^2
9.	$6x^5$	**10.**	$64x^3$	**11.**	$2x + 2$	**12.**	nx^{n-1}
13.	$1/2\sqrt{x}$	**14.**	$3\sqrt{x}$	**15.**	$\frac{7}{2}x^{2\frac{1}{2}}$	**16.**	$-1/2\sqrt{x^3}$

17. 0 **18.** $-\frac{1}{4}x^{-1\frac{1}{4}}$ **19.** $1/5\sqrt[5]{x^4}$ **20.** $6x+6$
21. $\frac{1}{2}nx^{\frac{1}{2}n-1}$ **22.** $2x+3$ **23.** $2x+1$ **24.** $4x-1$
25. $2x-2$ **26.** 1 **27.** 1 **28.** $2x-\dfrac{2}{x^3}$
29. $\dfrac{1}{b}\,x^{\frac{1}{b}-1}$ **30.** $\frac{1}{2}bx^{\frac{1}{2}b-1}$ **31.** 12 **32.** 4
33. -1 **34.** $1, 2$ **35.** $-2, -3$ **36.** 16
37. $6x+12$ **41.** $50, 18, -14;\ -32$ **42.** $13, 160;\ 22, 76$

Exercise 7.3 page 187

1. (a) 4 (b) 6 (c) −2 (d) 0 (e) 25 (f) 6
(g) $-1\frac{1}{3}$ (h) −1 (i) 2 (j) 2

2. (a) $(3, -7);\ (-\frac{1}{3}, 8\frac{5}{27})$ (b) $(2, 0);\ (-\frac{2}{3}, 12\frac{4}{27})$ (c) $(-1, -4);\ (2, 5)$
(d) $(3, 4);\ (-3, -4)$ (e) $(-4, -4\frac{4}{5})$

3. (a) $y = x+1$ (b) $x+y = 10$ (c) $5y+4x+3 = 0$
(d) $3y+4x = 2$ (e) $x+y = 6$

4. 1 **5.** 3 **7.** $-\frac{1}{4}$ **8.** $y = 3x-14;\ \frac{98}{3}$

9. $(-1, 4);\ y+8x+4 = 0;\ y+4x = 0$
$(\frac{1}{3}, \frac{4}{9});\ 9y-24x+4 = 0;\ 9y+12x = 8$

10. $(2, 4)$ **11.** $y = 2(x-1);\ (3, 0)$ **12.** $y = \frac{9}{4}$

Exercise 7.4 page 189

1. (a) $5\,\text{m/s};\ 2\,\text{m/s}^2$ (b) $150\,\text{m/s};\ 20\,\text{m/s}^2$ (c) $-\frac{1}{2}\,\text{m/s};\ \frac{3}{4}\,\text{m/s}^2$
(d) $32\,\text{m/s};\ 2\,\text{m/s}^2$ (e) $196\,\text{m/s};\ 4\,\text{m/s}^2$

2. 20 m/s; 31·62 m/s **3.** 90 m/s; 60 m/s down; 120 m/s down
4. 5·4 m; no **5.** when $t = 0$ or $\frac{1}{3}$ s; when $t = \frac{1}{6}$ s
6. 8 m/s; 1000 m **7.** 15 m/s; 18·75 s **8.** $-8\,\text{m/s}^2$ or $+8\,\text{m/s}^2$; $-5\frac{1}{3}$ m/s
9. 720 m **10.** 1·464 s; 250 m **11.** No. Yes, after 1 hour

Exercise 7.5 page 192

1. 0, min, 2 **2.** −2, min, −7 **3.** $-\frac{1}{2}$, max, $4\frac{1}{4}$ **4.** 1 or 2, max 6, min 5
5. −3 or −2, max −23, min −24 **6.** ±1, max −2, min +2
7. No turning values **8.** 1·26, min −4·56 **9.** 2, max 48
10. ±1, both min 2 (If you don't believe this, try sketching the curve.)
11. $31\,250\,\text{cm}^3$ **12.** $217{\cdot}1\,\text{cm}^3$ **13.** 12·17 cm **14.** 17·32 by 24·49 cm
15. £4000 **16.** 180 m **17.** $31\,250\,\text{cm}^3$ **18.** $553{\cdot}6\,\text{cm}^2$
19. 2·041 by 4·082 by 1·633 cm **20.** $2419\,\text{cm}^3$

Exercise 7.6 page 194

1. $3x^2;\ x^3+c$

2. (a) $\frac{1}{4}x^4+c$ (b) x^5+c (c) $x^7/21+c$ (d) $\frac{1}{3}x^3+2x+c$
(e) $\frac{1}{3}x^3+x^2+x+c$ (f) $-1/x+c$ (g) $\frac{2}{3}\sqrt{x^3}+c$ (h) $-x^{-3}+c$
(i) $\frac{2}{5}\sqrt{x^5}+c$ (j) $7x+c$ (k) $\frac{3}{5}\,x^{1\frac{2}{3}}+c$ (l) $\frac{1}{5}x^5+1/x+c$
(m) c

3. (a) $\frac{7}{3}$ (b) $20\frac{1}{4}$ (c) $\frac{1}{12}$ (d) $4\frac{2}{3}$ (e) $\frac{2}{3}$ (f) $-\frac{3}{8}$
(g) $\frac{1}{2}$ (h) 136

4. $s = 20t + 7\frac{1}{2}t^2 + 30$
5. 18 m; 290 m; 32 414 km
6. $s = 3t^2 + ct + d$
7. 12 m/s
8. 100 m
9. 1980 m; 990 m/s
10. 997 m/s
11. $y = x^2 - 3x + 2$
12. $y = \frac{2}{3}x^3 - \frac{1}{2}x^2$

Exercise 7.7 page 197

1. 15 sq. units; 14 sq. units
2. $56{\cdot}8\ \text{cm}^2$; $52\ \text{cm}^2$; $56{\cdot}56\ \text{cm}^2$
3. 8·65 sq. units; 8·65 sq. units
4. $830\ \text{m}^2$; $2490\ \text{m}^3$

Exercise 7.8 page 199

1. $41\frac{2}{3}$ sq. units
2. 63 sq. units
3. 36 sq. units
4. $85\frac{1}{3}$ sq. units
5. $20\frac{5}{6}$ sq. units
6. $\frac{1}{6}$ sq. unit
7. $\frac{1}{6}$ sq. unit
8. $50\frac{2}{3}$ sq. units
9. $\frac{1}{3}$ sq. unit
10. $3\frac{1}{3}$ sq. units
11. $\frac{1}{6}$ sq. unit
12. $1\frac{5}{6}$ sq. units
13. $1\frac{13}{24}$ sq. units

Miscellaneous exercise 7 page 200

1. 2; −6
2. $10\frac{2}{3}$
3. $1\frac{1}{3}$ sq. units
4. $\dfrac{1}{2\sqrt{x}} - \dfrac{1}{x^2}$
5. $3975\ \text{m}^3$
6. (a) $v = 36 - 3t^2$; 24 m/s (b) $a = -6t$; $-12\ \text{m/s}^2$ (c) 29 m
7. $0{\cdot}355\ \text{m}^3$
8. $y = 2x + 7$; $y = 2x + \frac{193}{27}$; (0, 7); $(0, \frac{193}{27})$; 0·0663
9. −1, +1, 90°
10. (a) 1 s, 6 s (b) $141\frac{2}{3}$ m (c) $12\ \text{m/s}^2$
11. $\frac{24}{25}\ \text{cm}^2/\text{min}$; $0\ \text{cm}^2/\text{min}$
12. $6{\cdot}036\ \text{m}^3$
13. 1·386 sq. units
14. $6\frac{2}{3}$ sq. units
15. −16, +16
16. $y = x^2 - x^3/3 - \frac{3}{8}$
17. $y = (x + at^2) \div t$
18. £53·35
19. (a) 4 s; 48 m (b) 9 m (c) 24 m/s; 0 m/s
20. $a = 16, b = -9$, $553\frac{1}{3}$ sq. units

Part 8

Exercise 8.1 page 203

1. (a) 0·6632 rad (b) 0·7348 rad (c) 1·3145 rad (d) 2·4498 rad
(e) 3·2212 rad
2. (a) 85° 57′ (b) 120°20′ (c) 82° 30′ (d) 3°26′ (e) 210°18′
3. 10·12 cm
4. 107°26′; 1·875 rad
5. 209·5 radians per second; 209·5 m/s
6. 1·0472 rad
7. 0·9898 m
8. 534·7 r.p.m.
9. 7·33 cm
10. 3·2 rad; 7·638 r.p.m.
11. (a) 0·8 rad (b) 45°50′ (c) 3·894 cm (d) $10\ \text{cm}^2$
(e) $8{\cdot}968\ \text{cm}^2$ (f) $1{\cdot}032\ \text{cm}^2$

Exercise 8.2 page 205

1. (a) $\log a + \log b -$ og c (b) $\log a - \log b - \log c$

(c) $2 \log a + \log b - 3 \log c$ (d) $\frac{1}{2}(\log a + \log b + \log c)$

(e) $2 \log a + 3 \log b + 4 \log c$ (f) $\frac{1}{3}\log a + \frac{1}{4}\log b - \log c$

(g) $2(\log a + \log b)$ (h) $\frac{1}{3}(\log a + \log b + \log c)$

2. (a) $\log 2 + 2 \log 3$ (b) $\log 3 + 4 \log 2$ (c) $4 \log 3$ (d) $3(\log 2 + \log 3)$

3. (a) 0·77815 (b) 0·17609 (c) 1·5563 (d) 1·77815 (e) $\bar{2}$·60206

(f) 0·389075 (g) 1·25527 (h) 1·85733 (i) 0·7365 (j) 1·104755

4. 16 **5.** 5623 **6.** 99 **7.** 2·154 **8.** 10·05

9. $3\frac{5}{9}$ **10.** 0·618 **11.** 3·082 **12.** 1·5725 **13.** 6·236 *or* 1·764

14. 3·3725 **15.** 3·1925 **16.** 0·2573 **17.** 8·11 **18.** 7·6535

19. 1·531 **20.** 2·045 **21.** 2·4575 **22.** 3·732 *or* 0·268 **23.** 17

Exercise 8.3 page 206

1. $(x+1)(x+2)$ **2.** $(x-2)(x-1)$ **3.** $(x+3)(x+4)$

4. $(x+1)(x-1)(x+2)$ **5.** $(x+1)(x+3)(x+5)$ **6.** $(x-2)(x+3)(x-4)$

7. $(x-2)(x+2)(x+6)$ **8.** $(x-3)(x+3)(x+1)$ **9.** $(x+1)(x-1)(x+7)$

10. $(x+3)(x+4)(x-5)$ **11.** $(2x+1)(x+1)(x+2)$ **12.** $(2x-1)(x-1)(x+2)$

13. $(2x+3)(x+1)(x-1)$ **14.** $(2x+1)(x-2)(x+2)$ **15.** $(3x+1)(x+1)(x+2)$

16. $(3x+1)(x-1)(x-2)$ **17.** $(3x+1)(2x-1)(x+2)$ **18.** $(4x+1)(x+1)(x-1)$

19. $(2x+1)(2x-1)(x+2)$ **20.** $(2x-3)(x+6)(x+2)$ **21.** $(x^2+x+1)(x+1)$

22. $(x^2+x-1)(x-2)$ **23.** $(x^2+3x+1)(x+1)$ **24.** $(x^2-x-1)(x+3)$

25. $(2x^2+x+1)(2x+1)$ **26.** $(x+1)$ **27.** $(x-1)$ **28.** $(x+1)$

29. $(2x+1)$ **30.** $(x+1)(x+2)$ **31.** $a=-2, b=-5$

32. $a=0, b=30$ **33.** $a=1, b=-6, (x^2+3)$ **34.** $a=6, b=11, c=6$

35. $a=-58, b=-15, (4x+1)$ **36.** $a=-3$ *or* -2 **38.** $2b^n$

39. $a=3, b=72; (x+5)(2x+1)(x-7)$ **40.** $-(x-y)(y-z)(z-x)$

Exercise 8.4 page 209

1. 30, 240 **2.** 60, 630 **3.** −26, −48 **4.** $22\frac{1}{2}$, 180 **5.** $-22\frac{1}{2}, -110$

6. $-32\frac{1}{2}, -147\frac{1}{4}$ **7.** $5\frac{1}{6}, 162\frac{1}{2}$ **8.** $5\frac{5}{6}, 45\frac{5}{6}$ **9.** 1, 88

10. $-19\frac{7}{15}, -69\frac{13}{15}$ **11.** $10a+9b, 55a+45b$

12. $\frac{1}{2}(35a+33b), 111a+99b$ **13.** $10/\sqrt{7}, 45/\sqrt{7}$

14. $n(n+1)$ **15.** 5, 8, 11 **16.** $3\frac{1}{2}, 5\frac{1}{2}, \ldots 17\frac{1}{2}$ **17.** $2\frac{1}{2}, 1, -\frac{1}{2}, -2, -3\frac{1}{2}$

18. $3a, 5a, 7a, 9a$ **19.** x^2-x+1, x^2-2x+2 **20.** 3, 6, 9, ... 24

21. −2, 0, 2, ... 18 **22.** 3, 1, −1, −3, −5 **23.** 5, 7, 9

24. 6, 8, 10 **25.** 200 **26.** 9 **27.** 3, 5, 7, 9, ...

28. 56 **29.** 5 or 6 **30.** $-(m+n)$

Exercise 8.5 page 211

1. 64, 126 **2.** 2187, 3280 **3.** −512, −341 **4.** $34\frac{11}{64}, 96\frac{33}{64}$

5. $-\frac{1}{64}, -\frac{63}{64}$ **6.** $27\sqrt{3}, 40(\sqrt{3}-1)$ **7.** $\frac{64}{243}, 8\frac{115}{243}$

8. $1\frac{113}{512}, \frac{461}{512}$ **9.** $-\frac{4}{2187}, 2\frac{2186}{2187}$ **10.** 0·000 007 68, 3·749 998 08

11. 4 **12.** $7\frac{1}{2}$ **13.** 2 **14.** $-2\frac{2}{5}$

15. $6\frac{2}{3}$ **16.** $-1\frac{1}{4}, \frac{5}{8}$ **17.** 9, 27, 81, 243 **18.** $\frac{1}{2}, \frac{1}{16}$

Exercise 8.6 page 213

1. 10, 3 **2.** 60, $\frac{7}{20}$ **3.** $\frac{1}{3}, \frac{2}{3}$ **4.** 147, 2
5. 32, $7\frac{1}{9}$ **6.** 16, 1·587 **7.** 12, 9 **8.** $1\frac{1}{2}, -3\frac{1}{2}$
9. $17\frac{1}{2}, -7$ **10.** 1·535 *or* −2·035 **11.** $\frac{3}{4}$
12. $\pm\frac{9}{4}$ **13.** 96 g **14.** 1 : 32 **15.** 38°C
16. £1350 **17.** £6009 **18.** Increase of 35·8%

Exercise 8.7 page 214

1. $\frac{1}{2}\sqrt{2}$ **2.** $\frac{1}{3}\sqrt{3}$ **3.** $\frac{2}{5}\sqrt{5}$ **4.** $\frac{5}{7}\sqrt{7}$
5. $\frac{2}{33}\sqrt{11}$ **6.** $\sqrt{2}-1$ **7.** $-\frac{1}{11}(1+2\sqrt{3})$ **8.** $\frac{2}{3}(\sqrt{5}-\sqrt{2})$
9. $-(2+\sqrt{3})$ **10.** $17-12\sqrt{2}$ **11.** $5\sqrt{2}-4\sqrt{3}$ **12.** $\frac{1}{2}(3\sqrt{15}-7\sqrt{5})$
13. $8\sqrt{2}-11$ **14.** $\sqrt{6}+2\sqrt{3}-\sqrt{2}-2$ **15.** $\frac{1}{19}(13+7\sqrt{5})$
16. 14 **17.** 18 **18.** $49-20\sqrt{6}$ **19.** $24\sqrt{2}$
20. $99-70\sqrt{2}$ **21.** $17+12\sqrt{2}$ **22.** $6+2(\sqrt{2}+\sqrt{3}+\sqrt{6})$

Exercise 8.8a page 216

1. $2, \sqrt{2}$ **2.** $\frac{4}{3}\sqrt{3}, \frac{8}{3}\sqrt{3}$ **3.** $\sqrt{3}, 3$ **4.** $\frac{3}{2}$
5. $\frac{7}{2}$ **6.** 18 **7.** $\sqrt{6}$ **8.** 3
9. $3\sqrt{3}$
10. (a) $\sqrt{3}$ (b) $\frac{1}{3}$ (c) $2(1-\frac{1}{3}\sqrt{3})$ (d) 1
(e) $\frac{1}{3}$ (f) $4+\sqrt{3}$

Exercise 8.8b page 217

1. 0·8, 0·6
2. (a) 0·866 (b) 0·7071 (c) 0·5736 (d) 0·91 (e) 0·8007
3. 30° **4.** 45° **5.** 60° **6.** 45° **7.** 50°46′ **8.** 60°

Exercise 8.9a page 219

1. $1\frac{3}{8}$ cm **2.** $\frac{4}{5}$ cm **3.** $4\frac{3}{8}$ cm, $7\frac{5}{8}$ cm **4.** 20 cm **5.** 11 cm
6. 6·136 cm, 5·625 cm **7.** 4 cm **8.** 4·677 cm **9.** $5\frac{1}{3}$ cm
10. 18·5 cm

Exercise 8.9b page 221

1. 2·5 cm **2.** 12·5 cm **3.** 6·892 cm **4.** 8·617 cm
5. 4·243 cm **6.** 7·036 cm **7.** 7·616 cm **8.** 7·81 cm
9. 9·899 cm **10.** 7·036 cm **11.** 3·808 cm, 8·216 cm
12. 3 cm, 1 cm; ABDEC is a straight line **13.** $1\frac{2}{3}$ cm
14. 4·523 cm, 5·924 cm, 6·862 cm.

Exercise 8.9c page 221

1. Acute **2.** Obtuse **3.** Obtuse **4.** Acute
5. Obtuse **6.** Right-angled **7.** Acute **8.** Obtuse
9. Acute **10.** Acute **11.** 23·04 cm, twenty-three
12. Yes

Exercise 8.10 page 222

1. 9·03 km, 041°22′ **2.** 343·6 m, 35′ **3.** 6·624 m, 4·88 m, 3·375 m
4. 10·28 m **5.** 47·8 m **6.** 37·33 m **7.** 80·35 m
8. (a) 41°12′ (b) 3·518 cm (c) 44·26 cm^2 **9.** 4·118 m
10. 19·2 cm **11.** 17·59 cm **12.** 13·21 m

Exercise 8.11 page 225

1. 204·8 π cubic units **2.** 0·6 π cubic units **3.** $\frac{1}{6}\pi$ cubic units
4. 0·059 π cubic units **5.** $85\frac{1}{3}\pi$ cubic units **6.** $\frac{1}{3}\pi r^2 h$ cubic units
7. $161\frac{2}{3}\pi$ cubic units **8.** $\frac{5}{24}\pi r^3$ cubic units **9.** 9·066 π cubic units
10. $\frac{6}{5}\pi$ cubic units

Exercise 8.12 page 227

1. 50·27 cm^2/s **2.** 0·0221 cm/s **3.** 75·41 cm^2/s **4.** 1·2 cm^3/h
5. $1\frac{2}{3}$ km/h **6.** 1·309 cm/s **7.** (a) $\frac{1}{2}$ m/s, (b) 0·3535 m/s
8. (a) 871·4 cm^3/s increase (b) 1152 cm^3/s decrease **9.** 0·008 95 m/s
10. $\pi y^2/2$ cubic units; $2{\cdot}83/\pi$ cm/s **11.** 0·7813 cm/s
12. (a) 0·3978 cm/s (b) 0·5612 cm/s

Exercise 8.13 page 229

1. (a) 4 (b) $\frac{5}{3}$ (c) $\frac{4}{9}$ (d) $\frac{2}{5}$ (e) 6 (f) −0·8125
2. (a) Yes (b) Yes (c) Yes (d) No
3. (a) $(-\frac{5}{2}, 0), (0, \frac{5}{3})$ (b) $(3, 0), (0, \frac{3}{2})$ (c) (0·7, 0), (0, −2·8)
(d) (0, 0), (0, 0) (e) (0·21, 0), (0, −0·6) (f) (1·749, 0), (0, 0·03)
4. (a), (b), (d), and (f) **5.** (b), (c), (d), and (f)
6. (a), (d), (f), (g), (h), (j), (k), (l), (n), and (o)
7. (a) 60°57′ (b) 34°59′ (c) 168°41′ (d) 45°
(e) 108°26′ (f) 165°58′
8. (a) $y = 4x - 1$ (b) $3y + 5x + 1 = 0$ (c) $4y = 9x - 2$
(d) $y = x + 2$ (e) $y + x = 5$ (f) $2x + y = 2$
9. (a) $\sqrt{3}y = x$ (b) $y = \sqrt{3}x + 3$ (c) $x + 2y = 9$
10. (3, 3)

Exercise 8.14 page 232

1. 4·147 cm, 22°31′ **2.** (a) 109°28′ (b) 70°32′ **3.** 58°40′
4. 31°, 19°28′ **5.** 2·812 cm, 10°7′ and 169°53′
6. 62°32′, 37°38′ **7.** (a) 8·66 cm (b) 2·887 cm (c) 5·773 cm
8. (a) 16·07 cm (b) 71°52′ **9.** (a) 15·27 cm (b) 79°6′
10. (a) 16·33 cm (b) 54°45′

Miscellaneous exercise 8 page 233

1. 12·65 cm **2.** 6·532 cm **3.** Eight: 11, 12, 13, 14, 16, 17, 18, and 19 cm
4. One : 15 cm **5.** (a) 5·831 cm (b) 5 cm (c) 7·071 cm
6. (a) 90° (b) 90° (c) 45° **7.** 10 cm^3 **8.** 2·16 cm
9. (a) 4·226 cm (b) 4·364 cm (c) 10·91 cm^2 (d) 9·575 cm^2 (e) 1·335 cm^2
10. (a) 3·472 cm (b) 307·8 cm^2 (c) 6·4 cm^2

11. (a) 41°49′ (b) 21·41 cm (c) 21·89 cm (d) 328·4 cm^2
12. 48°11′, 60°, 300°, 311°49′
13. 199°28′, 210°, 330°, 340°32′
14. 45°, 135°, 225°, 315°
15. 0°, 90°, 180°, 270°, 360°
16. 45°, 135°, 225°, 315°
17. $21\frac{1}{3}\pi$ cubic units
18. $5 + 3\sqrt{2} - \sqrt{3} - \sqrt{6}$
19. $2 - \sqrt{2} - 6\sqrt{3} + 4\sqrt{6}$
20. $7 + 7\sqrt{2} + 3\sqrt{3} + 3\sqrt{6}$
21. $\frac{1}{2}(7 + 5\sqrt{2} + 7\sqrt{3} + 5\sqrt{6})$

Part 9

Exercise 9.1 page 235

1. (a) {2, 3, 5, 7, 11} (b) {1, 4, 9, 16, 25} (c) {1, 3, 6, 10, 15}
(d) {5, 10, 15, 20, 25}
2. (a) The first five odd numbers (b) The first five multiples of 3
(c) The first five cubic numbers (d) The first five powers of 2
3. (a) True (b) False (c) False (d) False
4. (a) $A \cap B = \{2, 4\}$; $A \cup B = \{2, 4, 6, 8\}$
(b) $A \cap B = \{5, 6\}$; $A \cup B = \{3, 4, 5, 6, 7, 8\}$
(c) $A \cap B = \phi$; $A \cup B = \{1, 2, 3, 4, 5, 6, 7, 8\}$
(d) $A \cap B = \{4, 16\}$; $A \cup B = \{1, 4, 8, 9, 12, 16\}$
5. (a) {2, 4, 6, 8} (b) ϕ (c) ℰ (d) ϕ
7. (a) {2, 10} (b) {5, 15} (c) {3, 6, 12}
8. (a) {2, 3, 4, 5, 6} (b) {1, 3, 6, 7} (c) {2, 4, 6, 7}
11. (a) True (b) False (c) True
12. (a) {rhombuses, squares} (b) {squares}

Exercise 9.2 page 237

1. (a) {2, 3, 4, 5, 6, 7, 8} (b) {2} (c) {3, 5, 7, 9}
(d) {4, 6, 8, 9} (e) {9}

2.

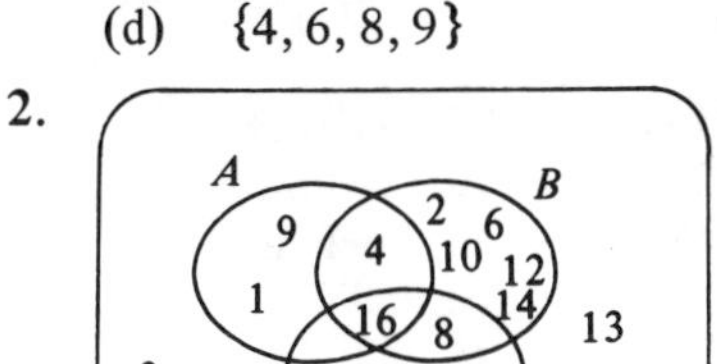

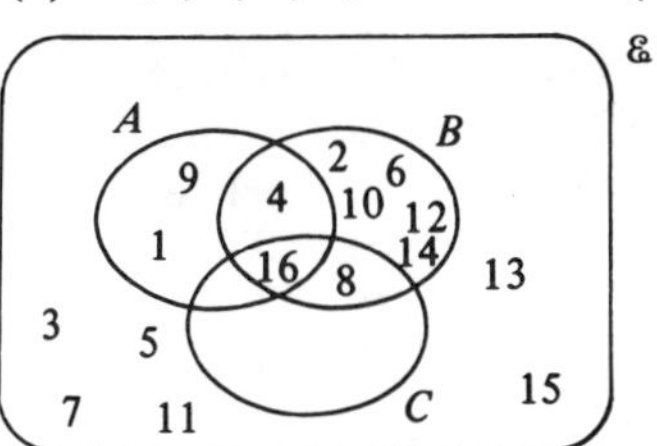

3.

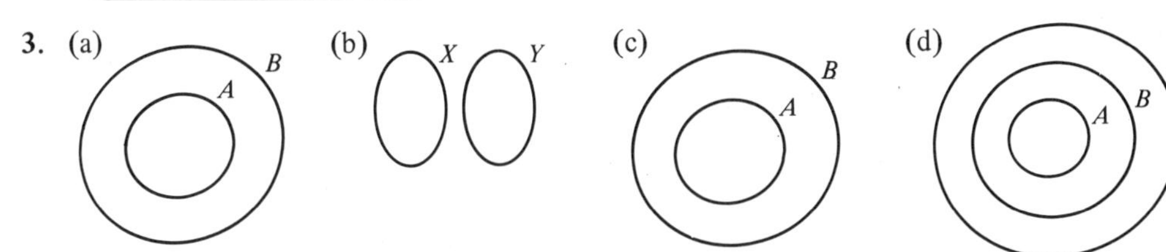

4. 87 **5.** 8 **6.** 9 **7.** 16 **8.** 2 **9.** 19 **10.** 130

Exercise 9.3 page 239

1. True statements are (a), (b), (c), (e), (f), (h), and (j).

2. (a) $x > 4$ (b) $x \geqslant 6$ (c) $x > -5$ (d) $x \ngtr 3$
(e) $x \nless -10$ (f) $x \leqslant 4$ (g) $-\frac{1}{2} < x < 3$ (h) $-8 < x \leqslant 8$
(i) $4 < x < 5$ or $-4 > x > -5$ (j) $4 \leqslant x \leqslant 16$

3. (a) $\{z : z < 5\}$ (b) $\{y : y \geqslant 1\}$ (c) $\{x : x < 2\}$ (d) $\{z : z > 13\}$
(e) $\{x : x \ngtr 25\}$

5. $\{-1, 0, 1, 2, 3\}$ **6.** $\{2, 3, 4\}$ **7.** $\{5 < x \ngtr 8\}$

8. $\{x : x \geqslant 23\}$

Exercise 9.4 page 241

4. $a = 5, b = 6$; or $a = 6, b = 5$ **5.** 30

6. (a) 40 cm^2 (b) 10 cm^2 **7.** (a) 15 (b) 5

8. 84 buses, 8 trains **9.** 4 caravans, 24 tents

Exercise 9.5a page 243

1.	10000	**2.**	10001	**3.**	11011	**4.**	11011	**5.**	100100
6.	100000	**7.**	1110	**8.**	1111	**9.**	1101	**10.**	110100100
11.	1110111	**12.**	1011011	**13.**	110111	**14.**	1101001	**15.**	100011110
16.	111101010			**17.**	111001110			**18.**	10001111
19.	10010	**20.**	100011	**21.**	110001	**22.**	111001	**23.**	1010101
24.	1000110111			**25.**	5	**26.**	12	**27.**	29
28.	93	**29.**	78	**30.**	85	**31.**	40	**32.**	130
33.	1114	**34.**	1242	**35.**	12332	**36.**	10202	**37.**	22
38.	3	**39.**	104	**40.**	132	**41.**	403	**42.**	332
43.	121	**44.**	121	**45.**	1403	**46.**	20301	**47.**	13013
48.	34414	**49.**	10	**50.**	40	**51.**	103	**52.**	41

Exercise 9.5b page 244

1.	144	**2.**	1T1	**3.**	523	**4.**	1T87	**5.**	1321
6.	EE85	**7.**	13	**8.**	86	**9.**	157	**10.**	2TE
11.	TTE	**12.**	203E	**13.**	316	**14.**	2482	**15.**	9TT0
16.	382T	**17.**	2893	**18.**	T912	**19.**	12	**20.**	3T
21.	78	**22.**	88	**23.**	179	**24.**	1072	**25.**	17
26.	35	**27.**	412	**28.**	1653	**29.**	1523	**30.**	1726
31.	base six	**32.**	base nine	**33.**	base 5	**34.**	base 6 or above		
35.	base 7								

Exercise 9.6 page 246

1. (a) reflection in x-axis (b) reflection in y-axis
(c) reflection in $y = x$ (d) rotation $+90°$ about (0, 0)
(e) rotation 180° about (0, 0) (f) enlargement scale factor 2, centre (0, 0)
(g) translation $\begin{pmatrix}-2\\3\end{pmatrix}$ (h) shear 2 units parallel to y-axis
3. (a) rhombus (b) rhombus (c) square (d) parallelogram (e) rectangle
4. (a) $(-2, -4)$ (b) $(2, 4)$ (c) $(0, 6)$ (d) $(-4, -2)$ (e) $(2, -4)$
(f) $(-1, 2)$ (g) $(1, 2)$ (h) $(2, 0)$
5. (a) reflection in y-axis (b) reflection in $y = x$
(c) reflection in x-axis (d) rotation 180° about (0, 0)
(e) enlargement scale factor 2 centre (0, 0)
(f) rotation $-90°$ about (0, 0) (g) reflection in $y = -x$
(h) enlargement scale factor -2 centre (0, 0)
(i) reflection in $x + y = 4$
(j) reflection in $x + y = 4$, then rotation $-90°$ about (0, 0)

Exercise 9.7 page 247

1. (b) rotation 90° anticlockwise about (0, 1).
2. (c) reflection in the line $x + y = 4$
3. (c) translation $\begin{pmatrix}0\\6\end{pmatrix}$
4. (d) (i) rotation 90° anticlockwise about (0, 0)
(ii) rotation 90° anticlockwise about (0, 0)
5. (c) Yes
6. (c) and (d).
7. (b) $\frac{1}{3}$ (d) $-1\frac{1}{2}$

Exercise 9.8 page 249

1. (a) 1 axis reflective symmetry only (b) 3 axes, rotational symmetry order 3
(c) none (d) 1 axis reflective symmetry only
(e) 8 axes, rotational symmetry order 8 (f) infinite
(g) 2 axes, rotational symmetry order 2 (h) 2 axes, rotational symmetry order 2
(i) 1 axis reflective symmetry only (j) 1 axis reflective symmetry only
(k) 2 axes, rotational symmetry order 2 (l) rotational symmetry order 2 only
(m) none (n) 1 axis reflective symmetry only
(o) 1 axis reflective symmetry only (p) rotational symmetry order 2 only
3. (a) 1 axis reflective symmetry only (b) 3 axes, rotational symmetry order 3
4. (a) 4 (b) 2 (c) 2
7. 4 axes, rotational symmetry order 4
8. (a) $(0, 0), (2, 0), (2, -2), (0, -2)$ (b) $(0, 0), (-2, 0), (-2, 2), (0, 2)$
(c) $(0, 0), (0, 2), (2, 2), (2, 0)$ (d) $(0, 0), (-2, 0), (-2, -2), (0, -2)$

Exercise 9.9 page 252

1. (a) $\mathbf{a} + \mathbf{b}$ (b) $-\mathbf{b} - \mathbf{a}$ (c) $\mathbf{b} + \mathbf{c}$ (d) $\mathbf{a} + \mathbf{b} + \mathbf{c}$
2. (a) $\mathbf{a} + \mathbf{b}$ (b) $\mathbf{b} - 2\mathbf{a}$ (c) $\mathbf{a} - \mathbf{b}$
3. (a) $-\mathbf{c}$ (b) $-\mathbf{a}$ (c) $\mathbf{b}$ (d) $\mathbf{0}$
4. (a) $\mathbf{b} - \mathbf{a}$ (b) $\mathbf{a} + \mathbf{b}$ (c) $\mathbf{a}$
AB is parallel and equal to DC. ABCD is a parallelogram.

5. (a) **2b** (b) **a** (c) **2b** − **a** (d) **2b** − **a**
(i) CM is parallel to OA, CM = ½OA; (ii) AM = MD
6. (a) **a** (b) **2b** (c) **a** + **b** (d) **2a** + **2b**
(e) **a** + **b** ABRC is a parallelogram.
7. (a) **a** + **b** (b) **a** − **b**
8. $\frac{\mathbf{b}+\mathbf{a}}{2}$ 9. (a) $(-2\frac{1}{2}, -1\frac{1}{2})$ (b) $(-\frac{1}{4}, -1\frac{1}{4})$

Exercise 9.10 page 254

1. (a) $\begin{pmatrix}-1 & 1\\ 6 & 0\end{pmatrix}$ (b) $\begin{pmatrix}-2 & -4\\ 1 & -3\end{pmatrix}$ (c) $\begin{pmatrix}3 & 3\\ 0 & 8\end{pmatrix}$ (d) $\begin{pmatrix}-2 & 2\\ 5 & -5\end{pmatrix}$
(e) $\begin{pmatrix}3 & 6\\ 2 & 7\end{pmatrix}$
2. (a) $\begin{pmatrix}3a & -a\\ -a & 9a\end{pmatrix}$ (b) $\begin{pmatrix}-a & 5a\\ 7a & -a\end{pmatrix}$ (c) $\begin{pmatrix}2a & 4a\\ 6a & 8a\end{pmatrix}$ (d) $\begin{pmatrix}8a & -12a\\ -16a & 20a\end{pmatrix}$
(e) $\begin{pmatrix}-a & 12a\\ 17a & 2a\end{pmatrix}$
3. (a) $\begin{pmatrix}4 & -2\\ 2 & -4\end{pmatrix}$ (b) $\begin{pmatrix}4 & 2\\ -2 & -4\end{pmatrix}$ (c) $\begin{pmatrix}-4 & 2\\ 2 & -4\end{pmatrix}$ (d) $\begin{pmatrix}-4 & 2\\ 2 & -4\end{pmatrix}$
(e) $\begin{pmatrix}-4 & 2\\ -2 & 4\end{pmatrix}$ (f) $\begin{pmatrix}1 & 0\\ 0 & 1\end{pmatrix}$
4. (a) $\begin{pmatrix}0 & -3a^2\\ 2a^2 & -5a^2\end{pmatrix}$ (b) $\begin{pmatrix}7a^2 & 10a^2\\ 15a^2 & 22a^2\end{pmatrix}$ (c) $\begin{pmatrix}3a^2 & 0\\ 0 & 3a^2\end{pmatrix}$
(d) $\begin{pmatrix}5a^2 & 8a^2\\ -7a^2 & -10a^2\end{pmatrix}$ (e) $\begin{pmatrix}15a^2 & 15a^2\\ 10a^2 & 10a^2\end{pmatrix}$
5. (a) $x = 4, y = 1$ (b) $x = 8, y = -1$ (c) $x = 3, y = 2$
(d) $x = 1, y = -2$
6. (a) $\begin{pmatrix}3 & 3\\ 6 & 6\end{pmatrix}$ (b) $\begin{pmatrix}6 & 6\\ 3 & 3\end{pmatrix}$ (c) $\begin{pmatrix}-3 & -3\\ 3 & 3\end{pmatrix}$ (d) $\begin{pmatrix}-6 & -6\\ 6 & 6\end{pmatrix}$
(e) $\begin{pmatrix}0 & 0\\ 0 & 0\end{pmatrix}$; no; no.
7. (a) 8 (b) −1 (c) −1 8. $\begin{pmatrix}1 & 1\\ 2 & 1\end{pmatrix}$; $\begin{pmatrix}a+c & b+d\\ 2a+c & 2b+d\end{pmatrix}$

9.

×	I	A	B	C
I	I	A	B	C
A	A	C	I	B
B	B	I	C	A
C	C	B	A	I

10. No.

Exercise 9.11 page 256

1. (a) $\begin{pmatrix} 1 & -2 \\ -1 & 3 \end{pmatrix}$ (b) $\begin{pmatrix} 3 & 2 \\ 4 & 3 \end{pmatrix}$ (c) $\begin{pmatrix} 5 & -7 \\ -2 & 3 \end{pmatrix}$
   (d) $\begin{pmatrix} -13 & 4 \\ 16 & -5 \end{pmatrix}$ (e) $\begin{pmatrix} 18 & -13 \\ 7 & -5 \end{pmatrix}$
2. (a) $\begin{pmatrix} 0 & 1 \\ -1 & 0 \end{pmatrix}$ (b) $-\frac{1}{2}\begin{pmatrix} 4 & -6 \\ -3 & 4 \end{pmatrix}$ (c) $\frac{1}{7}\begin{pmatrix} 2 & -3 \\ 1 & 2 \end{pmatrix}$
   (d) $\frac{1}{7}\begin{pmatrix} -3 & 4 \\ 2 & -5 \end{pmatrix}$ (e) $\frac{1}{2ab}\begin{pmatrix} b & b \\ -a & a \end{pmatrix}$
3. (a) $x = 1, y = 1$ (b) $x = 2, y = 1$ (c) $x = 1, y = -1$
   (d) $x = -3, y = 2$ (e) $x = -13, y = -11$ (f) $x = 0, y = -2$
4. (a) not possible: the same line (b) $x = 3, y = -2$
   (c) not possible: parallel lines (d) $a = 2, b = 1$
   (e) $c = 6, d = -8$ (f) $x = 0, y = 0$ (g) $x = 2, y = -1$
   (h) not possible: parallel lines (i) $s = 78, t = 120$
5. (a) 8 (b) $-\frac{140}{121}$
6. $x = 3, y = 1, z = -4$

Exercise 9.12 page 259

1. (a) unchanged (b) reflection in $y = x$ (c) rotation $-90°$ about (0, 0)
   (d) enlargement scale factor 2 centre (0, 0) (e) a stretch along x-axis
   (f) shear parallel to x-axis (g) shear parallel to y-axis
   (h) a stretch along x-axis with a shrink along y-axis
   (i) maps on to a line (j) reflection and shear
2. (a) $\begin{pmatrix} 1 & 0 \\ 0 & -1 \end{pmatrix}$ (b) $\begin{pmatrix} -1 & 0 \\ 0 & -1 \end{pmatrix}$ (c) $\begin{pmatrix} 2 & 0 \\ 0 & 2 \end{pmatrix}$ (d) $\begin{pmatrix} 0 & -1 \\ 1 & 0 \end{pmatrix}$
   (e) $\begin{pmatrix} 1 & 2 \\ 0 & 1 \end{pmatrix}$ (f) $\begin{pmatrix} k & 0 \\ 0 & 1 \end{pmatrix}$ (g) $\begin{pmatrix} 0 & 2 \\ -2 & 0 \end{pmatrix}$
   (h) $\begin{pmatrix} \frac{1}{\sqrt{2}} & -\frac{1}{\sqrt{2}} \\ \frac{1}{\sqrt{2}} & \frac{1}{\sqrt{2}} \end{pmatrix}$
3. (a) shear parallel to y-axis (b) reflection in $y = x$
   (c) reflection and shear (d) shear and reflection
4. (a) shear parallel to y-axis (b) reflection in $y = -x$
   (c) reflection and shear (d) shear and reflection
5. (a) rotation $-90°$ about (0, 0) (b) rotation $+90°$ about (0, 0)
   (c) rotation and enlargement (d) rotation and enlargement
   (e) rotation and enlargement (f) rotation and enlargement

6. (b) $\begin{pmatrix} 0 & 1 \\ -1 & 0 \end{pmatrix}$

(c) (i) $\begin{pmatrix} -1 & 0 \\ 0 & -1 \end{pmatrix}$ (ii) $\begin{pmatrix} 0 & 1 \\ -1 & 0 \end{pmatrix}$ (iii) $\begin{pmatrix} -1 & 0 \\ 0 & 1 \end{pmatrix}$ (iv) $\begin{pmatrix} 0 & -1 \\ 1 & 0 \end{pmatrix}$

(v) $\begin{pmatrix} 0 & -1 \\ -1 & 0 \end{pmatrix}$ (vi) $\begin{pmatrix} 0 & 1 \\ 1 & 0 \end{pmatrix}$

7. (a) (i) $\begin{pmatrix} 0 & -1 \\ 1 & 0 \end{pmatrix}$ (ii) $\begin{pmatrix} -1 & 0 \\ 0 & -1 \end{pmatrix}$ (iii) $\begin{pmatrix} 0 & 1 \\ -1 & 0 \end{pmatrix}$ (iv) $\begin{pmatrix} \frac{\sqrt{3}}{2} & -\frac{1}{2} \\ \frac{1}{2} & \frac{\sqrt{3}}{2} \end{pmatrix}$

(v) $\begin{pmatrix} \frac{1}{2} & -\frac{\sqrt{3}}{2} \\ \frac{\sqrt{3}}{2} & \frac{1}{2} \end{pmatrix}$ (vi) $\begin{pmatrix} -\frac{1}{2} & -\frac{\sqrt{3}}{2} \\ \frac{\sqrt{3}}{2} & -\frac{1}{2} \end{pmatrix}$ (vii) $\begin{pmatrix} \frac{1}{\sqrt{2}} & -\frac{1}{\sqrt{2}} \\ \frac{1}{\sqrt{2}} & \frac{1}{\sqrt{2}} \end{pmatrix}$

(viii) $\begin{pmatrix} \frac{1}{\sqrt{2}} & \frac{1}{\sqrt{2}} \\ -\frac{1}{\sqrt{2}} & \frac{1}{\sqrt{2}} \end{pmatrix}$

(b) (i) $+45°$ (ii) $+233°$

8.

×	A	B	C	D
A	B	C	D	A
B	C	D	A	B
C	D	A	B	C
D	A	B	C	D

Two rotations in succession can be produced by a single rotation.

Exercise 9.13 page 262

1. (a) one-to-one (b) many-to-one (c) one-to-one
   (d) one-to-many (e) many-to-many (f) one-to-one
   (g) many-to-one (h) many-to-many (i) one-to-many
   (j) one-to-one
2. (a) $\{-9, -5, -1, 3, 7\}$ (b) $\{4, 1, 0\}$ (c) $\{15, 3, -1\}$
   (d) $\{-2, -1{\cdot}6, 0, 1{\cdot}6, 2\}$ (e) $\{3, 0, -3\}$ (f) $\{\frac{1}{4}, \frac{1}{2}, 1, 2, 4\}$
3. (a) $\{\frac{1}{2}, 1, 1\frac{1}{2}\}$ (b) $\{-2, -1, 0, 1, 2\}$ (c) $\{-1\frac{1}{2}, 0, 2\}$
   (d) $\{-3, -\sqrt{8}, -\sqrt{7}, \sqrt{7}, \sqrt{8}, 3\}$
4. (a) 2 (b) 2 (c) $x^2 - 3x + 2$ (d) $\frac{1}{x^2} - \frac{3}{x} + 2$
   (e) $x^2 - x$
5. (a) $\frac{x-1}{3}$ (b) $2x - 1$ (c) $\frac{2}{x}$ (d) $\pm\sqrt{x-1}$ (e) $x^2 - 1$
6. (a) $x^2 + 2x$ (b) x^2 (c) $\pm\sqrt{x}$ (d) $\pm\sqrt{x+1} - 1$
   (e) $\pm\sqrt{x}$ (f) $x^2(x^2-2)$ $(gf)^{-1} = f^{-1}g^{-1}$
7. (a) $2x + 1$ (b) $3x - 1$ (c) $13 - 4x$ (d) x^2 (e) 2^x

Exercise 9.14 page 264

1. (a) yes (b) no (c) yes (d) yes
2. (a) 0 (b) 1 (c) −2 (d) −8 (e) $4\frac{1}{2}$
3. (a) 1 (b) 1·69 (c) 0·04
4. (a) ± 12 (b) $\pm\frac{3}{4}$ (c) +1 or −1·44 (d) $\pm\sqrt{2n^2}$
5. $a^2 = 3b^2$
6. (a) yes; yes; yes (b) 0 (c) 2; 3
7. (a) y (b) x; no inverse (c) yes; yes; no

8.

*	1	3	5	7	9
1	1	3	5	7	9
3	3	9	5	1	7
5	5	5	5	5	5
7	7	1	5	9	3
9	9	7	5	3	1

(a) yes; yes; yes
(b) yes, 1

9.

×	P	Q	R	S
P	P	Q	R	S
Q	Q	P	S	R
R	R	S	Q	P
S	S	R	P	Q

(a) **P**
(b) **P**; **Q**; **S**; **R**.

10. (a) No (b) Yes; 1 (c) Yes $\begin{pmatrix}0 & 0\\0 & 0\end{pmatrix}$ (d) $\begin{pmatrix}1 & 0\\0 & 1\end{pmatrix}$ (e) Yes; the empty set.

Exercise 9.15 page 268

1. (a) 120 (b) 168° (c) 54°
8. (b) 34·65, 33, 29
9. 73·28
11. (c) 17, $71\frac{2}{3}\%$

Exercise 9.16 page 272

1. (a) 6, 1 (b) 3·2, 0·15 (c) 1, 0·5 (d) 144, 1·5 (e) 7, 1·5
2. (a) 3, 12, 0·5, 12, 0·55, 0·55 (b) 13, 22, 0·5, 24, 3·2, 2·4
   (c) 12, 7, 4, 6·1, 3·7, 3·6 (d) 5, 5, 0·5, 5, 0·8, 0·8
   (e) 8, 104, 2, 105·2, 2·2, 2·1 (f) 15, 45·5, 2·5, 45, 3, 3
3. (a) 27 (b) 7 (c) 19
4. (a) 20 (b) 76·7%
5. (a) 38 (b) 22 (c) 43

Exercise 9.17 page 274

1. (a) $\frac{4}{9}$ (b) $\frac{4}{9}$ (c) $\frac{1}{3}$ (d) $\frac{1}{3}$ (e) $\frac{8}{9}$ (f) $\frac{4}{9}$
2. $\frac{4}{7}$; 49
3. (a) $\frac{1}{9}$ (b) $\frac{1}{12}$ (c) $\frac{1}{6}$ (d) $\frac{1}{18}$
4. (a) (i) $\frac{4}{11}$ (ii) $\frac{3}{11}$ (b) $\frac{1}{55}$
5. $\frac{13}{102}$
6. $\frac{1}{4}$
7. $\frac{17}{105}$
8. (a) $\frac{125}{216}$ (b) $\frac{91}{126}$ (c) $\frac{1}{216}$
9. (a) $\frac{1}{8}$ (b) $\frac{1}{36}$ (c) $\frac{125}{324}$ (d) 0·000 003 69
10. $\frac{1}{720}$

11. (a) $\frac{1}{5}$ (b) $\frac{1}{11}$

12. (a) $\frac{1}{9}, \frac{1}{3}, \frac{1}{18}, \frac{1}{18}, \frac{1}{3}, \frac{1}{9}$
(b) $\frac{1}{81}, \frac{1}{6}, \frac{1}{6}, \frac{1}{4}, \frac{10}{81}, \frac{223}{324}$

Miscellaneous exercise 9 page 276

1. 43_8

2. (a) $A \cap B$

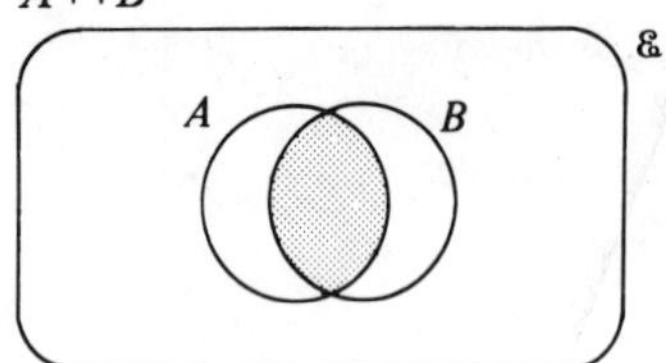

(b) $(A \cap B)'$

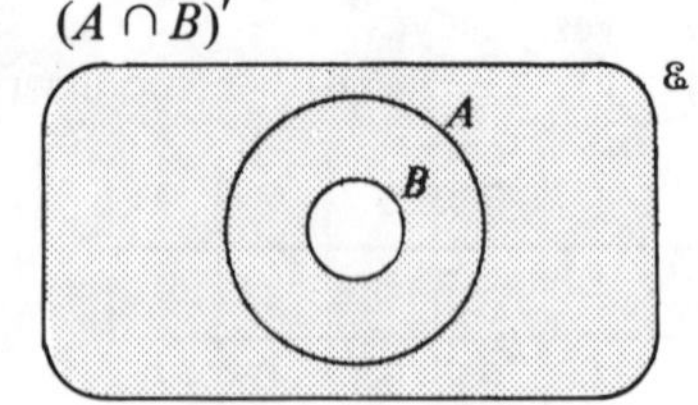

(c) $(A \cap B) \cup C$

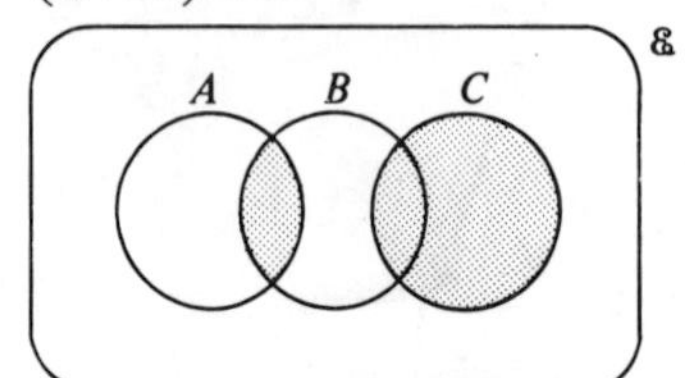

(d) $A' \cap B$

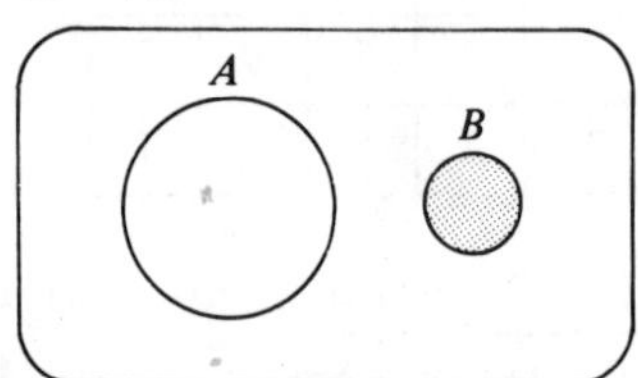

3. (a) (i) $\frac{1}{365}$ (ii) $\frac{7}{365}$ (iii) $\frac{104}{365}$ (b) $\frac{4}{15}$
4. (c) oblique square-based pyramid; 3.
6. (a) (i) base 8 (ii) base 9
(b) (i) $x = 11_2, y = 10_2$ (ii) $x = 101_2$ or -1_2
7. (d) rotation 90° clockwise (e) reflection in $y = -x$
10. (a) $A \cup B$ (b) $A \cap B$ (c) A' (d) $A \cap B'$ (e) $A' \cup B$
(f) $(A \cup C) \cap B$
12. (a) (i) $\frac{10}{31}$ (ii) $\frac{21}{31}$ (b) $\frac{18}{31}$ (c) $\frac{25}{961}$ (d) $\frac{494}{961}$
13. (b) rotation +53° 8′ about (0, 0) (c) $\begin{pmatrix} 0{\cdot}6 & 0{\cdot}8 \\ -0{\cdot}8 & 0{\cdot}6 \end{pmatrix}$
14. (a) (i) $\dfrac{1}{2x-1}$ (ii) $\dfrac{2}{x} - 1$ (iii) $\dfrac{1}{2x-1}$ (iv) $\dfrac{2}{x+1}$
15. 0·047 86
16. (a) 12 cm (b) 76° and 72°
17. (a)

Δ	1	3	5	7	9
1	0	1	3	6	0
3	1	3	6	0	4
5	3	6	0	4	9
7	6	0	4	9	5
9	0	4	9	5	2

(b) no
(c) yes (symmetrical about leading diagonal)

18. (a) the number is greater than 5 (b) $x > 3$
(c) the length is less than 22 cm
19. between 60% and 65%
20. (a) 1·5 tonnes (b) 2·14 tonnes